SolidWorks 2007
for Designers

CADCIM Technologies

525 St. Andrews Drive
Schererville, IN 46375
USA
(www.cadcim.com)
(www.cadcimtech.com)

Contributing Authors
Sham Tickoo
Professor
Department of Mechanical Engineering Technology
Purdue University Calumet
Hammond, Indiana
U.S.A.

Deepak Maini
Sr. CAD Engineer
CADCIM Technologies

CADCIM Technologies

SolidWorks 2007 for Designers
Sham Tickoo

ISBN 1-932709-26-6

Cover designer: *Deepak Maini*
Sales Manager: *Santosh Tickoo*
Technical editor: *Amol P. Kanthe*
Copy editor: *Pragya Katariya*
Cover illustration: *Created by Deepak Maini using SolidWorks, PhotoWorks, and Photoshop software*
Typeface: *10/12 New Baskerville Bt*

www.cadcim.com

DEDICATION

*To teachers, who make it possible to disseminate knowledge
to enlighten the young and curious minds
of our future generations*

*To students, who are dedicated to learning new technologies
and making the world a better place to live*

THANKS

*To the faculty and students of the MET department of
Purdue University Calumet for their cooperation*

To engineers of CADCIM Technologies for their valuable help

Free Teaching Resources for Faculty

The following teaching resources are available for free to faculty:

1. *Online technical support by contacting techsupport@cadcim.com.*
2. *All part files, assembly files, and drawing files used for illustrations, tutorials, and exercises in this book.*
3. *Customizable PowerPoint presentations for every chapter of the book.*
4. *Instructor's guide with answers to review questions and solution to exercises.*
5. *Course outlines.*
6. *Students projects.*

To access the web site that contains these teaching aids, please contact the author, Prof. Sham Tickoo, at the following address.

> **stickoo@calumet.purdue.edu**
> *or*
> **tickoo@cadcim.com**

Free Learning Resources for Students
Note:
These resources are available only for the users who buy the textbook from our web site www.cadcim.com or the university/college bookstores. We need proof of purchase when you request the technical support

1. *Free online technical support by contacting techsupport@cadcim.com.*
2. *All Part, Assembly, and Drawing files used in illustrations and tutorials in this book.*
3. *Additional student projects.*
4. *Tips and Notes.*

For more information, please visit www.cadcim.com

Table of Contents

Chapter 3: Editing and Modifying Sketches

Chapter 4: Adding Relations and Dimensions to Sketches

Chapter 5: Advanced Dimensioning Techniques and Base Feature Options

Chapter 6: Creating Reference Geometries

Chapter 7: Advanced Modeling Tools-I

Chapter 8: Advanced Modeling Tools-II

Chapter 9: Editing Features

Chapter 10: Advanced Modeling Tools-III

Chapter 11: Advanced Modeling Tools-IV

Chapter 12: Assembly Modeling-I

Chapter 13: Assembly Modeling-II

Chapter 14: Working With Drawing Views-I

Chapter 15: Working With Drawing Views-II

Preface

SolidWorks 2007

SolidWorks, developed by SolidWorks Corporation, is one of the world's fastest growing solid modeling software. It is a parametric feature-based solid modeling tool that not only unites the three-dimensional (3D) parametric features with two-dimensional (2D) tools, but also addresses every design-through-manufacturing process. SolidWorks is also known as standard in 3D. The latest in the family of SolidWorks, SolidWorks 2007 includes a number of customer requested enhancements. This implies that SolidWorks is completely tailored to the customer's needs. Based mainly on the user feedback, this solid modeling tool is remarkably user-friendly and it allows you to be productive from day one.

The 2D drawing views of the components are easily generated in the **Drawing** mode. The drawing views that can be generated include detailed, orthographic, isometric, auxiliary, section, and so on. You can use any predefined standard drawing document to generate the drawing views. Besides displaying the model dimensions in the drawing views or adding reference dimensions and other annotations, you can also add the parametric Bill Of Materials (BOM) and balloons in the drawing view. If a component in the assembly is replaced, removed, or a new component is assembled, the modification will be automatically reflected in the BOM placed in the drawing document. The bidirectional associative nature of this software ensures that any modification made in the model is automatically reflected in the drawing views and any modification made in the dimensions in drawing views automatically updates the model.

SolidWorks 2007 for Designers is a text book written with an intent of helping users who are interested in 3D design. This book is written with the tutorial point of view with learn-by-doing as the theme. Real world mechanical engineering industry examples and tutorials have been used to ensure that the user relates the knowledge of the book with the actual mechanical industry designs. The main features of the book are as follows.

- **Tutorial Approach**

    The author has adopted the tutorial point-of-view with learn-by-doing as the theme throughout the book. This approach guides the users through the process of creating the models in the tutorials.

- **Real-world Mechanical Engineering Projects as Tutorials**

  The author has used the real-world mechanical engineering projects as tutorials in this book so that the reader can correlate the tutorials with the real-time models in the mechanical engineering industry.

- **Coverage of major SolidWorks Modes**

  All major modes of SolidWorks are covered in this book. These include the **Part** mode, the **Assembly** mode, and the **Drawing** mode.

- **Tips and Notes**

  Additional information related to the topics is provided to the users in the form of tips and notes.

- **Learning Objectives**

  The first page of every chapter summarizes the topics that are covered in that chapter.

- **Tools Section**

  Each chapter begins with the tools section that provides the detailed explanation of the SolidWorks tools and commands.

- **Self-Evaluation Test, Review Questions, and Exercises**

  Each chapter ends with a Self-Evaluation Test that enables the users to assess their knowledge of the chapter. The answers of Self-Evaluation Test are given at the end of the chapter. Review Questions and Exercises, given at the end of each chapter, can be used by the Instructors as test questions and exercises.

- **Heavily Illustrated Text**

  The text in this book is heavily illustrated with the help of around 700 line diagrams and 800 screen captures that support the tools sections and tutorials.

Features of the Text

Learning Objectives   The first page of every chapter summarizes the topics that will be covered in that chapter.

Tutorials   These are real-world mechanical, automobile engineering projects that are explained in a step-by-step method.

Self-Evaluation Test   These are the questions given at the end of each chapter. Answer to these questions are also given at the end of the chapter so that users can verify their answers.

Review Questions   These are the questions that are given at the end of the chapter. However, the answer to these questions are not given in the book and so the instructor can use them as test questions. The teaching faculty can get answers to these questions in the Instructor's Guide provided by the author.

Note   The author has provided additional information to the users, about the topics in the form of notes.

Tip   Special information and techniques are provided in the form of tips that allow the users to increase their efficiency.

New   This indicates the new commands or tools introduced in SolidWorks 2007.

Enhanced   This indicates the existing commands and tools that are enhanced in SolidWorks 2007.

Chapter 1

Introduction to SolidWorks 2007

Learning Objectives

After completing this chapter, you will be able to:

- *Understand how to start SolidWorks.*
- *Learn about the system requirements to run SolidWorks.*
- *Learn about various modes of SolidWorks.*
- *Understand various important terms and definitions of SolidWorks.*
- *Automatically save files in SolidWorks.*
- *Change the color scheme of SolidWorks.*

INTRODUCTION TO SolidWorks 2007

Welcome to the world of Computer Aided Designing (CAD) with SolidWorks. If you are a new user of this software package, you will be joining hands with thousands of users of this parametric, feature-based, and one of the most user-friendly software packages. If you are familiar with the previous releases of this software, you will be able to upgrade your designing skills with the tremendous improvement in this latest release.

SolidWorks, developed by SolidWorks Corporation, USA, is a feature-based, parametric solid-modeling mechanical design and automation software. SolidWorks, also known as the standard in 3D, is the first CAD package to use the Microsoft Windows graphic user interface. The use of the drag-drop (DD) functionality of Windows makes this CAD package extremely easy to learn. The Windows graphic user interface makes it possible for the mechanical design engineers to innovate their ideas and implement them in the form of virtual prototypes or solid models, large assemblies, subassemblies, and detailing and drafting.

SolidWorks is one of the products of SolidWorks Corporation, which is a part of Dassault Systemes. SolidWorks also works as the platform software for a number of software. This implies that you can also use other compatible software within the SolidWorks window. There are a number of software provided by the SolidWorks Corporation, which can be used as Add-Ins with SolidWorks. Some of the software that can be used on SolidWorks's working platform are listed below.

1. SolidWorks Animator
2. PhotoWorks
3. FeatureWorks
4. COSMOS/Works
5. COSMOS/Motion
6. COSMOS/Flow
7. eDrawings
8. SolidWorks Piping
9. CAMWorks
10. Toolbox
11. Mold Base

As mentioned earlier, SolidWorks is a parametric, feature-based and easy to use mechanical design automation software. It enables you to convert the basic 2D sketch into a solid model using simple but highly effective modeling tools. SolidWorks does not restrict you to 3D solid output, but it extends to bidirectional associative generative drafting. It also enables you to create the virtual prototype of a sheet metal component and its flat pattern, which helps you in complete process planning for designing and creating a press tool. SolidWorks helps you to extract the core and the cavity of a model that has to be molded or casted. With SolidWorks, you can also create complex parametric shapes in the form of surfaces. Some of the important modes of SolidWorks are discussed next.

Part Mode

The **Part** mode of SolidWorks is a feature-based parametric environment in which you can create solid models. You are provided with three default planes named as the **Front Plane**, **Top Plane**, and the **Right Plane**. First, you need to select the sketching plane to create the sketch for the base feature. On selecting the sketching plane, you enter the sketching environment. The sketches for the model are drawn in the sketching environment using easy to use tools. After drawing the sketches, you can dimension them and apply the required relations in the same sketching environment. The design intent is captured easily by adding relations and equations and using the design table in the design. You are provided with the standard hole library known as the hole wizard in the **Part** mode. You can create simple holes, tapped holes, counterbore holes, countersink holes, and so on using this wizard. The holes can be of any standard such as ISO, ANSI, JIS, and so on. You can also create complicated surfaces using the surface modeling available within the **Part** mode. Annotations such as weld symbols, geometric tolerance, datum references, and surface finish symbols can be added to the model within the **Part** mode. The standard features that are used frequently can be saved as library features and retrieved when needed. The palette feature library is also provided in SolidWorks, which contains a number of standard mechanical parts and features. You can also create the sheet metal components in the **Part** mode of SolidWorks using the related tools. Besides, you can also analyze the part model for various stresses applied to the model in the real physical conditions. COSMOSXpress is a very easy and user-friendly tool for stress analysis in SolidWorks. It helps you to reduce the cost and time in testing your design in real physical testing conditions (destructive tests). You can analyze the component during modeling in the SolidWorks windows. In addition, you can work with the weld modeling within the **Part** mode of SolidWorks by creating steel structures and adding weld beads. All standard weld types and welding conditions are available for your reference. You can extract the core and the cavity in the **Part** mode by using the mould design tools.

Assembly Mode

In the **Assembly** mode, you can assemble components of the assembly with the help of the required tools. There are two types of methods of assembling the components:

1. Bottom-up assembly
2. Top-down assembly

In the bottom-up assembly approach, the assembly is created by assembling the previously created components and maintaining their design intent. In the top-down approach, the components are created in the assembly mode. You may begin with some ready-made parts and then create other components in the context of the assembly. You can refer to the features of some components of the assembly to drive the dimensions of the other components. The **SmartMates** option allows you to assemble all the components using a single button. While assembling the components of an assembly, you can also animate the assembly by dragging. Besides you can also check the working of your assembly. Collision detection is one of the major features of the SolidWorks assembly. Using this feature, you can rotate and move the components and detect the collision between the components that you have assembled. You can see the realistic motion of the assembly by using physical dynamics. Physical simulation is used to simulate the assembly with the effects of motors, springs, and gravity on the assemblies.

Drawing Mode

The **Drawing** mode is used for the documentation of the parts or the assemblies created earlier, in the form of drawing views and the details in the drawing views. There are two types of drafting done in SolidWorks:

1. Generative drafting
2. Interactive drafting

Generative drafting is the process of generating drawing views of the part or assembly created earlier. The parametric dimensions and annotations added to the component in the **Part** mode can be generated in the drawing views. Generative drafting is bidirectional associative in nature. Automatic BOMs and balloons can be added while generating the drawing views of an assembly.

In interactive drafting, you have to create the drawing views by sketching them using the normal sketching tools, after which you have to add dimensions to them.

SYSTEM REQUIREMENTS

The system requirements to ensure the smooth running of SolidWorks on your system are as follows:

- Microsoft Windows XP Professional or Windows 2000 Professional.
- Intel Pentium, Xeon, or AMD Athlon-based computer.
- 256 MB RAM minimum (512 MB to 1 GB or higher recommended).
- Graphic card OpenGL (recommended).
- Mouse or any other compatible pointing device.
- Internet Explorer version 5.5 or higher recommended.

GETTING STARTED WITH SolidWorks

Install SolidWorks on your system and then start it by choosing the **Start** button available on the lower left corner of the screen. Choose **Programs** to display the **Program** menu. Choose **SolidWorks 2007 SP0.0** to display the cascade menu and then choose **SolidWorks 2007 SP0.0**, as shown in Figure 1-1.

Figure 1-1 Starting SolidWorks using the taskbar shortcut

The system will now prepare to start SolidWorks. The SolidWorks window will be displayed on the screen. On opening SolidWorks for the first time, the **SolidWorks License Agreement** dialog box will be displayed, as shown in Figure 1-2; choose the **Accept** button from this dialog box.

> **Tip**. *You can also start* **SolidWorks 2007** *by double-clicking on the* **SolidWorks 2007 SP0.0** *shortcut icon from the desktop of your computer. You need to create the shortcut icon of* **SolidWorks 2007** *if it is not created by default. The shortcut icon of* **SolidWorks 2007** *is created by choosing the* **Start** *button available on the lower left corner of the screen. Choose* **Programs** *to display the* **Program** *menu and from it, choose* **SolidWorks 2007 SP0.0** *to display the cascading menu. Move the cursor on* **SolidWorks 2007 SP0.0** *and right-click to display the shortcut menu. Move the cursor to the* **Send To** *option; a cascading menu is displayed. Choose the* **Desktop (create shortcut)** *option from the cascade menu. The* **SolidWorks 2007** *shortcut icon will be placed on the desktop of your computer.*

SolidWorks License Agreement   ☒

Please read the following license agreement. You must accept the license agreement to continue using SolidWorks.

SolidWorks Corporation License and Subscription Service Agreement

The terms and conditions that follow set forth a legal agreement ("Agreement") between you (either an individual or an entity), the end user, and SolidWorks Corporation, a Delaware corporation with its principal place of business at 300 Baker Avenue, Concord, Massachusetts 01742 USA ("SolidWorks"), relating to the computer software known as SolidWorks®, and certain other software licensed by SolidWorks (including the COSMOS line of analysis products and the PDMWorks line of product data management products in all countries) if applicable (the "Software").   The term "Software" includes and these terms and conditions also apply to (i) any updates or upgrades to the Software that you may receive from time to time under a subscription service or other support arrangement, (ii) any add-in modules to the SolidWorks software you may order and install from time to time, and (iii) software from third parties such as the Adobe® PDF library that is incorporated into the SolidWorks software. You may not load or use the Software in any computer or copy it without a license from SolidWorks. SolidWorks hereby offers you a non-exclusive license on the terms set out in this Agreement. You should carefully read these terms and conditions BEFORE opening the case that contains the Software or installing and using the Software. Opening the case containing the Software or installing and using the Software will signify your agreement to be bound by these terms and conditions. If you do not agree to these terms and conditions, promptly return the case containing the Software and the accompanying items (including written materials) for a refund.

Press the PAGE DOWN key to see more text...

| Accept | | Do Not Accept |

*Figure 1-2 The **SolidWorks License Agreement** dialog box*

The SolidWorks 2007 window is opened and the **SolidWorks Resource Task Pane** is displayed on the right, as shown in Figure 1-3. This window can be used to open a new file or an existing file, and use the on-line tutorials. This window can also be used to visit the Web site of the SolidWorks partners.

Choose the **New Document** button from the **Getting Started** group in the **SolidWorks Resources Task Pane** to open a new file. Alternatively, you can also choose the **New** button from the **Standard** toolbar. The **New SolidWorks Document** dialog box is displayed, as shown in Figure 1-4.

Tip. *In the earlier releases of SolidWorks, the **Tip of the Day** dialog box was displayed by default when you started a new SolidWorks session. From the recent releases, the tip of the day will be displayed at the bottom of the **Task Pane**. You can choose **Next Tip** to view additional tips. These tips are extremely useful in helping you efficiently use SolidWorks. It is recommended that you view at least 2 to 3 tips every time you start a new session of SolidWorks 2007.*

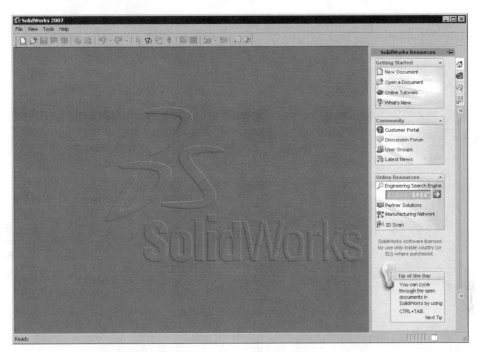

Figure 1-3 SolidWorks 2007 window and the **SolidWorks Resource Task Pane**

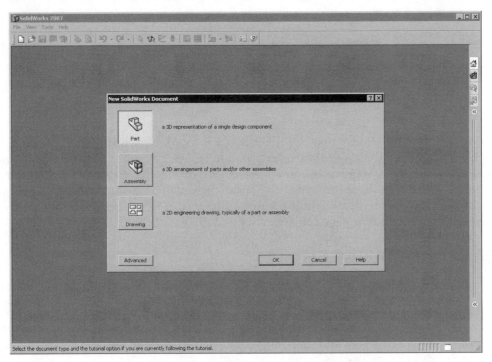

Figure 1-4 The **New SolidWorks Document** dialog box

Choose the **Part** button for creating a part model and then choose **OK** from the **New SolidWorks Document** dialog box to enter the **Part** mode of SolidWorks. Note that the **Task Pane** is automatically closed if you start a new file using the **Standard** toolbar. The initial screen display when you start a new part file of SolidWorks, using the **New** button in the **Standard** toolbar, is shown in Figure 1-5.

Figure 1-5 *Components of a new part document*

It is evident from the screen that SolidWorks is a very user-friendly solid modeling tool. Apart from the default **CommandManager** shown in Figure 1-5, you can also invoke a number of other **CommandManagers** by moving the cursor on the **CommandManager** and right-clicking to display the shortcut menu. Choose the **Customize CommandManager** option from the shortcut menu; a cascading menu is displayed. Using this cascading menu, you can select the **CommandManager** that you need to display.

COMMANDMANAGER

There are three options to invoke a tool in SolidWorks: the **CommandManager**, the use of the menu bars available on the top of the screen, and the shortcut menu. The menu bar and the shortcut menu are discussed later. While working with **CommandManager** you will realize that this is the most convenient method to invoke a tool. Different types of **CommandManagers** are used for different design environments. The **CommandManagers** available in various modes of SolidWorks are discussed next.

Part Mode CommandManagers

A number of **CommandManagers** can be invoked in the **Part** mode. The **CommandManagers** that are extensively used during the designing process in this environment are described next.

Sketch CommandManager

This **CommandManager** is used to enter and exit the 2D sketching environment and the 3D sketching environment. The tools available in the **CommandManager** are used to draw sketches for the features. This **CommandManager** is also used to add relations and smart dimensions to the sketched entities. The **Sketch CommandManager** is shown in Figure 1-6.

Figure 1-6 The Sketch CommandManager

Dimension/Relations CommandManager

This **CommandManager** is used to add various dimensions such as horizontal dimension, vertical dimension, ordinate dimension, and so on. The **Dimension/Relations CommandManager** is displayed in Figure 1-7.

Features CommandManager

This is one of the most important **CommandManagers** provided in the **Part** mode. Once the sketch is completed, you need to convert the sketch into a feature using the modeling tools. This **CommandManager** provides all the modeling options that are to be used for feature-based solid modeling. The **Features CommandManager** is shown in Figure 1-8.

Reference Geometry CommandManager

This **CommandManager** is used to create the reference geometry features like planes, axes, coordinate systems, points, and mate references. The **Reference Geometry CommandManager**, along with all its options, is shown in Figure 1-9.

*Figure 1-7 The **Dimension/Relations CommandManager***

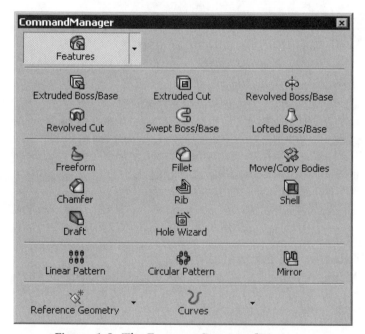

*Figure 1-8 The **Features CommandManager***

*Figure 1-9 The **Reference Geometry CommandManager***

Sheet Metal CommandManager

This **CommandManager** provides you the tools that are used in creating the sheet metal parts. As mentioned earlier, in SolidWorks, you can create sheet metal parts while working in the **Part** mode. This is done with the help of the **Sheet Metal CommandManager** shown in Figure 1-10.

Figure 1-10 The Sheet Metal CommandManager

Surfaces CommandManager

The options available in this **CommandManager** are used to create complicated surface features. These surface features are also converted into the solid features. The **Surfaces CommandManager** is shown in Figure 1-11.

Figure 1-11 The Surfaces CommandManager

Curves CommandManager

The options available in this **CommandManager** are used to create the curves, such as the projected curve, split line, curve through points, helical curve, and so on. The **Curves CommandManager** is shown in Figure 1-12.

Figure 1-12 The Curves CommandManager

Molds CommandManager

The options in this **CommandManager** are used to design the mold and extract its core and cavity. The **Molds CommandManager** is shown in Figure 1-13.

Figure 1-13 The Molds CommandManager

View CommandManager

This **CommandManager** is used to zoom, pan, and orient the model. The shading mode of the solid model can also be changed using this toolbar. You can also create the section view of a model using the option available in this **CommandManager**. The **View CommandManager**, along with all its buttons, is shown in Figure 1-14.

Figure 1-14 The View CommandManager

Standard Views CommandManager

This **CommandManager** is used to orient the model using the standard view options. The **Standard Views CommandManager** is shown in Figure 1-15.

Figure 1-15 The Standard Views CommandManager

Tools CommandManager

This **CommandManager** is used to measure the distance between two entities, add the equations in the design, calculate the mass properties of a solid model, and so on. The **Tools CommandManager** is shown in Figure 1-16.

Assembly Mode CommandManagers

The **CommandManager** in the **Assembly** mode is used to assemble the components, create an explode line sketch, and simulate the assembly. This **CommandManager** is discussed next.

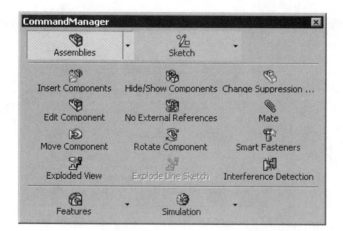

*Figure 1-16 The **Tools** CommandManager*

Assemblies CommandManager

This **CommandManager** is used to apply various types of mates to the assembly. Mates are the constraints that can be applied to the components to restrict their degree of freedom. You can also move and rotate the component in the assembly, change the hidden and the suppression state of the assembly and individual component, edit the component of the assembly, and so on. The **Assemblies CommandManager** is shown in Figure 1-17.

*Figure 1-17 The **Assemblies** CommandManager*

Drawing Mode CommandManagers

A number of **CommandManagers** can be invoked in the **Drawing** mode. The **CommandManagers** that are extensively used during the designing process in this mode are described next.

Drawings CommandManager

This **CommandManager** is used to generate the drawing views from an existing model or an assembly. The views that can be generated using this **CommandManager** are model view, three standard views, projected view, section view, aligned section view, detail view, crop view, relative view, auxiliary view, and so on. The **Drawings CommandManager** is shown in Figure 1-18.

Figure 1-18 The Drawings CommandManager

Tip. *You can also create 2D drawings and drawing views using the normal sketching tools available in the **Sketch Tools** toolbar. The **Sketch Tools** toolbar is also available in the **Drawing** mode.*

Annotations CommandManager

The **Annotations CommandManager** is used to generate the model items and to add the notes, balloons, geometric tolerance, surface finish symbols, and so on to the drawing views. The **Annotations CommandManager** is shown in Figure 1-19.

Figure 1-19 The Annotations CommandManager

DIMENSIONING STANDARD AND UNITS

While installing SolidWorks on your system, you can specify the units and the dimensioning standard for dimensioning the model. You are provided with many dimensioning standards such as ANSI, ISO, DIN, JIS, BSI, and GOST. You are also provided with various units such as millimeters, centimeters, inches, and so on. This book follows millimeters as the units and ISO as the dimensioning standard. Therefore, it is recommended that you install SolidWorks with ISO as the dimensioning standard and millimeters as units.

IMPORTANT TERMS AND THEIR DEFINITIONS

Before you proceed further in SolidWorks, it is very important for you to understand the following terms. These terms have been widely used in this book.

Feature-based Modeling

Feature is defined as the smallest building block that can be modified individually. In SolidWorks, the solid models are created by integrating a number of these building blocks. A model created in SolidWorks is a combination of a number of individual features with each feature related to the other, directly or indirectly. These features understand their fit and function properly, and therefore can be modified any time during the design process. If the proper design intent is maintained while creating the model, these features automatically adjust their values to any change in their surrounding. This provides greater flexibility to the design.

Parametric Modeling

The parametric nature of a software package is defined as its ability to use the standard properties or parameters in defining the shape and size of a geometry. The main function of this property is to derive the selected geometry to a new size or shape without considering its original dimensions. You can change or modify the shape and size of any feature at any stage of the design process. This property makes the designing process very easy. For example, consider the design of the body of a pipe housing shown in Figure 1-20.

In order to change the design by modifying the diameter of the holes and the number of holes on the front, top, and the bottom face, you need to simply select the feature and change the diameter and the number of instances in the pattern. The modified design is shown in Figure 1-21.

Bidirectional Associativity

As mentioned earlier, SolidWorks has different modes such as the **Part** mode, **Assembly** mode, and **Drawing** mode. There exists a bidirectional associativity between all these modes, which ensures that any modification made in the model in any one of the modes of SolidWorks is automatically reflected in the other mode immediately. For example, if you modify the dimension of a part in the **Part** mode, the change will be reflected in the **Assembly** and the **Drawing** modes. Similarly if you modify the dimensions of a part in the drawing views

Figure 1-20 *Body of pipe housing*   **Figure 1-21** *Design after modifications*

generated in the **Drawing** mode, the changes will be reflected in the **Part** and **Assembly** modes. Consider the drawing views shown in Figure 1-22. These are the drawing views of the body of the pipe housing shown in Figure 1-20. Now, when you modify the model of the body of pipe housing in the **Part** mode, the changes will be reflected in the **Drawing** mode automatically. Figure 1-23 shows the drawing views of the pipe housing after increasing the diameter and the number of holes.

Figure 1-22 *Drawing views of the body part before making the modifications*

Windows Functionality

SolidWorks is the first Windows-based 3D CAD package. It uses the graphical user interface of Windows, as also its drag and drop and the copy paste functionality. For example, consider a case where you had created a hole feature on the front planar surface of a model. Now, to create another hole feature on the top planar surface of the same model, select the hole feature and press CTRL+C (copy) on the keyboard. Next, select the top planar surface of the

Figure 1-23 Drawing views after modifications

base feature and press CTRL+V (paste). You can also drag and drop the standard features from the feature pallet library on the face of the model on which the feature has to be added. Therefore, SolidWorks is the easiest to learn 3D CAD package for mechanical engineers.

Geometric Relations

Geometric relations are the logical operations that are performed to add a relationship (like tangent or perpendicular) between the sketched entities, planes, axes, edges, or vertices. When adding the relations, one entity can be a sketched entity and the other can be a sketched entity, or an edge, face, vertex, origin, plane, and so on. There are two methods to create the geometric relations:

1. Automatic Relations
2. Add Relations

Automatic Relations

The sketching environment of SolidWorks has been provided with the facility of autorelations. This facility ensures that the geometric relations are applied to the sketch automatically while creating it. Automatic relations are also provided in the **Drawing** mode while working with interactive drafting.

Add Relations

Add relations is used to add geometric relations manually to the sketch. The 16 types of geometric relations that can be manually applied to the sketch are as follows:

Horizontal

This relation forces the selected line segment to become a horizontal line. You can also select two points and force them to be aligned horizontally.

Vertical

This relation forces the selected line segment to become a vertical line. You can also select two points and force them to be aligned vertically.

Collinear

This relation forces the two selected entities to be placed in the same line.

Coradial

This relation is applied to two selected arcs, circles, or an arc and a circle to force them to become equi-radius and at the same time share the same centerpoint.

Perpendicular

This relation is used to make the selected line segment perpendicular to another selected segment.

Parallel

This relation is used to make the selected line segment parallel to another selected segment.

Tangent

This relation is used to make the selected line segment, arc, spline, circle, or ellipse tangent to another arc, circle, spline, or ellipse.

Note

In case of splines, the relations are applied to their control points.

Concentric

This relation forces two selected arcs, circles, a point and an arc, a point and a circle, or an arc and a circle to share the same centerpoint.

Midpoint

This relation forces a selected point to be placed on the midpoint of a line.

Intersection

This relation forces a selected point to be placed at the intersection of two selected entities.

Coincident

This relation is used to make two points, a point and a line, or a point and an arc coincident.

Equal

The equal relation forces the two selected lines to become equal in length. This relation is also used to force two arcs, or two circles, or an arc and a circle to have equal radii.

Symmetric

The symmetric relation is used to force the selected entities to become symmetrical about a selected centerline, so that they remain equidistant from the centerline.

Fix

This relation is used to fix the selected entity to a particular location with respect to the coordinate system of the current sketch. The endpoints of the fixed line, arc, spline, or an elliptical segment are free to move along the line.

Pierce

This relation forces the sketched point to be coincident to the selected axis, edge, or curve where it pierces the sketch plane. The sketched point in this relation can be the endpoint of the sketched entity.

Merge

This relation is used to merge two sketched points or endpoints.

Library Feature

Generally, in a mechanical design, some features are used frequently. In most of the other solid modeling tools, you need to create these features whenever you need them. However, SolidWorks allows you to save these feature in a library so that you can retrieve them whenever you want. This saves a lot of designing time and effort of a designer.

Feature Palette

The feature palette is also a very unique feature of SolidWorks. Using the feature palette library, you can access some ready-to-use drop-down standard mechanical parts such as shafts, keyways, forming parts for a sheet metal, and so on.

Design Table

Design tables are used to create a multi-instance parametric component. For example, some components in your organization have the same geometry but different dimensions. Instead of creating each component of the same geometry with a different size, you can create one component and then using the design table, create different instances by changing the dimension as per your requirement. Using the design table, you can access all those components with the same geometry having different sizes in a single part file.

Equations

Equations are the analytical and numerical formulae applied to the dimensions during the sketching of the feature sketch or after sketching the feature sketch. The equations can also be applied to the placed features.

Collision Detection

Collision detection is used to detect the interference and collision between the parts of an assembly when the assembly is in motion. While creating the assembly in SolidWorks, you can detect the collision between the parts by moving and rotating them.

What's Wrong Functionality

While creating a feature of the model or after editing a feature created earlier, if the geometry of the feature is not compatible and the system is not able to construct that feature, then the **What's Wrong** functionality is used to detect the possible error that occurs while creating the feature.

2D Command Line Emulator

The 2D command emulator is an Add-In of SolidWorks. You can activate this by choosing **Tools** > **Add-Ins** from the menu bar. On choosing this option, the **Add-Ins** dialog box is displayed. Select the **SolidWorks 2D Emulator** check box and choose **OK** from the **Add-Ins** dialog box. A command section is displayed at the bottom of the graphics area. This 2D Command line emulator is useful for invoking the commands by typing them. You can type the commands in the 2D Command line emulator.

COSMOSXpress

In SolidWorks, you are provided with COSMOSXpress, which is an analysis tool to execute the static or stress analysis. In COSMOSXpress you can only execute the linear static analysis. Using the linear static analysis, you can calculate the displacement, strain, and stresses applied on a component with the effect of material, various loading conditions, and restraint conditions applied on a model. A component fails when the stress applied to it reaches a certain permissible limit. The Static Nodal stress plot of the crane hook designed in SolidWorks and analyzed using COSMOSXpress is shown in Figure 1-24.

Figure 1-24 *The crane hook analyzed using COSMOSXpress*

Physical Dynamics

Physical Dynamics is used to observe the motion of the assembly. With this option selected, the component dragged in the assembly applies a force to the component that it touches. As a result, the other component is moved or rotated within its allowable degrees of freedom.

Physical Simulation

Using **Physical Simulation** you can simulate the assemblies created in the assembly environment of SolidWorks. You can assign and simulate the effect of different simulation elements such as linear, rotary motors, and gravity to the assemblies. After creating a simulating assembly, you can record and replay simulation.

Seed Feature and Seed Component

The original feature that is used as the parent feature to create any type of pattern or mirror feature is known as the seed feature. You can edit or modify only a seed feature. You cannot edit the instances of the pattern feature.

The original component that is used to create a derived pattern, local pattern, or a mirrored component is known as the seed component.

FeatureManager Design Tree

The **FeatureManager Design Tree** is one the most important components of SolidWorks screen. It contains the information about the default planes, material, lights, and all the features that are added to the model. When you add features to the model using various modeling tools, the same are also displayed in the **FeatureManager Design Tree**. You can easily select and edit the features using the **FeatureManager Design Tree**. When you invoke any tool to create a feature, the **FeatureManager Design Tree** is replaced by the respective **PropertyManager**. At this stage, the **FeatureManager Design Tree** is displayed in the drawing area.

Absorbed Features

Features that are directly involved in creating other features are known as absorbed features. For example, the sketch of an extruded feature is an absorbed feature of the extrude feature.

Child Features

The features that are dependent on their parent and whose existence is not possible without their parent features are known as child features. For example, consider a cube with filleted edges. If you delete the cube, the fillet feature will also be deleted because its existence is not possible without its parent feature.

Dependent Features

Dependent features are those that depend on their parent feature but can still exist without the parent feature with some minor modifications. If the parent feature is deleted, then by specifying other references and modifying the feature, you can retain the same feature.

AUTO-BACKUP OPTION

SolidWorks also allows you to set the option to save the SolidWorks document automatically after a regular interval of time. While working on a design project, if the system crashes, you may loose the unsaved design data. If the auto-backup option is turned on, your data is saved automatically after regular intervals. To turn this option on, choose **Tools** > **Options** from the menu bar; the **System Options - General** dialog box is displayed. Select the **Backup/**

Recover option from the display area provided on the left of this dialog box. Now, choose the **Save auto recover info every** check box. The spinner and the drop-down list provided on the right of the check box are enabled. Using this spinner and drop-down list, you can set the number of changes or minutes after which the document would be saved automatically. By default, the backup files are saved in *X:\Documents and Settings\Admisitrator <name of your machine>\Local Settings\TempSWBackupDirectory* location (where *X* is the drive in which you have installed SolidWorks 2007 and the *Local Settings* folder is a hidden folder). You can also change the path of this location. To change this path, choose the button provided on the right of the edit box; the **Browse For Folder** dialog box is displayed. Using this, you can specify the location of the folder to save the backup files. If you need to save the backup files in the current folder, select the **Number of backup copies per document** check box and then select the **Save backup files in the same location as the original** radio button. You can set the number of backup files that you need to save using the **Number of backup copies per document** spinner. After setting all the options, choose the **OK** button from the **System Options - Backup/Recover** dialog box.

SELECTING HIDDEN ENTITIES

Sometimes, while working on a model, you need to select an entity that is either hidden behind another entity or is not displayed in the current orientation of the view. SolidWorks allows you to select these entities using the **Select Other** option. For example, consider a case where you need to select the back face of a model, which is not displayed in the current orientation. In such case, move the cursor over the visible face such that the cursor is also in line with the back face of the model. Now, right-click and choose **Select Other** from the shortcut menu; the cursor changes to the select other cursor and the **Select Other** list box is displayed. This list box displays all entities that can be selected. The item on which you move the cursor in the list box is highlighted in the drawing area. You can select the hidden face using this box.

COLOR SCHEME

SolidWorks allows you to use various color schemes as the background color for the screen, color and display style of **FeatureManager Design Tree**, and for displaying the entities on the screen. Note that the color scheme used in this book is neither the default color scheme nor the predefined color scheme. To set this color scheme, choose **Tools > Options** from the menu bar; the **System Options - General** dialog box is displayed. Select the **Colors** option from the left of this dialog box; the option related to the color scheme is displayed in the dialog box and the name of the dialog box is changed to **System Options - Colors** dialog box. In the list box available in the **Color scheme settings** area, the **Viewport Background** option is available. Select this option and choose the **Edit** button from the preview area on the right. Select white color from the **Color** dialog box and choose the **OK** button. Select the **Blue** option from the **PropertyManager color** drop-down list available in the **System colors** area and choose the **None** option from the **PropertyManager skin** drop-down list. Now, clear the **Match graphics area and FeatureManager backgrounds** check box. After setting the color scheme, you need to save it so that next time if you need to set this color scheme, you do not need to configure all the settings. You just need to select the name of the saved color scheme from the **Current Color Scheme** drop-down list. Choose the **Save As Scheme** button; the **Color Scheme Name** dialog box is displayed. Enter the name of the color scheme as **SolidWorks 2007** in the edit box in the **Color Scheme Name** dialog box and choose the **OK** button. Now, choose the **OK** button from the **System Options - Colors** dialog box.

Note
The colors of the entities that are mentioned in the description or tutorials in this book are those that are displayed if the operating system is Windows XP. However, if you use Windows 2000, the colors of the entities that you get on the screen may be different from those mentioned in this book.

SELF-EVALUATION TEST

Answer the following questions and then compare your answers with those given at the end of this chapter:

1. The **Part** mode of SolidWorks is a feature-based parametric environment in which you can create solid models. (T/F)

2. Generative drafting is the process of generating drawing views of the part or assembly created earlier. (T/F)

3. The tip of the day will be displayed at the bottom of the **Task Pane**. (T/F)

4. In SolidWorks, the solid models are not created by integrating a number of building blocks, called features. (T/F)

5. The _____ property ensures that any modification made in the model in any one of the modes of SolidWorks is automatically reflected in the other mode immediately.

6. The _____ relation forces two selected arcs, circles, a point and an arc, a point and a circle, or an arc and a circle to share the same centerpoint.

7. The _____ relation is used to make two points, a point and a line, or a point and an arc coincident.

8. The _____ relation forces the two selected lines to become equal in length.

9. The _____ is used to detect the interference and collision between the parts of an assembly when the assembly is in motion.

10. _____ are the analytical and numerical formulae applied to the dimensions during the sketching of the feature sketch or after sketching the feature sketch.

Answers to Self-Evaluation Test

1. T, **2.** T, **3.** T **4.** F, **5.** bidirectional associativity, **6.** concentric, **7.** coincident, **8.** **equal**, **9.** collision detection, **10.** Equations

Chapter 2

Drawing Sketches for Solid Models

Learning Objectives

After completing this chapter, you will be able to:
- *Understand the requirement of the sketching environment.*
- *Open a new part document.*
- *Understand various terms used in the sketching environment.*
- *Work with various sketching tools.*
- *Use the drawing display tools.*
- *Delete the sketched entities.*

THE SKETCHING ENVIRONMENT

Most products designed using SolidWorks are a combination of sketched, placed, and derived features. The placed and derived features are created without drawing a sketch, but the sketched features require a sketch to be drawn first. Generally, the base feature of any design is a sketched feature and is created using a sketch. Therefore, while creating any design, the first and foremost point is to draw the sketch for the base feature. Once you have drawn the sketch, you can convert it into the base feature and then add the other sketched, placed, and derived features to complete the design. In this chapter, you will learn to create the sketch for the base feature using various sketcher entities.

In general terms, a sketch is defined as the basic contour for the feature. For example, consider the spanner shown in Figure 2-1.

Figure 2-1 *Solid model of a spanner*

This spanner consists of a base feature, cut feature, mirror feature (cut on the back face), fillets, and an extruded text feature. The base feature of this spanner is shown in Figure 2-2. It is created using a single sketch drawn on the **Front Plane**, as shown in Figure 2-3. This sketch is drawn in the sketching environment using various sketching tools. Therefore, to draw the sketch of the base feature, you first need to invoke the sketching environment where you will draw the sketch.

Note
Once you are conversant with various options of SolidWorks, you can also use a derived feature or a derived part as the base feature.

The sketching environment of SolidWorks can be invoked any time in the **Part** mode or **Assembly** mode. You just have to specify that you want to draw the sketch of a feature and then select the plane on which you want to draw the sketch.

Note
You will learn how to invoke the sketching environment in SolidWorks 2007 later in this chapter.

Figure 2-2 *Base feature of the spanner*   *Figure 2-3* *Sketch for the base feature of the spanner*

STARTING A NEW SESSION OF SolidWorks 2007

To start a new session of SolidWorks 2007, choose **Start > Programs > SolidWorks 2007 SP0.0 > SolidWorks 2007 SP0.0** from the **Start** menu or double-click on the **SolidWorks 2007 SP0.0** icon placed on the desktop of your computer; the SolidWorks 2007 window will be displayed. If you are starting SolidWorks application for the first time after installing it, the **SolidWorks License Agreement** dialog box will be displayed. Choose **Accept** from this dialog box; the **Welcome to SolidWorks** dialog box will also be displayed, as shown in Figure 2-4. This dialog box welcomes you to SolidWorks and helps you customize SolidWorks installation. The options available in this dialog box are discussed next.

Figure 2-4 *The **Welcome to SolidWorks** dialog box*

Help customization Area

The options available in this area are used to define the type of help you need to invoke while working with SolidWorks. By default, the **I am new user. Show Quick Tips to help me get**

started radio button is selected in this area. With this radio button selected, you are provided with quick tips that will guide you through the process of starting as a new user. Keep this radio button selected if you are a new user of SolidWorks.

If you are an existing user of SolidWorks, select the **I am new to this version of SolidWorks. Show me Interactive What's New help** radio button. This ensures that the **Interactive What's New** help is displayed while you are working with the tools that are enhanced or introduced in this release of SolidWorks.

If you do not want to invoke any dynamic help topic, select the **Do not show me any dynamic help** radio button.

Work flow customization Area

The options available in the **Work flow customization** area of this dialog box are used to customize the default visibility of toolbars and menu bars. These customize the toolbars and menu bars on the basis of the area of your expertise, such as product design, machine design, and mold design. Select the check box that belongs to the area of your expertise.

This textbook follows the beginners point of view. Therefore, you need to keep the default radio button selected in the **Help customization** area and clear all check boxes in the **Work flow customization** area. Next, choose the **OK** button from the **Welcome to SolidWorks** dialog box. The **Welcome to SolidWorks** dialog will disappear and you can view the **SolidWorks 2007** window, as shown in Figure 2-5.

You will notice that **Task Pane** is displayed on the right of the SolidWorks 2007 window. This **Task Pane** is provided with various options that are used to start a new file, open an existing file, browse the related links of SolidWorks, and so on. The options available in the **Task Pane** are discussed next.

SolidWorks Resources Task Pane

By default, the **SolidWorks Resources Task Pane** is displayed when you start the SolidWorks session. Different options provided in the groups available in this **Task Pane** are discussed next.

Getting Started

The options available in this group are used to start a new document, open an existing document, and invoke the interactive help topics.

Community

The options available in this group are used to invoke various SolidWorks communities such as subscription services, discussion forum, user groups, and so on.

Online Resources

The options available in this group are used to invoke the discussion forum of SolidWorks, subscription services, solution partners, manufacturing network, and print 3D Web sites. With this release of SolidWorks, a search engine is provided in the **Online Resource Task**

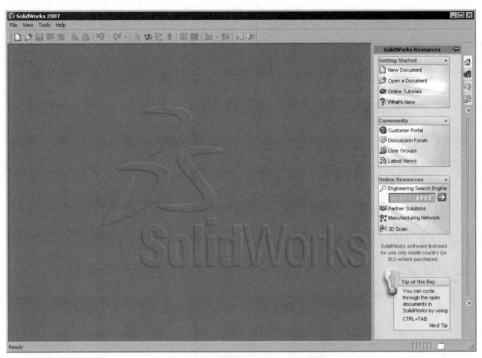

Figure 2-5 *The **SolidWorks 2007** window*

Pane. You just need to type the term on which you need some information and then choose the **Start searching** button; you will be redirected to the Web site of GlobalSpec search engine.

Tip of the Day
The **Tip of the Day** group provides you with a useful tip that will enhance your performance of using SolidWorks. Choose the **Next Tip** provided on the lower right corner of the **Tip of the Day** dialog box to switch to the next tip.

Design Library

The **Design Library Task Pane** is invoked by choosing the **Design Library** tab from the **Task Pane**. This **Task Pane** is used to browse the default **Design Library** available in SolidWorks or the toolbox components, and also to access the **3D ContentCentral** Web site. To access the toolbox components, **Toolbox Add-in** needs to be installed on your computer. To access the **3D ContentCentral** Web site, your computer needs to be connected to the Internet.

File Explorer

The **File Explorer Task Pane** is used to explore the files and folders that are saved on the hard disk of your computer.

View Palette
The **View Palette Task Pane** is used to drag and drop the drawing views into a drawing sheet.

STARTING A NEW DOCUMENT IN SolidWorks 2007

To start a new document in SolidWorks 2007, choose the **New Document** option from the **Getting Started** group of the **SolidWorks Resources Task Pane**; the **New SolidWorks Document** dialog box will be displayed, as shown in Figure 2-6. You can also invoke this dialog box by choosing the **New** button from the **Standard** toolbar. The options provided in this dialog box are discussed next.

*Figure 2-6 The **New SolidWorks Document** dialog box*

Part

The **Part** button is chosen by default in the **New SolidWorks Document** dialog box. Choose the **OK** button to start a new part document to create solid models or sheet metal components. When you start a new part document, you will enter the **Part** mode.

Assembly

Choose the **Assembly** button and then the **OK** button from the **New SolidWorks Document** dialog box to start a new assembly document. In the assembly document, you can assemble the components created in the part documents. You can also create components in the assembly document.

Drawing

Choose the **Drawing** button and then the **OK** button from the **New SolidWorks Document** dialog box to start a new drawing document. In a drawing document, you can generate or create the drawing views of the parts created in the part documents or the assemblies created in the assembly documents.

Note

*When you start a new file in SolidWorks, the **What would you like to do?** window is displayed, which assists you in working with SolidWorks. To close this window, choose the (X) button available close to the lower right corner of the SolidWorks window. The (X) button changes into the (?) button. You can choose this button to again display **What would you like to do?** window.*

Tip. *If you invoke the **New SolidWorks Document** dialog box using the **Task Pane** and start a new document, the **Task Pane** will remain expanded even when the new document is started. If you invoke the **New SolidWorks Document** dialog box using the toolbar or menu bar, the **Task Pane** will collapse and remain collapsed after starting the new document. You will learn more about expanding and collapsing the **Task Pane** later in this chapter.*

UNDERSTANDING THE SKETCHING ENVIRONMENT

Whenever you start a new part document, by default you are in the part modeling environment. But you need to start the design by first creating the sketch of the base feature in the sketching environment. To invoke the sketching environment, choose the **Sketch** button from the **CommandManager** (Figure 2-7). Next, choose the **Sketch** button from the **Sketch CommandManager**. For your convenience, you can add the **Sketch** button to the **Standard** toolbar and invoke the sketching environment using this button. To do so, right-click on any toolbar and choose the **Sketch** option from the shortcut menu. Again, right-click on any toolbar and choose **Customize** from the shortcut menu. Now, drag the **Sketch** button from the **Sketch** toolbar and drop it on the **Standard** toolbar. After adding the button, exit the **Customize** dialog

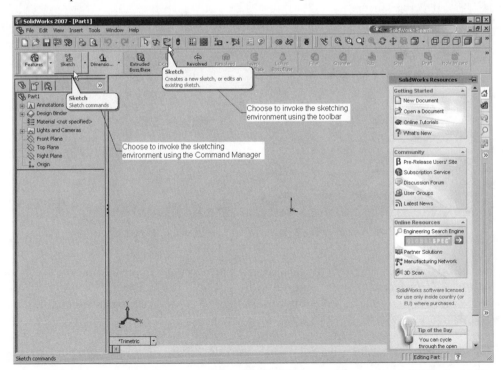

Figure 2-7 Different methods of invoking the sketching environment in SolidWorks 2007

> **Tip**. *To collapse the **Task Pane**, click anywhere in the drawing area, choose any one of the arrow symbols available on the right of the **Task Pane**, or click on the bar attached to these two arrows.*
>
> *To expand the **Task Pane** at any stage of the design cycle, choose any one of the arrows provided on the right of the **Task Pane**.*

box and the **Sketch** toolbar. Figure 2-7 shows the **Sketch** button added to the **Standard** toolbar. When you choose the **Sketch** button from the **Standard** toolbar or choose any tool from the **Sketch CommandManager**; the **Edit Sketch PropertyManager** is displayed and you are prompted to select the plane on which the sketch will be created. Also, the three default planes available in SolidWorks 2007 (**Front Plane**, **Right Plane**, and **Top Plane**) are temporarily displayed on the screen, as shown in Figure 2-8.

Figure 2-8 *Selecting the plane to draw the sketch of the base feature*

Depending on the requirement of the design, you can select any plane to draw the sketch of the base feature. The selected plane is automatically oriented normal to the view so that you can easily create the sketch. Also, the **CommandManager** now displays various sketching tools to draw the sketch.

The default screen appearance of a SolidWorks part document in the sketching environment is shown in Figure 2-9.

Figure 2-9 Default screen display of a part document in the sketching environment

SETTING THE DOCUMENT OPTIONS

When you install SolidWorks on your computer, you will be prompted to specify the dimensioning standards and units for measuring linear distances. The settings specified at that time are the default settings and whenever you start a new SolidWorks document, it will use these settings. However, if you want to modify these settings for a particular document, you can easily do so using the **Document Properties** dialog box. To invoke this dialog box, choose **Tools > Options**. When you invoke this option, the **System Options** dialog box will be displayed. In this dialog box, choose the **Document Properties** tab; the name of this dialog box will be changed to **Document Properties** dialog box. Setting the options for the current document using this dialog box is discussed next.

Modifying the Dimensioning Standards

To modify the dimensioning standards, invoke the **System Options** dialog box and then choose the **Document Properties** tab. You will notice that the **Detailing** option is selected by default in the area on the left to display the detailing options, as shown in Figure 2-10.

The default dimensioning standard that was selected while installing SolidWorks will be selected in the drop-down list provided in the **Dimensioning standard** area. You can select the required dimensioning standard from this drop-down list. The standards that are available are ANSI, ISO, DIN, JIS, BSI, GOST, and GB. You can select any one of these dimensioning standards for the current document.

Figure 2-10 *Setting the dimensioning standards*

Modifying the Linear and Angular Units

To modify the linear and angular units, invoke the **System Options** dialog box and then choose the **Document Properties** tab. In this tab, select the **Units** option from the area on the left to display the options related to linear and angular units, as shown in Figure 2-11. The default option for measuring the linear distances that was selected while installing SolidWorks will be available in the drop-down list in the **Length units** area. You can set the units from the options in the **Unit system** area. To specify units other than those in this area, choose the **Custom** radio button to invoke the options in the **Length units** area. You can set the units using the drop-down list provided in this area. The units that can be selected are angstroms, nanometers, microns, millimeters, centimeters, meters, microinches, mils, inches, feet, and feet & inches. You can also change the units for angular dimensions by selecting them from the drop-down list in the **Angular units** area. The angular units that can be selected are Degrees, Deg/Min, Deg/Min/Sec, and Radians.

Figure 2-11 *Setting the dimensioning units*

Modifying the Snap and Grid Settings

In the sketching environment of SolidWorks, you can make the cursor jump through a specified distance while creating the sketch. Therefore, if you draw a sketched entity, its length will change in the specified increment. For example, while drawing a line, if you make the cursor jump through a distance of 10 mm, the length of the line will be incremented by a distance of 10 mm. To do this, choose **Tools > Options** from the menu bar to display the **System Options** dialog box. To ensure that the cursor jumps through the specified distance, you need to invoke the snap option. Select the **Relations/Snap** branch of the **Sketch** option to display the related options. From the options available on the right, select the **Grid** check box and clear the **Snap only when grid is displayed** check box, if it is selected. This check box, when selected, snaps the sketched entities only when grid is displayed.

Now, choose the **Document Properties** tab to invoke the **Document Properties** dialog box. Select the **Grid/Snap** option to display the related options, see Figure 2-12. The distance through which the cursor jumps is dependent on the ratio between the values in the **Major grid spacing** and **Minor-lines per major** spinners available in the **Grid** area. For example, if you want that the coordinates should be incremented by 10 mm, you will have to make the ratio of the major and minor lines to 10. This can be done by setting the value of the **Major grid spacing** spinner to **100** and that of the **Minor-lines per major** spinner to **10**. Similarly, to make the cursor jump through a distance of 5 mm, set the value of the **Major grid spacing** spinner to **50** and that of the **Minor-lines per major** spinner to **10**.

Figure 2-12 Modifying the grid and snap settings

Tip. *If you want to display the grid in the sketching environment, select the* **Display grid** *check box from the* **Grid** *area of the* **Document Properties - Grid/Snap** *dialog box.*

While drawing a sketched entity by snapping through grips, the grips symbol is displayed below the cursor on the right.

Note
Remember that these settings will only be for the current documents. When you open a new document, it will have the settings that were defined while installing SolidWorks.

LEARNING ABOUT SKETCHER TERMS

Before you learn about the various sketching tools, it is important for you to understand some terms that are used in the sketching environment. These terms are discussed next.

Origin

The origin is a red color icon that is displayed at the center of the sketching environment screen. This icon consists of two arrows displaying the X and Y axes directions of the current sketching plane. The point of intersection of these two axes is the origin point and the coordinates of this point are 0,0.

Inferencing Lines

The inferencing lines are the temporary lines that are used to track a particular point on the screen. These lines are dashed lines and are automatically displayed when you select a sketching tool in the sketching environment. These lines are created from the endpoint of a sketched entity or from the origin. For example, if you want to draw a line from the point where two imaginary lines intersect, you can use the inferencing lines to locate the point and then draw the line from that point. Figure 2-13 shows the use of inferencing lines to locate the point of intersection of two imaginary lines.

Figure 2-13 *Using inferencing lines to locate a point*

Figure 2-14 shows the use of inferencing lines to locate the center of an arc. Notice that the inferencing lines are created from the endpoint of the line and from the origin.

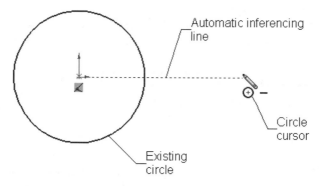

Figure 2-14 *Using inferencing lines to locate the center of a circle*

Note
The inferencing lines that are displayed on the screen will be either blue or yellow. The blue inferencing lines suggest that the relations are not added to the sketched entity and the yellow inferencing lines suggest that the relations are added to the sketched entity. You will learn about various relations in later chapters.

Select Tool

Toolbar:	Standard > Select

The **Select** tool is used to select a sketched entity or exit any sketching tool that is active. You can select the sketched entities by selecting them one by one using the left mouse button. You can also hold the left mouse button down and drag the cursor around the multiple sketched entities to define a box and select the multiple entities. There are two methods of selection, box selection and cross selection. You can also select multiple entities by pressing the SHIFT and CTRL keys. In this release of SolidWorks, a new tool has been added that allows you to invert the current selection. All these selection related tools are discussed next.

Note
*You can also invoke the **Select** tool or exit a sketching tool by pressing the ESC key.*

Invert Selection

Menu:	Tools > Invert Selection

With this release of SolidWorks, you are provided with an option to invert the selection set. By doing so, you can remove the entities in the current selection set and select all the other entities that are not in the current selection set. To invert the selection, select the entities that you do not want to be included in the final selection set and then choose **Tools > Invert Selection** from the menu bar. You can also, invoke the **Invert Selection** option from the shortcut menu. All the entities that were not selected earlier are now selected and the entities that were in the selection set earlier are now removed from the selection set.

Selecting Entities Using the Box Selection

A box is a window created by pressing the left mouse button and dragging the cursor from left to right in the drawing area. A box has a property that all entities that lie completely inside it will be selected. The selected entities will be displayed in green.

Selecting Entities Using the Cross Selection

When you press the left mouse button and drag the cursor from right to left in the drawing area, the cross selection method is invoked. The box drawn in the cross selection method consists of dashed lines. The cross selection method has a property that all entities that lie completely or partially inside the dashed box or the entities that touch the dashed box will be selected.

Selecting Entities Using the SHIFT and CTRL Keys

You can also use the SHIFT and CTRL keys on the keyboard to manage the selection procedure. If you have selected some entities and you need to select more entities using the windows or crossing selection, press and hold the SHIFT key. Now, create a window or a crossing selection; all the entities that touch the crossing or those inside the window are selected. You can also invert the current selection without invoking the **Invert Selection** tool. To do that, select the entities that you do not want to be included in the selection set and press the CTRL key. Now, drag a window or crossing; all the entities that touch the crossing or those inside the window are selected and the entities selected earlier are removed from the selection set.

Now, you are familiar with the important sketching terms. Next, you will learn about the sketching tools available in SolidWorks.

DRAWING LINES

CommandManager:	Sketch > Line
Menu:	Tools > Sketch Entities > Line
Toolbar:	Sketch > Line

Lines are one of the basic sketching entities available in SolidWorks. In general terms, a line is defined as the shortest distance between two points. As mentioned earlier, SolidWorks is a parametric solid modeling tool. This property allows you to draw a line of any length and at any angle and later force it to the desired length and angle. To draw a line in the sketching environment of SolidWorks, choose the **Line** tool from the **Sketch CommandManager**. You can also invoke the **Line** tool by pressing L on the keyboard. You will notice that the cursor, which was an arrow earlier, is replaced by the line cursor. The line cursor is actually a pencil-like cursor with a small inclined line below the pencil. Also, the **Insert Line PropertyManager** is displayed, as shown in Figure 2-15.

The **Message** rollout of the **Insert Line PropertyManager** informs you to edit the settings of the next line or sketch a new line. Using the options available in this **PropertyManager**, you can set the orientation and other sketching options of drawing a line. All these options are discussed next.

*Figure 2-15 The **Insert Line PropertyManager***

Orientation Rollout

The **Orientation** rollout is used to define the orientation of the line to be drawn. By default, the **As sketched** radio button is selected and you can draw the line in any orientation. If you select the **Horizontal** radio button, you can only draw horizontal lines. When you select this radio button, the **Parameters** rollout is displayed and you can specify the length of the line in the **Length** spinner provided in this rollout. If you select the **Add dimension** check box from this rollout, a dimension displaying the length of the line will be applied to the drawn line. You will learn more about dimensioning in the later chapters.

If you select the **Vertical** radio button, you can only draw vertical lines. The **Parameters** rollout is also displayed where you can set the parameters for drawing the vertical line.

The **Angle** radio button is selected to draw lines at a specified angle. When you select this radio button, the **Parameters** rollout is displayed, where you can set the values of the length of the line and the angle or orientation.

Options Rollout

The **For construction** check box available in this rollout is used to draw a construction line. You will learn more about construction lines later in this chapter. The **Infinite length** check box is used to draw a line of infinite length.

After setting the options in this **PropertyManager**, you need to draw the line. In SolidWorks, there are two methods of drawing lines. The first method is to draw continuous lines and the second method is to draw individual lines. Both these methods are discussed next.

Drawing a Chain of Continuous Lines

This is the default method of drawing lines. In this method, you just have to specify the start point and the endpoint of the line using the left mouse button. As soon as you specify the start point of the line, the **Line Properties PropertyManager** will be displayed. The options in the **Line Properties PropertyManager** will not be available at this stage.

After specifying the start point, move the cursor away from it and specify the endpoint of the line using the left mouse button. A line will be drawn between the two points. You will notice that the line is green and has filled circles at the two ends. The line will be displayed in green because it is still selected.

Move the cursor away from the endpoint of the line and you will notice that another line is attached to cursor. The start point of this line is the endpoint of the last line and the length of this line can be increased or decreased by moving the cursor. Because this line stretches like a rubber band as you move the cursor, it is called a rubber-band line. The point that you specify next on the screen will be taken as the endpoint of the second line and a line will be drawn such that the endpoint of the second line is taken as the start point of the new line and the point you specify is taken as the endpoint of the new line. Now, a new rubber-band line is displayed starting from the endpoint of the last line. This is a continuous process and you can draw a chain of as many continuous lines as you need by specifying the points on the screen using the left mouse button.

You can exit the continuous line drawing process by pressing the ESC key on the keyboard, by choosing the **Select** tool, or by double-clicking on the screen. You can also right-click to display the shortcut menu and choose the **End Chain** option from the shortcut menu.

Figure 2-16 shows a sketch drawn using continuous lines. This sketch is started from the lower left corner and the horizontal line is drawn first. To close the loop using the last line, as soon as you move the cursor close to the start point of the first line, you will notice that a red circle is displayed at the start point. If you specify the endpoint of the line at this stage, the loop will be closed and no rubber-band line will be displayed now. This is because the loop is already closed and you may not need another continuous line now. However, the **Line** tool is still active and you can draw other lines.

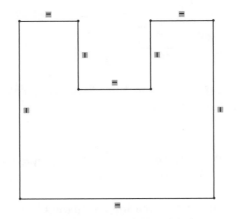

Figure 2-16 *Sketch drawn with the help of continuous lines*

Note

*When you exit the line drawing process by double-clicking on the screen or by choosing **End** **chain** from the shortcut menu, the current chain is ended but the **Line** tool is still active and you can draw other lines.*

Drawing Individual Lines

This is the second method of drawing lines. Using this method, you can draw individual lines and the start point of the next line will not necessarily be the endpoint of the last line. To draw individual lines, you need to press and hold the left mouse button down and drag the cursor from the start point of the line to the endpoint. Once you have dragged the cursor to the endpoint, release the left mouse button; a line will be drawn between the two points.

To make the process of sketching easy in SolidWorks, you are provided with the **PropertyManager**. The **PropertyManager** is a table that will be displayed on the left of the screen as soon as you select the first point of any sketched entity. The **PropertyManager** has all parameters related to the sketched entity such as the start point, endpoint, angle, length, and so on. You will notice that as you start dragging the mouse, the **Line Properties PropertyManager** is displayed on the left of the drawing area. All options in the **Line Properties PropertyManager** will be available when you release the left mouse button. Figure 2-17 shows a partial view of the **Line Properties PropertyManager**.

*Figure 2-17 Partial display of the **Line Properties**
PropertyManager*

Note

*The **Line Properties PropertyManager** will also display additional options about relations.
You will learn more about relations in later chapters.*

After you have drawn the line, modify the parameters in the **Line Properties PropertyManager** to make the line to the desired length and angle. You can also dynamically modify the line by holding its endpoints and dragging them.

Line Cursor Parameters

When you draw lines in the sketching environment of SolidWorks, you will notice that a numeric value is displayed above the line cursor, see Figure 2-18. This numeric value indicates the length of the line you draw. This value is the same as that in the **Length** spinner of the **Line Properties PropertyManager**. The only difference is that in the **Line Properties PropertyManager**, the value will be displayed with more precision.

Figure 2-18 The length of the line displayed on the screen while drawing the line

The other thing that you will notice while sketching is that sometimes when you are drawing vertical or horizontal lines, a ▬ or ▮ symbol is displayed below the line cursor. These are the symbols of the **Vertical** and **Horizontal** relations. SolidWorks automatically applies these relations to the lines. These relations ensure that the lines you draw are vertical or horizontal and not inclined. Figure 2-19 shows the symbol of the **Vertical** relation on a line and Figure 2-20 shows the symbol of the **Horizontal** relation on a line.

*Figure 2-19 Symbol of the **Vertical** relation*   *Figure 2-20 Symbol of the **Horizontal** relation*

Note

*In addition to the **Horizontal** and **Vertical** relations, you can apply a number of other relations such as **Tangent**, **Concentric**, **Perpendicular**, **Parallel**, and so on. You will learn about all these relations in later chapters.*

*The other options of the **Line Properties PropertyManager** will be discussed in later chapters.*

Drawing Tangent or Normal Arcs Using the Line Tool

SolidWorks allows you to draw tangent or normal arcs originating from the endpoint of the line while drawing continuous lines. Note that these arcs can be drawn only if you have drawn at least one line, arc, or spline. To draw such arcs, draw a line by specifying the start point and the endpoint. Move the cursor away from the endpoint of the last line to display the rubber-band line. Now, when you move the cursor back to the endpoint of the last line, the arc mode is invoked and the line cursor is replaced by the arc cursor. The angle and the radius of the arc is displayed above the arc cursor. You can also invoke the arc mode by right-clicking and choosing **Switch to arc** from the shortcut menu or pressing the A key from the keyboard.

To draw a tangent arc, invoke the arc mode by moving the cursor back to the endpoint of the last line. Now, move the cursor through a small distance along the tangent direction of the line; a dotted line will be drawn. Next, move the cursor in the direction in which the arc should be drawn. You will notice that a tangent arc is drawn. Specify the endpoint of the tangent arc using the left mouse button. Figure 2-21 shows an arc tangent to an existing line.

*Figure 2-21 Drawing a tangent arc using the **Line** tool*

To draw a normal arc, invoke the arc mode. Now, move the cursor through a small distance in the direction normal to the line and then move it in the direction of the endpoint of the arc; the normal arc will be drawn, as shown in Figure 2-22.

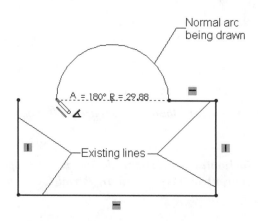

*Figure 2-22 Drawing a normal arc using the **Line** tool*

As soon as the endpoint of the tangent or normal arc is defined, the line mode will be invoked again. You can continue drawing lines using the line mode or move the cursor back to the endpoint of the arc to invoke the arc mode.

Note
*If the arc mode is invoked by mistake while drawing lines, you can cancel the arc mode and invoke the line mode again by pressing the A key from the keyboard. Alternatively, you can right-click and choose **Switch to Line** from the shortcut menu or move the cursor back to the endpoint and press the left mouse button to invoke the line mode.*

Drawing Construction Lines or Centerlines

CommandManager:	Sketch > Centerline
Menu:	Tools > Sketch Entities > Centerline
Toolbar:	Sketch > Centerline

Construction lines or centerlines are those that are drawn only for the aid of sketching. These lines are not considered while converting the sketches into features. You can draw a construction line similar to the sketched line by using the **Centerline** tool. You will notice that when you draw a construction line, the **For Construction** check box in the **Line Properties PropertyManager** is selected. You can also draw a construction line by sketching the line using the **Line** tool and then selecting the **For Construction** check box available in the **Line Properties PropertyManager**. When you select this check box, the line turns into a centerline.

DRAWING CIRCLES

CommandManager:	Sketch > Circle
Menu:	Tools > Sketch Entities > Circle
Toolbar:	Sketch > Circle

In SolidWorks, there are two methods of drawing circles. The first method is by specifying the center point of a circle and then defining its radius. The second method is to draw a circle by defining three points that lie on its periphery. Both these methods are discussed next. To draw a circle, choose the **Circle** button from the **Sketch CommandManager**; the **Circle PropertyManager** will be displayed, as shown in Figure 2-23.

Drawing Circles by Defining Their Centerpoints

When you invoke the **Circle PropertyManager**, the **Center creation** radio button is selected by default in the **Parameters** rollout. This radio button is selected to draw a circle by specifying its center. You will notice that the arrow cursor is replaced by the circle cursor. The circle cursor consists of a pencil and two concentric circles below the pencil. Specify the center point of the circle and then move the cursor to define its radius. The current radius of the circle is displayed above the circle cursor. This radius will change as you move the cursor. The coordinates of the center point of the circle and the radius, updated dynamically, are shown in the **Circle PropertyManager**. You can define any arbitrary radius of the circle and then modify it to the desired value by using the **Circle PropertyManager**. Figure 2-24 shows a circle being drawn using the **Center creation** option of the **Circle** tool.

Figure 2-23 *The Circle PropertyManager*

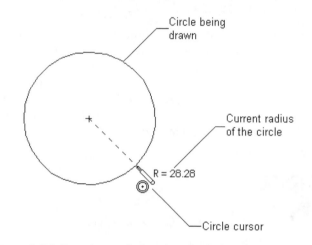

Figure 2-24 *Drawing a circle using the Center creation option*

Drawing Circles by Defining Three Points

The **Perimeter creation** radio button is used to draw a circle by defining three points on it. To draw a circle using this option, invoke the **Circle PropertyManager** and select the **Perimeter creation** radio button from the **Parameters** rollout. The select cursor will be replaced by a three point circle cursor. Specify the first point of the circle in the drawing area. Now, specify the other two points on the circle. The resulting circle will be highlighted in green and you can set its parameters in the **Circle PropertyManager**. Figure 2-25 shows a circle being drawn by specifying three points on it.

Drawing Construction Circles

If you want to sketch a construction circle, draw a circle using the **Circle** tool and then select the **For construction** check box available in the **Circle PropertyManager**.

DRAWING ARCS

In SolidWorks, you can draw arcs using three methods: **Tangent/Normal Arc**, **Centerpoint Arc**,

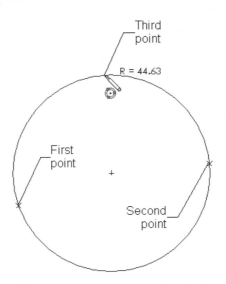

*Figure 2-25 Drawing a circle using the **Perimeter creation** option*

Tip. *To convert a construction entity back to the sketched entity, invoke the **Select** tool and then select the construction entity; the entity will turn green and the **PropertyManager** will be displayed on the left of the drawing area. From the **PropertyManager**, clear the **For Construction** check box; the construction entity will again be changed into a sketched entity and it will be displayed with a continuous line.*

and **3 Point Arc**. All these methods can be invoked separately by choosing their respective buttons from the **Sketch CommandManager**. These methods are discussed next.

Drawing Tangent/Normal Arcs

CommandManager:	Sketch > Tangent Arc
Menu:	Tools > Sketch Entities > Tangent Arc
Toolbar:	Sketch > Tangent Arc

The tangent arcs are those that are drawn tangent to an existing sketched entity. The existing sketched entities include sketched and construction lines, arcs, and splines. The normal arcs are those that are drawn normal to an existing entity. You can draw tangent and normal arcs using the **Tangent Arc** tool.

To draw a tangent arc, invoke the **Tangent Arc** tool; the arrow cursor will be replaced by the arc cursor. Move the arc cursor close to the endpoint of the entity you want to select as the tangent entity. You will notice that a red circle is displayed at the endpoint. Also, a yellow symbol displaying two concentric circles appears below the pencil. Now, press the left mouse button once and move the cursor along the tangent direction through a small distance and then move the cursor to size the arc. The arc will start from the endpoint of the tangent entity and its size will change as you move the cursor. Note that the angle and the radius of the tangent arc are displayed above the arc cursor, see Figure 2-26.

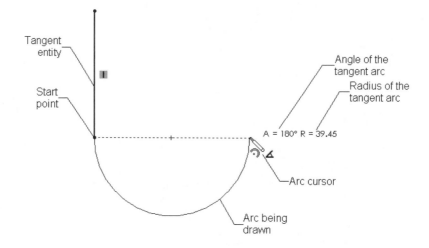

Figure 2-26 *Drawing a tangent arc*

To draw a normal arc, invoke the **Tangent Arc** tool. Move the arc cursor close to the endpoint of the entity you want to select as the normal entity. A red circle will be displayed at the endpoint and a yellow symbol displaying two concentric circles that appear below the pencil. Now, press the left mouse button once and move the cursor along the normal direction through a small distance and then move the cursor to size the arc, refer to Figure 2-27.

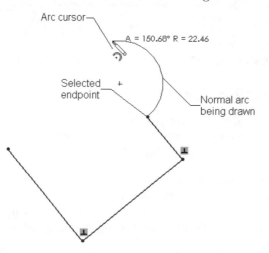

Figure 2-27 *Drawing a normal arc*

 Tip. *You can invoke the list of recently used commands by right-clicking in the drawing area. The cascading menu that is displayed when you choose the **Recent Command** option from the shortcut menu displays the eight most recent commands.*

While drawing the arc, as soon as you start moving the cursor after specifying the start point, the **Arc PropertyManager** will be displayed. However, the options in the **Arc PropertyManager**

*Figure 2-28 Partial display of the **Arc PropertyManager***

are not enabled at this stage. These options are enabled only after you have completed drawing the tangent or normal arc.

You can draw an arbitrary arc and then modify its value using the **Arc PropertyManager**. Figure 2-28 shows a partial view of the **Arc PropertyManager**.

Note
*When you select a tangent entity to draw a tangent arc, the **Tangent** relation is applied between the start point of the arc and the tangent entity. Therefore, if you change the coordinates of the start point of the arc, the tangent entity will also be modified accordingly.*

Drawing Centerpoint Arcs

CommandManager:	Sketch > Centerpoint Arc
Menu:	Tools > Sketch Entity > Centerpoint Arc
Toolbar:	Sketch > Centerpoint Arc

The center point arcs are those that are drawn by defining the center point, start point, and endpoint of the arc. When you invoke this tool, the arrow cursor is replaced by the arc cursor. As mentioned earlier, an arc cursor consists of a pencil and an arc below the pencil.

To draw a center point arc, invoke the **Centerpoint Arc** tool and then move the arc cursor to the point that you want to specify as the center point of the arc. Press the left mouse button once at the location of the center point and then move the cursor to the point from where you want to start the arc. You will notice that a dotted circle is displayed on the screen. The size of this circle will modify as you move the mouse. This circle is drawn for your reference and the center point of this circle lies at the point that you specified as the center of the arc. Press the left mouse button once at the point that you want to select as the start point of the arc. Next, move the cursor to specify the endpoint of the arc. You will notice that the reference circle is no longer displayed and an arc is being drawn with the start point as the point that you specified after specifying the center point. Also, the **Arc PropertyManager**, similar to the one that is shown in the tangent arc, is displayed on the left of the drawing area. Note that the options in the **Arc PropertyManager** will not be available at this stage.

If you move the cursor in the clockwise direction, the resulting arc will be drawn in the clockwise direction. However, if you move the cursor in the counterclockwise direction, the resulting arc will be drawn in the counterclockwise direction. Specify the endpoint of the arc using the left mouse button. Figure 2-29 shows the reference circle that is drawn when you move the mouse button after specifying the center point of the arc and Figure 2-30 shows the resulting center point arc.

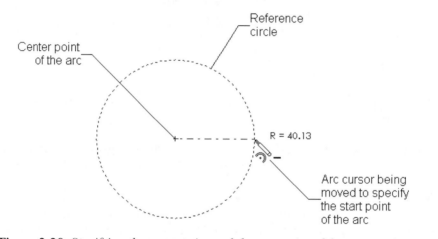

Figure 2-29 Specifying the center point and the start point of the center point arc

Figure 2-30 Moving the cursor to specify the start point and the endpoint of the arc

Drawing 3 Point Arcs

CommandManager:	Sketch > 3 Point Arc
Menu:	Tools > Sketch Entities > 3 Point Arc
Toolbar:	Sketch > 3 Point Arc

The three point arcs are those that are drawn by defining the start point and endpoint of the arc, and a point somewhere on the arc. When you invoke this tool, the arrow cursor is replaced by the arc cursor.

To draw a three point arc, invoke the **3 Point Arc** tool and then move the arc cursor to the point that you want to specify as the start point of the arc. Press the left mouse button once at the location of the start point and then move the cursor to the point that you want specify as the endpoint of the arc. As soon as you start moving the cursor after specifying the start point, a reference arc will be drawn and the **Arc PropertyManager** will be displayed. However, the options in the **Arc PropertyManager** will not be available at this stage.

Using the left mouse button, specify the endpoint of the arc. You will notice that the reference arc is no longer displayed. Instead, a solid arc is displayed and the cursor is attached to it. As you move the cursor, the arc will also be modified dynamically. Using the left mouse button, specify a point on the screen to create the arc. The last point that you specify will determine the direction of the arc. The options in the **Arc PropertyManager** will be displayed once you draw the arc. You can modify the properties of the arc using the **Arc PropertyManager**. Figure 2-31 shows the reference arc that is drawn by specifying the start point and the endpoint of the arc and Figure 2-32 shows the resulting three point arc.

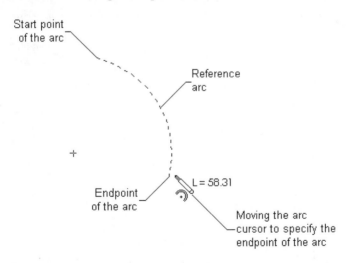

Figure 2-31 Specifying the start point and the endpoint of the arc

Figure 2-32 Specifying a point on the arc to draw it

DRAWING RECTANGLES

CommandManager:	Sketch > Rectangle
Menu:	Tools > Sketch Entities > Rectangle
Toolbar:	Sketch > Rectangle

In SolidWorks, the rectangles are drawn by specifying two opposite corners of the rectangle. To draw a rectangle, invoke the **Rectangle** tool; the arrow cursor will be replaced by the rectangle cursor. Move the cursor to the point that you want to specify as the first corner of the rectangle. Press the left mouse button once at the first corner and then move the cursor and specify the other corner of the rectangle using the left mouse button. You will notice that the length and width of the rectangle are displayed above the rectangle cursor. The length is measured along the X axis and the width is measured along the Y axis. Figure 2-33 shows a rectangle being drawn by specifying two opposite corners.

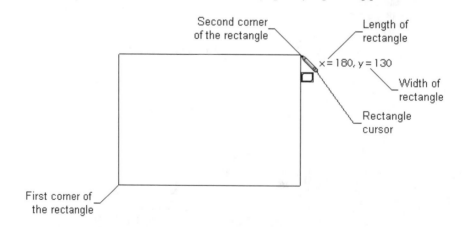

Figure 2-33 Drawing a rectangle by specifying two opposite corners

Tip. *You can also dislodge the **Task Pane** from its position by double-clicking on the gray bar at the top where its name is displayed. Now, you can move it at the desired location. To place it back on its original position, again double-click on the gray bar or choose the **Dock Task Pane** button provided on the top-right corner of the **Task Pane**.*

Note

*When you draw a rectangle, the **PropertyManager** will not be displayed. This is because a rectangle is considered as a combination of four individual lines. Therefore, after drawing the rectangle, if you select one of the lines of the rectangle using the **Select** tool, the **Line Properties PropertyManager** will be displayed. You can modify the parameters of the selected line using the **Line Properties PropertyManager**.*

*Remember that because the relations are applied to all four corners of the rectangle, if you modify the parameters of one of the lines using the **Line Properties PropertyManager**, the other three lines will also be modified accordingly.*

*You can convert a rectangle into a construction rectangle by selecting all lines together using a window and then selecting the **For construction** check box from the **PropertyManager**.*

DRAWING PARALLELOGRAMS

Menu:	Tools > Sketch Entities > Parallelogram

In SolidWorks, the **Parallelogram** tool can be used to draw a parallelogram and also to draw a rectangle at an angle. The methods used to draw both these entities are discussed next.

Drawing a Rectangle at an Angle

To draw a rectangle at an angle, invoke the **Parallelogram** tool from the menu bar. The cursor will be replaced by the parallelogram cursor. Move the cursor to the point you want to specify as the start point of one of the edges of the rectangle. Press the left mouse button once at this point and move the cursor to size the edge. You will notice that a reference line is being drawn. Depending on the current position of the cursor, the reference line will be horizontal, vertical, or inclined at some angle. The current length of the edge and its angle will be displayed above the parallelogram cursor. Using the left mouse button, specify the endpoint of the edge such that the resulting reference line is at an angle.

Next, move the cursor to specify the width of the rectangle. You will notice that a reference rectangle is drawn at an angle. Also, irrespective of the current position of the cursor, the width will be specified normal to the first edge, either above or below. Using the left mouse button, specify a point on the screen to define the width of the rectangle. The reference rectangle will be converted into a sketched rectangle. Figure 2-34 shows a rectangle drawn at an angle.

Drawing a Parallelogram

To draw a parallelogram, invoke the **Parallelogram** tool from the menu bar. The cursor will be replaced by the parallelogram cursor. Specify two points on the screen to define one edge of the parallelogram. Next, press the CTRL key from the keyboard once and then move the mouse to define the width of the parallelogram. You will notice that the width is no longer added normal to the first edge. As you move the mouse, a reference parallelogram will be drawn. The size and shape of the reference parallelogram will depend on the current location of the cursor.

Specify a point on the screen to define the parallelogram. Figure 2-35 shows a parallelogram drawn at an angle.

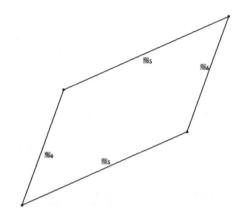

Figure 2-34 *Rectangle at an angle*   **Figure 2-35** *Parallelogram at an angle*

Note
*Similar to rectangles, each edge of a parallelogram is considered as a separate line. Also, in the case of parallelograms, the **PropertyManager** is not displayed while you are drawing it.*

DRAWING POLYGONS

Menu:	Tools > Sketch Entities > Polygon

A polygon is defined as a multisided geometric figure in which the length of all sides and the angle between them are the same. In SolidWorks, you can draw a polygon with the number of sides ranging from 3 to 40. The dimensions of a polygon are controlled using the diameter of a construction circle that is inscribed inside the polygon or circumscribed outside the polygon. If the construction circle is inscribed inside the polygon, the diameter of the construction circle will be taken from the edges of the polygon. If the construction circle is circumscribed about the polygon, the diameter of the construction circle will be taken from the vertices of the polygon.

To draw a polygon, invoke the **Polygon** tool; the **Polygon PropertyManager** will be displayed, as shown in Figure 2-36.

Set the parameters such as the number of sides, inscribed or circumscribed circle, and so on, in the **Polygon PropertyManager**. You can also modify these parameters after drawing the polygon. When you invoke this tool, the arrow cursor will be replaced by the polygon cursor. Press the left mouse button at the point that you want to specify as the center point of the polygon and then move the cursor to size the polygon. The length of each side and the rotation angle of the

Tip. *You can also invoke the tools to draw lines, arcs, circles, or rectangles using the shortcut menu that is displayed when you right-click in the drawing area.*

*Figure 2-36 The **Polygon PropertyManager***

polygon will be displayed above the polygon cursor as you drag it. Using the left mouse button, specify a point on the screen after you get the desired length and rotation angle of the polygon. You will notice that based on whether you selected the **Inscribed circle** or the **Circumscribed circle** radio button in the **Polygon PropertyManager**, a construction circle will be drawn inside or outside the polygon. After you have drawn the polygon, you can modify the parameters such as the center point of the polygon, the diameter of the construction circle, the angle of rotation, and so on using the **Polygon PropertyManager**. If you want to draw another polygon, choose the **New polygon** button provided below the **Angle** spinner in the **Polygon PropertyManager**.

Figure 2-37 shows a six-sided polygon with the construction circle inscribed inside the polygon and Figure 2-38 shows a five-sided polygon with the construction circle circumscribed outside the polygon. Note that the reference circle is retained with the polygon. Remember that this circle will not be considered while converting the polygon into a feature.

Figure 2-37 *Six-sided polygon with construction circle inscribed inside the polygon*

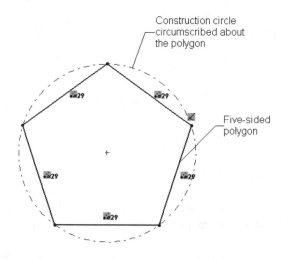

Figure 2-38 *Five-sided polygon with construction circle circumscribed outside the polygon*

DRAWING SPLINES

CommandManager:	Sketch > Spline
Menu:	Tools > Sketch Entities > Spline
Toolbar:	Sketch > Spline

In SolidWorks, you can draw a spline by continuously specifying the endpoints of the spline segments using the left mouse button. This method of drawing splines is similar to that of drawing continuous lines. After specifying all points of the spline, right-click and choose **Select** to exit the **Spline** tool. Choosing **End Spline** will exit the current spline but the **Spline** tool will still be active and you can draw another spline. Figure 2-39 shows a spline drawn with its start point at the origin.

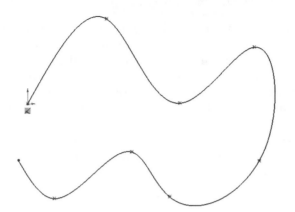

Figure 2-39 Sketched spline with its start point at the origin

Note
*Handles are provided on the points that were used to draw a spline. These handles are displayed when you select the spline using the **Select** tool. You will learn more about these handles in the later chapters while editing splines.*

Similar to drawing individual lines, you can also create individual spline segments by specifying the start point and then dragging the mouse to specify the endpoint.

Tip. *After creating the spline, when you select it using the **Select** tool, the **Spline PropertyManager** is displayed. The current handle will be displayed with a cyan filled square and its number and the corresponding X and Y coordinates will be displayed in the **Spline PropertyManager**. You can modify these coordinates to modify the selected spline. A double-sided arrow will also be displayed along with the handle. You will learn more about this in the later chapters.*

PLACING SKETCHED POINTS

CommandManager:	Sketch > Point
Menu:	Tools > Sketch Entities > Point
Toolbar:	Sketch > Point

To place a sketched point, choose the **Point** tool from the **CommandManager** and then specify the point on the screen where you want to place it. The **Point PropertyManager** will be displayed with the X and Y coordinates of the current point. You can modify the location of the point by modifying its X and Y coordinates in the **Point PropertyManager**.

DRAWING ELLIPSES

Menu: Tools > Sketch Entities > Ellipse

In SolidWorks, an ellipse is drawn by specifying its center point and then specifying the two ellipse axes by moving the mouse. To draw an ellipse, invoke the **Ellipse** tool from the menu bar; the arrow cursor will be replaced by the ellipse cursor. Move the cursor to the point that you want to specify as the center point of the ellipse. Press the left mouse button once at the center point of the ellipse and then move the cursor to specify one of the ellipse axes. You will notice that a reference circle is drawn and two values are displayed above the ellipse cursor, see Figure 2-40. The first value that shows R = * is the radius of the first axis that you are defining and the second value that shows r = * is the radius of the other axis. While defining the first axis, the second axis is taken equal to the first axis. This is the reason why a reference circle is drawn and not a reference ellipse.

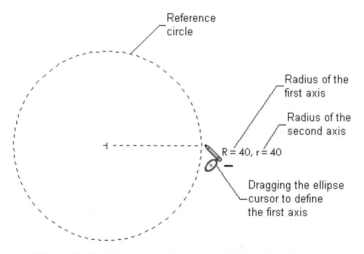

Figure 2-40 *Dragging the cursor to define the first axis*

Specify a point on the screen to define the first axis. Next, move the cursor to size the other ellipse axis. You will notice that the **Ellipse PropertyManager** is displayed. As you move the cursor, the second value above the ellipse cursor that shows r = * will change dynamically. Using the left mouse button, specify a point on the screen to define the second axis of the ellipse, see Figure 2-41.

DRAWING ELLIPTICAL ARCS

Menu: Tools > Sketch Entities > Partial Ellipse

In SolidWorks, the process of drawing an elliptical arc is similar to that of drawing an ellipse. You will follow the same process of defining the ellipse first. The point that you specify on the screen to define the second axis of the ellipse is taken as the start point of the elliptical arc. You can define the endpoint of the elliptical arc by specifying a point on the screen, as shown in Figure 2-42.

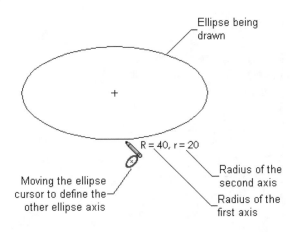

Figure 2-41 Defining the second axis of the ellipse

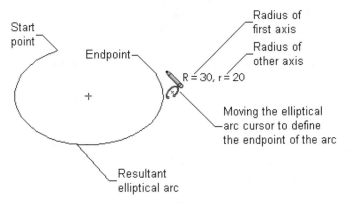

Figure 2-42 Drawing the elliptical arc

You can also set the parameters of the elliptical arc in the **Ellipse PropertyManager** shown in Figure 2-43.

DRAWING PARABOLIC CURVES

Menu: Tools > Sketch Entities > Parabola

In SolidWorks, you can draw a parabolic curve by specifying the focus point of the parabola and then specifying two points on the guide of the parabolic curve. To draw a parabolic curve, invoke the **Parabola** tool from the menu bar; the cursor will be replaced by the parabola cursor. Move the cursor to the point that you want to specify as the focal point of the parabola. Press the left mouse button once at the focal point and then move the cursor to define the apex point and size the parabola. You will notice that a reference parabolic arc is displayed. As you move the cursor away from the focal point, the parabola will be flattened. After you get the basic shape of the parabolic curve, specify a point on the screen using the left mouse button. This point is taken as the apex of the parabolic curve. Next, specify two points on the screen with respect to the reference parabola to define the guide of the parabolic curve, see Figure 2-44.

Figure 2-43 *Partial view of the **Ellipse PropertyManager***

Figure 2-44 *Drawing the parabola*

As you move the mouse after specifying the focal point of the parabola, the **Parabola PropertyManager** will be displayed. But the options in the **Parabola PropertyManager** will not be available. These options will be available only after you have drawn the parabola. Figure 2-45 shows a partial view of the **Parabola PropertyManager**.

DRAWING DISPLAY TOOLS

The drawing display tools are one of the most important tools provided in any of the solid modeling software. These tools allow you to modify the display of a drawing by zooming or panning it. Some of the drawing display tools available in SolidWorks are discussed in this chapter. The remaining tools are discussed in the later chapters.

*Figure 2-45   Partial view of the **Parabola** PropertyManager*

Zoom to Fit

Menu: View > Modify > Zoom to Fit
Toolbar: View > Zoom to Fit

 The **Zoom to Fit** tool is used to increase or decrease the drawing display area so that all sketched entities or dimensions are fitted inside the current view.

Zoom to Area

Menu: View > Modify > Zoom to Area
Toolbar: View > Zoom to Area

 The **Zoom to Area** tool is used to magnify a specified area so that the part of the drawing inside the magnified area can be viewed in the current window. The area is defined by a window that is created by dragging the cursor and specifying two opposite corners of the window. When you choose this tool, the cursor is replaced by a magnifying glass cursor. Press and hold the left mouse button down and drag the cursor to specify the two opposite corners of the window. The area enclosed inside the window will be magnified.

Zoom In/Out

Menu: View > Modify > Zoom In/Out
Toolbar: View > Zoom In/Out

 The **Zoom In/Out** tool is used to dynamically zoom in or out of the drawing. When you invoke this tool, the cursor is replaced by the zoom cursor. To zoom out of a drawing, press and hold the left mouse button down and drag the cursor in the downward direction. Similarly, to zoom in a drawing, press and hold the left mouse button down and drag the cursor

> **Tip**. *You can also use the keyboard shortcuts to invoke some of the drawing display tools. For example, to invoke the **Zoom to Fit** tool, press the F key. Similarly, to zoom out of a drawing, press the Z key and to zoom in, press the SHIFT+Z keys.*

in the upward direction. As you drag the cursor, the drawing display will be modified dynamically. After you get the desired view, exit this tool by choosing the **Select** tool from the **Sketch** toolbar. You can also exit this tool by right-clicking and choosing **Select** from the shortcut menu or by pressing the ESC key.

Zoom to Selection

Menu:	View > Modify > Zoom to Selection
Toolbar:	View > Zoom to Selection

 The **Zoom to Selection** tool is used to modify the drawing display area such that the selected entity is fitted inside the current display. After selecting the entity, choose the **Zoom to Selection** button. The drawing display area will be modified such that the selected entity fits inside the current view.

Pan

Menu:	View > Modify > Pan
Toolbar:	View > Pan

 The **Pan** tool is used to drag the view in the current display. This process is similar to changing the view by using the scroll bars available in the drawing area.

> **Tip**. *You can also invoke the **Pan** tool using the CTRL key and the arrow keys on the keyboard. For example, to pan toward the right, press the CTRL key and then press the right arrow key a few times. Similarly, to pan upward, press the CTRL key and then press the up arrow key a few times.*

Redraw

Menu:	View > Redraw

The **Redraw** tool is used to refresh the screen. Sometimes when you draw a sketched entity, some unwanted elements remain on the screen. To remove these unwanted elements from the screen, choose this tool. The screen will be refreshed and all the unwanted elements will be removed. You can also invoke this tool by pressing the CTRL+R keys from the keyboard.

DELETING SKETCHED ENTITIES

You can delete the sketched entities by selecting them using the **Select** tool and then pressing the DELETE key on the keyboard. You can select the entities by selecting them individually or select more than one entity by defining a window or crossing around the entities. When you select the entities, they turn green. When they turn green, press the DELETE key on the keyboard. You can also delete the sketched entities by selecting them and choosing the **Delete** option from the shortcut menu that is displayed on right-clicking.

TUTORIALS

Tutorial 1

In this tutorial, you will draw the sketch of the model shown in Figure 2-46. The sketch is shown in Figure 2-47. You will not dimension the sketch. The solid model and the dimensions are given for your reference only. **(Expected time: 30 min)**

Figure 2-46 Solid model for Tutorial 1

Figure 2-47 Sketch of the model

The steps that will be followed to complete this tutorial are listed below:

a. Start SolidWorks and then start a new part document.
b. Switch to the sketching environment.
c. Draw the sketch of the model using the **Line** and **Circle** tools, refer to Figures 2-50 through 2-52.
d. Save the sketch and then close the document.

Starting SolidWorks and Starting a New Part Document

1. Start SolidWorks by choosing **Start > Programs > SolidWorks 2007 > SolidWorks 2007** or by double-clicking on the shortcut icon of SolidWorks 2007 available on the desktop of your computer.

    The **SolidWorks 2007** window is displayed along with the **SolidWorks Resources Task Pane** on its right. The **Getting Started**, **Online Resources**, and **Tip of the Day** groups are displayed in this **Task Pane**.

    You can get many valuable tips from the **Tip of the Day** group. These tips are helpful to make full utilization of this CAD package.

2. Choose the **New Document** option from the **Getting Started** group of the **SolidWorks Resources Task Pane** to display the **New SolidWorks Document** dialog box.

3. The **Part** button is chosen by default. Choose the **OK** button from the **New SolidWorks Document** dialog box shown in Figure 2-48; a new SolidWorks part document is started. Also, the part modeling environment is active by default.

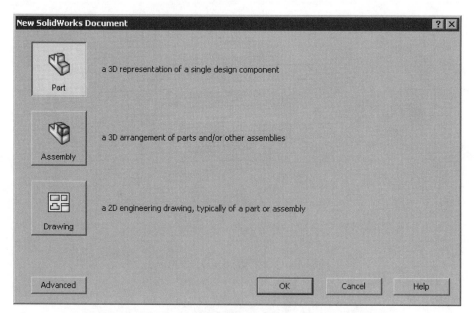

Figure 2-48 The New SolidWorks Document dialog box

Tip. *If the shortcut icon of SolidWorks is not created automatically on the desktop of your computer when you install SolidWorks, you can create it manually. To create the shortcut icon on the desktop, choose* **Start > Programs > SolidWorks 2007** *to display the SolidWorks cascading menu. Right-click on* **SolidWorks 2007** *in the cascading menu and then choose* **Send To > Desktop (create shortcut)** *from the shortcut menu.*

Because you first need to draw the sketch of the feature, you need to invoke the sketching environment.

4. Choose the **Sketch** button from the **Standard** toolbar; the **Edit Sketch PropertyManager** is displayed and you are prompted to select a plane on which you want to draw the sketch.

5. Select **Front Plane** from the drawing area; the sketching environment is invoked and the plane is oriented normal to the view. You will notice that a red origin is displayed at the center of the screen, indicating the sketching environment. The default screen appearance of the sketching environment of SolidWorks is shown in Figure 2-49.

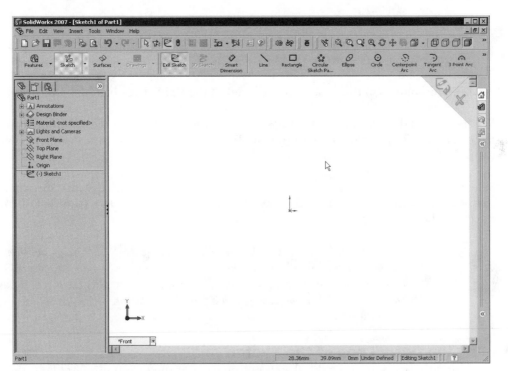

Figure 2-49 Screen display in the sketching environment

Setting Units and Grid

It is assumed that while installing SolidWorks, you selected the option of measuring the length in millimeters. This is the reason why the length will be measured in millimeter in the current file. But if you selected some other unit, you need to make some initial settings of changing the linear and angular units before you proceed with drawing the sketch.

1. Choose **Tools > Options** from the menu bar to invoke the **System Options - General** dialog box.

2. Choose the **Document Properties** tab; the name of the dialog box is changed to **Document Properties - Detailing**.

3. Select the **Units** option from the area on the left to display the options related to linear and angular units.

4. Select the **MMGS (millimeter, gram, second)** radio button from the **Unit system** area if it is not selected by default. Also, select the **Degrees** option from the drop-down list provided in the **Angular units** area.

Note

*If you had selected **Millimeters** as the unit while installing SolidWorks, you can skip the points discussed earlier in this section.*

5. Select **Grid/Snap** from the area on the left. Select the **Grid** check box, if it is cleared.

6. Set the value of the **Major grid spacing** spinner to **100** and the value of the **Minor-lines per major** spinner to **20**. Now, choose the **Go To System Snaps** button; the system options related to relations and snap are displayed.

7. Select the **Grid** check box from the **Sketch Snaps** area, if it is cleared. Make sure that you clear the **Snap only when grid is displayed** check box, if it is selected. Choose **OK** to exit the dialog box.

Tip. *If the grid is displayed on the screen when you invoke the sketching environment for the first time, then you can set the option to turn off the grid display. Right-click in the drawing area to display the shortcut menu. The **Display Grid** option has a check mark on its left, indicating that this option is chosen. Select this option again to turn the grids off.*

Drawing the Outer Loop of the Sketch

It is a good practice to draw the sketch on one side of the origin, preferably in the first quadrant. This is because while generating the part program for manufacturing the part, you will have a reference for work origin in advance.

The sketch of the model consists of an outer loop, two circles inside the outer loop, and a cavity. Therefore, it will be drawn using the **Line** and **Circle** tools. You will first draw the outer loop and then the inner entities. Note that in the sketching environment, the lower left corner of the SolidWorks window displays three main areas. The first area displays the X, Y, and Z coordinates of the current location of the cursor. These coordinates will be modified as you move the cursor around the drawing area. You will use the coordinate display to draw the sketch of the model.

You will start drawing the sketch from the lower left corner of the sketch and the outer loop will be drawn using the continuous lines.

1. Choose the **Line** button from the **Sketch CommandManager** to invoke the **Line** tool; the arrow cursor is replaced by the line cursor.

2. Move the cursor in the first quadrant close to the origin; the coordinates of the point are displayed close to the lower left corner of the screen.

3. Press the left mouse button at the point whose coordinates are 10 mm, 10 mm, 0 mm and then move the cursor horizontally toward the right.

    You will notice that the symbol of the **Horizontal** relation is displayed below the line cursor and the length of the line is displayed above the line cursor.

    As the length of the first horizontal line at the lower left corner of the sketch is 10 mm, you will move the mouse until the length of the line above the line cursor is shown as 10.

4. Press the left mouse button when the length of the line that is displayed above the line cursor shows a value of 10. Make sure the **Horizontal** relation symbol is displayed below the cursor.

    The first horizontal line is drawn. Because you are drawing continuous lines, the endpoint of the last line is automatically selected as the start point of the next line.

5. Move the line cursor vertically upward. The symbol of the **Vertical** relation is displayed below the line cursor and the length of the line is displayed above the line cursor.

6. Press the left mouse button when the length of the line displayed above the line cursor shows a value of 10 and the **Vertical** relation symbol is displayed below the cursor.

    A vertical line of length 10 mm will be drawn and displayed in green. Also, as this is the line that is selected now, the previous line will no longer be highlighted and therefore will be displayed in blue.

7. Move the line cursor horizontally toward the right. Press the left mouse button when the length of the line above the line cursor shows a value of 10. This draws the next horizontal line of 10 mm length.

8. Move the line cursor vertically downward and press the left mouse button when the length of the line on the line cursor shows a value of 10.

> **Tip**. *If by mistake you invoke the arc mode while drawing lines, move the cursor back to the endpoint of the previous line and press the left mouse button. The line mode will be invoked again.*

9. Move the line cursor horizontally toward the right and press the left mouse button when the length of the line on the line cursor shows a value of 30.

10. Move the line cursor vertically upward and press the left mouse button when the length of the line on the line cursor shows a value of 10.

11. Move the line cursor horizontally toward the right and press the left mouse button when the length of the line on the line cursor shows a value of 10.

12. Move the line cursor vertically downward and press the left mouse button when the length of the line on the line cursor shows a value of 10.

13. Move the line cursor horizontally toward the right and press the left mouse button when the length of the line on the line cursor shows a value of 10.

14. Move the line cursor vertically upward and press the left mouse button when the length of the line on the line cursor displays a value of 40.

    The next line that you need to draw is an inclined line that makes an angle of 135-degrees. To draw this line, you need to move the cursor in a direction that makes an angle of 135-degrees.

15. Move the line cursor such that the line is drawn at an angle of 135-degrees and the length of the line displays a value of 14.14 above the cursor. The angle can be checked from the **Angle** spinner in the **Parameters** rollout of the **Line PropertyManager**.

16. Press the left mouse button at this location to specify the endpoint of the inclined line.

17. Move the line cursor horizontally toward the left and press the left mouse button when the length of the line on the line cursor displays a value of 50.

    You will notice that some yellow inferencing lines are displayed when you move the cursor.

18. Move the line cursor in the direction diagonally downward where the value of the angle displays a value of 135-degrees and the length of the lines displays a value of 14.14.

19. Press the left mouse button at this location.

20. Move the cursor vertically downward to the start point of the first line.

    You will notice that when you move the cursor close to the start point of the first line, a red circle is displayed. Symbols of the **Vertical** and **Coincident** relations are displayed on the right of the cursor. The length of the line shows a value of 40.

21. Press the left mouse button when the red circle is displayed. Right-click to display the shortcut menu and choose the **Select** option to exit the **Line** tool.

This completes the sketch of the outer loop. Note that the display of the sketch is small. Therefore, you need to modify the drawing display area such that the sketch fits the screen. This is done using the **Zoom to Fit** tool.

22. Choose the **Zoom to Fit** button from the **View** toolbar to fit the current sketch on the screen. The outer loop of the sketch is completed and is shown in Figure 2-50. Note that in this figure, the display of the grid is temporarily turned off for a better visibility. This can be done by clearing the **Display grid** check box from the **Grid** area of the **Document Properties - Grid/Snap** dialog box.

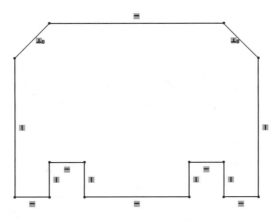

Figure 2-50 Outer loop of the sketch

Drawing Circles

The circles will be drawn using the **Circle** tool. You will use the inferencing line originating from the start points and endpoints of the inclined lines to specify the center point of the circles. At a given time, you can snap to grid or use inferencing lines to draw the sketches. Therefore, you need to turn off the snapping to grid.

1. Choose **Tools > Options** from the menu bar to invoke the **System Options - General** dialog box. Select **Relations/Snaps** from the left of this dialog box. Clear the **Grid** check box and choose the **OK** button from this dialog box.

2. Choose the **Circle** button from the **Sketch CommandManager** to invoke the **Circle** tool.

When you invoke the **Circle** tool, the arrow cursor will be replaced by the circle cursor.

3. Move the circle cursor close to the lower endpoint of the right inclined line and then move it toward the left. Remember that you will not press the left mouse button at this moment.

An inferencing line is displayed originating from the lower endpoint of the right inclined line. When you move the cursor toward the left, you will notice that at the point where the cursor is vertically in line with the upper endpoint of the right inclined line, another inferencing line originates from the upper endpoint of the right inclined line. This inferencing line will intersect the inferencing line generated from the lower endpoint of the inclined line.

4.   Press the left mouse button at the point where the inferencing lines from both the endpoints of the inclined lines intersect. Now, move the circle cursor toward the left to define a circle.

5.   Press the left mouse button when the radius of the circle displayed above the circle cursor shows a value close to 5.

6.   The **Circle PropertyManager** is displayed. Set the value of the **Radius** spinner to 5 from this **PropertyManager**.

7.   Similarly, draw the circle on the left using the inferencing lines generating from the endpoints of the left inclined line. The sketch, after drawing the two circles inside the outer loop, is shown in Figure 2-51. In this figure also, the grids are turned off for clarity.

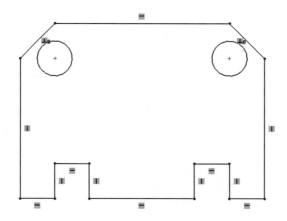

Figure 2-51 Sketch after drawing the two inner circles

8.   Right-click in the drawing area and choose **Select** to exit the **Circle** tool.

Drawing the Sketch of the Inner Cavity

Next, you will draw the sketch of the inner cavity. You will start drawing with the lower horizontal line. Before proceeding further, you need to invoke the snap to grid option.

1.   Select the **Grid** option from the **System Options - Relations/Snaps** dialog box. Now, invoke the **Line** tool by pressing the L key on the keyboard; the arrow cursor is replaced by the line cursor.

2.   Move the line cursor to a location whose coordinates are 30 mm, 25 mm, 0 mm.

3. Press the left mouse button at this point and move the cursor horizontally toward the right. Press the left mouse button when the length of the line above the line cursor shows a value of 30.

4. Move the line cursor vertically upward and press the left mouse button when the length of the line on the line cursor displays a value of 10.

5. Move the line cursor horizontally toward the left and press the left mouse button when the length of the line on the line cursor displays a value of 10.

6. Move the line cursor vertically downward and press the left mouse button when the length of the line on the line cursor displays a value of 5.

7. Move the line cursor horizontally toward the left and press the left mouse button when the length of the line on the line cursor displays a value of 10.

8. Move the line cursor vertically upward and press the left mouse button when the length of the line on the line cursor displays a value of 5.

9. Move the line horizontally toward the left and press the left mouse button when the length of the line on the line cursor displays a value of 10.

10. Move the line cursor vertically downward to the start point of the first line. Press the left mouse button when the red circle is displayed. The length of the line at this point will show a value of 10.

11. Right-click and choose **Select** from the shortcut menu. This completes the sketch for Tutorial 1.

12. Choose the **Zoom to Fit** button from the **Standard** toolbar to fit the display of the sketch on the screen. The final sketch for Tutorial 1 is shown in Figure 2-52.

Saving the Sketch

It is recommended that you create a separate folder for saving the tutorial files of this book. When you invoke the option to save a document, the default folder *My Documents* will be displayed. You will create a folder with the name *SolidWorks* in the *My Documents* folder and then create the folder of each chapter inside the *SolidWorks* folder. As a result, you can save the tutorials of a chapter in the folder of that chapter.

1. Choose the **Save** button from the **Standard** toolbar to invoke the **Save As** dialog box. Create the *SolidWorks* folder inside the *My Documents* folder and then create the *c02* folder inside the *SolidWorks* folder.

2. Enter the name of the document as *c02tut1* in the **File name** edit box and choose the **Save** button. The document will be saved in the *My Documents\SolidWorks\c02* folder.

3. Close the document by choosing **File > Close** from the menu bar.

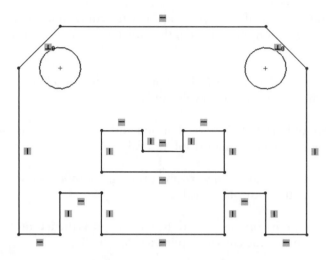

Figure 2-52 *Final sketch for Tutorial 1*

 Tip. *If you open a document that was saved in the sketching environment, it will be opened in the sketching environment only and not in the part modeling environment.*

Tutorial 2

In this tutorial, you will draw the basic sketch of the revolved solid model shown in Figure 2-53. The sketch of the revolved solid model is shown in Figure 2-54. Do not dimension the sketch. The solid model and dimensions are given only for your reference.

(Expected time: 30 min)

Figure 2-53 *Revolved model for Tutorial 2*

Figure 2-54 *Sketch for the revolved model*

The steps that will be followed to complete this tutorial are listed below.

a.   Start a new part document.
b.   Switch to the sketching environment.
c.   Modify the settings of the snap and grid so that the cursor jumps through a distance of 5 mm instead of 10 mm.
d.   Draw the sketch of the model using the **Line** tool, refer to Figure 2-55.
e.   Save the sketch and then close the document.

Starting a New Document

1.   Choose the **New** button from the **Standard** toolbar to invoke the **New SolidWorks Document** dialog box.

2.   The **Part** button is chosen by default in the **New SolidWorks Document** dialog box. Choose **OK**.

A new SolidWorks part document is started. As mentioned earlier, when you start a new part document, the part modeling environment is active by default. But, because you first need to draw the sketch of the revolved model, the sketching environment needs to be invoked.

3.   Choose the **Sketch** button from the **Standard** toolbar to display the **Edit Sketch PropertyManager**. Select **Front Plane**.

A red origin and the **Sketch CommandManager** are displayed. Also, the confirmation corner is displayed with the **Exit Sketch** and **Delete Sketch** options on the upper right corner of the drawing area. This indicates that the sketching environment is activated.

Modifying the Snap and Grid Settings and the Dimensioning Units

Before you proceed with drawing the sketch, you need to modify the grid and snap settings so that you can make the cursor jump through a distance of 5 mm.

1. Choose **Tools > Options** from the menu bar to invoke the **System Options - General** dialog box. Choose the **Document Properties** tab.

2. Select the **Grid/Snap** option from the area on the left to display the options related to linear and angular units. Set the value of the **Major grid spacing** spinner to **50**. Make sure the value of the **Minor-lines per major** spinner is **10**.

    The coordinates close to the lower left corner of the SolidWorks window will show an increment of 5 mm instead of the default increment of 25 mm when you exit the dialog box.

    If you had selected a unit other than millimeter while installing SolidWorks, you need to change the unit for the current drawing.

3. Select the **Units** option from the area on the left of the **Document Properties - Grid/Snap** dialog box.

4. Select the **MMGS (millimeter, gram, second)** radio button from the **Unit system** area.

5. Make sure the **Grid** check box is selected in the **System Options - Relations/Snaps** dialog box. After setting all parameters, choose the **OK** button.

Drawing the Sketch

As evident from Figure 2-52, the sketch will be drawn using the **Line** tool. You will start drawing the sketch from the lower left corner of the sketch.

1. Choose the **Line** button from the **Sketch CommandManager**; the arrow cursor is replaced by the line cursor.

2. Move the line cursor to a location whose coordinates are 40 mm, 0 mm, 0 mm.

3. Press the left mouse button down at this point and move the cursor horizontally toward the right. Press the left mouse button again when the length of the line above the line cursor shows a value of 20.

4. Move the line cursor vertically upward and press the left mouse button when the length of the line on the line cursor displays a value of 20.

5. Move the cursor horizontally toward the left and press the left mouse button when the length of the line on the line cursor displays a value of 5.

6. Move the line cursor vertically upward and press the left mouse button when the length of the line on the line cursor displays a value of 25.

7. Move the line cursor horizontally toward the right and press the left mouse button when the length of the line on the line cursor displays a value of 20.

8. Move the line cursor vertically upward and press the left mouse button when the length of the line on the line cursor displays a value of 5.

9. Move the line cursor horizontally toward the left and press the left mouse button when the length of the line on the line cursor displays a value of 50.

10. Move the line cursor vertically downward and press the left mouse button when the length of the line on the line cursor displays a value of 5.

11. Move the line cursor horizontally toward the right and press the left mouse button when the length of the line on the line cursor displays a value of 20.

12. Move the line cursor vertically downward and press the left mouse button when the length of the line on the line cursor displays a value of 25.

13. Move the line cursor horizontally toward the left and press the left mouse button when the length of the line on the line cursor displays a value of 5.

14. Move the line cursor vertically downward to the start point of the first line. Press the left mouse button when the red circle is displayed. The length of the line at this point will be 20 mm.

15. Right-click and choose **Select** from the shortcut menu.

    The sketch is completed but does not fit the screen. Therefore, you need to modify the display area such that the sketch fits the screen.

16. Choose the **Zoom to Fit** button from the **View** toolbar to fit the sketch on the screen. The final sketch for Tutorial 2 is shown in Figure 2-55. In this figure, the display of the grid is turned off for clarity.

 Tip. *You will notice that the bottom horizontal line in the sketch is black and the remaining lines are blue. In the next chapter, you will learn about the reason why some entities in the sketch have a different color.*

Saving the Sketch

1. Choose the **Save** button from the **Standard** toolbar to invoke the **Save As** dialog box.

2. Enter the name of the document as *c02tut2* in the **File name** edit box and choose the **Save** button.

    The document will be saved in the *\My Documents\SolidWorks\c02* folder.

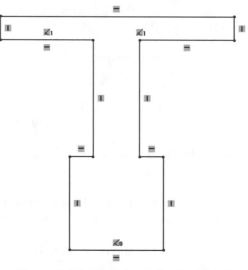

Figure 2-55 *Final sketch for Tutorial 2*

3.   Close the document by choosing **File > Close** from the menu bar.

Tutorial 3

In this tutorial, you will draw the basic sketch of the model shown in Figure 2-56. The sketch to be drawn is shown in Figure 2-57. Do not dimension the sketch; the solid model and dimensions are given for your reference only.   **(Expected time: 30 min)**

Figure 2-56 *Solid model for Tutorial 3*

Figure 2-57 *Sketch for Tutorial 3*

The steps that will be followed to complete this tutorial are listed below.

a. Start SolidWorks and then start a new part file.
b. Switch to the sketching environment.
c. Modify the settings of the snap and grid so that the cursor jumps through a distance of 5 mm instead of 10 mm.
d. Draw the outer loop of the sketch using the **Line** tool, refer to Figure 2-58.
e. Draw the inner circle using the **Circle** tool, refer to Figure 2-59.
f. Save the sketch and then close the file.

Starting a New File

1. Choose the **New** button from the **Standard** toolbar to invoke the **New SolidWorks Document** dialog box.

2. The **Part** button is chosen by default in the **New SolidWorks Document** dialog box. Choose the **OK** button.

    A new SolidWorks part document will be started. As you first need to draw the sketch of the revolved model, you need to invoke the sketching environment.

3. Choose the **Sketch** button from the **Standard** toolbar; the **Edit Sketch PropertyManager** is displayed. Select **Front Plane**.

    A red origin is displayed and the **Sketch CommandManager** is displayed above the drawing area. Also, the confirmation corner with the **Exit Sketch** and **Delete Sketch** options is displayed on the upper right corner of the drawing area. This indicates that the sketching environment is activated.

Modifying the Snap and Grid Settings and Dimensioning Units

As the dimensions in the sketch are multiples of 5, you need to modify the grid and snap settings so that you can make the cursor jump through a distance of 5 mm instead of 10 mm.

1. Choose **Tools > Options** from the menu bar to invoke the **System Options - General** dialog box. Choose the **Document Properties** tab.

2. Select the **Grid/Snap** option from the area on the left to display the options related to linear and angular units. Set the value of the **Major grid spacing** spinner to **50**. Make sure the value of the **Minor-lines per major** spinner is **10**.

   The coordinates displayed close to the lower left corner of the SolidWorks window will show an increment of 5 mm instead of the default increment of 10 mm when you close the dialog box.

3. Make sure the **Grid** check box is selected in the **System Options - Relations/Snaps** dialog box. Choose **OK** to close the dialog box.

Drawing the Outer Loop

As evident from Figure 2-57, the sketch consists of an outer loop and an inner circle. Therefore, this sketch will be drawn using the **Line** and **Circle** tools. You will start drawing from the lower left corner of the sketch. As the length of the lower horizontal line is 150 mm, you need to modify the drawing display area such that the drawing area in the first quadrant is increased. This can be done using the **Pan** tool.

1. Choose the **Pan** button from the **View** toolbar; the arrow cursor is replaced by the pan cursor.

2. Press and hold the left mouse button down and drag the cursor toward the bottom left corner of the screen.

   You will notice that the origin also moves toward the bottom left corner of the screen, thus increasing the drawing area in the first quadrant.

3. After dragging the origin close to the lower left corner, release the left mouse button.

4. Choose the **Line** button from the **Sketch CommandManager**; the pan cursor is replaced by the line cursor.

5. Move the line cursor to a location whose coordinates are 40 mm, 0 mm, 0 mm.

6. Press and hold the left mouse button down at this point and move the cursor horizontally toward the right. Press the left mouse button again when the length of the line above the line cursor shows a value of 150.

7. Move the line cursor vertically upward and press the left mouse button when the length of the line on the line cursor displays a value of 40.

    The next entity that has to be drawn is a tangent arc. As mentioned earlier, you can draw a tangent arc using the **Line** tool also. Drawing arcs from within the **Line** tool is a recommended method when you need to draw a sketch that is a combination of lines and arcs. This increases the productivity by reducing the time taken in invoking the tools for drawing an arc and then invoking the **Line** tool to draw lines.

8. Move the line cursor away from the endpoint of the last line and then move it back to the endpoint.

    The arc mode is invoked and the line cursor is replaced by the arc cursor. Also, the **Arc PropertyManager** is displayed in place of the **Line Properties PropertyManager**.

9. Move the arc cursor vertically upward to a small distance.

10. When the dotted line is displayed, move the cursor toward the left.

    You will notice that a tangent arc is being drawn. The angle of the tangent arc and its radius are displayed above the arc cursor.

11. Press the left mouse button when the angle value above the arc cursor shows 180 and the radius shows a value of 30 to complete the arc.

    The required tangent arc is drawn. As mentioned earlier, the line mode is automatically invoked after you have drawn the arc using the **Line** tool. Therefore, the arc cursor will be replaced by the line cursor and the **Arc PropertyManager** will be replaced by the **Line Properties PropertyManager**.

12. Move the line cursor vertically downward and press the left mouse button when the length of the line on the line cursor displays a value of 20.

13. Move the line cursor horizontally toward the left and press the left mouse button when the length of the line on the line cursor displays a value of 30.

14. Move the line cursor vertically downward and press the left mouse button when the length of the line on the line cursor displays a value of 5.

15. Move the line cursor horizontally toward the left and press the left mouse button when the length of the line on the line cursor displays a value of 25.

16. Move the line cursor vertically upward and press the left mouse button when the length of the line on the line cursor displays a value of 5.

17. Move the line cursor horizontally toward the left and press the left mouse button when the length of the line on the line cursor displays a value of 35.

18. Move the line cursor to the start point of the first line. Press the left mouse button when the red circle is displayed.

    The length of the line at this point will be 20 mm

19. Right-click and choose **Select** from the shortcut menu to exit the **Line** tool.

20. Choose the **Zoom to Fit** button to fit the sketch on the screen. This completes the outer loop of the sketch. The sketch, after drawing the outer loop, is shown in Figure 2-58.

Figure 2-58 Sketch after drawing the outer loop

Drawing the Circle

The circle in the sketch will be drawn using the **Circle** tool. The center point of the circle will be the center point of the arc, which will be displayed by a plus sign. This plus sign is automatically drawn when you draw the arc. You can select this center point to draw the circle.

1. Choose the **Circle** button from the **Sketch CommandManager** to invoke the **Circle** tool; the arrow cursor is replaced by the circle cursor.

2. Move the circle cursor close to the center point of the arc and press the left mouse button when the red circle is displayed.

3. Move the cursor toward the left and when the radius of the circle above the circle cursor shows a value of 15, press the left mouse button. A circle of 15 mm radius is drawn.

4. This completes the sketch for Tutorial 3. Right-click and choose the **Select** option from the shortcut menu to exit the **Circle** tool.

The final sketch for Tutorial 3 is shown in Figure 2-59.

Figure 2-59 *Final sketch for Tutorial 3*

Saving the Sketch

1. Choose the **Save** button from the **Standard** toolbar to invoke the **Save As** dialog box.

2. Enter the name of the document as *c02tut3* in the **File name** edit box and choose the **Save** button.

3. Close the document by choosing **File > Close** from the menu bar.

Tutorial 4

In this tutorial, you will draw the sketch of the model shown in Figure 2-60. The sketch of the model is shown in Figure 2-61. Do not dimension the sketch. The dimensions and the solid model are given for your reference only. **(Expected time: 30 min)**

Figure 2-60 *Model for Tutorial 4*

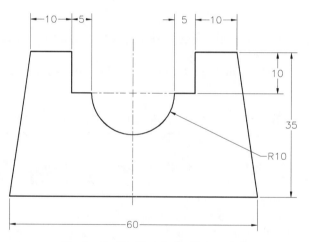

Figure 2-61 *Sketch for Tutorial 4*

The steps that will be followed to complete this tutorial are listed below.

a.   Start SolidWorks and then start a new part document.
b.   Switch to the sketching environment.
c.   Modify the settings of the snap and grid so that the cursor jumps through a distance of 5 mm instead of 10 mm.
d.   Draw the sketch using the **Line** tool, refer to Figure 2-62.
e.   Save the sketch and then close the file.

Opening a New File

1. Choose the **New** button from the **Standard** toolbar to invoke the **New SolidWorks Document** dialog box.

2. The **Part** button is chosen by default in the **New SolidWorks Document** dialog box. Now, choose the **OK** button.

As you first need to draw the sketch of the model, the sketching environment needs to be invoked.

3. Choose the **Sketch** button from the **Standard** toolbar and select the **Front Plane** to invoke the sketching environment.

Modifying the Snap and Grid Settings and Dimensioning Units

As evident in Figure 2-61, the dimensions in the sketch are multiples of 5. Therefore, you need to modify the grid and snap settings so that the cursor jumps through a distance of 5 mm instead of 10 mm.

1. Choose **Tools > Options** from the menu bar to invoke the **System Options - General** dialog box. Choose the **Document Properties** tab.

2. Select the **Grid/Snap** option from the area on the left to display the options related to linear and angular units. Set the value of the **Major grid spacing** spinner to **50** and the value of the **Minor-lines per major** spinner to **10**.

The coordinates displayed close to the lower left corner of the SolidWorks window show an increment of 5 mm when you close this dialog box.

3. Make sure the **Grid** check box is selected in the **System Options - Relations/Snaps** dialog box. Choose **OK** to close the dialog box.

Drawing the Sketch

The sketch will be drawn using the **Line** tool. The arc in the sketch will also be drawn using the same tool. You will start drawing from the lower left corner of the sketch.

1. Invoke the **Line** tool by pressing the L key on the keyboard; the arrow cursor is replaced by the line cursor.

2. Move the line cursor to a point whose coordinates are 30 mm, 0 mm, 0 mm.

3. Press the left mouse button at this point and move the cursor horizontally toward the right. Press the left mouse button again when the length of the line above the line cursor shows a value of 60.

The bottom horizontal line of 60 mm length is drawn.

4. Choose the **Zoom to Fit** button from the **View** toolbar to increase the display of the line that is drawn.

    As mentioned earlier, you can also invoke the drawing display tools while some other tool is active. After modifying the drawing display, the tool that was active before invoking the drawing display tool will be restored and you can continue using that tool. Therefore, after the drawing display area is modified, the **Line** tool will be restored and you can continue drawing lines.

5. Move the line cursor along a direction that makes an angle close to 98-degrees with the positive X axis direction. The angle can be checked from the **Angle** spinner in the **Parameters** rollout of the **Line Properties PropertyManager**.

6. Press the left mouse button when the length of the line displayed above the line cursor shows a value of 35.36.

7. Move the line cursor horizontally toward the left and press the left mouse button when the length of the line above the line cursor shows a value of 10.

8. Move the line cursor vertically downward and press the left mouse button when the length of the line above the line cursor shows a value of 10.

9   Move the line cursor horizontally toward the left and press the left mouse button when the length of the line above the line cursor shows a value of 5.

    Next, you need to draw the arc that is normal to the last line.

10. Move the line cursor away from the endpoint of the last line and then move it back close to the endpoint.

    The arc mode is invoked and the line cursor is replaced by the arc cursor. Also, the **Line Properties PropertyManager** is replaced by the **Arc PropertyManager**.

11. Move the arc cursor vertically downward up to the next grid point.

12. Move the arc cursor toward the left.

    You will notice that a normal arc is being drawn and the angle and radius of the arc is displayed above the arc cursor.

13. Press the left mouse button when the angle value on the arc cursor is 180 and the radius value is 10. An arc normal to the last line is drawn and the line mode is activated.

14. Move the line cursor horizontally toward the left and press the left mouse button when the length of the line on the line cursor shows a value of 5.

15. Move the line cursor vertically upward and press the left mouse button when the length of the line on the line cursor shows a value of 10.

16. Move the line cursor horizontally toward the left and press the left mouse button when the length of the line on the line cursor shows a value of 10.

17. Move the line cursor to the start point of the first line and press the left mouse button when the red circle is displayed.

18. Press the ESC key to exit the **Line** tool.

This completes the sketch. However, you need to modify the drawing display area such that the sketch fits the screen.

19. Choose the **Zoom to Fit** button from the **View** toolbar to modify the drawing display area. The final sketch for Tutorial 4, without the grid display, is shown in Figure 2-62.

Figure 2-62 *Final sketch for Tutorial 4*

Saving the Sketch

1. Choose the **Save** button from the **Standard** toolbar to invoke the **Save As** dialog box.

2. Enter the name of the document as *c02tut4* in the **File name** edit box and choose the **Save** button.

3. Close the document by choosing **File > Close** from the menu bar.

SELF-EVALUATION TEST

Answer the following questions and then compare your answers with those given at the end of this chapter:

1. The base feature of any design is a sketched feature and is created by drawing the sketch. (T/F)

2. You can also invoke the **3Pt Arc** tool from within the **Line** tool. (T/F)

3. By default, the cursor jumps through a distance of 5 mm. (T/F)

4. When you save a file in the sketching environment, it is opened in the part modeling environment when you open it the next time. (T/F)

5. You can convert a sketched entity into a construction entity by selecting the _____ check box provided in the **PropertyManager**.

6. To draw a rectangle at an angle, you need to use the _____ tool.

7. The _____ are the temporary lines that are used to track a particular point on the screen.

8. You can also invoke the _____ tool or exit a sketching tool by pressing the ESC key.

9. When you select a tangent entity to draw a tangent arc, the _____ relation is applied between the start point of the arc and the tangent entity.

10. The rectangle is considered as a combination of individual _____.

REVIEW QUESTIONS

Answer the following questions:

1. The three point arcs are drawn by defining the start and end points of the arc, and a point on the arc. (T/F)

2. You can also delete the sketched entities by selecting them and choosing the **Delete** option from the shortcut menu, which is displayed on right-clicking. (T/F)

3. The origin is a blue icon that is displayed in the middle of the sketcher screen. (T/F)

4. In SolidWorks, circles are drawn by specifying the center point of the circle and then entering the radius of the circle in the dialog box that is displayed. (T/F)

5. When you open a new SolidWorks document, it is not maximized in the SolidWorks window. (T/F)

6. In SolidWorks, a polygon is considered as a combination of which of the following entities?

    (a) Lines   (b) Arcs
    (c) Splines   (d) None

7. Which one of the following options is not displayed in the **New SolidWorks Document** dialog box?

    (a) **Part**   (b) **Assembly**
    (c) **Drawing**   (d) **Sketch**

8. Which one of the following entities is not considered while converting a sketch into a feature?

    (a) Sketched circles   (b) Sketched lines
    (c) Construction lines   (d) None

9. When you select a line of the rectangle, which of the following **PropertyManagers** will be displayed?

    (a) **Line Properties PropertyManager**   (b) **Line/Rectangle PropertyManager**
    (c) **Rectangle PropertyManager**   (d) None

10. While drawing an elliptical arc, which of the following **PropertyManagers** will be displayed?

    (a) **Arc PropertyManager**   (b) **Ellipse PropertyManager**
    (c) **Elliptical Arc PropertyManager** (d) None

EXERCISES

Exercise 1

Draw the sketch of the model shown in Figure 2-63. The sketch to be drawn is shown in Figure 2-64. Do not dimension the sketch. The solid model and dimensions are given for your reference only.   **(Expected time: 30 min)**

Figure 2-63 Solid model for Exercise 1

Figure 2-64 Sketch for Exercise 1

Exercise 2

Draw the sketch of the model shown in Figure 2-65. The sketch to be drawn is shown in Figure 2-66. Do not dimension the sketch. The solid model and dimensions are given for your reference only.   **(Expected time: 30 min)**

Figure 2-65 Solid model for Exercise 2

Figure 2-66 Sketch for Exercise 2

Answers to Self-Evaluation Test

1. T, **2.** T, **3.** F, **4.** F, **5. For Construction**, **6. Parallelogram**, **7.** inferencing lines, **8. Select**, **9. Tangent**, **10.** lines

Chapter 3

Editing and Modifying Sketches

Learning Objectives

After completing this chapter, you will be able to:
- *Edit sketches using various editing tools.*
- *Create rectangular patterns of sketched entities.*
- *Create circular patterns of sketched entities.*
- *Write text in the sketching environment.*
- *Modify sketched entities.*
- *Modify sketches by dynamically dragging sketched entities.*

EDITING SKETCHED ENTITIES

SolidWorks provides you with a number of tools that can be used to edit the sketched entities. Using these tools, you can trim, extend, offset, or mirror the sketched entities. You can also perform various other editing operations. The tools to perform these operations are discussed next.

Trimming Sketched Entities

CommandManager:	Sketch > Trim Entities
Menu:	Tools > Sketch Tools > Trim
Toolbar:	Sketch > Trim Entities

 The **Trim Entities** tool is used to trim the unwanted entities in a sketch. You can use this tool to trim a line, arc, ellipse, parabola, circle, spline, or centerline that is intersecting another line, arc, ellipse, parabola, circle, spline, or centerline. You can also extend the entities using the **Trim** tool. To use the trim option, choose the **Trim Entities** button from the **Sketch CommandManager**; the **Trim PropertyManager** will be displayed, as shown in Figure 3-1.

Figure 3-1 The Trim PropertyManager

The options available in this **PropertyManager** to trim the sketched entities are discussed next.

Power trim

When the **Power trim** button is chosen in the **Options** rollout, the **Message** rollout provided in this **PropertyManager** will inform you about the procedure of trimming and extending the sketched elements using this option. To trim the unwanted portion of the sketch using this option, press and hold the left mouse button down and drag the cursor. You will notice that a gray-colored drag trace line is displayed along the path of the cursor. When you drag and place the cursor on an unwanted sketched entity, it will be trimmed and a small red-colored box will be displayed in its place. You can continue trimming entities by dragging the cursor on them. After trimming all unwanted entities, release the left mouse button.

To extend the sketched entities using this tool, press and hold the left mouse button down and then press the SHIFT key. Now, drag the cursor to the entity that needs to be extended. As the cursor reaches the entity, it will be extended to the nearest intersection. If there is no intersection on the path of the entity, it will not be extended. You can continue extending entities by dragging the cursor on the elements. After extending all the required entities, release the SHIFT key and the left mouse button.

Note

You can also drag the endpoint of a selected entity to another entity to extend it to that entity. However, in this case, the orientation of the entity will be altered.

Corner

The **Corner** button available in the **Options** rollout is used to trim or extend elements in such a manner that the resulting elements form a corner. To trim unwanted elements using this option, choose the **Corner** button from the **Options** rollout; you will be prompted to select an entity. Select the entity from the geometry area. You need to make sure that you select the area of the entity that you want to retain. Now, you will be prompted to select another entity. Select the second entity from the geometry area, refer to Figure 3-2. The portion of the entities from where the selection was made will be retained and the other portion will be removed, resulting in a corner, as shown in Figure 3-3.

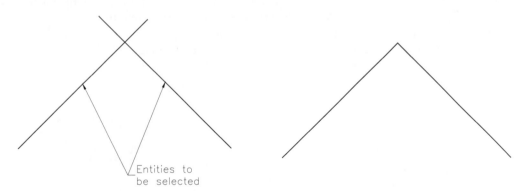

Figure 3-2 Entities to be selected for trimming   *Figure 3-3 Trimmed entities*

You can also extend the entities using this tool. To do so, choose the **Corner** button from the **Options** rollout. Select the entities to be extended; the selected entities will be extended to their apparent intersection, refer to Figures 3-4 and 3-5.

Trim away inside

The **Trim away inside** button available in the **Options** rollout is used to trim the inside portion of the selected entity. This portion is defined by two bounding entities. To trim the entities using

Figure 3-4 *Entities selected for extending*   **Figure 3-5** *Sketch after extending*

this tool, invoke the **Trim PropertyManager** and choose the **Trim away inside** button from the **Options** rollout. The **Message** rollout will inform you to select two bounding entities and then to select the entities to be trimmed. Select the bounding entities from the drawing area, refer to Figure 3-6. Now, select the entities to be trimmed from the drawing area. As you select an entity to be trimmed, the portion of the entity inside the bounding entities will be removed and the portion outside that will be retained, refer to Figure 3-6.

Trim away outside

The **Trim away outside** button available in the **Options** rollout is used to trim the outside portion of the selected entity. This portion is defined by two bounding entities. To trim the entities using this tool, invoke the **Trim PropertyManager** and choose the **Trim away outside** button from the **Options** rollout. The **Message** rollout will inform you to select two bounding entities, and then to select the entities to be trimmed. Select the bounding entities from the drawing area, refer to Figure 3-7. Now, select the entities to be trimmed from the drawing area. As you select an entity to be trimmed, the portion of the entity outside the bounding entities will be removed and the portion inside that will be retained, refer to Figure 3-7.

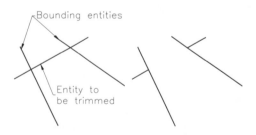

Figure 3-6 *Entities trimmed using the **Trim away** inside option*   **Figure 3-7** *Entities trimmed using the **Trim away** outside option*

Trim to closest

The **Trim to closest** tool is used to trim the selected entity to its closest intersection. To trim entities using this tool, invoke the **Trim PropertyManager** and choose the **Trim to closest** button from the **Options** rollout; the cursor will be replaced by the trim cursor. Move the trim cursor near to the portion of the sketched entity to be removed. The entity or the portion of the entity to be removed will be highlighted in red. Press the left mouse button to remove the highlighted entity. Figure 3-8 shows the entities to be trimmed and Figure 3-9 shows the sketch after trimming the entities.

Figure 3-8 *Entities to be trimmed*   **Figure 3-9** *Sketch after trimming the entities*

You can also use this option to extend the sketched entities. To do this, move the trim cursor to the entity to be extended. When the sketched entity turns red, drag the cursor; the entity to be

Tip. *In SolidWorks, all buttons are not displayed by default in toolbars or* ***CommandManagers***. *You need to customize them and add buttons according to your need and specifications. The next topic is Extending Sketched Entities. The* ***Extend*** *tool button is not available in the* ***Sketch CommandManager*** *by default. To insert the* ***Extend Entities*** *button in the* ***Sketch CommandManager***, *follow the procedure given below.*

1. Choose ***Tools*** *>* ***Customize*** *from the menu bar to display the* ***Customize*** *dialog box.*
2. Choose the ***Commands*** *tab from the* ***Customize*** *dialog box.*
3. Select ***Sketch*** *from the* ***Categories*** *area of the* ***Customize*** *dialog box.*
4. Press and hold the left mouse button down on the ***Extend Entities*** *button from the* ***Buttons*** *area of the* ***Customize*** *dialog box; the description of the* ***Extend Entities*** *button will be displayed in the* ***Description*** *area.*
5. Drag the mouse to the ***Sketch CommandManager*** *and release the left mouse button to place the* ***Extend Entities*** *button on this* ***CommandManager***.
6. Choose ***OK*** *from the* ***Customize*** *dialog box.*

You can insert the other tool buttons in the ***Sketch CommandManager*** *or any other* ***CommandManager*** *by following the same procedure. To remove the tool button from a* ***CommandManager***, *invoke the* ***Customize*** *dialog box and drag the tool button you want to remove from the* ***CommandManager*** *to the graphics area.*

When you customize and add a tool to the ***CommandManager***, *it will automatically be added to the toolbar also.*

extended will be displayed in green. Drag the cursor to the entity up to which it will be extended. You will notice the preview of the extended entity in red color. Release the left mouse button when the preview of the extended entity appears.

Extending Sketched Entities

CommandManager:	Sketch > Extend Entities	*(Customize to Add)*
Menu:	Tools > Sketch Tools > Extend	
Toolbar:	Sketch > Extend Entities	*(Customize to Add)*

The **Extend Entities** tool is used to extend the sketched entity to intersect the next available entity. The tool is used to extend a line, arc, ellipse, parabola, circle, spline, or centerline to intersect another line, arc, ellipse, parabola, circle, spline, or centerline. The sketched entity is extended up to its intersection with another sketched entity or a model edge. Choose the **Extend Entities** button from the **Sketch CommandManager** and move the extend cursor close to the portion of the sketched entity to be extended. The entity to be extended will be displayed in red and its preview will also be displayed in red. Press the left mouse button to complete the extend operation. Figure 3-10 shows the sketched entities before extending and Figure 3-11 shows the sketched entities after extending.

Tip. *If the preview of the sketched entity to be extended is shown in the wrong direction, move the extend cursor to a position on the other half of the entity and observe the new preview.*

Entities to be selected for extending

Figure 3-10 Sketched entities before extending

Figure 3-11 Sketched entities after extending

Tip. *You can toggle between the **Trim Entities** and **Extend Entities** tools using the shortcut menu that will be displayed on right-clicking when one of these tools is active.*

Filleting Sketched Entities

CommandManager:	Sketch > Sketch Fillet
Menu:	Tools > Sketch Tools > Fillet
Toolbar:	Sketch > Sketch Fillet

A fillet creates a tangent arc at the intersection of two sketched entities. It trims or extends the entities to be filleted, depending on the geometry of the sketched entity. You can apply a fillet two nonparallel lines, two arcs, two splines, an arc and a line, a spline and a line, or a spline and an arc. The fillet between two arcs, or between an arc and a line depends on the compatibility of the geometry to be extended or filleted along a given radius. You can invoke the **Sketch Fillet** tool first and then select the entities to be filleted. You can also hold the CTRL key down and first select two entities to be filleted and then invoke this tool. When you invoke this tool, the **Sketch Fillet PropertyManager** will be displayed, as shown in Figure 3-12.

*Figure 3-12 The **Sketch Fillet PropertyManager***

Set the value of the **Fillet Radius** spinner and press ENTER or choose the **Apply** button from the **Sketch Fillet** dialog box. You can also select the sketched entities after invoking the **Sketch Fillet PropertyManager**. You can also select the intersection points of the entities to be filleted. You can also select the nonintersecting entities for creating a fillet. While filleting the nonintersecting entities, the selected entities will be extended to form a fillet. If the **Keep constrained corners** check box is selected, the dimension and geometric relations applied to the sketch will not be deleted. If you clear the **Keep constrained corners** check box, you will be prompted to delete the relations applied to the corners of the sketched entities to be filleted. The **Undo** button will be displayed in the **Sketch Fillet PropertyManager** when you create at least one sketch fillet. Figures 3-13 and 3-14 show the sketched entities before and after applying the radius.

Figure 3-13 Sketched entities before and after creating a fillet

Figure 3-14 Sketched entities before and after creating a fillet

Note
The consecutive fillets with the same radius are not dimensioned individually; an automatic equal radii relation is applied to all fillets.

The fillet creation between two splines, a spline and a line, and a spline and an arc depends on the compatibility of the spline to be trimmed or extended.

Tip. *The other method of creating a sketched fillet between two entities is to drag a window around the entities to be filleted. To fillet the entities using this method, invoke the Sketch Fillet PropertyManager. Set the fillet radius spinner to the required value. Now, drag the cursor to create a window around the two entities to be filleted such that they are enclosed inside the window. As soon as you release the left mouse button, the fillet will be created between the two selected entities.*

You can also select a vertex to fillet the two entities that form that vertex.

Chamfering Sketched Entities

CommandManager:	Sketch > Sketch Chamfer	*(Customize to Add)*
Menu:	Tools > Sketch Tools > Chamfer	
Toolbar:	Sketch > Sketch Chamfer	*(Customize to Add)*

The **Sketch Chamfer** tool is used to apply a chamfer to adjacent sketch entities. The chamfer can be specified by angle-distance or distance-distance options. You can apply a chamfer between two nonparallel lines; the lines may be intersecting lines or nonintersecting lines. The creation of a chamfer between two nonintersecting lines depends on the length of the lines and the chamfer distance. To create a chamfer, choose the **Sketch Chamfer** button from the **Sketch CommandManager** and select two entities to be chamfered. You can also select the two entities before invoking the **Chamfer** tool. When you invoke this tool, the **Sketch Chamfer PropertyManager** will be displayed, as shown in Figure 3-15. The options available in the **Sketch Chamfer PropertyManager** are discussed next.

Figure 3-15 The Sketch Chamfer PropertyManager

Angle-distance

The **Angle-distance** radio button is selected to create the chamfer by specifying the angle and the distance, refer to Figure 3-16. When you select this radio button, the **Direction 1 Angle** spinner will be displayed below the **Distance 1** spinner. The **Distance 1** spinner is used to specify the distance and the **Direction 1 Angle** spinner is used to specify the angle. Note that the angle will be measured from the first entity that you selected.

Distance-distance

The **Distance-distance** radio button is selected to create the chamfer by specifying the distances along both the selected lines, refer to Figure 3-16. When you invoke the **Sketch Chamfer**

Figure 3-16 *Creating various types of chamfers*

PropertyManager, the **Distance-distance** radio button and the **Equal distance** check box are selected by default. Therefore, you can create an equal distance chamfer between the selected entities. The distance value can be specified in the **Distance 1** spinner.

Equal distance

The **Equal distance** check box is selected to specify an equal distance in both directions for creating the sketched chamfer. This check box is selected by default. If you clear this check box, you can specify two different distances for creating the chamfer, refer to Figure 3-16. When you clear this check box, the **Distance 2** spinner will be displayed below the **Distance 1** spinner to set the value of the distance in the second direction. Note that the distance 1 value will be measured along the first entity that you selected and the distance 2 value along the second entity.

You can also use the shortcut menu that is invoked to use various methods of creating a chamfer.

Note

If you apply a sketch chamfer to the entities that are constrained using some relations or dimensions, the SolidWorks warning box will be displayed. This window will show the message: At least one sketch constraint is about to be lost, Chamfer anyway? Choose the Yes button from this warning box. You will learn more about the relations and dimensions that constrain the sketch in later chapters.

Offsetting Sketched Entities

CommandManager:	Sketch > Offset Entities
Menu:	Tools > Sketch Tools > Offset Entities
Toolbar:	Sketch > Offset Entities

Offsetting is one of the easiest methods of drawing parallel lines or concentric arcs and circles. You can select the entire chain of entities as a single entity or select an individual entity to be offset. You can offset selected sketched entities, edges, loops, faces, and curves. With this release of SolidWorks, you can also select parabolic curves, ellipses, and elliptical arcs to be offset. When you choose the **Offset Entities** button from the **Sketch Tools** toolbar, the **Offset Entities PropertyManager** will be displayed, as shown in Figure 3-17. The options available in the **Offset Entities PropertyManager** are discussed next.

*Figure 3-17 The **Offset Entities PropertyManager***

 Note
*While performing any kind of editing operation, if you want to clear the current selection set, right-click in the drawing area and choose **Clear Selections** from the shortcut menu.*

Offset Distance

The **Offset Distance** spinner is used to set the distance through which the selected entity needs to be offset. You can set the value of the offset distance using this spinner or by dragging the offset entity in the drawing area.

Add Dimension

The **Add dimension** check box is selected by default in the **Parameters** rollout. When selected, this check will add a dimension representing the offset distance between the parent entity and the resulting offset entity.

Reverse

The **Reverse** check box is selected to change the direction of the offset. Note that while offsetting the entities by dragging, you do not need this check box. This is because you can change the direction of the offset by dragging the entities in the required direction.

Select Chain

The **Select chain** check box is selected to select the entire chain of continuous sketched entities that are in contact with the selected entity. When you invoke the **Offset** tool, the **Select chain** check box will be selected by default. If you clear this check box, only the selected sketched entity will be offset.

Bi-directional

The **Bi-directional** radio button is selected to create the offset of the selected entity in both directions of the selected entity. If the **Bi-directional** check box is selected, the **Reverse** check box will not be available in the **Parameters** area.

Make Base Construction

The **Make base construction** check box is selected to convert the parent entity or the base entity into a construction entity.

Cap Ends

The **Cap ends** check box is available only if the **Bi-directional** check box is selected. When selected, this option closes the ends of the bidirectionally offset entities. You can select the type of cap to close the ends. If you are offsetting a closed entity on both directions, this option will not be available.

Figure 3-18 shows a new chain of entities created by offsetting the chain of entities and Figure 3-19 shows offsetting of a single entity.

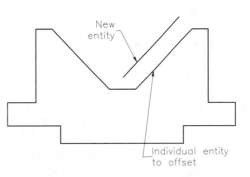

Figure 3-18 *Offsetting a chain of entities*   *Figure 3-19* *Offsetting a single entity*

Mirroring Sketched Entities

CommandManager:	Sketch > Mirror Entities
Menu:	Tools > Sketch Tools > Mirror
Toolbar:	Sketch > Mirror Entities

The **Mirror Entities** tool is used to create the mirror image of the selected entities. The entities are mirrored about a centerline. When you create the mirrored entity, SolidWorks applies the symmetric relation between the sketched entities. If you change the entity, its mirror image will also change. To mirror the existing entities, choose the **Mirror Entities** button from the **Sketch CommandManager**; the **Mirror PropertyManager** will be displayed, as shown in Figure 3-20.

Figure 3-20 The Mirror PropertyManager

You are prompted to select entities to be mirrored. Select the entities from the drawing area. The name of the selected entities will be displayed in the **Entities to mirror** selection box. After selecting all entities to be mirrored, click once in the **Mirror about** selection box. After selecting an entity, if you pause the mouse on that entity, the **Select** symbol will also be displayed. If you right-click while this symbol is displayed below the cursor, the selection mode in the next selection box will be activated automatically. You will be prompted to select a line or a linear model edge to mirror about. Select a line or a centerline from the drawing area that will be used as the mirror line. The preview of the mirrored image will be displayed. You need to make sure that **Copy** check box is selected in the **Mirror PropertyManager**. If you clear this check box, the parent selected entities will be removed and only the mirror image will be retained when you mirror the sketched entities. Choose the **OK** button from the **Mirror PropertyManager**.

Figure 3-21 shows the sketched entities with the centerline and Figure 3-22 shows the resulting mirror image of the sketched entities.

Figure 3-21 Selecting the sketched entities and the *Figure 3-22 Sketch after mirroring the geometry*
centerline

Mirroring While Sketching (Dynamic Mirror Entities)

CommandManager:	Sketch > Dynamic Mirror Entities	*(Customize to Add)*
Menu:	Tools > Sketch Tools > Dynamic Mirror	
Toolbar:	Sketch > Dynamic Mirror Entities	*(Customize to Add)*

 The **Dynamic Mirror Entities** tool is used to mirror the entities about a symmetry line while sketching. This tool is recommended when you are drawing symmetric sketches. To use this tool, choose the **Dynamic Mirror Entities** button from the **Sketch CommandManager**; the **Mirror PropertyManager** will be displayed, as shown Figure 3-23.

Figure 3-23 The Mirror PropertyManager

The **Message** rollout of the **Mirror PropertyManager** informs you to select a sketch line or a linear model edge to mirror about. Select a line or a centerline from the drawing that will be used as symmetry line. The symmetry symbols appear at both ends of the centerline to indicate that automatic mirroring is activated, as shown in Figure 3-24. Now, start drawing the sketch. The sketched entity that you draw on one side of the centerline will automatically be created on the other side of the mirror line (centerline). As evident in Figure 3-25, the entities are mirrored automatically while sketching. Figure 3-26 shows the complete sketch with automatic mirroring.

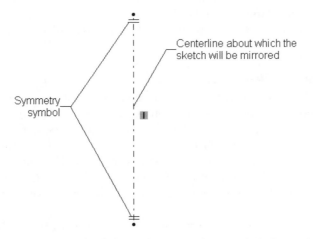

Figure 3-24 The centerline and the symmetry symbols that indicate that automatic mirroring is activated

Figure 3-25 *Sketching using automatic mirroring active*

Figure 3-26 *Sketch drawn with automatic mirroring*

 Note
*After completing the sketch using the automatic mirroring option, you can clear this option by choosing the **Dynamic Mirror Entities** button from the **Sketch CommandManager**.*

Moving Sketched Entities

CommandManager:	Sketch > Move Entities
Menu:	Tools > Sketch Tools > Move
Toolbar:	Sketch > Move Entities

The **Move Entities** tool is used to move the selected entities from its base location to a desired location. To do this, invoke the **Move Entities** tool by choosing the **Move Entities** button from the **Sketch CommandManager**. Remember that this tool will be available only when at least one sketched entity is drawn. When you invoke this tool, the **Move PropertyManager** will be displayed, as shown in Figure 3-27, and you will be prompted to select sketch items or annotations. The options available in this **PropertyManager** are discussed next.

Entities to Move Rollout

The options available in this rollout are used to select the entities to be moved. You will notice that the **Sketch items or annotations** selection box is active in this rollout. The names of the entities selected to be moved will be displayed in this selection box. To remove an entity from the selection set, select it again from the drawing area. Alternatively, you can select its name from the **Sketch items or annotations** selection box and right-click to invoke the shortcut menu. Choose the **Delete** option from the shortcut menu. If you choose the **Clear Selection** option from the shortcut menu, all the entities in the selection set are removed from it.

You will notice that by default, the **Keep relations** check box is cleared. If you move the sketched entities with this check box cleared, the relations applied to the entities to be moved are removed. If you select this check box and then move the entities, then the relations applied to the sketched entities are retained even if you move the entities. You will learn more about relations later in this chapter.

Figure 3-27 The Move PropertyManager

Parameters Rollout

The **Parameters** rollout is used to specify the origin and destination positions of moving the sketched entities. The options available in this rollout are discussed next.

From/To

You will notice that the **From/To** radio button is selected by default. This option let you to move the selected entities from one point to another. To move the selected entities using this option, click once in the **Base point** selection box; you are prompted to define the base point. Click anywhere in the drawing area to specify the base point; a yellow circle is displayed where the start point is specified and you are prompted to define the destination point. Select a point anywhere in the drawing area to place the selected entities.

X/Y

The **X/Y** radio button is selected to move the selected entities by specifying the relative coordinates of X and Y. When you select this radio button, the **Delta X** and the **Delta Y** spinners are displayed below this radio button. Set the value of destination coordinates in these spinners.

Repeat

The **Repeat** button, when chosen, will further move the selected entities with the same incremental distance.

Figure 3-28 shows the selected entities being moved using the **Move Entities** tool. In this figure, the upper and right edges of a rectangle are selected to be moved.

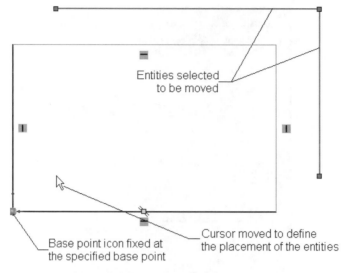

Figure 3-28 *Moving the selected entities*

Rotating Sketched Entities

CommandManager:	Sketch > Rotate Entities	*(Customize to Add)*
Menu:	Tools > Sketch Tools > Rotate	
Toolbar:	Sketch > Rotate Entities	*(Customize to Add)*

To rotate the sketched entities, invoke the **Rotate Entities** tool by choosing the **Rotate Entities** button from the **Sketch CommandManager**. You can also select the entities and right-click to display the shortcut menu. In this menu, choose **Rotate Entities** to invoke this tool. When you invoke this tool, the **Rotate PropertyManager** will be displayed, as shown in Figure 3-29, and you will be prompted to select sketch items or annotations.

The entities that you select to rotate are displayed in the **Sketch items or annotations** selection box of the **Entities to Rotate** rollout. Next, click in the base point selection box in the **Parameters** rollout; you will be prompted to specify the base point about which to rotate.

As soon as you specify the base point, the **Angle** spinner in the **Parameters** rollout will be highlighted. You can specify the angle of rotation using this spinner. You can also drag the mouse on the screen to define the angle of rotation.

Figure 3-30 shows a rectangle being rotated by dragging the cursor to define the angle of rotation. The lower right vertex of the rectangle is taken as the base point of rotation.

Scaling Sketched Entities

CommandManager:	Sketch > Scale Entities	*(Customize to Add)*
Menu:	Tools > Sketch Tools > Scale	
Toolbar:	Sketch > Scale Entities	*(Customize to Add)*

*Figure 3-29 The **Rotate PropertyManager***

Figure 3-30 Dragging the mouse to rotate the rectangle

To scale the sketched entities, invoke the **Scale Entities** tool by choosing the **Scale Entities** button from the **Sketch Tools CommandManager**. You can also select the entities and right-click to display the shortcut menu. In this menu, choose **Scale Entities** to invoke this tool. When you invoke this tool, the **Scale PropertyManager** will be displayed, as shown in Figure 3-31, and you will be prompted to select sketch items or annotations.

The entities that you select to be scaled are displayed in the **Sketch items or annotations** selection box of the **Entities to Scale** rollout. After selecting the entities to be rotated, right-click; you will be prompted to specify the base point about which to scale.

Figure 3-31 *The Scale PropertyManager*

As soon as you specify the base point, the **Scale Factor** spinner in the **Parameters** rollout will be highlighted. You can specify the rotation angle using this spinner.

You can also create more than one instance of the selected entities by selecting the **Copy** check box. On doing so, the **Number of Copies** spinner is displayed. You can set the number of instances that you need to create using this spinner. These copies will be created with an incremental scale factor.

Copying Sketched Entities

CommandManager:	Sketch > Copy Entities	(Customize to Add)
Menu:	Tools > Sketch Tools > Rotate	
Toolbar:	Sketch > Copy Entities	(Customize to Add)

The **Copy Entities** tool allows you to copy the selected sketched entities from one location to the other. Note that if you select dimensions also along with the entities to be copied, those dimensions will also be copied along with the sketched entities. To copy the sketched entities, choose the **Copy Entities** button from the **Sketch CommandManager**; the **Copy PropertyManager** is displayed, as shown in Figure 3-32.

Select the entities that you need to copy and then select the **From/To** radio button. Next, click once in the **Base Point** selection box and then specify the base point. Now, move the cursor; you will notice that the selected entities will also move as you move the cursor. Click anywhere in the drawing area where you need to place the copied entities. Another set of selected entities will be attached to the cursor. Again click to place the copied entities. If you select the **X/Y** radio button to copy the entities, then you can not place multiple copied entities.

CREATING PATTERNS

While sketching the base feature of a model, sometimes you may need to place the sketched

Figure 3-32 *The Copy PropertyManager*

entities in a particular arrangement such as along linear edges or around a circle. For example, refer to Figures 3-33 and 3-34, which show the base features with the slots. These slots are created with the help of linear and circular patterns of the sketched entities. The tools that are used to create linear and circular patterns of sketched entities are discussed next.

Figure 3-33 *Base feature with slots created about linear edges*

Figure 3-34 *Base feature with slots created around a circle*

Creating Linear Sketch Patterns

CommandManager:	Sketch > Linear Sketch Pattern *(Customize to Add)*
Menu:	Tools > Sketch Tools > Linear Pattern
Toolbar:	Sketch > Linear Sketch Pattern *(Customize to Add)*

In SolidWorks, the linear pattern of the sketched entities is created using the **Linear Sketch Pattern** tool. To create the linear pattern, select the sketched entities using the **Select** tool and then choose this button from the **Sketch CommandManager**; the **Linear Pattern PropertyManager** will be displayed, as shown in Figure 3-35, and the preview of the linear pattern will be shown on the screen in the background. Also, the arrow cursor will be replaced by the linear pattern cursor. Note that if you have not selected the sketched entities to be patterned before invoking this tool, you will have to select them one by one using the linear pattern cursor. You cannot define a window to select more than one entity using the linear pattern cursor. The name of selected instances are displayed in the **Entities to Pattern** rollout.

*Figure 3-35 The **Linear Pattern** PropertyManager*

The options available in this **PropertyManager** are discussed next.

Direction 1 Rollout

The options available in the **Direction 1** rollout are used to define the first direction, distance between the instances, number of instances, and the angle of pattern direction.

When you invoke the **Linear Pattern PropertyManager**, you will notice that only the options in the **Direction 1** rollout are active. Also, a callout is also attached to the direction arrow. The edit boxes available in this callout are used to define the distance between the pattern instances and the number of instances to be patterned. Alternatively, you can define these values in the **Distance** and the **Instances** spinners provided in this **Direction 1** rollout. To select any existing line or model edge to define direction 1, click in the selection box in the **Direction 1** area and select the line or the edge. The default direction is parallel to the X-axis. Clicking on the direction arrow or choosing the **Reverse direction** button from the **Direction 1** rollout reverses the pattern direction. The **Angle** spinner is used to define the angle of the direction of the pattern. By default, the direction of pattern is set to 360-degrees. If the **Add dimension** check box is selected, a dimension is attached between the parent instance and the first instance of pattern.

You can also define the distance between the instances by dragging the selected point provided on the tip of the direction arrow. Figure 3-36 shows the preview of the entities being patterned in the first direction. Figure 3-37 shows a linear pattern at an angle of 30-degrees.

Figure 3-36 Preview of the linear pattern with three instances along direction 1 and one instance along direction 2

Figure 3-37 Preview of the linear pattern at an angle of 30-degrees along direction 1

Direction 2 Rollout

You will notice that the preview in the second direction is not displayed. This is because the value of the number of instances is set to 1 in the **Number** spinner. This means only one instance is available in the second direction which is the parent instance. If you set the value of the number of instances to more than 1, then the options available in this rollout are enabled. All the options available in this rollout are the same, except the **Add angle dimension between axes** check box. This check box is selected by default and is used to apply an angular dimension to the reference direction lines of both the directions.

Figure 3-38 shows a linear pattern created by specifying instances on both the directions.

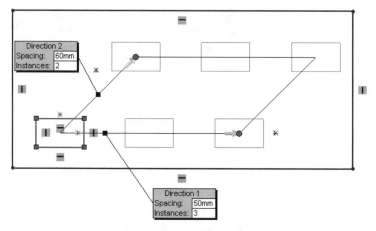

Figure 3-38 *Preview of the linear pattern at an angle of 0-degree along direction 1 and 45-degrees along direction 2*

Tip. *You can also specify the spacing and angle value dynamically in the preview of the linear pattern. To do this, press the left mouse button on the control points displayed at the end of the arrow in the pattern preview and drag the cursor. After placing the arrow at the desired location, release the left mouse button. The new spacing and angle values will be displayed in their respective spinners.*

Instances to Skip Rollout

The **Instances to Skip** rollout is used to temporarily remove some of the instances from the pattern. By default, this rollout is not invoked. To invoke it, click on the down arrow on the right of it. As soon as you activate the selection box in this rollout, pink dots are displayed in the center of each pattern instance. To temporarily remove an instance from a pattern, move the cursor on the pink dot; a hand symbol is displayed and the matrix of its location is displayed in the tooltip below this symbol. Click at this location to remove the instance; the display of the instance is turned off and the matrix of its location is displayed in the selection box. Also, the pink dot will change to a red dot. Similarly, you can remove as many instances that you do not want to be included in the pattern.

To restore the temporarily removed instances, select the red dot of the instance that you need to restore from the drawing area. Alternatively, you can select the name of the instance from the **Instances to Skip** rollout and then press the DELETE key on the keyboard.

 Tip. *You can also add entities in the current selection set or remove them from the current selection set by selecting them using the linear pattern cursor. As you add or remove the instances, the effect can be seen dynamically in the preview of the pattern.*

Creating Circular Sketch Patterns

CommandManager:	Sketch > Circular Sketch Pattern *(Customize to Add)*
Menu:	Tools > Sketch Tools > Circular Pattern
Toolbar:	Sketch > Circular Sketch Pattern *(Customize to Add)*

 In SolidWorks, the circular pattern of the sketched entities is created using the **Circular Sketch Pattern** tool. To create the circular pattern, select the sketched entities using the **Select** tool and then choose this button from the **Sketch CommandManager**; the **Circular Pattern PropertyManager** will be displayed, as shown in Figure 3-39, and the preview of the circular pattern will be shown on the screen in the background. Also, the arrow cursor will be replaced by the circular pattern cursor. The names of the selected entities will be displayed in the **Entities to Pattern** rollout.

*Figure 3-39 The **Circular Pattern** PropertyManager*

The options provided in the **Circular Pattern PropertyManager** are discussed next.

Parameters Rollout

The options available in the **Parameters** rollout are used to define the center point of the circular pattern, coordinates of the centerpoint of the reference circle, number of instances, angle between the instance or the total angle of pattern, radius of the reference circle, and so on. Figure 3-40 shows the parameters associated with the circular pattern. The options to define all these parameters are discussed next.

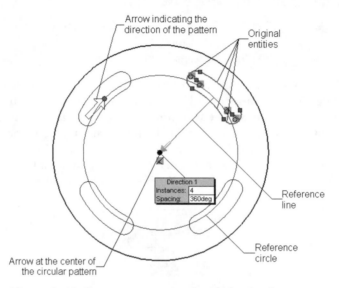

Figure 3-40 *Parameters associated with the circular pattern*

The **Reverse Direction** button is used to reverse the default direction of the circular pattern. The selection box on the right of this button is used to select the centerpoint of the circular pattern. By default, the origin is selected as the center of the circular pattern. You can modify this location using the **X Coordinate** and the **Y Coordinate** spinners. You can set the value of the number of instances using the **Number of Instances** spinner.

By default, the **Equal spacing** check box is selected and the value of angle in the **Angle** spinner is set to 360-degrees. This check box, when selected, makes sure that total number of instances are placed along the specified angle. If you modify the value of the angle in the **Angle** spinner, the total number of instances will be placed along the specified angle. If you clear this check box, then you need to specify the incremental angle between the instances using the **Angle** spinner.

The **Radius** spinner is used to modify the radius of the reference circle around which the circular pattern will be created. The **Arc Angle** spinner provided in this rollout is used to modify the angle between the center point of the original pattern instance and the center of the reference circle.

The **Add dimensions** check box is used to display the dimensions of the circular pattern

Note
If you know the location of the center point of the circular pattern, dragging the arrow at the center of the reference circle is the recommended method of defining the center of the circular pattern.

Instances to Skip

The **Instances to Skip** rollout is used to temporarily remove the instances from the pattern. The procedure of doing this is the same as that is discussed while creating the linear pattern.

Figure 3-41 shows the preview of the circular pattern with a 70-degrees incremental spacing between two successive instances. Figure 3-42 shows a circular pattern with the angle and radius dimension values displayed in the pattern.

Tip. *You can modify the total angle between the instances by pressing the left mouse button on the tip of the direction arrow and dragging the cursor.*

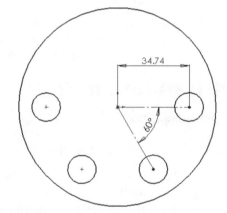

Figure 3-41 Creating circular pattern by defining incremental angle between individual instances

Figure 3-42 Radius and angle values placed in the circular pattern

EDITING PATTERNS

You can edit the patterns of the sketched entities by using the shortcut menu that will be displayed when you right-click on any instance of the pattern. Depending on whether you right-click on the instance of the linear or the circular pattern, the **Edit Liner Pattern** or the **Edit Circular Pattern** option will be available in the shortcut menu. Figure 3-43 shows the partial view of the shortcut menu that will be displayed when you right-click one of the instances of a circular pattern.

Select Other	
Zoom/Pan/Rotate	▶
Recent Commands	▶
Sketch Entities	▶
Smart Dimension	
More Dimensions	▶
Relations	
Fix	
Add Relation...	
Display/Delete Relations...	
Fully Define Sketch...	
Relations/Snaps Options...	
Selected Entity (Arc2)	
Show Curvature Combs	
Edit Circular Pattern	
Make Block	

Figure 3-43 *The partial view of the shortcut menu displayed on right-clicking on an instance of a circular pattern*

Depending on whether you choose the option to edit a linear pattern or a circular pattern, the **Linear Pattern** or the **Circular Pattern PropertyManager** will be displayed. Note that only those options that can be edited will be available in these **PropertyManagers**.

WRITING TEXT IN THE SKETCHING ENVIRONMENT

CommandManager:	Sketch > Text	*(Customize to Add)*
Menu:	Tools > Sketch Entities > Text	
Toolbar:	Sketch > Text	*(Customize to Add)*

You can also create text in the sketching environment of SolidWorks that can be later used to create join or cut features. To write the text, choose the **Text** button from the **Sketch CommandManager**; the **Sketch Text PropertyManager** will be displayed, as shown in Figure 3-44. Enter the text in the box available in the **Text** rollout. You will notice that by default, the text will be started from the sketch origin. However, the text will actually be placed at the location that you specify on the screen before or after writing the text. You can also change the format, font, justification, and so on using the options available in the **Text** rollout. Figure 3-45 shows the text created using the **Text** tool.

You can also create the text along a curve. To do so, you first need to create a curve. The curve can be an arc, a spline, a line, or a combination of a line, arc, and spline. Next, invoke the **Sketch Text PropertyManager** and select the curve or curves along which you need to create the text. Now, enter the text in the **Text** edit box; you will observe that the text is created along the arc. You can use the **Flip Horizontal** and **Flip Vertical** options to modify the display of the text. Figure 3-46 shows the text created along an arc.

Figure 3-44 *The Sketch Text PropertyManager*

Figure 3-45 *Sketch created using the Text tool*

Figure 3-46 Text created along the arc

Tip. *If the text that you write appears reversed, you can draw a line from left to right and then use it as an element to align the text.*

MODIFYING SKETCHED ENTITIES

Most of the sketches require modification at some stage of the design. Therefore, it is important for any designer to understand the process of modification in SolidWorks. Modification of various sketched entities is discussed next.

Modifying a Sketched Line

You can modify the sketched lines by using the **Line Properties PropertyManager**, which is displayed when you select it using the **Select** tool. Note that if the selected line is part of a rectangle, polygon, or a parallelogram, the entire object will be modified as you modify the line. This is because relations are applied to all lines of a rectangle, polygon, and a parallelogram.

Similarly, you can also modify the centerlines using the **Line Properties PropertyManager**, which will be displayed when you select a centerline.

Modifying a Sketched Circle

To modify a sketched circle, select it using the **Select** tool to display the **Circle PropertyManager**. The coordinate values of the center point of the circle and the value of the radius will be displayed. You can modify the values that you want.

 Tip. *The status of the sketched entity that you select for modification is displayed in the **Existing Relations** rollout of the **PropertyManager**, which is displayed. For example, if the selected sketched entity is fully defined, it will be displayed in the **PropertyManager** and if the entity is underdefined, the **PropertyManager** will display a message that the entity is underdefined.*

Modifying a Sketched Arc

To modify a sketched arc, select it using the **Select** tool. The **Arc PropertyManager** will be displayed with the coordinate values of the center point, start point, and endpoint. The values of the radius and the included angle will also be displayed. You can modify the values that you want.

Modifying a Sketched Polygon

To modify a sketched polygon, right-click on any one edge of the polygon to display the shortcut menu. Choose the **Edit polygon** option from the shortcut menu to display the **Polygon PropertyManager**. You can modify the selected polygon using the options in the **Polygon PropertyManager** or draw a new polygon.

 Note
*If you right-click on the reference circle that is automatically drawn when you draw a polygon, the **Edit polygon** option will not be available in the shortcut menu.*

Modifying a Spline

You can perform five types of modifications on a spline. The first is the modification of the coordinates of the selected control point. The second is adding more control points on the spline. The third is modifying the spline using the Spline Handles. The fourth is adding more

Spline Handles. The fifth is adding a curvature control symbol. These modifications are discussed in detail next.

Modifying a Spline Using the Control Polygon

With this release of SolidWorks, when you select a spline, control polygons are displayed on it. You can use them to modify the shape of the spline. To modify the spline using this method, select the control point of the control polygon, as shown in Figure 3-47.

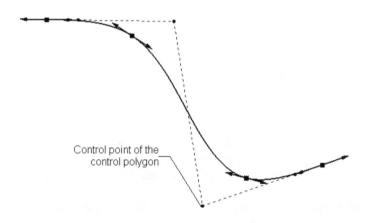

Figure 3-47 Control point of the control polygon

The **Spline Polygon PropertyManager** is displayed. Using this **PropertyManager**, you can modify the location of the coordinates of the control point. You can also modify the location of the control point by dragging it.

If the control polygon is not displayed by default, you need to select the spline and invoke the short cut menu. Now, choose the **Display Control Polygon** option from it. To turn off the display of the control polygon, you need to follow the same procedure.

Modifying the Coordinates of Control Points

To modify the control points of a spline, select it; the **Spline PropertyManager** will be displayed. A partial view of the **Spline PropertyManager** is displayed in Figure 3-48. All control points of the spline will be displayed and the current control point will also be displayed with a square with a filled circle inside it. The number and coordinates of the current handle will be displayed in the **Spline PropertyManager**. You can modify the coordinates using the spinner. You can select any other handle by using the **Spline Point Number** spinner.

Adding Control Points

To add control points to the spline, choose **Tools > Spline Tools > Insert Spline Point** from the menu bar. You can also select the spline and right-click to invoke the shortcut menu. In this menu, choose the **Spline Point** option. Now, select the points on the spline where you want to add the control point. A circle will be displayed at the point specified on the spline and the spline handle will also be displayed attached to the inserted point. You will learn more about the

Figure 3-48 *Partial view of the Spline PropertyManager*

spline handles later in this chapter. Similarly, you can add as many control points as you want to the spline. After adding the required number of control points, invoke the **Select** tool and then select the spline again. You will notice that the boxes of control points are displayed on all points you specified on the spline. You can display the coordinates of a control point using the **Spline Point Number** spinner available in the **Spline PropertyManager**.

Modifying a Spline Using the Spline Handles

The spline handle is a line with arrows on its both endpoints. The spline handles will be displayed when you select the spline using the **Select** tool. The default spline handles will be displayed in gray, which implies that they are not selected. When you move the cursor over a spline handle, it will be highlighted in red and a double-sided arrow will be displayed below the cursor. Select the spline handle when it is displayed in red; the spline handle will be displayed in green. The number of respective control points, and their coordinates are displayed in the **Parameters** rollout. Drag the cursor to dynamically modify the magnitude of the tangent and the radial direction of the tangent. As you drag the cursor, the values of the magnitude of the tangent and the radial direction of the tangent will be modified dynamically in the **Tangent Magnitude** and **Tangent Radial Direction** spinners, respectively. The **Tangent Driving** check box is also selected automatically when you drag the cursor. After modifying the shape of the spline, click anywhere in the drawing area to exit the current selection set. You will notice that currently modified spline handle is displayed in blue, which implies that the default setting of this spline handle is modified. Similarly, you can edit other spline handles.

With this release of SolidWorks, you can also apply dimensions to the spline handles to accurately shape the spline. You will learn more about dimensioning later in this chapter.

Adding/Deleting the Spline Handles

To add more spline handles, select the spline and right-click to invoke the shortcut menu. Choose the **Add Tangency Control** option from the shortcut menu; a blue-colored double-sided arrow will be displayed attached to the selected spline. Move the cursor to the location where you want to place the spline handle and click on that location. A spline control point will also be added along with the spline handle. You can also apply relations to the spline handles. You will learn more about relations in the later chapters. You can also delete the spline handles by selecting them and pressing the DELETE key on the keyboard.

Adding the Curvature Control

You can also add a curvature control symbol which is used to modify the curvature of the spline. To add a curvature control, select the spline and invoke the shortcut menu. Choose the **Add Curvature Control** option from it; the curvature control symbol ⤳ will be attached to the selected spline. Move the cursor to the location where you want to place the curvature control symbol. A spline handle will also be placed tangent to the spline at the location where the curvature control symbol is attached. Now, select and drag the circle placed at the bottom of the this symbol. You will notice that the curvature of the spline is modified dynamically as you drag the cursor. After modifying the shape of the spline, release the left mouse button. You can also delete the curvature control symbol by selecting it and pressing the DELETE key from the keyboard.

Modifying a Sketched Point

To modify a sketched point, select it using the **Select** tool; the **Sketched Point PropertyManager** will be displayed. You can modify the coordinates of the sketched point using this **PropertyManager**.

Modifying an Ellipse or an Elliptical Arc

To modify an ellipse or an elliptical arc, select it using the **Select** tool; the **Ellipse PropertyManager** will be displayed. You can modify the required parameters using the options available in this **PropertyManager**.

Modifying a Parabola

To modify a parabola, select it using the **Select** tool; the **Parabola PropertyManager** will be displayed. You can modify the parameters of the parabola from this **PropertyManager**.

Dynamically Modifying and Copying Sketched Entities

In the sketcher environment of SolidWorks, you can modify or copy the sketched entities by dynamically dragging them using the left mouse button. For example, consider a case where you create a sketch of a rectangle and you want to increase the size of the rectangle. You simply have to select any of the lines of the rectangle or any of its vertices and hold the left mouse button down to drag the cursor. Drag the sketch according to your requirement and then release the left mouse button. If you choose **Tools > Sketch Setting > Detach Segment on Drag** from the menu bar and select a line of a rectangle to drag, the line segment will be detached from the rectangle. This option is not activated by default. As a result, the segments are not detached on dragging.

You can also copy the sketched entities dynamically. Select the sketched entity or entities to be copied using the CTRL key or by dragging a window around them. Press and hold the CTRL key down. Now, press and hold the left mouse button down and drag the selected entity or entities. The preview of the copied entities will be displayed. Release the left mouse button at the location where you want to place the new entities. You can make multiple copies of the selected entities by repeating this procedure.

Splitting Sketched Entities

CommandManager:	Sketch > Split Entities	(Customize to Add)
Menu:	Tools > Sketch Tools > Split Curve	
Toolbar:	Sketch > Split Curve	(Customize to Add)

Using the **Split Entities** tool, you can split a sketched entity into two or more entities by specifying the split points. To split an entity, choose the **Split Entities** button from the **Sketch CommandManager**; the current cursor will be replaced by the split entities cursor. Move the cursor to an appropriate location where you want to split the sketched entity. When the cursor snaps to the entity, press the left mouse button to add a split point. Now, right click to display the shortcut menu and choose the select option from the shortcut menu. Using the select cursor, select the sketched entity. You will notice that the sketched entity is divided in two entities and a split point is added between the two sketched entities. You can add as many split points as you need. Remember that to split a circle, a full ellipse, or a closed spline, you need to split them at least at two points.

You can also delete the split points to convert the split entity into a single entity. To delete the split point, select the split point and press the DELETE key from the keyboard. You can also right-click on the split point to display the shortcut menu and choose the **Delete** option from the shortcut menu.

TUTORIALS

Tutorial 1

In this tutorial, you will create the base sketch of the model shown in Figure 3-49. The sketch of the model is shown in Figure 3-50. You will create the sketch of the base feature using the normal sketch tools and then modify and edit the sketch using various modifying options. Do not create the center marks and center lines. They are for your reference only.   (**Expected time: 30 min**)

Figure 3-49 *Solid Model for Tutorial 1*

Figure 3-50 *The sketch of the base feature*

The steps that will be followed to complete this tutorial are listed next.

a. Start SolidWorks and then start a new part document.
b. Maximize the part file document and then switch to the sketching environment.
c. Draw the outer loop of the sketch of the given model, refer to Figures 3-51 and 3-52.
d. Create the inner cavity using the **Centerpoint Arc** and **Tangent Arc** tools, refer to Figure 3-53.
e. Use the **Circular Sketch Step and Repeat** tool to create a circular pattern of the inner cavity, refer to Figure 3-54.
f. Complete the sketch by creating the circles that define the hole in the outer loop.
g. Using the **Circular Sketch Step and Repeat** tools, create the circles for the remaining holes in the outer loop, refer to Figure 3-55.

Starting SolidWorks and Starting a New SolidWorks Document

1. Start SolidWorks by choosing **Start > Programs > SolidWorks 2007 SP0.0 > SolidWorks 2007 SP0.0** or by double-clicking on the shortcut icon of **SolidWorks 2007 SP0.0** available on the desktop of your computer.

    The **SolidWorks Resources Task Pane** is displayed on the right of this window.

2. Choose the **New Document** option from the **Getting Started** group of the **SolidWorks Resources Task Pane**; the **New SolidWorks Document** dialog box will be displayed.

3. The **Part** button is chosen by default. Choose the **OK** button from this dialog box.

    A new SolidWorks part document is started. The **SolidWorks Resources Task Pane** is also displayed and some of the display of the drawing area is consumed by it. Therefore, you need to exit this **Task Pane**.

4. Click anywhere in the drawing area to exit the **SolidWorks Resources Task Pane**.

    By default, when you start a new part document, the part modeling environment is active. But because you need to draw the sketch of the feature, you need to invoke the sketching environment.

5. Choose the **Sketch** button from the **Standard** toolbar; the **Edit Sketch PropertyManager** is invoked and you are prompted to select the plane to create the sketch.

6. Select the **Front Plane**; the sketching environment is invoked and the plane is oriented normal to the view.

    You will notice that the red sketch origin is displayed along with the confirmation corner.

Modifying the Snap and Grid Settings and the Dimensioning Units

Before drawing the sketch, you need to modify the grid and snap settings to make the cursor jump through a distance of 10 mm.

1. Choose **Tools > Options** from menu bar and then choose the **Document Properties** tab to invoke the **Document Properties - Detailing** dialog box.

2. Choose the **Grid/Snap** option from the area on the left. Set the value of the **Minor-lines per major** spinner to **10** and the **Major grid spacing** spinner to **100**.

    The coordinates displayed close to the lower right corner of the SolidWorks window shows an increment of 10 mm when you move the cursor in the drawing area after exiting the dialog box.

3. If by default the grid is displayed when you invoke the sketching environment, you can remove its display by clearing the **Display grid** check box from the **Grid** area.

Tip. *You can also pan using the CTRL+middle mouse button. To use this option, hold the CTRL key down and then press the middle mouse button and drag the cursor.*

4. Choose the **Go To System Snaps** button and select the **Grid** check box. Next, clear the **Snap only when grid is displayed** check box, if it is selected.

    If you had selected a unit other than millimeter to measure the length while installing SolidWorks, you need to select the units for the current drawing.

5. Invoke the **Document Properties** tab and select the **Units** option from the area on the left of the **Document Properties - Grid/Snap** dialog box.

6. Select the **MMGS (millimeter, gram, second)** radio button from the **Unit system** area and **Degrees** from the drop-down list available in the **Angular units** area.

7. Choose the **OK** button after making the necessary settings.

Drawing the Outer Loop of the Sketch

As evident from Figure 3-50, the sketch consists of the outer loop and inner cavities. It is recommended that for complex sketches, you should first create the outer loop of the sketch. Therefore, you need to create the outer loop of the sketch first and then you can create the inner cavities.

The origin of the sketcher environment is placed in the middle of the drawing area and you have to create the sketch in the first quadrant. Therefore, it is recommended that you modify the drawing area using the **Pan** tool.

1. Choose the **Pan** button from the **View** toolbar to invoke the **Pan** tool; the select cursor is replaced by the pan cursor.

2. Press and hold the left mouse button down near the sketch origin and drag the cursor to the lower left corner of the drawing area; the sketch origin is moved near the lower left corner of the drawing area.

3. Choose the **Circle** button from the **Sketch CommandManager**; the pan cursor is replaced by the circle cursor.

4. Move the cursor to a location where the value of the coordinates is 70 mm, 70 mm, 0 mm.

5. Specify the center point of the circle at this location and move the cursor horizontally toward the right. When the radius above the circle cursor shows a value 50, press the left mouse button.

6. Choose the **Zoom to Area** button from the **View** toolbar. Using the left mouse button, drag the cursor to define a window such that the sketched circle and the sketch origin are placed in the window.

When you release the left mouse button the display area of the sketch is increased.

7. Choose the **Circle** button from the **Sketch CommandManager** and move the cursor to the right quadrant of the circle. All quadrants of the circle are displayed, and the right quadrant on which you have placed the cursor is displayed in red. The symbol of coincident constraint is displayed below the cursor.

8. Using the left mouse button, specify the center point of the circle at this location and move the cursor horizontally toward the right. When the value of the radius above the circle cursor shows a value 10, press the left mouse button.

9. Choose the **Trim Entities** button from the **Sketch CommandManager** and choose the **Trim to closet** button from the **Trim PropertyManager**.

10. Trim the part of the sketch so that the sketch looks similar to that shown in Figure 3-51.

11. Choose the **Circular Sketch Pattern** button from the **Sketch CommandManager**. You may have to customize this button to add in the **Sketch CommandManager**.

    The **Circular Pattern PropertyManager** is displayed and the cursor is replaced by the circular pattern cursor.

12. Using the circular pattern cursor, select the smaller trimmed circle. The preview of the circular pattern with the default setting is displayed in the drawing area.

    You will notice that the center of the circular pattern, which is displayed by an arrow, is placed at the origin. But because the origin is not the actual center of the circular pattern, you need to modify the center of the circular pattern. This can be done by entering the coordinates of the point in the **X coordinate** and the **Y coordinate** spinners available in the **Parameters** rollout of this **PropertyManager**. But the recommended method of modifying the center of the circular pattern is by dragging the arrow displayed at the center of the pattern.

13. Move the circular pattern cursor at the control point available at the end of the arrow displayed at the origin.

14. Press and hold the left mouse button down at the control point and drag it to the center of the outer trimmed circle in the sketch. Release the left mouse button when a red circle is displayed at the center point of the outer trimmed circle.

    You will notice that both **X coordinate** and the **Y coordinate** spinners shows the value of 70 mm. This is because the center of the outer trimmed circle is located at a distance of 70 mm along the X and Y axis directions.

15. Set the value of the **Number of Instances** spinner to **6**. Accept all other default values and choose the **OK** button to create the pattern.

16. Trim the unwanted portion of the outer trimmed circle using the **Trim Entities** tool. You need to use the **Trim to closet** button for this trimming. After trimming, the sketch should look similar to that shown in Figure 3-52.

Figure 3-51 *Sketch after trimming the unwanted entities*

Figure 3-52 *Outer loop of the sketch*

Drawing the Sketch of the Inner Cavity

Next, you need to draw the sketch of the inner cavities. You will draw the sketch of one of the cavities and then create a circular pattern of this cavity. The number of items in the circular pattern will be 3.

Before creating the sketch of the inner cavity, you need to create a centerline that will act as a reference for creating the sketch of the inner cavity.

1. Invoke the **System Options - Relations/Snaps** dialog box. Make sure that the **Angle** check box is selected and set the value of the **Snap Angle** spinner to **30**.

2. Choose the **Centerline** button from the **Sketch CommandManager**. Move the cursor close to the center of the outer circle. When the red circle is displayed, specify the start point of the centerline. Move the cursor to a location where the angle of the line is shown as exactly 30-degrees and the length is close to 35 in the **Parameters** rollout of the **PropertyManager**. At this point, specify the endpoint of the line.

3. Exit the **Centerline** tool and select the centerline; the **Line PropertyManager** is displayed. Set the value of the **Length** spinner to **35**.

4. Choose the **Circle** button from the **Sketch CommandManager**.

5. Move the cursor to the upper endpoint of the centerline. When the red circle is displayed, specify the center point. Move the cursor horizontally toward the right and draw a circle of radius close to 5 mm.

6. Set the value of the radius of the circle to **5** in the **Radius** spinner of the **Circle PropertyManager**.

7. Choose the **Circular Sketch Pattern** button from the **Sketch CommandManager**; the **Circular Pattern PropertyManager** is displayed and the circle is automatically selected to be patterned. This is because the circle was selected when you invoked this tool.

    Note that the center of the circular pattern is placed at the origin. You need to change the center of the circular pattern to the center of the outer trimmed circle.

8. Move the circular pattern cursor at the control point available at the end of the arrow displayed at the origin.

9. Press and hold the left mouse button down and drag the cursor to the center point of the outer trimmed circle. Release the left mouse when the red circle is displayed.

10. Set the value of the **Number of Instances** spinner to **2**.

11. Set the value of the **Spacing** spinner to 45-degrees and choose the **Reverse direction** button.

12. Choose **OK** from the **Circular Pattern PropertyManager**.

13. Choose the **Centerpoint Arc** button from the **Sketch CommandManager**.

14. Move the cursor to the center point of the outer trimmed circle and specify the center point of the arc. Now, move the cursor to the intersection of the centerline and the circle. Specify the start point of the arc when the intersection symbol appears.

15. Move the cursor in the counterclockwise direction. When the value of the angle above the arc cursor shows a value of 45-degrees, press the left mouse button to specify the endpoint of the arc. At this point, the second inner circle is highlighted in red.

    Next, you need to offset the arc created in the previous step through an offset distance of 10.

    The arc created earlier is displayed in green, indicating that it is already selected. If the arc is not selected, select the arc using the left mouse button before invoking the offset tool.

16. Choose the **Offset Entities** button from the **Sketch CommandManager**; the **Offset Entities PropertyManager** is displayed.

17. The default value of the **Offset Distance** spinner is **10**. Clear the **Reverse** check box, if selected. Choose the **OK** button from the **Offset Entities PropertyManager**.

18. Choose the **Trim Entities** button from the **Sketch CommandManager**. Trim the unwanted portion of the inner cavity and then exit this tool. If the sketch turns

red and the **SolidWorks** warning window appears, choose **OK** to close the window. The sketch, after completing the inner cavity, is shown in Figure 3-53.

Creating the Pattern of the Inner Cavity

Next, you need to create the pattern of the inner cavity using the **Circular Sketch Pattern** tool. The pattern of the inner cavity consists of three instances. The center point of the pattern lies at the center point of the outer trimmed circle.

Before invoking this option, exit the **Trim** tool if it is active. Next, press the CTRL key on the keyboard and using the left mouse button, select all entities of the inner cavity.

1. Choose the **Circular Sketch Pattern** button from the **Sketch CommandManager** toolbar to invoke the **Circular Pattern PropertyManager**.

2. Press and hold the left mouse button down at the control point of the arrow displayed at the origin. Drag it to the center of the outer trimmed circle in the sketch. Release the left mouse button when the red circle is displayed.

   You will notice that the **X coordinate** and **Y coordinate** spinners in the **Parameters** rollout show the value 70 mm. The default value of the number of items in the pattern is 4. But you need to modify this value because you need three items in the pattern.

3. Set the value of the **Number** spinner in the **Parameters** rollout to **3**. Accept all other default values and choose the **OK** button to create the pattern. If the sketch turned red earlier, it will turn back to blue and the **SolidWorks** information box will be displayed. Choose **OK** from this dialog box. The sketch after, creating the pattern of the inner cavity, is shown in Figure 3-54.

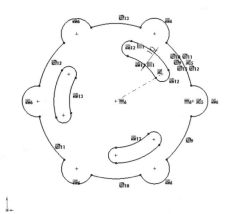

Figure 3-53 *The sketch of the outer loop and the inner cavity*

Figure 3-54 *Sketch after creating the pattern of the inner cavity*

Sketching the Holes

Next, you need to draw the sketch of the holes. As evident from Figure 3-50, you need to draw a total of six circles. After drawing the first circle, you need to draw the other five circles by creating a circular pattern of the parent circle.

1. Choose the **Circle** button from the **Sketch CommandManager**.

2. Select the center point of the trimmed circle at the left quadrant of the outer circle as the center point of the new circle.

3. Press and hold the CTRL key down and draw a circle of radius close to 5. Make sure you press the CTRL key so that the cursor does not snap to the points or grid.

4. Set the value of the **Radius** spinner to **5** in the **Circle PropertyManager**.

5. Choose the **Circular Sketch Pattern** button from the **Sketch CommandManager** to invoke the **Circular Pattern PropertyManager**.

6. Move the center of the circular pattern to the center point of the outer trimmed circle.

7. Set the value of the **Number** spinner to **6**. Accept all other default values and choose **OK** in this dialog box.

The final sketch of Tutorial 1 is shown in Figure 3-55.

Figure 3-55 *Final sketch for Tutorial 1*

Saving the Sketch

As mentioned earlier, it is recommended that you create a separate folder for saving the tutorial files of each chapter. When you invoke the option to save the document, the default folder that is displayed is the one in which you saved the last document. Browse to the */My Documents/SolidWorks* folder. Now, you will create another folder inside the *SolidWorks* folder and save the document.

1. Choose the **Save** button from the **Standard** toolbar to invoke the **Save As** dialog box.

2. Choose the **Create New Folder** button from the **Save As** dialog box. Enter the name of the folder as *c03* and press ENTER.

3. Enter the name of the document as *c03tut1* in the **File name** edit box and choose the **Save** button.

   The document will be saved in the */My Documents/SolidWorks/c03* folder.

4. Close the file by choosing **File** > **Close** from the menu bar.

 Tip. *If you do not want to display the symbols of the relations that are displayed on the sketched entities, choose **View** > **Sketch Relations** from the menu bar to clear this option.*

Tutorial 2

In this tutorial, you will create the base sketch of the model shown in Figure 3-56. The sketch of the model is shown in Figure 3-57. You will create the sketch with a mirror line and mirror tool. After creating the sketch, you will modify it by dragging the sketched entities.

(Expected time: 30 min)

Figure 3-56 Solid model for Tutorial 2   *Figure 3-57 Sketch of the model*

The steps that will be followed to complete this tutorial are listed below.

a. Start a new part document.
b. Maximize the part document and then switch to the sketching environment.
c. Create the centerlines and create a mirror line using one of the centerlines and the **Mirror Entities** tool.
d. Create the sketch in the third quadrant; the sketch will automatically be mirrored on the other side, refer to Figure 3-58.

    e.   Mirror the entire sketch along the second mirror line, refer to Figure 3-56.

    f.   Modify the sketch by dragging the sketched entities, refer to Figure 3-57.

Starting a New Document

1.   Choose the **New** button from the **Standard** toolbar to invoke the **New SolidWorks Document** dialog box.

2.   The **Part** button is chosen by default. Choose the **OK** button from the **New SolidWorks Document** dialog box to start a new SolidWorks part document.

    Next, you need to invoke the sketching environment.

3.   Choose the **Sketch** button from the **Standard** toolbar and select the **Front Plane** to invoke the sketching environment.

    Next, you need to modify the snap and grid settings.

4.   Invoke the **Document Properties - Grid/Snap** dialog box. Set the value of the **Major grid spacing** spinner to **100** and the **Minor-lines per Major** spinner to **10**.

    It is assumed that you have selected the unit of measurement as millimeter while installing SolidWorks. However, if you have selected any other unit while installation, you need to change it.

5.   Select the **Units** option available below the **Grid/Snap** option. Select the **MMGS (millimeter, gram, second)** option from the **Unit system** area. Choose the **Degrees** option from the drop-down list available in the **Angular units** area. Choose **OK** to exit the dialog box.

Drawing the Center Lines and Converting a Center Line Into a Mirror Line

    In this tutorial, you need to draw the sketch of the given model with the help of a mirror line. The sketches that are symmetrical along any axis are recommended to be drawn using the mirror line. The mirror line is drawn using the **Centerline** and **Dynamic Mirror Entities** tools. After drawing a mirror line, when you draw the entities on one side of the mirror line, the same entities are also automatically drawn on the other side of the mirror line. A symmetrical relation is also applied to the entities on both sides of the mirror line. Therefore, if you modify an entity on one side of the mirror line, the same modifications are reflected on the mirrored entity, and vice versa. First, you need to draw a mirror line.

1.   Choose the **Centerline** button from the **Sketch CommandManager**.

2.   Move the line cursor to a location where the value of the coordinates is 0 mm, 100 mm, 0 mm. You may have to zoom the drawing to reach that point.

3.   Specify the start point of the centerline at this point and move the cursor vertically downward and draw a line of 200 mm length. You may have to zoom and pan the drawing to draw a line of this length.

4. Now, double-click anywhere on the screen to end the current chain. You can also press the right mouse button anywhere on the drawing area to invoke the shortcut menu and choose the **End chain** option from it.

5. Move the line cursor to a location where the value of the coordinates is -100 mm, 0 mm, 0 mm.

6. Specify the start point of the centerline and move the cursor horizontally toward the right to draw a line of 200 mm length. Pan the drawing, if required.

7. Zoom to fit the drawing and then right-click to invoke the **Select** tool. The line cursor will be replaced by the select cursor.

8. Select the vertical centerline; it will be displayed in green.

9. Choose **Dynamic Mirror Entities** from the **Sketch CommandManager** to convert the selected centerline to a mirror line and activate the automatic mirror option.

    You can confirm the creation of the mirror line and the activation of the automatic mirror option by observing the symmetrical symbol applied to both ends of the centerline.

Drawing the Sketch

Next, you need to draw the sketch of the base feature. You will draw the sketch in the third quadrant and the same sketch will be created automatically on the other side of the mirror line. The symmetrical relation is applied between the parent entity and the mirrored entity.

1. Press the L key on the keyboard to invoke the **Line** tool.

2. Move the line cursor to a location where the value of the coordinates is 0 mm, -100 mm, 0 mm.

3. Specify the start point of the line at this location and move the cursor horizontally toward the left.

4. Specify the endpoint of the line when the length of the line above the line cursor shows a value 90.

    You will notice that as soon as you specify the endpoint of the line, a mirror image is automatically created on the other side of the mirror line. This line drawn as the mirrored entity is merged with the line drawn on the left. Therefore, the entire line becomes a single entity. Remember that the lines will merge only if one of the endpoints of the line you draw is coincident with the mirror line.

5. Move the cursor vertically upward and specify the endpoint of the line when the length of the line above the line cursor shows a value 30.

    You will notice that as soon as you specify the endpoint of a line, a mirror image is automatically created on the other side of the mirror line.

6.   Move the line cursor toward the right and specify the endpoint of the line when the length of the line above the line cursor shows a value 30. A mirror image is automatically created on the other side of the mirror line.

7.   Move the line cursor vertically upward and specify the endpoint of the line when the line cursor snaps the horizontal centerline. Exit the **Line** tool. The sketch, after creating the lines, is shown in Figure 3-58.

Mirroring the Entire Sketch

After creating one half of the sketch, you need to mirror the entire sketch about the horizontal centerline. But first, you need to disable the automatic mirroring.

1.   As evident from the symmetric relation symbol on the vertical centerline, automatic mirroring is activated. Choose the **Dynamic Mirror Entities** button again to disable automatic mirroring. Now, the vertical centerline will not work as a mirror line.

2.   Use the box selection method to select all the lines sketched earlier and also the horizontal centerline. Make sure you do not select the vertical centerline.

3.   Choose the **Mirror Entities** button from the **Sketch CommandManager**. The entire sketch is mirrored about the horizontal centerline. The sketch, after mirroring, is shown in Figure 3-59.

Figure 3-58 *Sketch after drawing the lines*   *Figure 3-59* *Sketch after mirroring the sketched entities*

Modifying the Sketch by Dragging

Next, you need to modify the sketch by dragging. While dragging the entities, you will observe that the corresponding mirrored entity will also be modified.

1.   Select the lower right vertical line. The **Line PropertyManager** will be displayed on the left of the drawing area.

You will notice that the value of the length in the **Length** spinner shows a value **30**. But the required length of this line is 20. Therefore, you need to edit the length of this line. In this tutorial, you will edit the sketch by dragging. You will observe that when you drag one line, all dependent lines are also modified. This is because they are created as mirror images.

2. Select the top horizontal line and then move the cursor to the right endpoint of this line. When the red circle appears, drag the cursor vertically downward. Release the left mouse button when the cursor snaps to the next grid point.

   You will observe that all sketched entities that are related to the dragged entity are also modified.

3. Select the lower left vertical line and drag one of its endpoint horizontally toward the right. Release the left mouse button when the cursor snaps to the next grid point on the right.

4. Select the middle left vertical line and drag one of the endpoints of the line horizontally toward the right. Release the left mouse button when the cursor snaps to the grid point on the left of the vertical centerline.

   The final sketch, after modifying the sketched entities by dragging, is shown in Figure 3-60.

Figure 3-60 *Final sketch for Tutorial 2*

Saving the Sketch

1. Choose the **Save** button from the **Standard** toolbar to invoke the **Save As** dialog box.

2. Browse to the *SolidWorks/c03* folder if it is not displayed by default.

3. Enter the name of the document as *c03tut2* in the **File name** edit box and choose the **Save** button.

The document will be saved in the */My Documents/SolidWorks/c03* folder.

4.   Close the document by choosing **File** > **Close** from the menu bar.

Tutorial 3

In this tutorial, you will create the basic sketch of the model shown in Figure 3-61. The sketch is shown in Figure 3-62. Do not dimension the sketch; the solid model and the dimensions are given only for your reference.   (**Expected Time: 30 min**)

Figure 3-61 *Solid model for Tutorial 3*

Figure 3-62 *Sketch for Tutorial 3*

The steps that will be followed to complete this tutorial are listed below.

a. Start a new part document.
b. Maximize the part file document and then switch to the sketching environment.
c. Create a centerline that will be used for reference.
d. Draw and edit the sketch using the **Mirror Entities** and **Trim Entities** tools, refer to Figure 3-63.
e. Offset the entire sketch, refer to Figure 3-64.
f. Complete the final editing of the sketch using the **Extend Entities** and **Trim Entities** tools, refer to Figures 3-65 and 3-66.

Starting a New Document

1. Choose the **New** button from the **Standard** toolbar to invoke the **New SolidWorks Document** dialog box.

2. The **Part** button is chosen by default. Choose the **OK** button from the **New SolidWorks Document** dialog box.

3. Choose the **Sketch** button from the **Standard** toolbar and select **Front Plane** to invoke the sketching environment.

4. Using the **Document Properties - Grid/Snap** dialog box, set the value of the **Major grid spacing** to **100** and the **Minor-lines per major** spinner to **10**.

Drawing the Centerline

Before drawing the sketch, you need to draw a centerline that will act as a reference for the other sketch entities. This centerline will also be used for mirroring.

1. Choose the **Centerline** button from the **Sketch CommandManager**.

2. Move the cursor to a location where the value of the coordinates is -70 mm, 0 mm, 0 mm.

3. Specify the start point at this location and move the cursor horizontally toward the right.

4. Specify the endpoint of the centerline when the value of the length of the centerline above the line cursor shows a value of 140.

5. Double-click anywhere in the drawing area to end the line creation.

Drawing the Outer Loop of the Sketch

Next, you need to draw the outer loop of the sketch using the sketch tools. As evident from Figure 3-62, the sketch is drawn using the **Circle** and **Line** tools.

1. Choose the **Circle** button from the **Sketch CommandManager**; the line cursor will be replaced by the circle cursor.

2.   Move the circle cursor to the origin and when the red circle is displayed, press the left mouse button to specify the center point of the circle.

3.   Move the cursor horizontally toward the right and draw a circle of 50 mm radius.

4.   Choose the **Zoom to Fit** button from the **View** toolbar to increase the display of the sketch.

5.   Choose the **Line** button from the **Sketch CommandManager** and move the cursor to a location where the value of the coordinates is -60 mm, 10 mm, 0 mm. Specify the start point of the line at this location.

6.   Move the cursor horizontally toward the right and press the left mouse button to specify the endpoint of the line when the line cursor snaps the circle. Exit the **Line** tool.

7.   Press the CTRL key on the keyboard and using the left mouse button, select the horizontal line created in the last step and the centerline. Both selected entities are displayed in green color.

8.   Choose the **Mirror Entities** button from the **Sketch CommandManager**; the mirror image of the lower horizontal line is created on the other side of the centerline.

9.   Choose the **Line** button from the **Sketch CommandManager** and move the cursor to the left endpoint of the upper horizontal line. Specify the start point of the line when the red circle is displayed.

10. Move the cursor vertically downward. Specify the endpoint of the line when the cursor snaps to the left endpoint of the lower horizontal line.

11. Choose the **Trim Entities** button from the **Sketch CommandManager**; the line cursor is replaced by the trim cursor. Trim the unwanted portion of the circle, as shown in Figure 3-63.

Offsetting the Entities

After drawing the outer loop of the sketch, you need to draw the inner cavity. The first step in drawing the inner cavity of the sketch is offsetting the entire sketch inwards.

1.   Choose the **Offset Entities** button from the **Sketch CommandManager**; the **Offset Entities PropertyManager** is displayed on the left of the drawing area.

2.   Set the value of the **Offset Distance** spinner to **4**. Select any one entity of the sketch; the entire sketch is selected.

When you select the sketch, the preview of the offset sketch is displayed in the drawing area. But the direction of the offset is outside the sketch. The required direction of offset should be inside the sketch. Therefore, you need to flip the direction.

3. Move the cursor inside the sketch and press the left mouse button to offset the sketch in the reverse direction. A dimension with a value of 4 is displayed with the sketch.

    The sketch, after offsetting the outer loop, is shown in Figure 3-64.

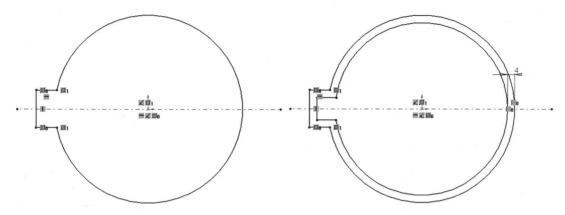

Figure 3-63 *Sketch of the outer loop*   *Figure 3-64* *Sketch after offsetting the outer loop*

4. Choose the **Extend Entities** button from the **Sketch CommandManager**. The select cursor is replaced by the extend cursor.

    If the **Extend Entities** button is not available in the **Sketch CommandManager**, you can invoke the extend option from **Tools > Sketch Tools > Extend**. As discussed earlier, you can insert the **Extend Entities** button in the **Sketch CommandManager** using the **Customize** dialog box.

5. Move the cursor close to the left end of the lower horizontal line of the inner sketch. You can preview the extended line in red.

    You need to move the cursor a little toward the left if the preview of the extended line appears on the right.

6. Press the left mouse button to extend the line.

7. Similarly, extend the upper horizontal line of the inner sketch. The sketch after extending the lines is shown in Figure 3-65.

8. Choose the **Trim Entities** button from the **Sketch CommandManager** and the extend cursor is replaced by the trim cursor.

9. Using the left mouse button, trim the unwanted entities. The final sketch is shown in Figure 3-66.

Saving the Sketch

1. Choose the **Save** button from the **Standard** toolbar to invoke the **Save As** dialog box.

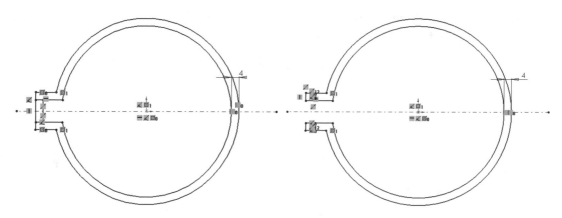

Figure 3-65 *Sketch after extending the lines*   **Figure 3-66** *Final sketch for Tutorial 3*

2.   Enter the name of the document as *c03tut3* in the **File name** edit box and choose the **Save** button. Close the file by choosing **File > Close** from the menu bar.

Tip. *Setting the snap and grid parameters for each document is a very tedious and time-consuming process. To overcome this problem, you can create a template in which all snap, grid, and units are set. Whenever you have to create a part document, you just need to select that template from the* **Template** *tab of the* **New SolidWorks Document** *dialog box. To create and save a template, create a new document in the Part mode and set the parameters of units, snap, and grid from the* **Document Properties** *dialog box. Choose the* **Save** *button from the* **Standard** *toolbar or choose* **File > Save** *from the menu bar. The* **Save As** *dialog box will be displayed. Browse* **X:/Program Files/SolidWorks/data/templates** *location to save the file.* **X:** *is the drive in which you have installed SolidWorks. Select the* **Part Templates (*.prtdot)** *option from the* **Save as type** *drop-down list. Enter the name of the template file in the* **File name** *edit box. Choose the* **Save** *button from the* **Save As** *dialog box.*

Next time when you invoke the **New SolidWorks Document** *dialog box to start a new part document, choose the* **Advanced** *button to display the advanced version of this dialog box. The advanced version of the* **New SolidWorks Document** *dialog box will have the* **Tutorial** *tab that lists the template that you created, along with the other default templates. Using the same procedure, you can also create the user-defined templates for drawing and assembly documents. You will learn more about drawing and assembly documents in later chapters.*

Next time when you invoke the **New SolidWorks Document** *dialog box, the advanced version of this dialog box will be displayed. To restore the original version, choose the* **Novice** *button.*

SELF-EVALUATION TEST

Answer the following questions and then compare your answers with those given at the end of this chapter:

1. The **Trim** option is also used to extend the sketched entities. (T/F)

2. In the sketching environment, you can apply fillets to two parallel lines. (T/F)

3. You can apply a fillet to two nonparallel and nonintersecting entities. (T/F)

4. You cannot offset a single entity; you have to select a chain of entities to create an entity using the **Offset Entities** tool. (T/F)

5. You can choose **Insert > Customize** from the menu bar to display the **Customize** dialog box. (T/F)

6. The design intent is not captured in the sketch created using the mirror line. (T/F)

7. The _____ tool is used to create a linear pattern in the sketcher environment of SolidWorks.

8. The _____ tool is used to create a circular pattern in the sketcher environment of SolidWorks.

9. To modify a sketched circle, select it using the _____ tool to display the _____ **PropertyManager**.

10. The _____ tool is used to invoke the automatic mirroring option.

REVIEW QUESTIONS

Answer the following questions:

1. You cannot extend the sketched entity using the trim tool. (T/F)

2. The preview of the entity to be extended is displayed in red. (T/F)

3. You cannot apply a sketch fillet to two nonintersecting entities. (T/F)

4. The sketched entities can be mirrored without using a centerline. (T/F)

5. The **Add angle dimension between axes** check box in the **Linear Pattern PropertyManager** is selected display the angular dimension between the two directions of the pattern. (T/F)

6. Which **PropertyManager** is displayed when you choose the **Sketch Fillet** button from the **Sketch CommandManager**?

    (a) **Sketch Fillet**   (b) **Fillet**
    (c) **Surface Fillet**   (d) **Sketching Fillet**

7. Which **PropertyManager** is displayed on the left of the drawing area when you choose **Tools > Sketch Tools > Chamfer** from the menu bar?

    (a) **Sketch Chamfer**   (b) **Sketcher Chamfer**
    (c) **Sketching Chamfer**   (d) **Chamfer**

8. Which tool is used to create an automatic mirror line?

    (a) **Dynamic Mirror Entities**   (b) **Mirror**
    (c) **Automatic Mirror**   (d) None

9. Which tool is used to break a sketched entity in two or more entities?

    (a) **Split Entities**   (b) **Trim Sketch**
    (c) **Break Curve**   (d) **Trim Curve**

10. Which tool is used to create a circular pattern in SolidWorks?

    (a) **Pattern**   (b) **Circular Pattern**
    (c) **Array**   (d) None

EXERCISES

Exercise 1

Create the sketch of the model shown in Figure 3-67. The sketch is shown in Figure 3-68. The solid model and dimensions are given only for reference. Create the sketch on one side and then mirror it on the other side. Make sure you do not use the mirror line option to draw this sketch. This is because if you draw the sketch using the mirror line, some relations are applied to the sketch. These relations interfere while creating fillets.   (**Expected time: 30 min**)

Figure 3-67 *Solid model for Exercise 1*

Figure 3-68 *Sketch for Exercise 1*

Exercise 2

Create the sketch of the model shown in Figure 3-69. The sketch is shown in Figure 3-70. The solid model and dimensions are given only for reference. Create the sketch using the sketching tools and then edit the sketch using the circular pattern tool and the trim tool.

(**Expected time: 30 min**)

Figure 3-69 *Solid model for Exercise 2*

Figure 3-70 *Sketch for Exercise 2*

Exercise 3

Create the sketch of the model shown in Figure 3-71. The sketch is shown in Figure 3-72. This model is created using a revolved feature; therefore, you will create the sketch on one side of the centerline. The solid model and dimensions are given only for reference.

(Expected time: 30 min)

Figure 3-71 Solid model for Exercise 3

Figure 3-72 Sketch for Exercise 3

Exercise 4

Create the sketch of the model shown in Figure 3-73. The sketch is shown in Figure 3-74. This model is created using a revolved feature; therefore, you will create the sketch on one side of the centerline. The solid model and dimensions are given only for reference.

(Expected time: 30 min)

Figure 3-73 Solid model for Exercise 4

Figure 3-74 Sketch for Exercise 4

Answers to Self-Evaluation Test
1. T, 2. F, 3. T, 4. F, 5. F, 6. F, 7. **Linear Pattern**, 8. **Circular Pattern**, 9. **Select**, **Circle**, 10. **Dynamic Mirror Entities**

Chapter 4

Adding Relations and Dimensions to Sketches

Learning Objectives

After completing this chapter, you will be able to:
- *Add geometric relations to sketches.*
- *Dimension sketches.*
- *Modify the dimensions of sketches.*
- *Understand the concept of fully defined sketches.*
- *View and examine the relations applied to sketches.*
- *Open an existing file.*

ADDING GEOMETRIC RELATIONS TO SKETCHES

Geometric relations are the logical operations that are performed to add a relationship (such as tangent or perpendicular) between the sketched entities, planes, axes, edges, or vertices. The relations applied to the sketched entities are used to capture the design intent. Geometric relations constrain the degree of freedom of the sketched entities. There are two methods of applying relations to the sketch.

1.   Add Relations PropertyManager
2.   Automatic Relations

Adding Relations Using the Add Relations PropertyManager

CommandManager:	Sketch > Add Relation
Menu:	Tools > Relations > Add
Toolbar:	Sketch > Add Relation

The **Add Relations PropertyManager** is widely used to apply relations to the sketch in the sketching environment of SolidWorks. It is invoked using the **Add Relation** button from the **Sketch CommandManager**. Alternatively, you can select an entity and right-click in the drawing area. Next, choose the **Add Relation** option from the shortcut menu. The **Add Relations PropertyManager** is shown in Figure 4-1. While adding the relations, the confirmation corner is also displayed at the top right corner of the drawing area. The options available in the **Add Relations PropertyManager** are discussed next.

Figure 4-1 The Add Relations PropertyManager

Selected Entities Rollout

The **Selected Entities** rollout displays the name of the entities that are selected to apply the relations. The entities that you select are displayed in green and are added in the area under the

Selected Entities rollout. You can remove the selected entity from the selection set by selecting the same entity again in the drawing area.

> **Tip**. *You can also remove the selected entity from the selection set by selecting that entity in the **Selected Entities** rollout and right-clicking to invoke the shortcut menu. Choose the **Delete** option from this menu to remove the entity from the selection set. If you choose the **Clear Selections** option from the shortcut menu, all entities will be removed from the selection set.*

Existing Relations Rollout

The **Existing Relations** rollout displays the relations that are already applied to the selected sketch entities. It also shows the status of the sketch entities. You can delete the already existing relation from this rollout. Select the already existing relation from the selection box and right-click to display the shortcut menu. Choose the **Delete** option from this shortcut menu to delete the selected relation. If you choose the **Delete All** option, all relations displayed in the selection box of the **Existing Relations** rollout will be deleted.

Add Relations Rollout

The **Add Relations** rollout is used to apply the relations to the selected entity. The list of relations that can be applied to the selected entity or entities is shown in the **Add Relations** rollout. The most appropriate relation for the selected entities appears in bold letters.

> **Tip**. *You can apply a relation to a single entity or between two or more entities. To apply a relation between two or more entities, at least one entity should be a sketched entity. The other entity or entities can be sketch entities, edges, faces, vertices, origins, plane, or axes. The sketch curves from other sketches that form lines or arcs, when projected on the sketch plane, can also be included in the relation.*

All relations that can be applied to the sketches using the **Add Relations** rollout are discussed next.

Horizontal

The **Horizontal** relation forces one or more selected lines or centerlines to become horizontal. You can also select an external entity such as an edge, plane, axis, or sketch curve on an external sketch that projects as a line to apply this relation. Using the **Horizontal** relation you can also force two or more points to become horizontal. A point can be a sketch point, a center point, an endpoint, a control point of a spline, or an external entity such as origin, vertex, axis, or point in an external sketch that projects as a point. To use this relation, invoke the **Add Relations PropertyManager**. Select the entity or entities to apply the **Horizontal** relation. Choose the **Horizontal** button from the **Add Relations** rollout provided in the **Add Relations PropertyManager**. You will notice that the name of the horizontal relation is displayed in the **Existing Relations** rollout.

Vertical

The **Vertical** relation forces one or more selected lines or centerlines to become vertical. Using the **Vertical** relation, you can also force two or more points to become vertical. To use this relation, invoke the **Add Relations PropertyManager** and select the entity or entities to apply the **Vertical** relation. Choose the **Vertical** button from the **Add Relations** rollout. You will notice that the name of the vertical relation is displayed in the **Existing Relations** rollout.

Collinear

The **Collinear** relation forces the selected lines to lie on the same infinite line. To use this relation, select the lines to apply the **Collinear** relation. Choose the **Collinear** button from the **Add Relations** rollout.

Coradial

The **Coradial** relation forces the selected arcs or circles to share the same radius and the same center point. You can also select an external entity that projects as an arc or a circle in the sketch to apply this relation. To use this relation, invoke the **Add Relations PropertyManager**. Select two arcs or circles, or an arc and a circle to apply the **Coradial** relation. Choose the **Coradial** button from the **Add Relations** rollout.

Perpendicular

The **Perpendicular** relation forces the selected lines to become perpendicular to each other. To use this relation, invoke the **Add Relations PropertyManager**. Select two lines and choose the **Perpendicular** button from the **Add Relations** rollout. Figure 4-2 shows two lines before and after applying the perpendicular relation.

Parallel

The **Parallel** relation forces the selected lines to become parallel to each other. To use this relation, invoke the **Add Relations PropertyManager**. Select two lines and choose the **Parallel** button from the **Add Relations** rollout. Figure 4-3 shows two lines before and after applying this relation.

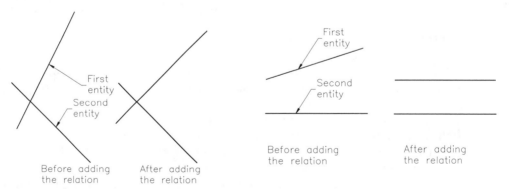

Figure 4-2 *Entities before and after applying the* *Perpendicular relation*

Figure 4-3 *Entities before and after applying the* *Parallel relation*

ParallelYZ

The **ParallelYZ** relation forces a line in the three-dimensional (3D) sketch to become parallel to the YZ plane with respect to the selected plane. To use this relation, invoke the **Add Relations PropertyManager**. Select the line in the 3D sketch and then select a plane. Next, choose the **ParallelYZ** button from the **Add Relations** rollout.

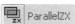

Note

You will learn more about the 3D curves in later chapters.

ParallelZX

The **ParallelZX** relation forces a line in the 3D sketch to become parallel to the ZX plane with respect to the selected plane. To use this relation, invoke the **Add Relations PropertyManager**. Select the line in the 3D sketch and then select a plane. Next, choose the **ParallelZX** button from the **Add Relations** rollout.

AlongZ

The **AlongZ** relation forces a line in the 3D sketch to become normal to the selected plane. To use this relation, invoke the **Add Relations PropertyManager**. Select the line in the 3D sketch and then select a plane. Next, choose the **AlongZ** button from the **Add Relations** rollout.

Tangent

The **Tangent** relation forces the selected arc, circle, spline, or ellipse to become tangent to the other arc, circle, spline, ellipse, line, or edge. To use this relation, invoke the **Add Relations PropertyManager**. Select two entities and choose the **Tangent** button from the **Add Relations** rollout. Figures 4-4 and 4-5 show the entities before and after applying this relation.

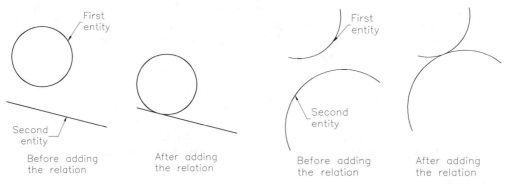

Figure 4-4 Applying the Tangent relation to a line and a circle

Figure 4-5 Applying the Tangent relation to two arcs

Concentric

The **Concentric** relation forces the selected arc or circle to share the same center point with the other arc, circle, point, vertex, or circular edge. To use this relation, invoke the **Add Relations PropertyManager**. Select the required entity to apply the **Concentric** relation and then choose the **Concentric** button from the **Add Relations** rollout.

Equal

 The **Equal** relation forces the selected lines to have equal length and the selected arcs, circles, or arc and circle to have equal radii. To use this relation, invoke the **Add Relations PropertyManager**. Select the required entity to apply the **Equal** relation and choose the **Equal** button.

Intersection

 The **Intersection** relation forces the selected point to move at the intersection of two selected lines. To use this relation, invoke the **Add Relations PropertyManager**. Select the required entity to apply the **Intersection** relation. Choose the **Intersection** button from the **Add Relations** rollout.

Coincident

 The **Coincident** relation forces the selected point to be coincident with the selected line, arc, circle, or ellipse. To use this relation, invoke the **Add Relations PropertyManager**. Select the required entity to apply the **Coincident** relation. Choose the **Coincident** button from the **Add Relations** rollout.

Midpoint

 The **Midpoint** relation forces the selected point to move to the midpoint of a selected line. To use this relation, invoke the **Add Relations PropertyManager**. Select the point and the line to the midpoint of which the point will be moved. Choose the **Midpoint** button from the **Add Relations** rollout.

Symmetric

 The **Symmetric** relation forces two selected lines, arcs, points, and ellipses to remain equidistant from a centerline. This relation also forces the entities to have the same size and orientation. To use this relation, invoke the **Add Relations PropertyManager**. Select the required entity to apply the **Symmetric** relation and select a centerline. Choose the **Symmetric** button from the **Add Relations** rollout.

Fix

 The **Fix** relation forces the selected entity to be fixed at the specified position. If you apply this relation to a line or an arc, its location will be fixed but you can change its size by dragging the endpoints. To use this relation, invoke the **Add Relations PropertyManager**. Select the required entity and choose the **Fix** button.

Merge Points

 The **Merge Points** relation forces two sketch points or endpoints to merge in a single point. To use this relation, invoke the **Add Relations PropertyManager**. Select the required entities to apply the **Merge Points** relation and choose the **Merge Points** button from the **Add Relations** rollout.

Pierce

The **Pierce** relation forces a sketch point or an endpoint of an entity to be coincident with an entity of another sketch. To use this relation, invoke the **Add Relations PropertyManager**. Select the required entities to apply the **Pierce** relation and choose the **Pierce** button from the **Add Relations** rollout.

Tip. *You can also apply the relations using the **Properties PropertyManager**. This **PropertyManager** is automatically invoked if you select more than one entity from the drawing area. The possible relations for the selected geometry will be displayed in the **Add Relations** rollout. Choose the relation you want to apply to the selected geometry.*

*Another method of applying relations to the sketches is by selecting the entity or entities to which you have to apply the relation and then right-clicking to display the shortcut menu. The relations that can be applied to the selected entities will be displayed in the shortcut menu under the **Relations** section. Choose the relation from the shortcut menu.*

Automatic Relations

Automatic relations are applied automatically to the sketch while drawing. For example, you will notice that when you specify the start point of the line and move the cursor horizontally toward the right or left, the horizontal line symbol is displayed below the line cursor. This is the symbol of the **Horizontal** relation that is applied to the line while drawing. If you move the cursor vertically downward or upward, the vertical line symbol for the **Vertical** relation will be displayed below the line cursor. If you move the cursor to the intersection of two or more sketched entities, the intersection symbol will appear below the cursor. Similarly, other relations are also automatically applied to the sketch while it is being created.

You can activate the automatic relations option if it is not available. To do so, choose **Tools > Options** from the menu bar; the **System Options - General** dialog box will be displayed. Select the **Sketch** option from the area on the left. Select the **Automatic Relations** check box from the **System Options - Sketch** dialog box and choose the **OK** button. The relations that can be applied automatically are listed below.

1.   Horizontal
2.   Vertical
3.   Coincident
4.   Midpoint
5.   Intersection
6.   Tangent
7.   Perpendicular

Tip. *You will observe that while sketching, two types of inferencing lines are displayed. One is displayed in blue and the other in brown. The brown inferencing line indicates that the relation is applied automatically to the sketch. The blue inferencing line indicates that no automatic relation is applied.*

DIMENSIONING THE SKETCH

After drawing the sketches and adding the relations, dimensioning is the most important step in creating a design. As mentioned earlier, SolidWorks is a parametric software. This property of

SolidWorks ensures that irrespective of the original size, the selected entity is driven by the dimension value you specify. Therefore, when you apply and modify a dimension of an entity, it is forced to change its size in accordance with the specified dimension value.

In SolidWorks, you can use the **Smart Dimension** tool to dimension any kind of entity. You can also select the individual type of dimensioning tool from the **Dimension/Relations CommandManager**. This **CommandManager** is not available by default. To invoke it, right-click on the **Sketch CommandManager** and choose **Customize Command Manager** from the shortcut menu; the **Customize CommandManager** flyout will be displayed. In this flyout, choose the **Dimension/Relations** option and then click anywhere on the screen. Again, right-click on the **Sketch CommandManager** and choose **Dimension/Relations** to display the tools available in this **CommandManager**. Figure 4-6 shows the default dimension types available in the **Dimension/Relations CommandManager**.

*Figure 4-6 The **Dimension/Relations CommandManager***

If you use the **Smart Dimension** tool, the type of dimension that will be applied will depend on the type of entity selected. For example, if you select a line, a horizontal, vertical, or aligned dimension will be applied. If you select a circle, a diametric dimension will be applied. Similarly, if you select an arc, a radial dimension will be applied. However, if you want to apply a particular type of dimension, choose its tool from the **Dimension/Relations CommandManager** and then apply the dimension.

In SolidWorks 2006, as soon as you place the dimension, the **Modify** dialog box will be displayed, as shown in Figure 4-7. You can enter a new value in this box to modify the dimension. You can modify the default dimension value using the spinner or by entering a new value in the edit box available in the **Modify** dialog box. With this release, a thumbwheel is also provided below the spinner. You can drag this thumbwheel to the right to increase the value and to the left to decrease it.

*Figure 4-7 The **Modify** dialog box*

Tip. *If the **Modify** dialog box is not displayed when you place the dimension, you need to set its preference manually. To do this, invoke the **System Options - General** dialog box and select the **Input dimension value** check box.*

The buttons available in the **Modify** dialog box are discussed next.

The **Save the current value and exit the dialog** button is used to accept the current value and exit the dialog box. The **Restore the original value and exit the dialog** button is used to restore the last dimensional value applied to the sketch and exit the dialog box. The **Regenerate the model with the current value** button is used to preview the geometry of the sketch with the new modified dimensional value. The **Reset spin increment value** button is used to enter a new spin increment value. This is the value that is added to or subtracted from the current value when you click once on the spinner arrow. If you choose this button, the **Increment** dialog box will be displayed. The **Mark dimensions to be imported into a drawing** button is chosen to make sure that the selected dimension is generated as a model annotation in the drawing views. If this button is not chosen, the dimensions will not be generated.

Tip. *You can also enter the arithmetic symbols directly into the edit box of the **Modify** toolbar to calculate the dimension. For example, if you have a dimension as a complex arithmetic function such as (220*12.5)-3+150, which is equal to 1247, you do not need to calculate this using the calculator. Just enter the statement in the edit box and press ENTER. SolidWorks will automatically solve the function to get the value of the dimension.*

The types of dimensions that can be applied to the sketches in the sketching environment of SolidWorks 2006 are discussed next.

Horizontal/Vertical Dimensioning

CommandManager:	Dimension/Relations > Horizontal/Vertical Dimension
Menu:	Tools > Dimension > Horizontal/Vertical
Toolbar:	Dimension/Relations > Horizontal/Vertical Dimension

These dimensions are used to define the horizontal or vertical dimensions of a selected line or between two points. The points can be the endpoints of lines or arcs, or the center points of circles, arcs, ellipses, or parabolas. You can dimension a vertical or a horizontal line by directly selecting it. Choose the **Horizontal/ Vertical Dimension** button from the **Dimension/Relations CommandManager**. You can also right-click in the drawing area and choose the **More Dimensions > Horizontal/Vertical** option from the shortcut menu to activate these tools. When you move the cursor on the line, it will be highlighted and turn red. As soon as you select the line, it will turn green, and the dimension will be attached to the cursor. Move the cursor and place the dimension at an appropriate place using the left mouse button. As the priority of editing the dimension as it is placed is set by default, the **Modify** dialog box will be displayed with the default value in it. Enter the new value of the dimension in the **Modify** dialog box and press ENTER. Figure 4-8 shows the horizontal and vertical dimensioning of lines.

Figure 4-8 Linear dimensioning of lines

If the dimension is selected in the drawing area, the **Dimension PropertyManager** will be displayed, as shown in Figure 4-9. The options available in the **Dimension PropertyManager** are discussed next.

*Figure 4-9 The **Dimension PropertyManager***

Favorites

The **Favorites** rollout, shown in Figure 4-10, is used to create, save, delete, and retrieve the dimension style in the current document. You can also retrieve the dimension styles saved in other documents using this rollout. The options available in this rollout are discussed next.

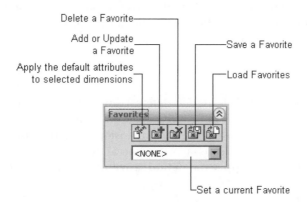

Delete a Favorite

Add or Update a Favorite

Save a Favorite

Apply the default attributes to selected dimensions

Load Favorites

Set a current Favorite

Figure 4-10 The *Dimension Favorite* rollout

Apply the default attributes to selected dimensions

The **Apply the default attributes to selected dimensions** button is used to apply the default attributes to the selected dimension or dimensions. The attributes include the tolerance, precision, arrow style, dimension text, and so on. This option is generally used when you have modified the settings applied to a dimension and then you want to restore the default settings on that dimension.

Add or Update a Favorite

The **Add or Update a Favorite** button is used to add a dimension style to the current document for a selected dimension. After invoking the **Dimension PropertyManager**, set the attributes using various options provided in this **PropertyManager**. Now choose the **Add or Update a Favorite** button; the **Add or Update a Favorite** dialog box will be displayed, as shown in Figure 4-11. Enter the name of the dimension style in the edit box and press ENTER or choose the **OK** button from this dialog box. The dimension style will be added to the current document.

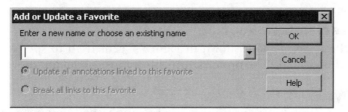

Figure 4-11 The *Add or Update a Favorite* dialog box

You can apply the new dimension style to the selected dimension by selecting the dimension style from the drop-down list in the **Favorite** rollout. You can also update the dimension style. To update a dimension style, select the dimension and set the options of the dimension style according to your need and then choose the **Add or Update a Favorite** button to invoke the **Add or Update a Favorite** dialog box. Select the dimension style to update from the drop-down list provided in the dialog box. The two radio buttons in this dialog box are enabled. Select the **Update all the annotations linked to this favorite** radio button and choose the **OK** button to update all the dimensions linked with the selected favorite. If you select the **Break all links to this favorite** radio button and choose the **OK** button, then the link between the other dimensions having the same favorite and the selected favorite will be broken.

Delete a Favorite

The **Delete a Favorite** button is used to delete a dimension style. Select the dimension style or favorite from the **Set a current Favorite** drop-down list and choose the **Delete a Favorite** button. Note that even after you delete the dimension style, the properties of the dimensions will be the same as with the deleted favorite. You can set the properties of a dimension to the default settings using the **Apply the default attributes to the selected dimension** button.

Save a Favorite

The **Save a Favorite** button is used to save a dimension style so that it can be retrieved in some other document. Select the dimension style or favorite from the **Set a current Favorite** drop-down list and choose the **Save a Favorite** button. The **Save As** dialog box will be displayed. Browse the folder in which you want to save the favorite and enter its name in the **File name** edit box. Choose the **Save** button from the **Save As** dialog box. The extension for the file in which the favorite is saved is *.sldfvt*.

Load Favorites

The **Load Favorites** button is used to open a saved favorite in the current document. The properties of that favorite will be applied to the selected dimension. To load a favorite, choose the **Load favorite** button to invoke the **Open** dialog box. Browse the folder in which the favorite is saved. Now, select the file with the extension *.sldfvt* and choose the **Open** button; the **Add or Update a Favorite** dialog box will be displayed. Choose the **OK** button from this dialog box.

Tip. *You can load more than one favorite by pressing the CTRL key and selecting the favorites from the **Open** dialog box. All favorites will be displayed in the **Set a current Favorite** drop-down list.*

Tolerance/Precision Rollout

The **Tolerance/Precision** rollout shown in Figure 4-12 is used to specify the tolerance and precision in the dimensions. The options available in this rollout are discussed next.

Tolerance Type

The **Tolerance Type** drop-down list is used to apply the tolerance to the dimension. By default, the **None** option is selected. Therefore, no tolerance is applied to the dimensions. The other tolerance methods available in this drop-down list are discussed next.

Basic

The basic dimension is the one that is enclosed in a rectangle. To display a basic dimension, select a dimension that you want to display as a basic dimension and then select the **Basic** option from the **Tolerance Display** drop-down list. You will notice that

Figure 4-12 *The **Tolerance/Precision** rollout*

the dimension is enclosed in a rectangle, suggesting that it is a basic dimension, see Figure 4-13.

Bilateral

The bilateral tolerance provides the maximum and minimum variation in the value of the dimension that is acceptable in the design. To apply the bilateral tolerance, select the dimension and then the **Bilateral** option from the **Tolerance Type** drop-down list. The **Maximum Variation** and **Minimum Variation** edit boxes will be enabled. These edit boxes are used to apply the value of the maximum and minimum variation to a dimension. The **Show parentheses** check box will also be displayed. If you select the **Show parentheses** check box, the bilateral tolerance will be displayed with parentheses. The dimension with a bilateral tolerance is shown in Figure 4-14.

Figure 4-13 *Basic dimension*   **Figure 4-14** *Bilateral tolerance*

Note

The dimension standard used in the sketches in this book is the ISO standard.

Limit

In the limit dimension, the dimension is displayed as its maximum and minimum allowed values. To apply this tolerance type, select the dimension to display as limit dimension and select the **Limit** option. The **Maximum Variation** and **Minimum Variation** edit boxes will be enabled to enter the value of the maximum and minimum variation. The dimension, along with the limit tolerance, is shown in Figure 4-15.

Symmetric

The symmetric tolerance is displayed with plus and minus signs. To use this tolerance, select the dimension and select the **Symmetric** option; the **Maximum Variation** edit box will be displayed to enter the value of the tolerance. You can select the **Show parentheses** check box to show the tolerance in parentheses. The dimension, along with the symmetric tolerance, is shown in Figure 4-16.

Figure 4-15 *Limit tolerance*   *Figure 4-16* *Symmetric tolerance*

MIN

In this type of dimensional tolerance, the **min.** symbol is added to the dimension as a suffix. This implies that the dimensional value is the minimum value that is allowed in the design. To display this dimensional tolerance, select the dimension and the **MIN** option from the **Tolerance Type** drop-down list. The dimension, along with the minimum tolerance, is shown in Figure 4-17.

MAX

In this type of dimensional tolerance, the **max.** symbol is added to the dimension as suffix. This implies that the dimensional value is the maximum value that is allowed in the design. To display this dimensional tolerance, select the dimension and the **MAX** option from the **Tolerance Type** drop-down list. The dimension, along with the maximum tolerance, is shown in Figure 4-18.

Fit

The **Fit** option is used to apply the fit according to the **Hole Fit** and **Shaft Fit** systems. The **Tolerance/Precision** rollout with the **Fit** option selected is shown in Figure 4-19. Specify the type of fit from the **Classification** drop-down list. The **Classification** drop-down list is used to define the **User Defined** fit, **Clearance** fit, **Transitional** fit, and **Press** fit. To apply the fit using the hole fit system or the shaft fit system, select the dimension and the **Fit** option from the **Tolerance Type** drop-down list. The **Classification** drop-down list, the **Hole Fit** drop-down list, and the **Shaft Fit** edit drop-down list will be displayed below the **Tolerance Type** drop-down list. Choose the type of fit from the **Classification** drop-down list and select the standard of fit from the **Hole Fit** drop-down list or the **Shaft Fit** drop-down list. If you choose the **Clearance**, **Transitional**, or **Press**

Figure 4-17 Minimum tolerance   *Figure 4-18* Maximum tolerance

Figure 4-19 The **Tolerance/Precision** rollout with the **Fit** option selected from the **Tolerance Type** drop-down list

option from the **Classification** drop-down list and the standard of fit from the **Hole Fit** drop-down list, only the standards that match the selected hole fit will be displayed in the **Shaft Fit** drop-down list and vice versa. If you choose the **User Defined** option from the **Classification** drop-down list, you can choose any standard from the **Hole Fit** and **Shaft Fit** drop-down lists. The **Stacked with line display** button is chosen to display the stacked tolerance with a line. You can also display the tolerance as stacked without a line using the **Stacked without line display** button. If you choose the **Linear display** button, the tolerance will be displayed in the linear form. The dimension, along with the hole fit and shaft fit, is shown in Figure 4-20.

Fit with tolerance

The **Fit with tolerance** option in the **Tolerance Type** drop-down list is used to display the tolerance along with the hole fit and shaft fit in a dimension. To apply the fit with the tolerance, select the dimension and the **Fit with tolerance** option from the **Tolerance Type** drop-down list. Select the type of fit from the **Classification** drop-down list. Now, select the fit standard from the **Hole Fit** drop-down list or the **Shaft Fit** drop-down list. The tolerance will be displayed with the fit standard only if you select one fit system from the hole drop-down list or from the shaft drop-down list. The tolerance will be displayed along with the fit standard in the drawing area. In this release of SolidWorks the tolerance is calculated automatically, depending on the type and standard of the fit selected. The **Show parentheses** check box can be selected to show the tolerance in parentheses. The dimension, along with the fit and tolerance, is shown in Figure 4-21.

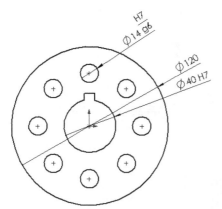

Figure 4-20 Hole fit and shaft fit

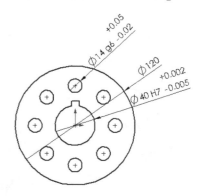

Figure 4-21 Fit with tolerance

Fit (tolerance only)

The **Fit (tolerance only)** option in the **Tolerance Type** drop-down list is used to display the tolerance in a dimension based on the hole fit or shaft fit.

Block

The **Block** option in the **Tolerance Type** drop-down list is used to display the block type tolerance in a dimension.

Primary Unit Precision

The **Primary Unit Precision** drop-down list is used to specify the precision of the number of places after the decimal for dimensions. By default, the selected precision is two places after the decimal.

Tolerance Precision

The **Tolerance Precision** drop-down list is used to specify the precision of the number of places after the decimal for tolerance. By default, the selected precision is two places after the decimal.

Dimension Text Rollout

The **Dimension Text** rollout, shown in Figure 4-22, is used to add the text and symbols to the dimension. The text box provided in this rollout is used to add the text to the dimension. The **<DIM>** displayed in the text box symbolizes the dimensional value. You can add the text before or after the dimension value.

This rollout also provides buttons to modify the text justification and add symbols such as **Diameter**, **Degree**, **Plus/Minus**, **Centerline**, and so on to the dimension text. You can add more symbols by choosing the **More Symbols** button from the **Dimension Text** rollout. When you choose this button, the **Symbols** dialog box will be displayed, as shown in Figure 4-23.

Figure 4-22 The **Dimension Text** *rollout*

Figure 4-23 The **Symbols** *dialog box*

Display Options Rollout

The options available in the **Display Options** rollout are used to display the dimension value in parentheses, display dual dimensions, and convert the normal dimension into inspection dimension.

Witness/Leader Display Rollout

The **Witness/Leader Display** rollout shown in Figure 4-24 is used to specify the arrow style in the dimensions. The options available in this rollout are discussed next.

Figure 4-24 The **Witness/Leader Display** *rollout*

Outside

The **Outside** button is used to display the arrows outside the dimension line. Select a dimension from the drawing area and choose the **Outside** button from the **Witness/Leader Display** rollout.

Inside

The **Inside** button is used to display the arrows inside the dimension line. Select a dimension from the drawing area and choose the **Inside** button from the **Witness/Leader Display** rollout.

Note

You can also click on the control point displayed on the arrowhead to reverse the direction of the arrowheads.

Smart

The **Smart** button is used to display the dimension inside or outside the dimension line, depending on the surrounding geometry. The **Smart** button is chosen by default in the **Witness/Leader Display** rollout.

Style

The **Style** drop-down list is used to select the arrowhead style. The unfilled triangular arrow is selected by default. You can select any arrowhead style for a particular dimension or dimension style. To change the arrow style, select the dimension from the drawing area and then the arrowhead style from the **Style** drop-down list.

The **More Properties** button is used to invoke the **Dimension Properties** dialog box to modify the properties of the dimension. All options available in the **Dimension PropertyManager** are available in the **Dimension Properties** dialog box with some additional options. You can modify the dimension properties from the **Dimension PropertyManager** or from the **Dimension Properties** dialog box.

Horizontal/Vertical Dimensioning Between Points

As mentioned earlier, you can add a horizontal or a vertical dimension between two points. To do so, choose the required button from the **Dimension/Relations CommandManager**. Select the first point, and then the second point. Specify a point to place the dimension; the **Modify** dialog box will be displayed. Enter a new dimension value in this dialog box and press ENTER. Figures 4-25 and 4-26 show the horizontal and vertical linear dimensioning between two points.

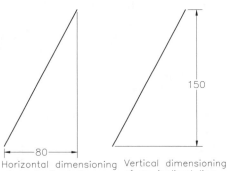

Figure 4-25 *Applying horizontal and vertical dimensions to two points*

Figure 4-26 *Applying horizontal and vertical dimensions to inclined lines*

You can also apply horizontal or vertical (linear) dimensioning to a circle. However, note that these types of dimensions can only be applied to a circle by using the **Smart Dimension** tool. To apply this type of dimension to a circle, choose the **Smart Dimension** button and select the circle. The dimension will be attached to the cursor. If you want to create the vertical dimension, move the cursor to the right or left of the sketch. If you want to create the horizontal dimension, move the cursor to the top or bottom of the sketch. Using the left mouse button, place the dimension and enter a new value in the **Modify** dialog box. The linear dimensioning of the circle is shown in Figure 4-27.

Aligned Dimensioning

CommandManager:	Sketch > Smart Dimension
Menu:	Tools > Dimension > Smart
Toolbar:	Sketch > Smart Dimension

 Aligned dimensions are used to dimension lines that are at an angle with respect to the X axis and the Y axis. These types of dimensions measure the actual distance of the inclined lines. You can directly select the inclined line to apply this dimension or select two points. The points that can be used to apply aligned dimensions include the endpoints of a line, arc, parabolic arc, or spline and the center points of arcs, circles, ellipse, or parabolic arc. To apply an aligned dimension to an inclined line, choose the **Smart Dimension** button from the **Sketch CommandManager** and select the line. Move the cursor at an angle such that the dimension line is parallel to the inclined line. Place the dimension at an appropriate place and enter a new value in the **Modify** dialog box.

To apply an aligned dimension between two points, choose the **Smart Dimension** button and select the first point to apply the dimension. Next, select the second point to apply the dimension. The dimension will be attached to the cursor. Move the cursor such that the dimension line is parallel to the imaginary line that joins the two points. Now, place the dimension at an appropriate location. Enter a new value in the **Modify** dialog box and press ENTER. Figure 4-28 shows aligned dimensioning of a line and an aligned dimension between two points.

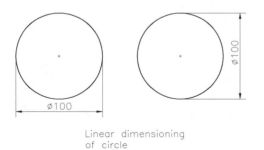

Linear dimensioning
of circle

Aligned dimensioning of inclined line and
between two points

Figure 4-27 *Linear dimensioning of a circle*   ***Figure 4-28*** *Aligned dimensioning*

Angular Dimensioning

CommandManager:	Sketch > Smart Dimension
Menu:	Tools > Dimension > Smart
Toolbar:	Sketch > Smart Dimension

Angular dimensions are used to dimension angles. You can select two line segments or use three points to apply angular dimensions. You can also use angular dimensioning to dimension an arc. All these options of angular dimensioning are discussed next.

Angular Dimensioning Between Two Line Segments

To apply angular dimensions between two lines, choose the **Smart Dimension** button from the **Sketch CommandManager** and select the first line segment; a dimension will be attached to the cursor. Now, select the second line segment; an angular dimension will be attached to the cursor. Place the angular dimension and enter the new value of angular dimension in the **Modify** dialog box. You need to be very careful while placing the angular dimension. This is because depending on the location of the dimension placement, the interior angle, exterior angle, major angle, or minor angle is displayed. Figures 4-29 through 4-32 illustrate various angular dimensions, depending on the dimension placement point.

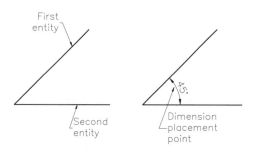

Figure 4-29 Angular dimension displayed according to the dimension placement point

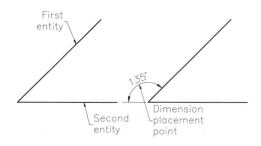

Figure 4-30 Angular dimension displayed according to the dimension placement point

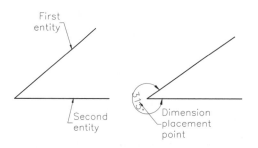

Figure 4-31 Angular dimension displayed according to the dimension placement point

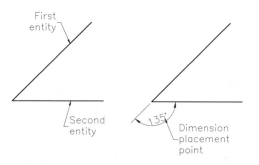

Figure 4-32 Angular dimension displayed according to the dimension placement point

Angular Dimensioning Between Three Points

While adding angular dimensions between three points, you need to be extremely careful in selecting the points. Remember that the first point that you select is the angle vertex point. To apply angular dimensions between three points, choose the **Smart Dimension** button from the **Sketch CommandManager**. Select the first point using the left mouse button. This is the angle vertex point. Select the second point; a linear dimension will be attached to the cursor. Next, select the third point; an angular dimension will be attached to the cursor. Place the angular dimension and enter a new value of angular dimension in the **Modify** dialog box. Figure 4-33 shows the angular dimensioning between three points.

Angular Dimensioning of an Arc

You can use angular dimensions to dimension an arc. In the case of arcs, the three points that should be used are the endpoints and the center point of the arc. Figure 4-34 shows the angular dimensioning of an arc.

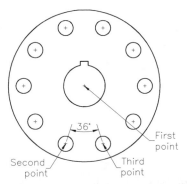

Figure 4-33 *Angular dimension displayed according to the dimension placement point*

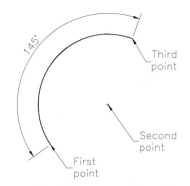

Figure 4-34 *Angular dimension displayed according to the dimension placement point*

Diameter Dimensioning

CommandManager:	Sketch > Smart Dimension
Menu:	Tools > Dimension > Smart
Toolbar:	Sketch > Smart Dimension

Diameter dimensions are applied to dimension a circle or an arc in terms of its diameter. To apply the diameter dimension, choose the **Smart Dimension** button from the **Sketch CommandManager**. Select a circle or an arc and place the dimension. In SolidWorks, when you select a circle to dimension, the diameter dimension is applied to it by default. However, when you select an arc, the radius dimension is applied to it. To apply the diameter dimension to an arc, select the arc and place the radius dimension. Next right-click to display the shortcut menu and choose the **Properties** option; the **Dimension Properties** dialog box will be displayed. Select the **Diameter dimension** check box and choose **OK**. Figure 4-35 shows a circle and an arc with the diameter dimension.

Radius Dimensioning

CommandManager:	Sketch > Smart Dimension
Menu:	Tools > Dimension > Smart
Toolbar:	Sketch > Smart Dimension

Radius dimensions are applied to dimension a circle or an arc in terms of its radius. As mentioned earlier, by default the dimension applied to a circle is in the diameter form and the dimension applied to an arc is a radius dimension. To apply a radius dimension, choose the **Dimension** button from the **Sketch** toolbar and select an arc. A radius dimension will be attached to the cursor. Using the left mouse button, place the dimension at an appropriate place. To convert the diameter dimension to the radius dimension, clear the **Diameter dimension** check box from the **Dimension Properties** dialog box. Figure 4-36 illustrates the radial dimensioning of a circle and an arc.

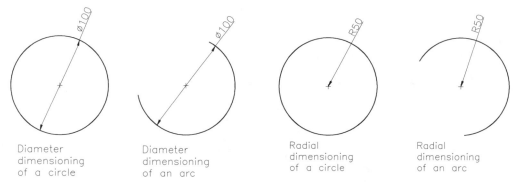

Diameter
dimensioning
of a circle

Diameter
dimensioning
of an arc

Radial
dimensioning
of a circle

Radial
dimensioning
of an arc

Figure 4-35 Diameter dimensioning of a circle and an arc

Figure 4-36 Radial dimensioning of a circle and an arc

Linear Diameter Dimensioning

CommandManager:	Sketch > Smart Dimension
Menu:	Tools > Dimension > Smart
Toolbar:	Sketch > Smart Dimension

Linear diameter dimensioning is used to dimension the sketch of a revolved component. An example of a revolved component is shown in Figure 4-37. The sketch for a revolved component is drawn using simple sketcher entities, as shown in Figure 4-38. If you dimension the sketch of the base feature of the given model using the linear dimensioning method, the same dimensions will be generated in the drawing views. This may be confusing because in the shop floor drawing, you need the diameter dimension of a revolved model. To overcome this problem, it is recommended that you create a linear diameter dimension, as shown in Figure 4-38. To create a linear diameter dimension, choose the **Smart Dimension** button from the **Sketch CommandManager**. Select the entity to be dimensioned and then select the centerline around which the sketch will be revolved. Move the cursor to the other side of the centerline; a linear diameter dimension will be displayed. Place the dimension and enter a new value in the **Modify** dialog box.

Figure 4-37 A revolved component

Figure 4-38 Sketch for the revolved feature and linear diameter dimension

Ordinate Dimensioning

The ordinate dimensions are used to dimension the sketch with respect to a specified datum. Depending on the requirement of the design, the datum can be an entity in the sketch or the origin. The ordinate dimensions are of two types, horizontal and vertical. The method of creating these types of ordinate dimensions is discussed next.

Horizontal Ordinate Dimensioning

CommandManager:	Dimension/Relations > Horizontal Ordinate Dimension
Menu:	Tools > Dimension > Horizontal Ordinate
Toolbar:	Dimension/Relations > Horizontal Ordinate Dimension

Horizontal ordinate dimensions are used to dimension the horizontal distances of the selected entities from the specified datum, see Figure 4-39. Note that when you apply the ordinate dimensions, the **Modify** dialog box is not displayed to modify the dimension values. After placing all ordinate dimensions, you need to exit the tool and then double-click on the dimensions to modify their values.

To apply a horizontal ordinate dimension, choose the **Horizontal Ordinate Dimension** button from the **Dimension/Relations CommandManager**; you will be prompted to select an edge or a vertex. Note that the first entity that you select is taken as the datum entity from where the remaining entities will be measured. Select the first entity and place the dimension above or below it. You will notice that the dimension shows a value of 0; refer to the dimension of the left vertical line in Figure 4-39.

After placing the first dimension, you will again be prompted to select an edge or a vertex. Select the edge that you need to dimension using the first selected edge as the datum. As soon as you select the edge, a horizontal dimension between the datum and this entity will be placed. Similarly, continue placing the dimensions to apply multiple horizontal ordinate dimensions, refer to Figure 4-39.

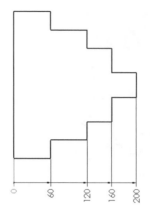

Figure 4-39 *Horizontal ordinate dimensions*

Vertical Ordinate Dimensioning

CommandManager:	Dimension/Relations > Vertical Ordinate Dimension
Menu:	Tools > Dimension > Vertical Ordinate
Toolbar:	Dimension/Relations > Vertical Ordinate Dimension

Vertical ordinate dimensions are used to dimension the vertical distances of the selected entities from the specified datum, see Figure 4-40. To add a vertical ordinate dimension, choose the **Vertical Ordinate Dimension** button from the **Dimension/ Relations CommandManager**. You will be prompted to select an edge or a vertex. As mentioned earlier, the first entity that you select is taken as the datum entity from where the remaining entities will be measured. Select the first entity and place the dimension on the right or left of it. You will notice that the dimension shows a value of 0; refer to the dimension of the left vertical line in Figure 4-40.

Next, select the edge that you need to dimension using the first selected edge as datum. As soon as you select the edge, a vertical dimension will be placed between the datum and this entity. Similarly, continue placing the dimensions to create multiple horizontal ordinate dimensions, refer to Figure 4-40.

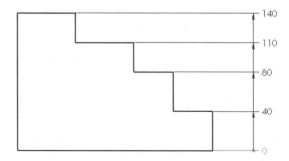

Figure 4-40 *Vertical ordinate dimensions*

CONCEPT OF A FULLY DEFINED SKETCH

It is very necessary for you to understand the concept of fully defined sketches. While creating a model, you first have to draw the sketch of the base feature and then proceed further for creating other features. After creating the sketches, you have to add the required relations and dimensions to constrain the sketch with respect to the surrounding environment. After adding the required relations and dimensions, the sketch may exist in one of the six states discussed below.

1. Fully Defined
2. Overdefined
3. Underdefined
4. Dangling
5. No Solution Found
6. Invalid Solution Found

Fully Defined

A fully defined sketch is the one in which all entities of the sketch and their positions are fully defined by the relations or dimensions, or both. In the fully defined sketch, all degrees of freedom of a sketch are constrained using relations and dimensions and the sketched entities cannot move or change their size and location unexpectedly. If the sketch is not fully defined, it can change its size or position at any time during the design because all degrees of freedom are not constrained. All entities in a fully defined sketch are displayed in black.

Overdefined

An overdefined sketch is the one in which some of the dimensions, relations, or both are conflicting or the dimensions or relations have exceeded the required number. The overdefined sketch is displayed in red. In an overdefined sketch, you need to delete the extra and conflicting relations or dimensions. It is recommended that you do not proceed further for creating the feature with an overdefined sketch. The overdefined sketch is changed to fully defined or underdefined sketch by deleting the conflicting relations or dimensions. Deleting the overdefining relations or dimensions is discussed later in this chapter.

Underdefined

An underdefined sketch is the one in which some of the dimensions or relations are not defined and the degree of freedom of the sketch is not fully constrained. In these types of sketches, the entities may move or change their size unexpectedly. As a result, the sketched entities of the underdefined sketch are displayed in blue. When you add relations and dimensions, the color of the entities in the sketch changes to black, suggesting that the sketch is fully defined. If the entire sketch is displayed in black and only some of the entities are shown in blue, this means that the entities in blue require some dimension or relation.

Tip. *In SolidWorks, it is not necessary that you fully dimension or define the sketches before you use them to create the features of the model. However, it is recommended that you fully define the sketches before you proceed further for creating the feature.*

*If you want to always use fully defined sketches before proceeding further, you can set the option by choosing **Tools** > **Options** from the menu bar to display the **System Option - General** dialog box. Select the **Sketch** option from the area on the left. Select the **Use fully defined sketches** check box and choose **OK** from this dialog box.*

Note

From this chapter onwards, you will work with fully defined sketches. Therefore, follow the above procedure to use the fully defined sketches in future.

Dangling

In the dangling sketch, the dimensions or relations applied to an entity lose their reference because of deletion of the entity from which they were referenced. These entities are displayed in brown. You need to delete the dangling entities, dimensions, or relations that conflict.

No Solution Found

In the no solution found state, the sketch is not solved with the current constraints. Therefore, you need to delete the conflicting dimensions or relations and add other dimensions or relations. The sketched entity, dimension, or relation will be displayed in pink.

Invalid Solution Found

In the invalid solution found state, the sketch is solved but will result in invalid geometry such as a zero length line, zero radius arc, or self-intersecting spline. The sketch entities for this state are displayed in yellow.

Sketch Dimension or Relation Status

In SolidWorks, when you are applying the dimensions and relations to the sketches, sometimes you apply the ones that are not compatible with the geometry of the sketched entities or that make the dimensioned entity overdefined. In addition to the fully defined state, the sketch dimensions or relations may have any of the following states.

1. Dangling
2. Satisfied
3. Overdefining
4. Not Solved
5. Driven

Tip. *The status bar of the SolidWorks window is divided into four areas while working in the sketching environment. The **Sketch Definition** area of the status bar always displays the status of the sketch, dimension, and relation. If the sketch is underdefined, the status area will display the **Under Defined** message; if the sketch is overdefined, the message displayed in the status area will be **Over Defined**; if the sketch is fully defined, the message displayed in the status area will be **Fully Defined**.*

Dangling

A dangling dimension or relation is the one that cannot be resolved because the entity to which it was referenced is deleted. The dangling dimension appears in brown.

Satisfied

A satisfied dimension is the one that is completely defined and is displayed in black.

Overdefining

An overdefining dimension or relation overdefines one or more entities in the sketch. The overdefining dimension appears in red.

Not Solved

The not solved dimension or relation is not able to determine the position of the sketched entities. A not solved dimension appears in pink.

Driven

The driven dimension's value is driven by other dimensions in the sketch that solve the sketch. The driven dimension appears in gray.

DELETING OVERDEFINING DIMENSIONS

In SolidWorks, when you add a dimension that overdefines a sketch, the sketch and dimension turn red. The **Make Dimension Driven?** dialog box is displayed, as shown in Figure 4-41.

*Figure 4-41 The **Make Dimension Driven?** dialog box*

The **Make Dimension Driven?** dialog box informs you that adding this dimension will overdefine the sketch or the sketch will not be solved. You are also prompted to specify whether you want to add the dimension as driven dimension. If you keep the **Make this dimension driven** radio button selected and choose **OK**, then that dimension will become a driven dimension. The driven dimension is displayed in gray and you cannot modify it. Its value depends on the value of the driver dimension. If you change the value of the driver dimension, the value of the driven dimension will be automatically changed.

If you select the **Leave this dimension driving** radio button and choose **OK**, then some of the entities and dimensions in the sketch will be displayed in red. Next, you need to delete the relation or dimension which is over defining the sketch. From this release of SolidWorks, the **Over Defined** option is displayed in the status bar, as shown in Figure 4-42.

Figure 4-42 The **Over Defined** button in the status bar

Click on the **Over Defined** option displayed in the status bar; the **SketchXpert PropertyManager** is displayed. Choose the **Manual Repair** button from the **Message** rollout; the relations or dimensions that are responsible for over defining the sketch are displayed in the **Conflicting Relations/Dimensions** rollout, as shown in Figure 4-43. Select any of the relation or dimension that is responsible for over defining the sketch and choose the DELETE key. If the over defining status of the sketch is removed, then the yellow **Message** area displays a message that the sketch can now find a valid solution. If a dimension or relation is still displayed in the **Conflicting Relations/Dimensions** rollout, then you need to delete it in order to remove the over defining status from the sketch.

You need to delete the red relation or the red dimension to make sure the sketch is no longer overdefined. When the sketch is not overdefined any more, the **Message** rollout in the **SketchXpert PropertyManager** will inform you that the sketch is no longer overdefined. Choose **OK** from the **PropertyManager**; the sketch will be displayed in black or blue, depending on the current state of the sketch.

You can also prevent the sketch from being overdefined by choosing the **Cancel** button from the **Make Dimension Driven?** dialog box. If you choose **Cancel** from the **Make Dimension Driven?** dialog box, the **SolidWorks** information dialog box will be displayed, with a message that the sketch is no longer overdefined.

Figure 4-43 The **SketchXpert PropertyManager**

Displaying and Deleting Relations

CommandManager:	Sketch > Display/Delete Relations
Menu:	Tools > Relations > Display/Delete
Toolbar:	Sketch > Display/Delete Relations

If the sketch is overdefined after adding the dimensions and relations, you need to delete some of the overdefining, dangling, or not solved relations or dimensions. You can view and delete the relations applied to the sketch using the **Display/ Delete Relations PropertyManager**. To invoke this **PropertyManager**, choose the **Display/Delete Relations** button from the **Sketch CommandManager**. You can also right-click in the drawing area to display the shortcut menu and choose the **Display/Delete Relations** option. You can also invoke this **PropertyManager** by clicking on the status of the sketch on the status bar provided on the bottom of the SolidWorks window. Whenever a sketch is overdefined or does not find any solution, a callout is displayed that prompts you to click on the status bar to resolve the conflict. Figure 4-44 shows the **Display/Delete Relations PropertyManager**. The options available in the **Display/Delete Relations PropertyManager** are discussed next.

Figure 4-44 The **Display/Delete Relations PropertyManager**

Relations Rollout

The **Relations** rollout is used to check, delete, and suppress the unwanted and conflicting relations. The status of the sketch or the selected entity is displayed in the **Information** area of this rollout. The options of the **Relations** rollout are discussed next.

Filter

The **Filter** drop-down list is used to select the filter to show the relations in the **Sketch Relation PropertyManager**. The options available in the **Filter** drop-down list are discussed next.

All in this sketch

The **All in this sketch** option is used to display all relations applied to the sketch. The first relation displayed in the list will be selected by default and will appear with a blue background. The status of the selected relations is displayed in the **Information** area of the **Relations** rollout. The overdefined relations are highlighted in red. If you select a relation highlighted in red in the **Relations** area, the status of the selected relation will be displayed as **Over Defining**. The dangling relation is highlighted in brown. When you select the dangling relation, the status of the relation will be displayed as **Dangling** in the **Information** area. Similarly, the not solved relation will be highlighted in yellow and the driven relation in gray.

Dangling

The **Dangling** option is used to display only the dangling relations applied to the sketch.

Overdefining/Not Solved

The **Overdefining/Not Solved** option is used to display only the overdefining and not solved relations. The dangling relations are also not solved relations. Therefore, they will also be displayed.

External

The **External** option is used to display the relations that have a reference with an entity outside the sketch. This entity can be an edge, vertex, or origin within the same model or it can be an edge, vertex, or origin of a different model within an assembly.

Defined In Context

The **Defined In Context** option is used to display only the relations that are in the context of a design. They are the relations between the sketched entity in one part and an entity in another part. These relations are defined while working with the top-down assemblies.

Locked

The **Locked** option is used to display only the locked relations.

Broken

The **Broken** option is used to display only the broken relations.

Note

*The **Locked** and **Broken** relations are applied while creating a part within the assembly environment. You will learn more about creating parts within the assembly in the later chapters.*

Selected Entities

The **Selected Entities** option is used to display the relations of only the selected set of entities. When you select this option from the **Filter** drop-down list, the **Selected Entities** selection box will be displayed in the **Relations** rollout. When you select an entity to display the relations, the name of the selected entity will be displayed in the **Selected Entities** area and the relations applied to this entity will be displayed in the **Relations** area. To remove the selected entity from the selection set, select the entity to be removed and right-click to display the shortcut menu. Choose the **Delete** option from the shortcut menu. If you choose the **Clear Selections** option, all entities will be removed from the selection set.

Suppressed

The **Suppressed** check box is selected to suppress the selected relation. When you suppress a relation, it will be displayed in gray in the **Relations** area. The status of the suppress relation will be displayed as **Satisfied** or **Driven** in the information area. If you suppress overdefining dimensions, the **SolidWorks** information dialog box will be displayed with a message that **The sketch is no longer over defined.** Choose the **OK** button from this dialog box.

Delete

The **Delete** button is used to delete the relation selected in the **Relations** area.

Delete All

The **Delete All** button is used to delete all relations that are displayed in the **Relations** area.

Undo last relation change

The **Undo last relation change** button is used to undo the **Delete**, **Replace**, and **Suppressed** options used earlier. The replace option is discussed later in this chapter.

Entities

The **Entities** rollout is used to display the entities that are referred to in the selected relation. This rollout is also used to display the status of the selected relation and the external reference, if any. By default, the **Entities** rollout is closed. You can open this rollout by clicking on the blue arrow displayed on the right of this rollout. The **Entities** rollout is shown in Figure 4-45. The options available in the **Entities** rollout are discussed next.

Figure 4-45 The Entities rollout

Entities used in the selected relation

The **Entities used in the selected relation** area is used to display the information about the entities used in the selected relation. The information about the name of the entity, the status of the entity, and the place where the entity is defined is provided. This area is divided into three columns, which are discussed next.

Entity
The **Entity** column is used to display the entity or entities to which the selected relation is applied.

Status
The **Status** column is used to display the status of the selected relation. The status can be **Fully Defined**, **Dangling**, **Over Defined**, or **Not Solved**.

Defined In
The **Defined In** column is used to display the placement of the entity. The entity can be placed in any of the following places.

Current Sketch
The **Current Sketch** option is displayed in the **Defined In** column when the entity is placed in the same sketch.

Same Model
The **Same Model** option is displayed in the **Defined In** column when the entity is defined to be placed in the same model. This means that the entity is placed in the same model, but outside the sketch. This entity can be an edge, vertex, or origin of the same model.

External Model
The **External Model** option is displayed in the **Defined In** column when the entity is placed in some other model but within the assembly. This entity can be an edge, vertex, or origin of a different model, but in the same assembly.

Tip. *By default, the **Override Dims on Drag** option is not selected from **Tools** > **Sketch Settings** menu in the menu bar. As a result, if you drag a dimensioned sketched entity, the entity will not be modified automatically. However, if the sketch is not fully defined, the entities that are not properly dimensioned or constrained will move. If you select this option, you can change a dimensioned sketched entity by dragging it. However, if the sketch is not fully defined, the entities that are not properly dimensioned or constrained will move.*

*By default, the **Automatic Solve** option is selected from the **Tools** > **Sketch Settings** menu in the menu bar. This option helps you solve the relations and dimensions automatically when you drag or modify a sketched entity. If you clear this option, a message will be displayed that will inform you that the sketch cannot be dragged because **Auto Solve** mode is off. It will further inform you to drag the sketch, please turn the **Auto Solve** mode on. If you modify the dimension value using the **Modify** dialog box, the dimension will not update automatically, and you have to update the new dimension manually. To update and solve the dimension, you have to choose the **Rebuild** button from the **Standard** toolbar or press CTRL+B on the keyboard.*

Tip. *By default, the relations applied to the sketched entities are displayed when you draw it or apply a relation to it. Therefore, sometimes the sketch looks untidy as all relations concerned with the sketch are displayed. To turn off the display of these relations, choose* **View > Sketch Relations** *from the menu bar. To turn on the display of these relations again, choose* **View > Sketch Relations** *from the menu bar.*

Entity

The **Entity** display box is used to display the name of the entity and the name of the part in which the selected entity is placed. This entity is selected in the **Entity** column of the **Entities used in the selected relation** area. The selected entity is also highlighted in the drawing area.

Owner

The **Owner** display box is used to display the name of the model in which the entity is placed when the **External Model** option is displayed in the **Defined In** column.

Assembly

The **Assembly** display box is used to display the path of the assembly in which the entity is placed when the **External Model** option is displayed in the **Defined In** column.

Replace

The **Replace** button is used to replace the selected entity from the **Entity** column with some other entity from the drawing area. When you select the entity from the drawing area, the entity will be displayed in the display box provided below the **Replace** button. Choose the **Replace** button to replace the entity. If the sketch is overdefined, you will be given a warning message. Sometimes after replacing the entity, the status of the entity is changed to not solved or overdefining. You need to undo the last operation.

Options

The check box available in this rollout is selected to display the **Display/Delete PropertyManager** when the sketch becomes overdefined or cannot be solved.

OPENING AN EXISTING FILE

Toolbar:	Standard > Open
Menu:	File > Open

The **Open** dialog box is used to open an existing SolidWorks part, assembly, or drawing document. You can also use this dialog box to import files from other applications saved in some standard file formats. Choose the **Open** button from the **Standard** toolbar, or press CTRL+O keys to invoke the **Open** dialog box, which is shown in Figure 4-46. The options available in this dialog box are discussed next.

Look in drop-down List

The **Look in** drop-down list is used to specify the drive or directory in which the file is saved. The location of the file and the folder that you browse is shown in this drop-down list.

Figure 4-46 The **Open** *dialog box*

File name

The name of the file selected is shown in the **File name** edit box. You can also enter the name of the file to open in this edit box.

Files of type

The **Files of type** drop-down list is used to specify the type of file to open. Using this drop-down list, you can select a particular type of file such as the part file, assembly file, drawing file, all SolidWorks files, and so on. You can also define the standard file format in this drop-down list to import the files saved in those file formats.

Open as read-only

The **Open as read-only** option is selected to open the document as a read-only file. This option is available in the flyout that will be displayed by choosing the down arrow available on the right of the **Open** button. If you modify the design in a read-only file, the changes will be saved in a new file. The original file will not be modified. This also allows another user to access the document while it is open on your computer.

Preview

The **Preview** check box is selected to display the **Preview** area in this dialog box. In the **Preview** area, you can preview the selected part, assembly, or drawing document before opening.

Advanced

The **Advanced** check box is selected to display the configurations available in the selected file. The configurations available in the selected file are displayed in the **Configurations** area.

View-Only

The **View-Only** check box is selected to open a SolidWorks document in the view only format. When you open a view-only file, only the tools related to viewing the models are enabled. The rest of the tools are not available. This is the reason why you cannot do any modification in the view-only document. You can use only the zoom, pan, or dynamically rotate tools. If you want to edit the design, right-click in the drawing area and choose the **Edit** option from the shortcut menu to edit the design.

Lightweight

The **Lightweight** check box is selected to open the assembly document using the lightweight parts. You will learn more about the lightweight parts in later chapters.

TUTORIALS

Tutorial 1

In this tutorial, you will draw the sketch of the model shown in Figure 4-47. This is the same sketch that was drawn in Tutorial 1 of Chapter 2. You will draw the sketch using the mirror line and then add the required relations and dimensions. The sketch is shown in Figure 4-48. The solid model is given only for reference.   (**Expected time: 30 min**)

Figure 4-47 Solid Model for Tutorial 1   *Figure 4-48 Sketch of the model*

The steps that will be followed to complete this tutorial are listed below.

a. Start SolidWorks and then start a new part document.
b. Maximize the part document and then invoke the sketching environment.
c. Create a mirror line using the **Centerline** and **Mirror** tools.
d. Draw the sketch of the model on one side of the mirror line so that it is automatically drawn on the other side, refer to Figures 4-49 through 4-54.
e. Add the required relations to the sketch, refer to Figures 4-55 and 4-56.
f. Add the required dimensions to the sketch and fully define the sketch, refer to Figure 4-57.
g. Save the sketch and then close the document.

Starting SolidWorks and Starting a New Part Document

1. Start SolidWorks by double-clicking on the shortcut icon of SolidWorks 2006 available on the desktop of your computer.

    The SolidWorks 2006 window is displayed and the **SolidWorks Resources Task Pane** is displayed on the right of the SolidWorks window.

2. Choose the **New** button from the **Standard** toolbar.

    The **New SolidWorks Document** dialog box is displayed.

3. The **Part** button is chosen by default. Choose the **OK** button from the **New SolidWorks Document** dialog box; a new SolidWorks part document is started.

4. Choose the **Sketch** button from the **Standard** toolbar and then select the **Front Plane** to invoke the sketching environment.

    In previous chapters, you used the grid and snap settings to create the sketches. However, from this chapter onwards, it is recommended that you do not use those settings. This way you can get familiar with drawing sketches at arbitrary locations and then using dimensions and relations to move them to their actual locations.

5. Invoke the **System Options - Relations/Snaps** dialog box and then clear the **Grid** check box from the **Sketch Snap** area.

6. Set the units for measuring linear dimensions to millimeters and the units for angular dimensions to degree using the **Document Properties - Units** dialog box. If you selected millimeters as units while installing SolidWorks, you can skip this point.

Drawing the Mirror Line

In this tutorial, you will draw the sketch of the given model with the help of the mirror line. As mentioned earlier, the sketches that are symmetrical along any axis are recommended to be drawn using the mirror line. The mirror line is drawn using the **Centerline** and **Mirror** tools. When you draw an entity on one side of the mirror line, the same entity is drawn automatically on the other side of it. Also, the symmetrical relation is applied to the entities on both sides of the mirror line. Therefore, if you modify an entity on one side of the mirror line, the same modification is reflected in the mirrored entity and vice versa. First, you need to draw a mirror line.

The origin of the sketching environment is placed at the center of the drawing area and you have to create the sketch in the first quadrant. Therefore, it is recommended that you modify the drawing area such that the area in the first quadrant is increased. This can be done using the **Pan** tool.

1. Choose the **Pan** tool button from the **View** toolbar. Press and hold the left mouse button down and drag the cursor toward the bottom left corner of the drawing area.

2. Choose the **Centerline** button from the **Sketch CommandManager** to display the **Insert Line PropertyManager**.

3. Move the line cursor to a location whose coordinates are close to 45 mm, 70 mm, 0 mm. You do not need to move the cursor exactly to this location. You can move it to a point close to this location.

4. Specify the start point of the centerline and move the line cursor vertically downward to draw a line of length close to 80 mm.

   As soon as you specify the endpoint of the centerline, a rubber-band line is attached to the line cursor. Right-click to display the shortcut menu and choose the **Select** option from the shortcut menu to end line creation and exit the **Line** tool.

5. Choose the **Zoom to Fit** button from the **View** toolbar to fit the sketch on the screen.

6. Select the centerline and convert it into a mirror line using the **Dynamic Mirror Entities** tool.

Drawing the Sketch

You will draw the sketch on the right of the mirror line and the same sketch will be automatically drawn on the other side of the mirror line.

1. Choose the **Line** button from the **Sketch CommandManager**; the arrow cursor is replaced by the line cursor.

2. Move the line cursor to a location where the coordinates are close to 45 mm, 10 mm, 0 mm. At this point, the cursor snaps to the mirror line and a coincident symbol is displayed below the cursor.

3. Specify the start point of the line at this point and move the cursor horizontally toward the right. Specify the endpoint of the line when its length above the line cursor shows a value close to 15. As soon as you press the left mouse button to specify the endpoint of the line, a line of the same length is drawn automatically on the other side of the mirror line. Figure 4-49 shows the mirrored entity created automatically on the other side of the mirror line. The display of relations in this figure is turned off by choosing **View > Sketch Relations** menu.

   Note that the mirrored entity that is automatically created on the left of the mirror line is merged with the line drawn on the right. Therefore, the entire line becomes a single entity. As mentioned earlier, the mirror image of the line is merged with the line you draw only if one of the endpoints of the line is coincident with the mirror line.

4. Move the cursor vertically upward. Specify the endpoint of the line when the length of the line on the line cursor displays a value close to 10. Figure 4-50 shows the sketch after drawing the vertical lines.

Figure 4-49 *Sketching using automatic mirroring*   **Figure 4-50** *Left line drawn by mirroring*

5. Move the line cursor horizontally toward the right. Specify the endpoint of the line when the length of the line on the line cursor displays a value close to 10.

6. Move the line cursor vertically downward. Specify the endpoint when the length of the line on the line cursor displays a value close to 10.

7. Move the line cursor horizontally toward the right. Specify the endpoint when the length of the line on the line cursor displays a value close to 10.

8. Move the line cursor vertically upward. Specify the endpoint when the length of the line on the line cursor displays a value close to 40.

9. Move the line cursor at an angle close to 135-degrees and specify the endpoint of the line. Figure 4-51 shows the sketch after drawing this inclined line.

10. Move the line cursor horizontally toward the left. Specify the endpoint when the cursor snaps to the mirror line and the mirror line is highlighted in red. Double-click anywhere in the drawing area to end the line creation. The sketch, after completing the outer loop, is shown in Figure 4-52.

    Next, you will draw the sketch of the inner cavity. To draw the sketch of the inner cavity, you will start with the lower horizontal line.

11. Move the line cursor to a location whose coordinates are close to 45 mm, 25 mm, 0 mm.

12. Specify the start point of the line at this point and move the cursor horizontally toward the right. Specify the endpoint when the length of the line above the line cursor shows a value close to 15.

13. Move the line cursor vertically upward. Specify the endpoint when the length of the line on the line cursor displays a value close to 10.

Figure 4-51 *Sketch after drawing the inclined line*

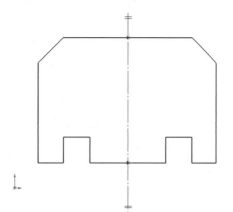

Figure 4-52 *Sketch after completing the outer profile of the sketch*

14. Move the line cursor horizontally toward the left. Specify the endpoint when the length of the line on the line cursor displays a value close to 10.

15. Move the line cursor vertically downward. Specify the endpoint when the length of the line on the line cursor displays a value close to 5.

16. Move the line cursor horizontally toward the left. Specify the endpoint when the line cursor snaps to the mirror line.

17. Double-click anywhere in the drawing area to end the line creation. The sketch, after completing the inner cavity, is shown in Figure 4-53.

18. Choose the **Circle** button from the **Sketch CommandManager** to invoke the circle tool.

19. Move the circle cursor to the point where the inferencing line originating from the endpoints of the right inclined line intersect.

20. Specify the center of the circle at this point and move the circle cursor toward the left to define the radius of the circle. Press the left mouse button when the radius of the circle above the circle cursor shows a value close to 5.

    The circle is automatically mirrored on the other side of the mirror line. The sketch, after drawing the circle, is shown in Figure 4-54.

21. Clear the automatic mirroring option by choosing the **Dynamic Mirror Entities** button again.

Adding the Required Relations

After drawing the sketch, you need to add the relations using the **Add Relations PropertyManager**. The relations are applied to a sketch to constrain its degree of freedom,

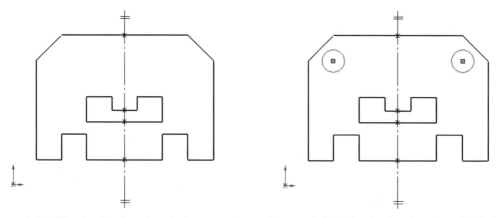

Figure 4-53 *Sketch after drawing the inner cavity*   **Figure 4-54** *Sketch after drawing the circle*

to reduce the number of dimensions in the sketch, and also to capture the design intent in the sketch.

1. Press the ESC key to remove the circles created previously from the selection set.

2. Choose the **Add Relation** button from the **Sketch CommandManager** to invoke the **Add Relations PropertyManager**. The confirmation corner is also displayed at the upper right corner of the drawing area.

3. Select the center point of the circle on the right and then select the lower endpoint of the right inclined line. The names of the selected entities are displayed in the **Selected Entities** rollout of the **Add Relations PropertyManager**.

    The relations that can be applied to the two selected entities are displayed in the **Add Relations** rollout of the **Add Relations PropertyManager**, as shown in Figure 4-55. The **Horizontal** option is highlighted, suggesting that the horizontal relation is the most appropriate relation for the selected entities.

Tip. *Sometimes unwanted inferencing lines are displayed when you are drawing a sketch. You can remove them by choosing **View** > **Redraw** from the menu bar. You can also redraw the drawing area by pressing CTRL+R keys.*

Note
*The names of the entities displayed in the **Selected Entities** rollout of the **Add Relations PropertyManager** may be different from those displayed on your computer screen.*

4. Choose the **Horizontal** button from the **Add Relations** rollout to apply the **Horizontal** relation to the selected entities.

5. Move the cursor to the drawing area and right-click to invoke the shortcut menu. Choose the **Clear Selections** option to remove the selected entities from the selection set.

Figure 4-55 *The Add Relations PropertyManager*

6. Select the center point of the circle on the right and the upper endpoint of the right inclined line.

   The relations that can be applied to the selected entities are displayed and the **Vertical** option is highlighted.

7. Choose the **Vertical** button from the **Add Relations PropertyManager**. Right-click in the drawing area and choose the **Clear Selections** option.

8. Select the entities shown in Figure 4-56. Choose the **Equal** button from the **Add Relations** rollout of the **Add Relations PropertyManager**.

9. Choose the **OK** button from the **Add Relations PropertyManager** or choose **OK** from the confirmation corner to close the **PropertyManager**. Click anywhere in the drawing area to clear the selected entities.

Applying Dimensions to the Sketch

Next, you will apply the dimensions and fully define the sketch. As mentioned earlier, the sketched entities are shown in blue, suggesting that the sketch is underdefined. It will be changed to black after you apply the required dimensions to the sketch. This suggests that the sketch is fully defined.

1. Choose **Tools > Options** from the menu bar to display the **System Options - General** dialog box. Select the **Input dimension value** check box, if cleared, and choose **OK** from

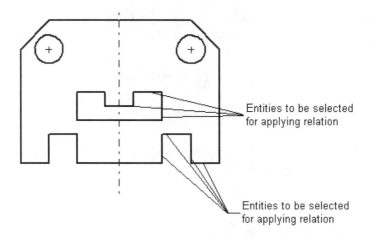

Entities to be selected
for applying relation

Entities to be selected
for applying relation

*Figure 4-56 Entities to be selected to apply the **Equal** relation*

the **System Options - General** dialog box. This check box is selected to invoke the **Modify** dialog box to enter a new dimension value and modify the sketch as you place the dimension.

2. Choose the **Smart Dimension** button from the **Sketch CommandManager**. You can also right-click in the drawing area and choose the **Smart Dimension** option to invoke the dimension option.

    The cursor is replaced by the dimension cursor.

3. Move the dimension cursor to the lower right horizontal line; the line is highlighted in red.

4. Select the line; a linear dimension is attached to the cursor.

5. Move the cursor downward and click to place the dimension below the line, refer to Figure 4-57. As you place the dimension, the **Modify** dialog box is displayed.

6. Enter the dimension value of **10** in this dialog box and press ENTER. The dimension is placed and the length of line is also modified to **10**.

7. Move the dimension cursor to the lower-middle horizontal line, refer to Figure 4-57. Select the line when the line changes to red; a dimension is attached to the cursor.

8. Move the cursor downward and click to place the dimension. Enter a value of **30** in the **Modify** dialog box and press ENTER.

9. Move the cursor to the outer left vertical line and when the color of the line changes to red, select the line; a dimension is attached to the cursor.

10. Move the cursor to the left and then click to place the dimension. Enter a value of **40** in the **Modify** dialog box and press ENTER.

11. Select the right inclined line; a dimension is attached to the cursor. Move the cursor vertically upward to apply the horizontal dimension to the selected line. Click to place the dimension at an appropriate place, see Figure 4-60.

12. Enter a value of **10** in the **Modify** dialog box and press ENTER.

13. Again, select the right aligned line; a dimension is attached to the cursor. Move the cursor horizontally toward the right to apply the vertical dimension for the selected line. Click to place the dimension at an appropriate place, see Figure 4-57.

14. Enter a value of **10** in the **Modify** dialog box and press ENTER.

15. Move the cursor to the left circle and when the circle is highlighted in red, select it. A diameter dimension is attached to the cursor. Move the cursor outside the sketch.

16. Place the diameter dimension. Enter a value of **10** in the **Modify** dialog box and press ENTER.

17. Select the lower horizontal line of the inner cavity; a linear dimension is attached to the cursor. Select the lower right horizontal line of the outer loop.

    A vertical dimension between the lower horizontal line of the inner cavity and the lower right horizontal line of the outer sketch is attached to the cursor.

18. Move the cursor horizontally toward the right and place the dimension. Enter a value of **15** in the **Modify** dialog box and press ENTER.

19. Select the inner right vertical line of the cavity and place the dimension outside the sketch. Enter a value of **5** in the **Modify** dialog box and press ENTER.

20. Select the lower left horizontal line of the outer sketch and the origin.

21. Move the cursor horizontally toward the left and place the dimension. Enter a value of **10** in the **Modify** dialog box.

    Notice that some of the entities are displayed in black. This suggests that these entities are now fully defined. But you have to fully define the entire sketch. So you need to add some more dimensions.

22. Select the left vertical line of the outer sketch and the origin. Move the cursor vertically downward and place the dimension. Enter a value of **10** in the **Modify** dialog box.

    Notice that all entities are displayed in black. This suggests that the sketch is fully defined. If the sketch is not fully defined, then you have to add a dimension between the outer right vertical line and the outer left vertical line. The value of the dimension should be maintained to 70. The fully defined sketch, after applying all required relations and dimensions, is shown in Figure 4-57.

Figure 4-57 *Fully defined sketch after applying all the required relations and dimensions*

Saving the Sketch

1. Choose the **Save** button from the **Standard** toolbar to invoke the **Save As** dialog box. Browse to the *My Documents\SolidWorks* folder. Choose the **Create New Folder** button from the **Save As** dialog box. Enter the name of the folder as *c04* and press ENTER.

2. Enter the name of the document as *c04tut1* in the **File name** edit box and choose the **Save** button. The document will be saved in the *\My Documents\SolidWorks\c04* folder. Close the document by choosing **File > Close** from the menu bar.

Tutorial 2

In this tutorial, you will draw the sketch of the model shown in Figure 4-58. You will draw the sketch using the mirror line and then add the required relations and dimensions. The sketch is shown in Figure 4-59. The solid model is given only for reference.   **(Expected time: 30 min)**

Figure 4-58 *Solid Model for Tutorial 2*

Figure 4-59 *Sketch of the solid model*

The steps that will be followed to complete this tutorial are listed below.

a. Start a new document file.
b. Maximize the part file document and then invoke the sketching environment.
c. Create a mirror line.
d. Draw the sketch on one side of the mirror line, refer to Figure 4-60.
e. Trim the arcs and circles and add the fillets, refer to Figures 4-61 through 4-63.
f. Add the required relations.
g. Add the required dimensions and fully define the sketch, refer to Figure 4-64.

Starting a New Document and Invoking the Sketching Environment

1. Choose the **New** button from the **Standard** toolbar to invoke the **New SolidWorks Document** dialog box.

2. The **Part** button is chosen by default. Choose the **OK** button; a new SolidWorks part document is started.

3. Choose the **Sketch** button from the **Standard** toolbar and select the **Front Plane** to invoke the sketching environment.

Drawing the Mirror Line

Similar to the last tutorial, you will draw the sketch of the given model with the help of a mirror line.

1. Increase the display of the drawing area using the **Zoom In/Out** tool and choose the **Centerline** button from the **Sketch CommandManager**.

2. Move the line cursor to a location whose coordinates are close to -102 mm, 0 mm, 0 mm. You do not need to move the cursor exactly to this location. You can move it to a point close to this location.

3. Specify the start point of the centerline at this point and move the line cursor horizontally toward the right. Specify the endpoint of the centerline when the length of the line shows a value close to 204. Double-click anywhere in the drawing area to end line creation.

4. Choose the **Zoom to Fit** button from the **View** tollbar to fit the sketch in the drawing area.

5. Convert the centerline to the mirror line and enable the automatic mirror option.

Drawing the Sketch

You will draw the sketch on the upper side of the mirror line and the same sketch will be automatically drawn on the other side of the mirror line.

1. Choose the **Centerpoint Arc** button from the **Sketch CommandManager**; the arrow cursor is replaced by the arc cursor.

2. Move the arc cursor close to the origin. Specify the center point of the arc when the cursor snaps the origin. Move the cursor horizontally toward the right. The cursor snaps to the mirror line. As you move the cursor, a reference circle is drawn. Specify the start point of the arc when the radius of the arc on the arc cursor shows a value close to 82.

3. Move the arc cursor in the counterclockwise direction. Specify the endpoint of the arc when the value of the angle above the arc cursor shows a value close to 30-degrees. The mirror image of the sketched entity is automatically created on the other side of the mirror line.

4. Move the arc cursor to the origin. Specify the center point of the arc. Move it horizontally toward the right. The cursor snaps to the mirror line and a reference circle is drawn. Specify the start point of the arc when the radius of the arc on the arc cursor shows a value close to 56.

5. Move the arc cursor in the counterclockwise direction. Specify the endpoint of the arc when the value of the angle above the arc cursor shows a value close to 30-degrees. The mirror image of the sketched entity is automatically created on the other side of the mirror line.

6. Choose the **Tangent Arc** button from the **Sketch CommandManager** .

7. Move the cursor to the upper endpoint of the left arc and when the red circle is displayed, specify the first point of the tangent arc. Move the cursor close to the upper endpoint of the right arc and when the red circle is displayed, specify the second point of the tangent arc.

8. Choose the **Circle** button from the **Sketch CommandManager**.

9. Move the cursor to the center point of the upper arc and when the red circle is displayed, specify the center point of the circle. Move the cursor horizontally toward the right. Press the left mouse button when the radius of the circle above the circle cursor shows a value close to 7.5.

10. Move the cursor to the origin and when the red circle is displayed, specify the center point

of the circle. Move the cursor horizontally toward the right. Press the left mouse button when the radius of the circle above the circle cursor shows a value close to 6.5.

The **SolidWorks** warning dialog box is displayed, which shows the warning message "**Unable to create the symmetric element**." This message is displayed because the circle is created on both sides of the mirror line. Therefore, a symmetric element is not created in this case.

11. Choose **OK** from the **SolidWorks** warning dialog box.

12. Move the cursor to the origin and when the red circle is displayed, specify the center point of the circle. Move the cursor horizontally toward the right. Press the left mouse button when the radius of the circle above the circle cursor displays a value close to 19. The **SolidWorks** warning dialog box is displayed.

13. Choose **OK** from the **SolidWorks** warning dialog box.

14. Choose the **Line** button from the **Sketch CommandManager**.

15. Move the line cursor to a location whose coordinates are close to 55 mm, 10 mm, 0 mm. The cursor snaps to the left arc.

16. Specify the start point of the line at this point and move the cursor horizontally toward the left. Specify the endpoint of the line when the line cursor snaps the outer circle. Double-click anywhere in the drawing area to end line creation.

17. Move the cursor to a location whose coordinates are close to -10 mm, 10 mm, 0 mm.

18. Specify the start point of the line on this location and move the cursor horizontally toward the left. Specify the endpoint when the length of the line above the line cursor shows a value close to 42.

19. Move the line cursor such that the line is drawn at an angle close to 105-degrees. Specify the endpoint when the length of line is close to 15.

Note
*You may need to scroll down the **Line PropertyManager** to view the angle. Move the cursor to the scroll bar, press and hold the left mouse button down, and drag the cursor vertically downward to scroll down the **Line PropertyManager**.*

20. Move the line cursor horizontally toward the left. Specify the endpoint when the length of the line above the line cursor shows a value close to 34.

21. Move the line cursor vertically downward. Specify the endpoint when the length of the line above the line cursor shows a value close to 10.

22. Move the line cursor such that the line is drawn at an angle close to 346-degrees. Specify the endpoint when the length of the line is around 27.

23. Move the line cursor vertically downward. Specify the endpoint when the line cursor snaps the mirror line. Double-click anywhere in the drawing area to end line creation.

The sketch, after drawing the required arcs, circles, and lines, is shown in Figure 4-63.

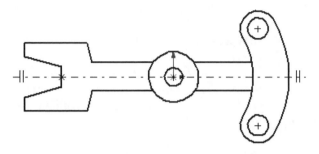

Figure 4-60 *Sketch after drawing all entities*

Trimming the unwanted entities

After drawing the sketch, you need to trim some of the unwanted sketched entities using the **Trim Entities** tool.

1. Choose the **Trim Entities** button from the **Sketch CommandManager** to display the **Trim PropertyManager**.

2. Choose the **Trim to closet** button from the **Options** rollout if it is not selected by default; the select cursor is replaced by the trim cursor.

3. Select the entities to be trimmed, as shown in Figure 4-61; the entities are dynamically trimmed.

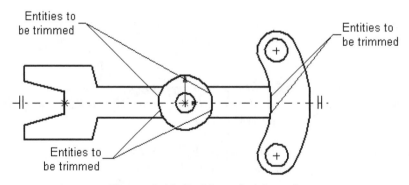

Figure 4-61 *Entities to be trimmed*

Filleting the Sketched Entities

Next, you need to fillet the sketched entities. The fillets are generally applied to avoid the stress concentration at sharp corners.

1. Choose the **Sketch Fillet** button from the **Sketch CommandManager**. Set the radius spinner to **5**.

2. Select the entities shown in Figure 4-62 to apply the fillet.

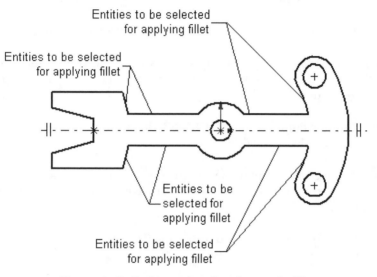

Figure 4-62 *Entities to be selected to apply fillet*

3. Choose the **OK** button from the **Sketch Fillet PropertyManager** to exit the **Fillet** tool. The sketch, after applying the fillets to it, is shown in Figure 4-63.

Figure 4-63 *Sketch after creating the fillets*

Adding Relations to the Sketch

Next, you need to add the required relations to the sketch.

1. Choose the **Add Relations** button from the **Sketch CommandManager** to invoke the **Add Relations PropertyManager**.

2. Select the lower left arc and the lower tangent arc; the **Tangent** button is highlighted in bold in the **Add Relations** rollout of the **Add Relations PropertyManager**. This suggests that the **Tangent** relation is the most appropriate relation for the selected entities.

3. Choose the **Tangent** button from the **Add Relations PropertyManager**.

4. Right-click in the drawing area and choose the **Clear Selections** option from the shortcut menu to clear the selections from the selection set. Select the right arc and the lower tangent arc; the **Tangent** button is highlighted.

5. Choose the **Tangent** button from the **Add Relations PropertyManager**. Clear the current selections from the selection set.

6. Select the upper right horizontal line and the upper left horizontal line that are coincident with the trimmed circle. Choose the **Collinear** button from the **Add Relations PropertyManager**.

7. Choose the **OK** button from the **Add Relations PropertyManager** or choose **OK** from the confirmation corner.

Adding Dimensions to the Sketch

Next, you will apply the required dimensions to the sketch and fully defined it.

1. Choose the **Smart Dimension** button from the **Sketch CommandManager** to invoke the dimension tool; the arrow cursor is replaced by the dimension cursor.

2. Select the right arc; a radius dimension is attached to the cursor. Move the cursor away from the sketch toward the right and place the dimension.

3. Enter a value of **82** in the **Modify** dialog box and press ENTER.

4. Select the left upper arc, refer to Figure 4-64; a radius dimension is attached to the cursor. Move the cursor away from the sketch toward the right and place the dimension.

5. Enter a value of **56** in the **Modify** dialog box and press ENTER.

6. Select the **Origin** and the center point of the upper circle; a dimension is attached to the cursor. Next, select the right endpoint of the mirror line; an angular dimension is attached to the cursor. Place the angular dimension outside the sketch.

7. Enter the angular dimension value of **30** in the **Modify** dialog box and press ENTER.

8. Select the upper right circle; a diameter dimension is attached to the cursor. Place the dimension outside the sketch.

9. Enter the diameter dimension value of **15** in the **Modify** dialog box and press ENTER.

10. Select the upper right horizontal line and the lower right horizontal line that coincide the trimmed circle, refer to Figure 4-64. A vertical dimension is attached to the cursor. Move the cursor vertically downward and click to place the dimension.

11. Enter a value of **20** in the **Modify** dialog box.

12. Select the smaller circle at the origin; a diameter dimension is attached to the cursor. Move the cursor upward and place the dimension outside the sketch.

13. Enter the diameter dimension value of **13** in the **Modify** dialog box.

14. Select the outer trimmed circle and place the radius dimension outside the sketch.

15. Enter the radial dimension value of **19** in the **Modify** dialog box.

16. Select the upper right inclined line; a dimension is attached to the cursor. Now, select the upper left horizontal line; an angular dimension is attached to the cursor. Place the dimension above the upper left horizontal line.

17. Enter the angular dimension value of **75** in the **Modify** dialog box.

18. Select the origin and the lower endpoint of the lower right inclined line. Move the cursor vertically downward and place the dimension.

19. Enter a value of **49** in the **Modify** dialog box.

20. Select the origin and the middle left vertical line, refer to Figure 4-64. Move the cursor vertically downward and place the dimension below the previous dimension.

21. Enter a value of **61** in the **Modify** dialog box.

22. Select the origin and the lower endpoint of the outer left vertical line. Move the cursor vertically downward and place the dimension below the last dimension.

23. Enter a value of **90** in the **Modify** dialog box.

24. Select the upper left inclined line and the lower left inclined line, refer to Figure 4-64; an angular dimension is attached to the cursor. Move the cursor horizontally toward the left and place the dimension.

25. Enter the angular dimension value of **28** in the **Modify** dialog box.

26. Select the upper left horizontal line and the lower left horizontal line; a linear dimension is attached to the cursor. Move the cursor horizontally toward the left and place the dimension.

27. Enter a value of **50** in the **Modify** dialog box.

28. Select the lower endpoint of the upper left vertical line and the upper endpoint of the lower left vertical line; a linear dimension is attached to the cursor. Move the cursor horizontally toward the left and left click to place the dimension.

29. Enter a value of **30** in the **Modify** dialog box.

All sketched entities are displayed in black, suggesting that the sketch is fully defined. The fully defined sketch is shown in Figure 4-64.

Figure 4-64 *Sketch after applying all relations and dimensions*

Saving the Sketch

1. Choose the **Save** button from the **Standard** toolbar to invoke the **Save As** dialog box.

2. Enter the name of the document as *c04tut2* in the **File name** edit box and choose the **Save** button.

3. Close the document by choosing **File > Close** from the menu bar.

Tutorial 3

In this tutorial, you will draw the sketch of a revolved model shown in Figure 4-65. The sketch is shown in Figure 4-66. The solid model is given only for your reference.

(Expected time: 30 min)

Figure 4-65 *Solid model of the piston*

Figure 4-66 *The sketch of the base feature*

The steps that will be followed to complete this tutorial are listed below.

a. Start a new part document and then invoke the sketching environment.
b. Draw a centerline that will be used to add the linear diameter dimensions to the sketch of the piston.
c. Create the sketch using various sketching tools.
d. Use the **Offset Entities** tool to offset the required lines, refer to Figure 4-67.
e. Draw the arcs and trim the unwanted entities, refer Figure 4-68.
f. Add the required relations.
g. Add the required dimensions and fully define the sketch, refer Figure 4-69.

Starting a New Part Document

1. Choose the **New** button from the **Standard** toolbar and start a new part document using the **New SolidWorks Document** dialog box.

2. Choose the **Sketch** button from the **Standard** toolbar and select the **Front Plane** to invoke the sketching environment for drawing the sketch.

Drawing the Sketch

To draw the sketch of the revolved model, you will first need to draw the centerline around which the sketch of the base feature will be revolved.

1. Choose the **Centerline** button from the **Sketch CommandManager**.

2. Draw a vertical centerline starting from the origin and having a length of 120 mm.

    Next, you will draw the sketch of the piston.

3. Right-click in the drawing area and choose the **Line** option from the shortcut menu. Move the cursor to a location whose coordinates are close to 58 mm, 0 mm, 0 mm. Click at this point to specify the start point of the line.

4. Draw a vertical line of dimension close to 100. Right-click and choose the **End chain** option from the shortcut menu.

5. Move the cursor to the lower endpoint of the line drawn earlier. Specify the start point of the line when the red circle is displayed. Move the cursor horizontally toward the left and draw a horizontal line of dimension close to 8.

6. Move the line cursor vertically upward and draw a vertical line of dimension close to 30.

7. Move the cursor horizontally toward the left and draw a horizontal line of dimension close to 7.

8. Move the line cursor vertically upward and draw a vertical line of dimension close to 70.

9. Right-click and choose the **3 Point Arc** option from the shortcut menu. Move the cursor near the upper endpoint of the right vertical line.

10. Specify the first point of the arc when the red circle is displayed. Move the cursor horizontally toward the left; the reference arc is attached to the cursor. Specify the second point of the arc when the value of the length is close to 116.

11. Move the cursor toward the right. Specify the third point of the arc when the value of the radius is close to 170.

12. Right-click and choose the **Line** option from the shortcut menu. Move the line cursor to a location whose coordinates are close to 58 mm, 90 mm, 0 mm. Specify the start point of

the line at this location and move the cursor horizontally toward the left to draw a line of a dimension close to 5. Double-click anywhere in the drawing area to end the line creation.

13. Choose the **Zoom To Fit** button from the **View** toolbar to fit the sketch to the drawing area.

Offsetting the Lines

Using the **Offset Entities** tool, you will offset the entities created earlier.

1. Select the line created previously using the select tool.

2. Choose the **Offset Entities** button from the **Sketch CommandManager** to invoke the **Offset Entities PropertyManager**. The confirmation corner is also displayed at the upper right corner of the drawing area.

3. Choose the **Keep Visible** button from the **Offset Entities PropertyManager** to pin the **PropertyManager**.

4. Set the value of **Offset Distance** spinner to **5**. Now, select the **Reverse** check box because you need to offset the entity in the reverse direction. The preview of the entity to be offset is modified in the drawing area.

5. Choose the **OK** button from the **Offset Entities PropertyManager**.

   You will notice that an entity is created at an offset distance of 5 from the original entity. Also, a dimension is applied between the newly created entity and the original entity with a value of **5**. This dimension is the offset distance between the two entities.

6. Select the newly created entity. Move the cursor vertically downward; the preview of the entity and the direction of the offset creation are also displayed. Press the left mouse button to offset the selected line.

   Repeat this procedure of offsetting the entities until you get eight entities, including the original entity.

7. Set the value of the **Offset Distance** spinner to **7** and clear the **Select chain** check box. Then select the upper arc. The preview of the offset arc is shown in the drawing area.

8. Choose the **OK** button twice on the **Offset Entities PropertyManager**.

Completing the Remaining Sketch

Next, you will complete the remaining sketch using the line tool.

1. Right-click and choose the **Line** option from the shortcut menu. Move the line cursor to the left endpoint of the original line that was used to create offset lines. When the red circle is displayed, specify the start point. Specify the endpoint of the line at the endpoint of the last offset line.

2. Move the cursor to the intersection point of the upper arc and the centerline. When the cursor snaps the intersection, draw a vertical line that snaps the intersection point of the lower arc and the centerline.

The sketch, after drawing the entities using various sketch tools and the offset tool, is shown in Figure 4-67.

Trimming the Unwanted Entities

Next, you will trim the unwanted entities using the trim tool.

1. Choose the **Trim Entities** button from the **Sketch CommandManager**.

2. Using the left mouse button trim the unwanted entities. The sketch, after trimming the unwanted entities, is shown in Figure 4-68.

Figure 4-67 *Sketch after creating various entities*

Figure 4-68 *Sketch after trimming the unwanted entities*

Adding the Required Relations

Now, you will add the required relations to the sketched entities.

1. Right-click and choose the **Select** option from the shortcut menu. Press and hold the CTRL key down and select one of the endpoints of the lower horizontal line and then select the origin. Release the CTRL key after selection. Right-click and choose the **Horizontal** option from the shortcut menu to add the horizontal relation to the selected entities. Click anywhere in the drawing area to clear the selection set.

2. Press and hold the CTRL key down and select the small horizontal lines on the right of the sketch. Release the CTRL key after making the selection and right-click to display the shortcut menu. Choose the **Equal** option from the shortcut menu to apply the equal relation.

3. Similarly, apply the **Equal** relation to all small vertical lines.

The **SolidWorks** warning message window is displayed. This warns you that the solution cannot be determined for the sketch. If the **Show property manager when the sketch becomes over defined or unsolved** check box is selected earlier in the **Display/Delete Relations Property Manager**, then this **PropertyManager** is displayed automatically and the warning message window is not displayed. You will notice that some of the entities of the sketch turn red. This indicates that the sketch is overdefined.

4. Choose **OK** from this message window or the **PropertyManager**.

    As discussed earlier, the overdefined sketch is not used to create any feature; therefore, you have to delete the conflicting relations. The sketch is overdefined after applying the previous relation. Therefore, if you delete the last applied relation using the **Undo** button from the **Standard** toolbar, then the sketch is not overdefined.

5. Choose the **Undo** button from the **Standard** toolbar. Click anywhere in the drawing area to clear the selections from the selection set.

    As evident from the color of the entities, which is blue, you still have to add some more relations or dimensions to fully define the sketch. The fully defined sketch is displayed in black.

6. Zoom out using the **Zoom In/Out** tool and apply the coincident relation between the center point of the upper arc and the centerline.

Adding Dimensions to the Sketch

After drawing and editing the sketch and applying the relations to it, you will add the required dimensions to fully define the sketch.

1. Select the dimension with a value of **7**, which is placed between the upper arcs and press the DELETE key on the keyboard.

    Delete this dimension because during the design and manufacturing practices the dimension between the tangents should be avoided.

2. Right-click and choose the **Smart Dimension** option from the shortcut menu to invoke this tool.

3. Select the outer upper right vertical line; a dimension is attached to the cursor. Now, select the centerline and move the cursor to the other side of the centerline. You will notice that the diameter dimension is displayed along the cursor.

4. Click to place the dimension above the sketch and enter a value of **116** in the **Modify** edit box and press ENTER.

5. Now, select the inner left vertical line and then select the centerline, refer to Figure 4-69. Move the cursor to the other side of the centerline and click to place the dimension below the sketch.

6. Enter a value of **86** in the **Modify** edit box and press ENTER.

   Add the remaining dimensions to fully define the sketch, refer to Figure 4-69.

7. Using the left mouse button, select one of the dimensions that are created after offsetting the entities and drag the cursor toward the right and using the left mouse button place the dimension at an appropriate place.

8. Arrange all dimensions using the above method. The fully defined sketch is shown in Figure 4-69. In this figure, the display of relations is turned off.

Figure 4-69 *Fully defined sketch after applying all the relations and dimensions*

Saving the Sketch

1. Choose the **Save** button from the **Standard** toolbar and save the sketch with the name given below.

   \My Documents\SolidWorks\c04\c04tut3.sldprt.

2. Choose **File > Close** from the menu bar to close the document.

SELF-EVALUATION TEST

Answer the following questions and then compare your answers with those given at the end of this chapter:

1. Some relations are automatically applied to the sketch while it is being drawn. (T/F)

2. When you choose the **Add Relations** button, the **Apply Relations PropertyManager** is displayed. (T/F)

3. You can modify the arrowhead style of a selected dimension. (T/F)

4. The dimension favorite created in one document cannot be retrieved in the other document. (T/F)

5. You can do modifications in the view-only file. (T/F)

6. The _____ **PropertyManager** is displayed using the **Add Relation** button from the **Sketch CommandManager**.

7. The _____ dimension is used to dimension a line that is at an angle with respect to the X axis or the Y axis.

8. A _____ defined sketch is the one in which all entities and their positions are described by the relations or dimensions, or both.

9. The _____ dimensions or relations are not able to determine the position of one or more sketched entities.

10. The _____ option is displayed in the **Defined In** column when the entity is defined as placed in the same sketch.

REVIEW QUESTIONS
Answer the following questions:

1. You can invoke the **Display/Delete Relations PropertyManager** using the **Display/Delete Relations** button from _____ **CommandManager**.

2. The linear diameter dimensions are applied to the sketches of _____ features.

3. You can modify the dimension to display the minimum or maximum distance between two circles using the _____ dialog box.

4. The _____ sketch geometry is constrained by too many dimensions and/or relations. Therefore, you have to delete the extra and conflicting relations or dimensions.

5. The _____ relation forces two selected lines, arcs, points, or ellipses to remain equidistant from a centerline.

6. In SolidWorks, by default, the dimensioning between two arcs, two circles, or between an arc and a circle is done from

    (a) Center point to center point   (b) Center point to tangent
    (c) Depends on the point where you select   (d) None

7. Which relation forces the selected arc to share the same center point with another arc or a point?

    (a) **Concentric**   (b) **Coradial**
    (c) **Merge points**   (d) **Equal**

8. Which type of dimensions change the color of the entities to red?

    (a) Underdefined   (b) Overdefined
    (c) Dangling   (d) None

9. Which dialog box is displayed when you modify a dimension?

    (a) **Modify Dimensional Value**   (b) **Insert a value**
    (c) **Modify**   (d) None

10. Which dialog box is displayed when you add an extra dimension to a sketch or add an extra relation that overdefines the sketch?

    (a) **Over defining**   (b) **Delete relation**
    (c) **Make Dimension Driven?**   (c) **Add Geometric Relations**

EXERCISES

Exercise 1

Create the sketch of the model shown in Figure 4-70. Apply the required relations and dimensions and fully define it. The sketch is shown in Figure 4-71. The solid model is given for reference only.   (**Expected time: 30 min**)

Figure 4-70 *Solid model for Exercise 1*   *Figure 4-71* *Sketch for Exercise 1*

Exercise 2

Create the sketch of the model shown in Figure 4-72. Apply the required relations and dimensions and fully define it. The sketch is shown in Figure 4-73. The solid model is given for reference only. **(Expected time: 30 min)**

Figure 4-72 Solid model for Exercise 2

Figure 4-73 Sketch for Exercise 2

Exercise 3

Create the sketch of the model shown in Figure 4-74. Apply the required relations and dimensions and fully define it. The sketch is shown in Figure 4-75. The solid model is given for reference only. **(Expected time: 30 min)**

Figure 4-74 Solid model for Exercise 3

Figure 4-75 Sketch for Exercise 3

Answers to Self-Evaluation Test
1. T, **2.** F, **3.** T, **4.** F, **5.** T, **6. Add Relations**, **7.** aligned, **8.** fully defined, **9. Dangling**, **10. All in this sketch**

Chapter 5

Advanced Dimensioning Techniques and Base Feature Options

Learning Objectives

After completing this chapter, you will be able to:

• *Fully define a sketch.*
• *Dimension the true length of an arc.*
• *Measure Distances and View Section Properties*
• *Create solid base extruded features.*
• *Create thin base extruded features.*
• *Create solid base revolved features.*
• *Create thin base revolved features.*
• *Dynamically rotate the view to display the model from all directions.*
• *Modify the orientation of the view.*
• *Change the display modes of the solid model.*
• *Apply materials and textures to the models.*

ADVANCED DIMENSIONING TECHNIQUES

In this chapter, you will learn about some of the advanced dimensioning techniques used in dimensioning the sketches in SolidWorks. With this release of SolidWorks, you will be able to apply all possible relations and dimensions to a sketch using a single tool, thus making a sketch fully defined sketch. The advanced dimensioning techniques are discussed next.

Fully Defining the Sketches

CommandManager:	Dimension/Relations > Fully Define Sketch
Menu:	Tools > Dimensions > Fully Define Sketch
Toolbar:	Dimension/Relations > Fully Define Sketch

The **Fully Define Sketch** tool is used to automatically apply all the required relations and dimensions to the sketch. To fully define a sketch, draw the sketch using the standard sketching tools. Choose the **Fully Define Sketch** button from the **Dimension/Relations CommandManager** to display the **Fully Define Sketch PropertyManager**, as shown in Figure 5-1. The options available in this **PropertyManager** are discussed next.

Entities to Fully Define

The **Entities to Fully Define** rollout is used to specify the entities to which the relations and dimensions have to be applied. The **All entities in sketch** radio button is selected by default. As a result, all entities drawn in the current sketching environment are selected to apply relations and dimensions. The **Selected entities** radio button is selected if you have to fully define only the selected entities. When you select this radio button, the **Selected Entities to Fully Define** selection box will be displayed in the **Entities to Fully Define** rollout. Select the entities to be dimensioned using the select cursor. The names of the selected entities will be displayed in the **Selected Entities to Fully Define** selection box. If you select one or more entities before invoking the **Fully Define Sketch PropertyManager**, the **Selected entities** radio button will be selected by default. Also, the names of the selected entities will be displayed in the **Selected Entities to Fully Define** selection box. The **Calculate** button is chosen to calculate and place the number of relations and dimensions required to fully define the sketch. When you choose this button, all the relations and dimensions required to fully define the sketch will be generated and placed.

Relations

The **Relations** rollout displays the buttons of all the relations. You can choose all buttons or only those of the relations that you want to apply to the sketch.

Dimensions

The **Dimensions** rollout is used to specify the type of dimensions that will be placed, reference for the dimensions, and the dimension placement. The options available in the **Dimensions** rollout are discussed next.

Horizontal Dimensioning Scheme

The **Horizontal Dimensioning Scheme** drop-down list is used to specify the dimensioning scheme to be applied to the horizontal dimensions in the sketch. The dimensioning schemes available in this drop-down list are discussed next.

*Figure 5-1 The **Fully Define Sketch PropertyManager***

Chain

The **Chain** option is used for the relative or incremental horizontal dimensioning of the sketch. When you invoke the **Fully Define Sketch PropertyManager** and select this scheme, the origin will be selected as the reference entity. This reference entity is used as a datum for generating dimensions. The name of the origin will be displayed in the **Datums - Vertical Model Edge, Model Vertex, Vertical Line or Point** selection box and the reference entity will be displayed in pink in the drawing area. You can also specify a user-defined reference entity after clicking in this selection box.

Note

Chain dimensioning should be avoided if the tolerances relative to a common datum are required in the part.

Baseline

The **Baseline** option is used for absolute or datum vertical dimensioning of the sketch. In this dimensioning method, the dimensions are applied to the sketch with respect to the common datum. When you invoke the **Fully Define Sketch PropertyManager**, this option is selected by default. Also, the origin will be selected as the reference entity and will be used as a datum for generating dimensions. The name of the origin will be displayed in the **Datums - Vertical Model Edge, Model Vertex, Vertical Line or Point** selection box. You can also specify a user-defined reference entity.

Ordinate

The **Ordinate** option is used for the ordinate dimensioning of the sketch. When you invoke the **Fully Define Sketch PropertyManager** and select this option, a point or a vertical line will be selected as the reference entity and will be used as a datum for generating dimensions. The name of the selected reference entity will be displayed in the **Datums - Vertical Model Edge, Model Vertex, Vertical Line or Point** selection box and the reference entity will be displayed in pink in the drawing area. You can also specify a user-defined reference entity.

Dimension placement

The **Dimension placement** area is used to define the position where the generated dimensions will be placed. Four radio buttons are available in this area. The first is the **Above sketch** radio button. If you use this option, the horizontal dimensions generated using the **Fully Define Sketch** tool will be placed above the sketch. The **Below sketch** radio button is selected by default and is used to place the dimensions below the sketch. The **Right of the sketch** radio button is selected to place the dimensions on the right of the sketch. The **Left of the sketch** radio button is selected to place the dimensions on the left of the sketch. This radio button is selected by default.

After specifying all parameters in the **Fully Define Sketch PropertyManager**, choose the **Calculate** button. Next, choose the **OK** button or choose the **OK** icon from the **Confirmation Corner**. The relations and dimension, with the selected dimension scheme, will be applied to the sketch. You can double-click on the dimensions to modify their values. Figure 5-2 shows the **Baseline** scheme with the origin as the datum. Figure 5-3 shows the **Ordinate** scheme with the origin as the datum.

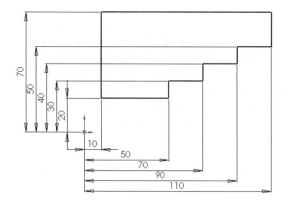

Figure 5-2 *Baseline dimension created using the origin as the reference entity*

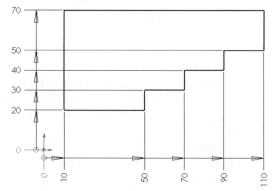

Figure 5-3 *Ordinate dimension created using the origin as the reference entity*

Dimensioning the True Length of an Arc

In SolidWorks, you can also apply the dimension of the true length of an arc, which is one of the advantages of the sketching environment of SolidWorks. To apply the dimension of the true length, invoke the **Smart Dimension** tool and select the arc using the dimension cursor. A radial dimension will be attached to the cursor. Move the cursor to any of the endpoints of the arc. When the cursor snaps the endpoint, use the left mouse button to specify the first endpoint of the arc. A linear dimension will be attached to the cursor; move the cursor to the second endpoint of the arc and when the cursor snaps the endpoint, select it. A dimension will be attached to the cursor. Move the cursor to an appropriate place to place the dimension. The dimension of the true length of the arc is shown in Figure 5-4.

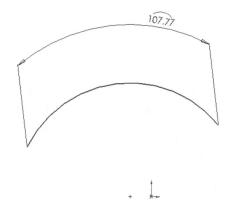

Figure 5-4 *Dimensioning the true length of an arc*

MEASURING DISTANCES AND VIEWING SECTION PROPERTIES

In SolidWorks, you can measure the distance of the entities and also view the section properties. These tools are discussed next.

Measuring Distances

CommandManager:	Tools > Measure
Menu:	Tools > Measure
Toolbar:	Tools > Measure

The **Measure** tool is used to measure the perimeter, angle, radius, and distance between lines, points, surfaces, and planes in sketches, 3D models, assemblies, or drawings. To use the measure tool, invoke the **Measure** toolbar by choosing the **Measure** button from the **Tools CommandManager**; the **Measure** toolbar will be displayed. The name of the document in which you are working will be displayed at the top of the **Measure** toolbar, refer to Figure 5-5. The current cursor will be replaced by the measure

Figure 5-5 *The* **Measure** *toolbar*

cursor. Using the measure cursor, select the entity or entities to be measured. The result related to the selected element or elements will be displayed in the callout or callouts attached to the selected entity or entities. You can also view the result in the **Measure** toolbar by expanding it. To expand the toolbar, choose the button with the down arrows on the right of the toolbar. The options in the **Measure** dialog box are discussed next.

Arc/Circle Measurements

The **Arc/Circle Measurements** button is used to specify the technique of measuring the distance between the selected arcs or circles. When you choose the **Arc/Circle Measurements** button a flyout will appear. The **Center to Center** option will be selected by default in this flyout. With this option selected, the center-to-center distance will be measured when you select two arcs or circles. If you choose the **Minimum Distance** option from this cascading menu, the minimum tangential distance between the two selected arcs or circles will be measured. However, if you choose the **Maximum Distance** option from this cascading menu, the maximum tangential distance between the selected arcs or circles will be measured.

Units/Precision

The **Units/Precision** button is used to set the type of units and their precision. To set the type and the precision of units, choose this button; the **Measure Units/Precision** dialog box will be displayed. The **Use document settings** radio button is selected by default in this dialog box. The default units and precision of the document are used while measuring the entities. You can also set the type of units and their precision for measuring the entities. To do so, select the **Use custom settings** radio button from this dialog box. The other options available in this dialog box will be invoked, as shown in Figure 5-6. These options are discussed next.

Length unit Area

The **Length unit** area is used to set the units and options of linear measurements of the entities. The **Unit** drop-down list is provided at the top right corner of the **Length unit** area. In this drop-down list, you can select any type of unit such as **Angstroms, Nanometers, Microns, Millimeters, Centimeters, Meters, Microinches, Miles, Inches**, **Feet**, and **Feet and Inches**. The **Decimal places** spinner is provided to control the decimal places. The other options in the **Length unit** area are discussed next.

Decimal

The **Decimal** radio button is available only when you select the units as **Microinches, Miles, Inches**, or **Feet and Inches** from the **Unit** drop-down list. This radio button is selected to display the dimension in the decimal form. You can also specify the decimal

Figure 5-6 *The **Measure Units/Precision***
dialog box

places using the **Decimal places** spinner provided on the right of the **Decimal** radio button.

Fractions

The **Fractions** radio button is available only when you select the units as **Microinches, Miles, Inches**, or **Feet and Inches** from the **Units** drop-down list. This radio button is selected to display the dimension in the fraction form. You can also set the value of the denominator using the **Denominator** spin box provided on the right of the **Fractions** radio button.

Round to nearest fraction

The **Round to nearest fraction** check box is selected to display the value in fractions by rounding the value to the nearest fraction.

Scientific Notation

The **Scientific Notation** check box is selected to display the value in the scientific notation units.

Angular unit Area

The **Angular unit** area is used to set the units for angular measurement. This area is provided with a drop-down list to specify the angular measurement units such as **Degrees, Deg/Min, Deg/Min/Sec**, and **Radians**. The **Decimal places** spinner is provided to specify the decimal places.

Show XYZ Measurement

The **Show XYZ measurement** button is chosen by default in the **Measure** toolbar and therefore shows the dx, dy, and dz values of the selected entities. If you clear this button, only the minimum distance between the selected entities will be displayed.

XYZ Relative To

The **XYZ Relative To** button is used to define the coordinate system along which the selected entities will be measured. By default, the part origin is selected as the coordinate system. To select any other coordinate system that you had created earlier, choose the **XYZ Relative To** button from the **Measure** toolbar. A flyout and all the coordinate systems that you have created along with the part origin will be displayed. Choose the coordinate system from this flyout. You will learn more about creating additional coordinate systems in the later chapters.

Projected On

The **Projected On** button is used to specify the location where the selected entity should be projected. You can project the selected entity on the screen or on a specific plane. The system will then calculate the measurement of the true projection. To specify the location, choose the **Projected On** button from the **Measure** toolbar; a callout will be displayed and you can select the location where you need to project the selected entity.

Determining Section Properties of Closed Sketches

CommandManager:	Tools > Section Properties
Menu:	Tools > Section Properties
Toolbar:	Tools > Section Properties

The **Section Properties** tool enables you to determine the section properties of the sketch in the sketching environment or of the selected planar face in the **Part** mode and the **Assembly** mode. Remember that the section properties of only the closed sketches with nonintersecting closed loops can be determined. The section properties include the area, centroid relative to the sketch origin, centroid relative to the part origin, moment of inertia, polar moment of inertia, angle between the principle axes and sketch axes, and principle moment of inertia.

To calculate the section properties, draw the sketch and then choose the **Section Properties** button from the **Tools CommandManager**; the **Section Properties** dialog box will be displayed as shown in Figure 5-7.

When you invoke the **Section Properties** dialog box, a 3D triad will be placed at the centroid of the sketch. The section properties of the sketch are displayed in the **Section Properties** dialog box. The **Selected Items** display box is used to display the name of the selected planar face or sketch whose section properties are to be calculated. When you are in the **Part** mode, select the face to calculate the section properties and choose the **Recalculate** button to display the properties. If you want to calculate the section properties of some other face, clear the previously selected face from the selection set. Now, select the new face and choose the **Recalculate** button.

Figure 5-7 *Resized view of the **Section Properties** dialog box*

The **Print** button available in the **Section Properties** dialog box is used to print the section properties. The **Copy** button is chosen to copy the section properties to the Clip board from where you can copy them to a program such as MS Word. The rest of the options in this dialog box are similar to those discussed in the previous section.

CREATING BASE FEATURES BY EXTRUDING SKETCHES

The sketches that you have drawn until now can be converted into base features by extruding using the **Extruded Boss/Base** tool. This tool is available in the **Features CommandManager**. After drawing the sketch, choose the **Features** button from the **CommandManager** to display the **Features CommandManager**. From the **Features CommandManager**, choose the **Extruded Boss/Base** button. The sketching environment will be closed and the part modeling environment will be invoked. Also, the preview of the feature that is created using the default options will be displayed in the trimetric view. The trimetric view gives a better display of the solid feature.

On the basis of the options and the sketch selected for extruding, the resulting feature can be a solid feature or a thin feature. If the sketch is closed, it can be converted into a solid feature or a thin feature. However, if the sketch is open, it can be converted only into a thin feature. The solid and thin features are discussed next.

Creating Solid Extruded Features

CommandManager:	Features > Extruded Boss/Base
Menu:	Insert > Boss/Base > Extrude
Toolbar:	Features > Extruded Boss/Base

After you have completed drawing and dimensioning the closed sketch and converted it into a fully defined sketch, invoke the **Features CommandManager** by choosing the **Features** button and then choose the **Extruded Boss/Base** button from the **Features CommandManager**. You will notice that the view is automatically changed to trimetric view and the **Extrude PropertyManager** is displayed, as shown in Figure 5-8.

Figure 5-8 The Extrude PropertyManager

You will notice that the preview of the base feature will be displayed in temporary graphics. Also, a transparent arrow will appear in front of the sketch. Figure 5-9 shows the preview of the sketch being extruded. Note that if the sketch consists of some closed loops inside the outer loop, they will be automatically subtracted from the outer loop while extruding.

The options available in the **Extrude PropertyManager** are discussed next.

Direction 1

The **Direction 1** rollout is used to specify the end condition for extruding the sketch in one direction from the sketch plane. The options available in the **Direction 1** drop-down list are discussed next.

Preview of the
base feature

Arrow for extrusion
in the first direction

Figure 5-9 *Preview of the feature being extruded*

Tip. *You can also extrude an underdefined or an overdefined sketch. However, if you extrude an underdefined sketch, a - sign will be displayed on the left of the sketch in the **Feature Manager**. Similarly, if you extrude an overdefined sketch, you will find a + sign on the left of the sketch in the **Feature Manager**. To check these signs, click on the + sign available on the left of **Extrude 1** in the **Feature Manager**. The sketch will be displayed and you can see the + or the - sign.*

End Condition

The **End Condition** drop-down list provides the options to define the termination of the extruded feature. Note that because this is the first feature, some of the options available in this drop-down list will not be used at this stage. Also, some additional options will be available later in this drop-down list. The options available to define the termination of the base feature are discussed next.

Blind

The **Blind** option is selected by default and is used to define the termination of the extruded base feature by specifying the depth of extrusion. The depth of extrusion can be specified in the **Depth** spinner, which will be displayed in this rollout when you select the **Blind** option. You can reverse the extrusion direction by selecting the **Reverse Direction** button provided on the left of this drop-down list. Figure 5-10 shows the preview of the feature being created by extruding the sketch using the **Blind** option.

You can also extrude a sketch to a blind depth by dynamically dragging the feature using the mouse. Invoke the **Extrude PropertyManager** and move the mouse to the transparent arrow and when the color of the arrow changes to red, press and hold the left mouse button. Now, drag the cursor to specify the depth of extrusion; the **Blind** callout will also be displayed below the cursor. The value of the depth of extrusion will change dynamically in this callout as you move the cursor. Release the left mouse button to specify the termination of the extruded feature. The preview of the sketch being dragged is shown in Figure 5-11. The select cursor will be replaced by the mouse cursor.

Figure 5-10 *Preview of the feature being extruded using the **Blind** option*

Figure 5-11 *Preview of the feature being extruded by dynamically dragging the arrow*

Use the right mouse button to complete the feature creation or choose the **OK** button from the **Extrude PropertyManager**.

Mid Plane

The **Mid Plane** option is used to create the base feature by extruding the sketch equally in both directions of the plane on which the sketch is drawn. For example, if the total depth of the extruded feature is 30 mm, it will be extruded 15 mm toward the front of the sketching plane and 15 mm toward the back. The depth of the feature can be defined in the **Depth** spinner, which is displayed below this drop-down list.

Figure 5-12 shows the preview of the feature being created by extruding the sketch using the **Mid Plane** option.

Figure 5-12 *Preview of the feature being extruded using the **Mid Plane** option*

Draft On/Off

The **Draft On/Off** button is used to specify a draft angle while extruding the sketch. Applying the draft angle will taper the resulting feature. This button is not chosen by default. Therefore, the resulting base feature will not have any taper. However, if you want to add a draft angle to the feature, choose this button; the **Draft Angle** spinner and the **Draft outward** check box will be available. You can enter the draft angle for the feature in the **Draft Angle** spinner. By default, the feature will be tapered inward, as shown in Figure 5-13.

If you want to taper the feature outward, select the **Draft outward** check box, which is displayed below the **Draft Angle** spinner. The feature created with the outward taper is shown in Figure 5-14.

Figure 5-13 *Feature created with outward draft*   **Figure 5-14** *Feature created with inward draft*

Note
*The **Direction of Extrusion** area will be discussed in later chapters.*

Tip. *You can also select the termination options using the shortcut menu that is displayed when you right-click in the drawing area.*

Direction 2

The **Direction 2** check box is selected to invoke the **Direction 2** rollout. This rollout is used to extrude the sketch with different values in the second direction of the sketching plane. This check box will not be available if you select the **Mid Plane** termination type.

Tip. *As soon as you select the **Direction 2** check box, another arrow will be displayed in the preview of the feature. You can use this arrow to define the depth of extrusion in the second direction.*

The options available in this rollout are similar to those in the **Direction 1** rollout. Note that unlike the **Mid Plane** termination option, the depth of extrusion and other parameters in both directions can be different. For example, you can extrude the sketch to a blind depth of 10 mm and an inward draft of 35-degrees in front of the sketching plane and to a blind depth of 15 mm and an outward draft of 0-degree behind the sketching plane, as shown in Figure 5-15.

After setting the values for both directions, choose the **OK** button or choose the **OK** icon from the confirmation corner. The feature will be created with the defined values.

Figure 5-15 Feature created in two directions with different values

 Note
*The **Selection Contours** rollout will be discussed in later chapters.*

Creating Thin Extruded Features

Thin extruded features can be created using a closed or an open sketch. If the sketch is closed, it will be offset inside or outside to create a cavity inside the feature, as shown in Figure 5-16.

Figure 5-16 Thin extruded feature created using a closed loop

If the sketch is open, as shown in Figure 5-17, the resulting feature will be as shown in Figure 5-18. To convert a closed sketch into a thin feature, choose the **Thin Feature** check box to invoke the **Thin Feature** rollout. The **Thin Feature** rollout, shown in Figure 5-19, is used to create a thin feature. However, if the sketch to be extruded is open, the **Thin Feature** rollout will be invoked automatically when you invoke the **Extrude PropertyManager**.

Figure 5-17 *Open loop to be converted into thin feature*

Figure 5-18 *Resultant thin feature created with fillets at sharp corners*

Figure 5-19 *The **Thin Feature** rollout*

The options available in the **Thin Feature** rollout of the **Extrude PropertyManager** are discussed next.

Type
The options provided in the **Type** drop-down list are used to select the method of defining the thickness of the thin feature. These options are discussed next.

One-Direction
The **One-Direction** option is used to add the thickness on one side of the sketch. The thickness can be specified in the **Thickness** spinner provided below this drop-down list. For the closed sketches, the direction can be inside or outside the sketch. Similarly, for open sketches, the direction can be below or above the sketch. You can reverse the direction of thickness using the **Reverse** check button available on the left of this drop-down list. This button will be available only when you select the **One-Direction** option from this drop-down list.

Mid-Plane
The **Mid-Plane** option is used to add the thickness equally on both sides of the sketch. The value of the thickness of the thin feature can be specified in the **Thickness** spinner provided below this drop-down list.

Two-Direction
The **Two-Direction** option is used to create a thin feature by adding different thicknesses on

both sides of the sketch. The thickness values in direction 1 and direction 2 can be specified in the **Direction 1 Thickness** spinner and the **Direction 2 Thickness** spinner, respectively. These spinners will be automatically displayed below the **Type** drop-down list when you select the **Two-Direction** option from this drop-down list.

Cap ends

The **Cap ends** check box will be displayed only when you select a closed sketch to convert into a thin feature. This check box is selected to cap the two ends of the thin extruded feature. Both ends will be capped with a face of the thickness you specify. When you select this check box, the **Cap Thickness** spinner will be displayed below this check box. The thickness of the end caps can be specified using this spinner.

Auto-fillet corners

The **Auto-fillet corners** check box will be displayed only when you select an open sketch to convert into a thin feature. If you select this check box, all sharp vertices in the sketch will be automatically filleted while converting into a thin feature. As a result, the thin feature will have filleted edges. The radius of the fillet can be specified in the **Fillet Radius** spinner, which will be displayed below the **Auto-fillet corners** check box when you select this check box.

Figure 5-20 shows the thin feature created by extruding an open sketch in both directions. Note that a draft angle is applied to the feature while extruding in the front direction and the **Auto-fillet corners** option is selected while creating this thin feature.

Figure 5-20 *Thin feature created in both directions*

 Note
Only the corners of the thin features that can accommodate the given radius will be filleted; other corners that cannot accommodate the given radius will not be filleted.

CREATING BASE FEATURES BY REVOLVING SKETCHES

CommandManager:	Features > Revolved Boss/Base
Menu:	Insert > Boss/Base > Revolve
Toolbar:	Features > Revolved Boss/Base

 The sketches that you have drawn until now can also be converted into base features by revolving using the **Revolved Boss/Base** tool. This tool is available in the **Features CommandManager**. Using this tool, the sketch is revolved about the revolution axis. The revolution axis could be an axis, an entity of the sketch, or an edge of another feature to create the revolved feature. Note that whether you use a centerline or an edge to revolve the sketch, the sketch should be drawn on one side of the centerline or the edge.

In SolidWorks, the right-hand thumb rule is used while determining the direction of revolution. The right-hand thumb rule states that if the thumb of your right hand points in the direction of the axis of revolution, the direction of the curled fingers will determine the default direction of revolution, see Figure 5-21.

Figure 5-21 Right-hand thumb rule

For example, consider a case in which you draw a centerline from left to right (direction of thumb in Figure 5-21) in the drawing area. Now, if you use this centerline to create a revolved feature, the default direction of revolution will be in the direction of the curled fingers.

 Note
*You can also reverse the direction of revolution using the button available in the **Revolve PropertyManager**.*

After drawing the sketch, as you choose this tool, you will notice that the sketching environment is closed and the part modeling environment is invoked. Similar to extruding the sketches, the resulting feature can be a solid feature or a thin feature, depending on the sketch and the options selected to be revolved. If the sketch is closed, it can be converted into a solid feature or a thin feature. However, if the sketch is open, it can be converted only into a thin feature. The solid and thin features are discussed next.

Creating Solid Revolved Features

After you have completed drawing and dimensioning the closed sketch and converted it into a fully defined sketch, choose the **Revolved Boss/Base** button from the **Features** toolbar. You will notice that the view is automatically changed to a 3D view and the **Revolve PropertyManager** is displayed, as shown in Figure 5-22. Also, the confirmation corner will be displayed and the preview of the base feature, created using the default options, will be displayed in temporary shaded graphics. The direction arrow will also be displayed in gray. If you have not drawn the centerline, you will be prompted to select an axis of revolution. Select an edge or entity you need to define as an axis of revolution. The options available in the **Revolve Parameters** rollout of the **Revolve PropertyManager** are discussed next.

*Figure 5-22 The **Revolve PropertyManager***

Tip. *Even if you can revolve the sketch using an edge in the sketch, you need to draw a centerline. This is because you can create linear diameter dimensions for the revolved features only using a centerline.*

Revolve Type

The **Revolve Type** drop-down list provides the options to define the termination of the revolved feature. The options available in this drop-down list to terminate the revolved feature are discussed next.

One-Direction

The **One-Direction** option is used to revolve the sketch on one side of the plane on which it is drawn. The angle of revolution can be specified in the **Angle** spinner displayed below

Tip. *You can dynamically specify the angle in a revolved feature by dragging the direction arrows. You can also use the right mouse button to display the shortcut menu; the options available in the **PropertyManager** are also available in the shortcut menu.*

this drop-down list. The default value of the **Angle** spinner is **360deg**. Therefore, if you revolve the sketch using this value, a complete round feature will be created. You can also reverse the direction of revolution of the sketch by choosing the **Reverse Direction** button, which will be displayed when you select this option. Figure 5-23 shows the sketch of the piston and Figure 5-24 shows the resulting piston created by revolving the sketch through an angle of 360-degrees. Note that the outer left vertical edge of the sketch that is vertically in line with the origin is used to revolve the sketch.

Figure 5-23 *Sketch of the piston to be revolved*

Figure 5-24 *Feature created by revolving the sketch through an angle of 360-degrees*

Figure 5-25 shows a piston created by revolving the same sketch through an angle of 270-degrees.

Figure 5-25 *Feature created by revolving the sketch through an angle of 270-degrees*

Mid-Plane

The **Mid-Plane** option is used to revolve the sketch equally on both sides of the plane on which it is drawn. The angle of revolution can be specified in the **Angle** spinner. When you choose this option, the **Reverse Direction** button will be unavailable.

Two-Direction

The **Two-Direction** option is used to create a revolved feature by revolving the sketch using different values on both sides of the plane on which it is drawn. The angle values in direction 1 and direction 2 can be specified in the **Direction 1 Angle** spinner and the **Direction 2 Angle** spinner, respectively. These spinners will be displayed below the **Revolve Type** drop-down list automatically when you select the **Two-Direction** option from this drop-down list.

Creating Thin Revolved Features

Thin revolved features can be created using closed or open sketches. If the sketch is closed, it will be offset inside or outside to create a cavity inside the feature as shown in Figure 5-26. In this figure, the sketch is revolved through an angle of 180-degrees.

Figure 5-26 *Thin feature created by revolving the sketch through an angle of 180-degrees*

If the sketch is open, as shown in Figure 5-27, the resulting feature will be similar to that shown in Figure 5-28.

Figure 5-27 *The open sketch to be revolved and the centerline to revolve the sketch*

Figure 5-28 *Thin feature created by revolving the open sketch through an angle of 180-degrees*

To convert a closed sketch into a thin feature, select the **Thin Feature** check box from the **Revolve PropertyManager** to invoke the **Thin Feature** rollout. However, if the sketch to be revolved is open and you invoke the **Revolved Boss/Base** tool, the **SolidWorks** information box will be displayed. This information box will inform you that the sketch is currently open and a non-thin revolved feature requires a closed sketch. You will be given an option of automatically closing the sketch. If you choose **Yes** from this dialog box, a line segment will be automatically drawn between the first and the last segment of the sketch and the **Revolve PropertyManager** will be displayed. However, if you choose **No** from this information box, the **Revolve PropertyManager** will be displayed and the **Thin Feature** rollout will be displayed automatically. The options available in the **Thin Feature** rollout of the **Revolve PropertyManager**, shown in Figure 5-29, are discussed next.

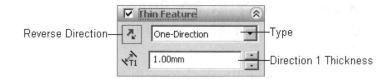

*Figure 5-29 The **Thin Feature** rollout*

Type

The options provided in the **Type** drop-down list are used to select the method of defining the thickness of the thin feature. These options are discussed next.

One-Direction

The **One-Direction** option is used to add the thickness on one side of the sketch. The thickness can be specified in the **Direction 1 Thickness** spinner provided below this drop-down list. For the closed sketches, the direction can be inside or outside the sketch. Similarly, for open sketches, the direction can be below or above the sketch. You can reverse the direction of thickness using the **Reverse Direction** button available on the right of this drop-down list. This button will be available only when you select the **One-Direction** option from this drop-down list.

Mid-Plane

The **Mid-Plane** option is used to add the thickness equally on both sides of the sketch. The value of the thickness of the thin feature can be specified in the **Direction 1 Thickness** spinner provided below this drop-down list.

Two-Direction

The **Two-Direction** option is used to create a thin feature by adding different thicknesses on both sides of the sketch. The thickness values in direction 1 and direction 2 can be specified in the **Direction 1 Thickness** spinner and the **Direction 2 Thickness** spinner, respectively.

Tip. *While defining the wall thickness of a thin revolved feature, remember that the wall thickness should be added such that the centerline does not intersect with the sketch. If the centerline intersects with the sketch, the sketch will not be revolved.*

These spinners will be displayed below the **Type** drop-down list automatically when you select the **Two-Direction** option from this drop-down list.

DYNAMICALLY ROTATING THE VIEW OF THE MODEL

In SolidWorks, you can dynamically rotate the view in the 3D space so that the solid models in the current document can be viewed from all directions. This allows you to visually maneuver around the model so that all its features can be clearly viewed. This tool can be invoked even when you are inside some other tool. For example, you can invoke this tool when the **Extrude Feature** dialog box is displayed. You can freely rotate the model in the 3D space or rotate it around a selected vertex, edge, or face. Both methods of rotating the model are discussed next.

Rotating the View Freely in 3D Space

Toolbar:	View > Rotate View
Menu:	View > Modify > Rotate

 To rotate the view freely in the 3D space, choose the **Rotate View** button from the **View** toolbar. You can also invoke this tool by choosing the **Rotate View** option from the shortcut menu that will be displayed when you right-click in the drawing area. When you are inside some other tool, use the right mouse button in the drawing area and choose the **Zoom/Pan/Rotate** > **Rotate View** option from the shortcut menu to invoke the rotate view tool. When you invoke this tool, the cursor will be replaced by the rotate view cursor. Now, press the left mouse button and drag the cursor to rotate the view. Figure 5-30 shows a model from different directions by rotating the view.

Figure 5-30 *Rotating the view to display the model from different directions*

Rotating the View Around a Selected Vertex, Edge, or Face

To rotate the view around a selected vertex, edge, or face, invoke the **Rotate View** tool and move the rotate view cursor close to the vertex, edge, or the face around which you want to rotate the view. When it is highlighted, select it using the left mouse button. Next, drag the cursor to rotate the view around the selected vertex, edge, or face.

Tip. *To resume rotating the view freely after you have completed rotating it around a selected vertex, edge, or face, double-click anywhere in the drawing area. Now when you drag the cursor, you will notice that the view is rotated freely in the 3D space.*

If a three-button mouse is configured to your computer, you can press and drag the middle mouse button to rotate the model freely in the 3D space. Note that in this case the rotate view cursor will not be displayed.

MODIFYING THE VIEW ORIENTATION

As mentioned earlier, when you invoke the **Extruded Boss/Base** tool or the **Revolved Boss/Base** tool, the view will be automatically changed to a trimetric view and the preview of the model will be displayed. In SolidWorks, you can manually change the view orientation using some predefined standard views or user-defined views. To invoke these standard views, choose the **Standard Views** button from the **View** toolbar; a flyout will be displayed, as shown in Figure 5-31. You can select the required standard view from this flyout.

*Figure 5-31 The **Standard View** flyout*

You can also orient the view of the model by clicking on the current view button provided on the lower left corner of the drawing area. As soon as you click on this button, a shortcut menu is displayed, as shown in Figure 5-32. Apart from the standard views, this shortcut menu also provides the **Normal To** option. This option is chosen to reorient the view normal to a selected face or plane. To do this, select the face normal to which you need to reorient the model and choose the **Normal To** option from this flyout. If you have not selected a face before invoking this option, the **Normal To PropertyManager** will be displayed and you will be prompted to select a reference along which the view will be reoriented.

The other options provided in this shortcut menu are discussed later in this chapter.

You can also invoke these standard views using the **Orientation** dialog

Figure 5-32 The shortcut menu

box. This dialog box is invoked by choosing the **View Orientation** option from the shortcut menu. This dialog box can also be invoked by pressing the SPACEBAR on the keyboard. Note that when you invoke this dialog box by pressing the SPACEBAR, the dialog box will be displayed at the location where the cursor is placed currently. The **Orientation** dialog box is shown in Figure 5-33.

You can invoke the view by double-clicking on it in this dialog box. The buttons available on top of this dialog box are discussed next.

Push-Pin

Figure 5-33 The ***Orientation*** *dialog box*

You will notice that the **Orientation** dialog box is automatically closed when you select a view or a point somewhere on the screen, or invoke a tool. If you want this dialog box to be retained on the screen, you can pin it at a location by choosing the **Push-Pin** button. This is the first button on top of this dialog box. Move the dialog box to the desired location and then choose this button. The dialog box will be pinned to that location and will not close when you perform any operation.

New View

The **New View** button is chosen to create a user-defined view and save it in the list of views in the **Orientation** dialog box. Using various drawing display tools and the **Rotate View** tool, modify the current view and then choose this button. When you choose this button, the **Named View** dialog box will be displayed. Enter the name of the view in the **View Name** edit box and then choose the **OK** button. You will notice that a user-defined view is created and it is saved in the list available in the **Orientation** dialog box.

Update Standard Views

The **Update Standard Views** button is chosen to modify the orientation of the standard views. For example, if you want that the view that is displayed when you invoke the **Back** option from this dialog box should be the front view, change the current view to the back view by double-clicking on it in the **Orientation** dialog box. Now, select the **Front** option from the list of views available in the **Orientation** dialog box and then choose the **Update Standard Views** button. The **SolidWorks** warning box will be displayed and you will be informed that if you change the standard view, all other named views in the model will also be changed. If you make the change using the **Yes** button, the current view that was originally the back view will become the front view. Also, all other views will be modified automatically.

Reset Standard Views

The **Reset Standard Views** button is chosen to reset the standard settings of all standard views in the current drawing. When you choose this button, the **SolidWorks** warning box will be displayed and you will be prompted to confirm whether you want to reset all standard views to their original settings or not. If you choose **Yes,** all the standard views will be reset to their default settings.

RESTORING PREVIOUS VIEW

In SolidWorks, while working on a model or viewing it from different directions, you need to temporarily change the view of the model. Once you have finished editing or viewing the model in the current view, you can restore the previous view using the **Previous View** button in the **View** toolbar. This tool saves ten previous views of the model.

DISPLAYING THE DRAWING AREA IN VIEWPORTS

With this release of SolidWorks, you can display the drawing area in multiple viewports. The procedure to do so is discussed next.

Displaying the Drawing Area in Two Horizontal Viewports

CommandManager:	Standard Views > Two View - Horizontal	*(Customize to Add)*
Menu:	Window> Viewport > Two View - Horizontal	
Toolbar:	Standard Views > Two View - Horizontal	*(Customize to Add)*

The **Two View - Horizontal** option is used to split the drawing view to display the model in two viewports placed horizontally, as shown in Figure 5-34. To display the model in this fashion, choose **Window > Viewport > Two View - Horizontal** from the menu bar. You will notice, that the drawing area is divided in two rows placed horizontally. The model is placed in the top orientation in the upper row and in the front orientation in the lower row. The type of orientation of both the models is displayed in the current view button provided on the lower left corner of each viewport.

To switch back to the single viewport, choose the **Single View** button from the **Standard Views** toolbar or choose **Window > Viewport > Single View** from the menu bar.

Displaying the Drawing Area in Two Vertical Viewports

CommandManager:	Standard Views > Two View - Vertical	*(Customize to Add)*
Menu:	View > Viewport > Two View - Vertical	
Toolbar:	Standard Views > Two View - Vertical	*(Customize to Add)*

The **Two View - Vertical** button is used to split the drawing view to display the model in two viewports placed vertically, as shown in Figure 5-35. To display the model in this fashion, choose **Window > Viewport > Two View - Vertical** from the menu bar. You will notice that the drawing area is divided in two columns placed vertically. The model is placed in the front orientation in the left column and in the right orientation in the right column.

Figure 5-34 *Drawing area divided in two rows horizontally using the* **Two View - Horizontal** *tool*

Figure 5-35 *Drawing area divided in two columns vertically using the* **Two View - Vertical** *tool*

Displaying the Drawing Area in Four Viewports

CommandManager:	Standard Views > Four Views	*(Customize to Add)*
Menu:	Window > Viewport > Four View	
Toolbar:	Standard Views > Four Views	*(Customize to Add)*

The **Four View** option is used to split the drawing view to display the model in four viewports, as shown in Figure 5-36. To display the model in this fashion, choose **Window > Viewport > Four View** from the menu bar. You will notice, that the drawing area is divided in four parts. The model is placed in the front, top, right, and trimetric orientations in each viewport. The types of orientation of all models are displayed in the current view button provided on the lower left corner of each viewport.

Figure 5-36 *Model displayed in four viewports*

Tip. *On creating multiple viewports, you will notice that current view button in one of the viewports is highlighted. This indicates that this viewport is currently active. To activate another viewport, click once in the drawing area in that viewport. After activating a viewport, you can change the model display in it. You will learn more about changing the model display later in this chapter.*

*You can choose **Window > Viewport > Link Views** from the menu bar to link the viewports. Now, if you pan or zoom one view while multiple viewports are being displayed, the model in all the other viewports will pan or zoom accordingly. Note, that this linking is not applicable for the viewport in which the model is displayed in 3D orientation. To break this link, choose **Window > Viewport > Link Views** from the menu bar.*

DISPLAY MODES OF THE MODEL

SolidWorks provides you with various predefined modes to display the model. You can select any of these display modes from the **View** toolbar. These modes are discussed next.

Wireframe

When you choose the **Wireframe** button, all hidden lines will be displayed along with the visible lines in the model. Sometimes it becomes difficult to recognize the visible lines and the hidden lines if you set this display mode for complex models.

Hidden Lines Visible

When you choose the **Hidden Lines Visible** button, the model will be displayed in the wireframe and the hidden lines in the model will be displayed as dashed lines.

Hidden Lines Removed

When you choose the **Hidden Lines Removed** button, the hidden lines in the model will not be displayed. Only the edges of the faces visible in the current view of the model will be displayed.

Shaded With Edges

The **Shaded With Edges** mode is the default mode in which the model is displayed. In this display mode, the model is shaded and the edges of the visible faces of the model are displayed.

Shaded

This display mode is similar to the **Shaded With Edges** mode, with the only difference that the edges of the visible faces will not be displayed.

Shadows In Shaded Mode

The **Shadows In Shaded Mode** button is used to display the shadow of the model. A light appears from the top of the model to display the shadow in the current view. With this option activated, the performance of the system is affected during the dynamic orientation. Remember that the position of the shadow is not changed when you rotate the model in the 3D space. To change the placement of the shadow, first remove the shadow in the shaded model using the **Shadow in Shaded Mode** button and rotate the model. After rotating the model, use the same button to activate the shadow in the shaded mode. Figure 5-37 shows a T-section with shadow in the shaded mode.

Perspective

 The **Perspective** button is not available in the **View** toolbar by default. You need to customize this toolbar to add this button. Using this button, you can display the perspective view of a model. Figure 5-38 shows the T-section with shadow in the perspective view.

Figure 5-37 Shadow in active shaded mode

Figure 5-38 T-section displayed in perspective view with shadow

You can also modify the settings of the perspective view. Choose **View** > **Modify** > **Perspective**

from the menu bar to invoke the **Perspective View PropertyManager**. Using the **Object Sizes Away** spinner of this **PropertyManager**, you can modify the observer's position.

ASSIGNING MATERIALS AND TEXTURES TO THE MODELS

You can assign materials and textures to the models. When you apply a material to a model, the physical properties such as density, young's modulus, and so on will be assigned to the model. When you apply a texture to a model or its face, the image of that texture will be applied to the model or its selected face. Physical properties are not applied to the model when you apply the texture. The method of assigning materials and textures is discussed next.

Assigning Materials to the Model

Toolbar:	Standard > Edit Material *(Customize to Add)*
Menu:	Edit > Appearance > Material

Whenever you assign a material to a model, all physical properties of the selected material are also assigned to the model. As a result, when you calculate the mass properties of the model, they will be based on the physical properties of the material. To assign a material to a model, choose the **Edit Material** button from the **Standard** toolbar; the **Materials Editor PropertyManager** will be displayed, as shown in Figure 5-39.

*Figure 5-39 Partial display of the **Materials Editor PropertyManager***

A number of material families are available in the **Materials** rollout. Click on the + sign located on the left of the material family to display all materials under that family. Select the material from that family.

You can change the scale and angle of the textures in the selected material using the **Scale** and **Angle** spinners available in the **Visual Properties** rollout.

Assigning Textures to the Model

Toolbar:	Standard > Edit Texture
Menu:	Edit > Appearance > Texture

In SolidWorks 2007, you can assign a texture to a model, feature, or a selected face. This can be done using the **Texture PropertyManager**, which will be displayed when you invoke the **Edit Texture** tool. Figure 5-40 shows this **PropertyManager**.

Figure 5-40 The Texture PropertyManager

The **Selection** rollout has some buttons available on the left. These buttons are the filters for making a selection to assign the textures. For example, if you want to assign the texture on a face of the model, choose the **Select Faces** button and clear all the remaining buttons. This allows you to select only a specified face. You can select the required face from the model. The selected face or model is displayed in the **Selected Entities** area of the **Selection** rollout.

Various texture families that you can select are available in the **Texture Tree** area of the **Texture Selection** rollout. Click on the + sign located on the left of a texture family to select a texture of that family. Figure 5-41 shows a model with the Gravel type of stone applied to its top face.

Figure 5-41 *Texture applied to the top face of a model*

The preview of the selected texture is displayed on the model or the face and also in the **Texture Preview** area of the **Texture Properties** rollout. You can use the **Scale** and **Angle** spinners available in this rollout to change the scale and angle of the selected texture.

You can remove the texture applied to a face or a model by choosing the **Remove Textures** button available below the **Selected Entities** area of the **Selection** rollout.

The drop-down list available below the **Texture Tree** area of the **Texture Selection** rollout lists the last ten textures used. You can also select a texture from this drop-down list.

TUTORIALS

Tutorial 1

In this tutorial, you will open the sketch drawn in Tutorial 2 of Chapter 4. You will then convert this sketch into an extruded model by extruding it in two directions, as shown in Figure 5-42. The parameters for extruding the sketch are given next.

Direction 1
Depth = 10 mm
Draft angle = 35-degrees

Direction 2
Depth = 15 mm
Draft angle = 0-degree

After creating the model, you will rotate the view using the **Rotate View** tool and then modify the standard views such that the front view of the model becomes the top view. You will then save the model with the current settings.   **(Expected time: 30 min)**

Figure 5-42 *Model for Tutorial 1*

The steps that will be followed to complete this tutorial are given next.

a. Open the document of Tutorial 2 of Chapter 4, refer to Figure 5-43.
b. Save this document in the *c05* folder with a new name.
c. Invoke the **Extruded Boss/Base** tool and convert the sketch into a model, refer to Figures 5-44 and 5-45.
d. Rotate the view using the **Rotate View** tool to view the model from all directions, refer to Figure 5-46.
e. Invoke the **Orientation** dialog box and then modify the standard view, refer to Figure 5-47.

Opening the Document of Tutorial 2 of Chapter 4

As the required document is saved in the *\My Documents\SolidWorks\c04* folder, you need to select this folder and then open the *c04tut2.sldprt* document.

1. Start SolidWorks 2007 by double-clicking on its shortcut icon on the desktop of your computer.

2. Choose the **Open a Document** option from the **SolidWorks Resources Task Pane** to display the **Open** dialog box.

3. Browse and select the *\My Documents\SolidWorks\c04* folder. All documents that were created in Chapter 4 are displayed in this folder.

4. Select the *c04tut2.sldprt* document and then choose the **Open** button. Close the **SolidWorks Resources Task Pane**.

Because the sketch was saved in the sketching environment in Chapter 4, it is opened in the sketching environment.

Saving the Document in the c05 Folder

It is recommended that when you open a document of some other chapter, you should save it in the folder of the current chapter with some other name before proceeding with modifying the document. This is because if you save the document in the folder of the current chapter, the original document of the other chapter will not be modified.

1. Choose **File > Save As** from the menu bar to display the **Save As** dialog box.

Because the *c04* folder was selected last to open the document, it will be the current folder.

2. Choose the **Up One Level** button available on the right of the **Save in** drop-down list to move to the *SolidWorks* folder. Create a new folder with the name *c05* using the **Create New Folder** button. Make the *c05* folder current by double-clicking on it.

3. Enter the new name of the document as *c05tut1* in the **File name** edit box and then choose the **Save** button to save the document.

The document is saved with the new name and is now opened in the drawing area, as shown in Figure 5-43.

Figure 5-43 *Sketch that will be opened in the drawing area*

Extruding the Sketch

Next, you need to invoke the **Extruded Boss/Base** tool and extrude the sketch using the parameters given in the tutorial description.

1. Choose the **Features** button from the **CommandManager** to display the **Features CommandManager**. From this **CommandManager**, choose the **Extruded Boss/Base** button. The sketch is automatically oriented in the trimetric view and the **Extrude PropertyManager** is displayed, as shown in Figure 5-44.

Because the sketch to be converted into a feature is closed, only the **Direction 1** rollout is displayed in the **Extrude PropertyManager**. The preview of the feature in the temporary shaded graphics with the default values is shown in the drawing area.

Figure 5-44 The Extrude PropertyManager

2. Choose the **Draft On/Off** button from the **Direction 1** rollout and then set the value of the **Draft Angle** spinner to **35**.

    These are the settings in direction 1. Next, you need to specify the settings for direction 2.

3. Select the **Direction 2** check box to invoke the **Direction 2** rollout.

    You will notice that the default values in this rollout are the same as you specified in the **Direction 1** rollout. Because the **Draft On/Off** button is chosen when you invoke the **Direction 2** rollout, you need to turn this button off. This is because you do not require the draft angle in the second direction.

4. Choose the **Draft On/Off** button from the **Direction 2** rollout to turn this option off. Set the value of the **Depth** spinner to **15** as the depth in the second direction is 15 mm. This completes the settings for the model in both directions.

5. Choose the **OK** button to create the feature or choose **OK** from the confirmation corner.

    It is recommended that you change the view to isometric view after creating the feature so that you can view the feature properly.

6. Choose the **Standard Views** button from the **View** toolbar to invoke the flyout and then choose **Isometric** from it. Turn off the display of the origin in the model by choosing **View > Origin** from the menu bar. The isometric view of the resulting solid model is shown in Figure 5-45.

Rotating the View

As mentioned earlier, you can rotate the view so that you can view the model from all directions.

1. Choose the **Rotate View** button from the **View** toolbar; the arrow cursor is replaced by the rotate view cursor.

2. Press and hold the left mouse button down and drag the cursor in the drawing area to rotate the view, as shown in Figure 5-46.

Figure 5-45 *Isometric view of the solid model*

Figure 5-46 *Rotating the view to display the model from different directions*

You will notice that the model is being displayed from different directions. Remember that when you rotate the view, the model is not being rotated. The camera that is used to view the model is being rotated around the model.

3. After viewing the model from all directions, choose **Isometric** from the flyout that is displayed when you choose the **Standard Views** button from the **View** toolbar.

Modifying the Standard Views

As mentioned in the tutorial description, you need to modify the standard views such that the front view of the model becomes the top view. This is done using the **Orientation** dialog box.

1. Press the SPACEBAR on the keyboard to invoke the **Orientation** dialog box.

    The orientation dialog box is automatically closed as soon as you perform any other operation. Therefore, you need to pin this dialog box so that it is not closed automatically.

2. Hold the **Orientation** dialog box by selecting it on the blue bar on the top of this dialog box and then drag it to the top right corner of the drawing area.

3. Choose the **Push Pin** button to pin this dialog box at the top right corner of the drawing area. Pinning the dialog box ensures that the dialog box is not automatically closed when you perform any other operation.

4. Double-click on the **Front** option in the list box of the **Orientation** dialog box.

    The current view is automatically changed to the front view and the model is now reoriented and displayed from the front.

5. Select the **Top** option from the list box by selecting it once.

    Make sure you do not double-click on this option. This is because if you double-click on this option, the model is reoriented and displayed from the top.

6. Now, choose the **Update Standard Views** button to update the standard views.

    The **SolidWorks** warning box is displayed and you are warned that modifying the standard views will change the orientation of any named view in this document.

7. Choose **Yes** from this warning box to modify the standard views.

8. Now, double-click on the **Isometric** option provided in the list box of the **Orientation** dialog box. You will notice that the isometric view is different now, see Figure 5-47.

Figure 5-47   *Model displayed from modified isometric view*

9. Choose the **Push Pin** button in the **Orientation** dialog box again and select a point anywhere in the drawing area to close the dialog box.

Saving the Model

As the name of the document was specified at the beginning, you just have to choose the save button now to save the document.

1.　Choose the **Save** button from the **Standard** toolbar to save the document.

　　The model is saved with the name *My Documents\SolidWorks\c05\c05tut1.sldprt*.

2.　Choose **File > Close** from the menu bar to close the document.

Tutorial 2

In this tutorial, you will open the sketch drawn in Exercise 1 of Chapter 4. You will then create a thin feature by revolving the sketch through an angle of 270-degrees, as shown in Figure 5-48. You will offset the sketch outward while creating the thin feature.

Figure 5-48 Revolved model for Tutorial 2

After creating the model, you will turn on the option to display the shadows and also apply the Copper material to the model.　　　　　　　　　　　　　　　　**(Expected time: 30 min)**

　　The steps that will be followed to complete this tutorial are given next.

a.　Open the sketch of Exercise 1 of Chapter 4, refer to Figure 5-49.
b.　Save it in the folder of the current chapter.
c.　Invoke the **Revolved Boss/Base** tool and revolve the sketch through an angle of 270-degrees, refer to Figure 5-51.
d.　Change the current view to isometric view and then display the model in shadow, refer to Figure 5-52.
e.　Assign copper material to the model, refer to Figure 5-53.

Opening the Document of Exercise 1 of Chapter 4

　　As the required document is saved in the *My Documents\SolidWorks\c04* folder, you need to select this folder and then open the *c04exr1.sldprt* document.

1. Choose the **Open** button from the **Standard** toolbar to display the **Open** dialog box. The *c05* folder is current in this dialog box.

2. Browse and select the *\My Documents\SolidWorks\c04* folder. All documents that were created in Chapter 4 are displayed in this folder.

3. Select the *c04exr1.sldprt* document and then choose the **Open** button. The document is opened in the sketching environment.

Saving the Document in the c05 Folder

As mentioned earlier, it is recommended that you save the document with a new name in the folder of the current chapter so that the original document is not modified.

1. Choose **File > Save As** from the menu bar to display the **Save As** dialog box. Because the *c04* folder was selected last to open the document, it is the current folder.

2. Browse and select the *c05* folder and double-click on it to make it current.

3. Enter the name of the document in the **File name** edit box as *c05tut2*. Choose the **Save** button to save the document. The sketch that is displayed in the drawing area is shown in Figure 5-49.

Revolving the Sketch

The sketch consists of two centerlines. The first centerline was used to mirror the sketched entities and the second was drawn to apply linear diameter dimensions. You need to revolve the sketch around the second centerline.

1. Choose the **Features** button from the **CommandManager** to display the **Features CommandManager**. From this **CommandManager**, choose the **Revolved Boss/ Base** button. The sketch is automatically oriented in the trimetric view and the **Revolve PropertyManager** is displayed.

    Because the sketch has two centerlines, SolidWorks cannot determine which one to use as an axis of revolution. This is the reason why you are prompted to select the axis of revolution.

2. Select the horizontal centerline that was used to create linear diameter dimensions as the axis of revolution. The preview of a complete revolved feature in temporary shaded graphics is displayed in the drawing area. Because the preview of the model is not displayed properly in the current view, you need to zoom the drawing.

3. Choose the **Zoom to Fit** button from the **View** toolbar or press the F key on the keyboard.

4. Set the value of the **Angle** spinner in the **Revolve PropertyManager** to **270**; the preview of the revolved model is also modified accordingly. If you enter the value in the **Angle** spinner, you need to click anywhere on the screen to make sure the preview is modified.

Figure 5-49 *Sketch for the revolved model*

Note that if the horizontal centerline was drawn from left to right, then the direction of revolution has to be reversed to get the required model; refer to the right-hand thumb rule. You can reverse the direction of revolution using the **Reverse Direction** button available on the left of the **Revolve Type** drop-down list.

5.   Select the **Thin Feature** check box to invoke the **Thin Feature** rollout, as shown in Figure 5-50. Set the value of the **Direction 1 Thickness** spinner to **5**. You will notice that the preview of the thin feature is shown outside the original sketch.

Figure 5-50 *The **Thin Feature** rollout*

6.   Choose the **OK** button to create the revolved feature. You will notice that the revolved feature is created.

7.   Choose the **Isometric** option from the flyout that is displayed on choosing the **Standard Views** button from the **View** toolbar.

You will notice that the sketch that was used to create the thin feature is still displayed. You need to turn off the display of this sketch.

8.   Click on the + sign located on the left of **Revolve-Thin1** in the **Feature Manager Design Tree**. The tree view expands and the sketch is displayed. Right-click on the sketch and choose **Hide** from the shortcut menu to hide the sketch. The revolved feature is shown in Figure 5-51.

Rotating the View

Next, you need to rotate the view so that you can view the model from all directions. As mentioned earlier, the view can be rotated using the **Rotate View** tool.

1. Choose the **Rotate View** button from the **View** toolbar; the arrow cursor is replaced by the rotate view cursor.

2. Press the left mouse button and drag the cursor in the drawing area to rotate the view.

3. Press the SPACEBAR to invoke the **Orientation** dialog box. In this dialog box, double-click on the **Isometric** option.

Displaying the Shadow

As mentioned in the tutorial description, you need to display the shadow of the model if it is not displayed by default. You can turn the display of the shadow on using the **View** toolbar.

1. Choose the **Shadows In Shaded Mode** button from the **View** toolbar; the shadow of the model is displayed below the model, see Figure 5-52.

Figure 5-51 *Model created by revolving the sketch*

Figure 5-52 *Model with the display of shadow turned on*

Assigning Materials to the Model

As mentioned earlier, you can assign a material to a model using the **Materials Editor PropertyManager**, which is displayed by choosing the **Edit Material** button. Note that you can also invoke this **PropertyManager** using the **Material** option available in the **Feature Manager Design Tree**.

1. Right-click on the **Material <not specified>** option in the **Feature Manager Design Tree** and choose the **Edit Material** option; the **Materials Editor FeatureManager** is displayed.

2. Click on the + sign located on the left of the **Copper and its Alloys** option from the list box

available in the **Materials** rollout. The tree view expands and the materials available under this family are displayed in the tree view.

3. Select the **Copper** option and choose **OK** from the **Materials Editor PropertyManager**. The model, after assigning the material, is shown in Figure 5-53.

Figure 5-53 Model after assigning Copper material

Saving the Model

As the name of the document was specified at the beginning, you just need to choose the save button now to save the document.

1. Choose the **Save** button from the **Standard** toolbar to save the model. If the SolidWorks warning box is displayed, choose **Yes** from it to rebuild the model before saving.

The model is saved with the name *\My Documents\SolidWorks\c05\c05tut2.sldprt*.

2. Choose **File > Close** from the menu bar to close the document.

Tutorial 3

In this tutorial, you will create the model shown in Figure 5-54. Its dimensions are shown in Figure 5-55. The extrusion depth of the model is 20 mm. After creating the model, rotate the view and then change the view back to isometric view before saving the model.

(Expected time: 45 min)

Figure 5-54 *Model for Tutorial 3*

Figure 5-55 *Dimensions of the model for Tutorial 3*

The steps that will be used to complete this tutorial are given next.

a.   Start a new SolidWorks part document and then invoke the sketching environment.
b.   Create the outer loop and then create the sketch of three inner cavities. Finally, draw the six circles inside the outer loop for the holes, refer to Figures 5-56 through 5-60.
c.   Invoke the **Extruded Boss/Base** tool and extrude the sketch through a distance of 20 mm, refer to Figure 5-61.
d.   Rotate the view using the **Rotate View** tool.
e.   Change the current view to isometric view and then save the document.

Starting a New Part Document

1. Choose the **New** button from the **Standard** toolbar and start a new part document using the **New SolidWorks Document** dialog box.

2. Choose the **Sketch** button from the **Standard** toolbar and select the **Front Plane** to invoke the sketching environment.

Drawing the Outer Loop

When the sketch consists of more than one closed loop, it is recommended that you draw the outer loop first and add relations and dimensions to it so that it is fully defined. Next, draw the inner loops one by one and add relations and dimensions to them. Therefore, you need to first draw the outer loop and add relations and dimensions to it.

1. Draw a circle in the first quadrant and then dimension it so that it is forced to a diameter of 100 mm.

2. Locate the center of the circle at a distance of 70 mm along the X and Y directions from the origin by adding dimensions in both directions. Choose the **Zoom to Fit** button to fit the display on the screen.

3. Draw a horizontal centerline from the center of the circle and then draw a circle with the center point at the intersection of the centerline and the bigger circle.

4. Trim the part of the sketch so that the sketch looks similar to that shown in Figure 5-56.

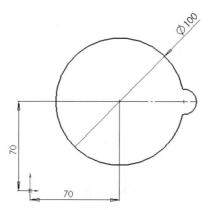

Figure 5-56 *Sketch after trimming the unwanted portion of circles*

5. Dimension the smaller arc so that it is forced to a radius of 10 mm. Add the **Coincident** relation to the center point of the smaller arc and the circumference of the bigger arc.

You will notice that as you add the dimensions and relations to the smaller arc, it turns black. This suggests that the sketch drawn so far is fully defined.

Next, you need to create a circular pattern of the smaller arc. The total number of instances in the pattern is 6 and the total angle is 360-degrees.

6. Select the smaller arc and then choose the **Circular Sketch Pattern** button from the **Sketch CommandManager**; the **Circular Pattern PropertyManager** is displayed.

7. Drag the center of the circular pattern to the center of the bigger arc.

8. Set the value of the **Number** spinner in the **Step** area to **6**. Accept all other default values and choose the **OK** button to create the pattern.

    You will notice that all instances of the pattern are black in color. This is because you have already applied the dimensions and relations to the original instance and so the other instances are also fully defined.

9. Trim the unwanted portion of the bigger arc. This completes the outer loop. The sketch at this stage should look similar to that shown in Figure 5-57.

Drawing the Sketch of the Inner Cavities

Now, you need to draw the sketch of the inner cavities. Draw the sketch of one of the cavities and then add the required relations and dimensions to it. Next, you need to create a circular pattern of this cavity. The number of instances in the circular pattern is 3.

1. Using the **Centerpoint Arc** tool, draw an arc with the center at the center point of the bigger arc of 100 mm diameter.

2. Dimension this arc such that it is forced to a radius of 30 mm. Also, add the angular dimensions to the two endpoints of the arc, refer to Figure 5-58. The arc turns black, suggesting that it is fully defined.

3. Offset the last drawn arc outward through a distance of 10 mm using the **Offset Entities** tool.

    The new arc created using the **Offset Entities** tool is also black. Also, a dimension with the value 10 mm is placed between the two arcs.

4. Close the two ends of the arc using the **Tangent Arc** tool. This completes the sketch of one of the inner cavities. All entities in the sketch at this stage should be displayed in black, as shown in Figure 5-58.

    Next, you need to create a circular pattern of the inner cavity.

5. Select all entities in the sketch of the inner cavity and then invoke the **Circular Pattern PropertyManager**.

6. Drag the center of the circular pattern to the center of the outer arc in the sketch.

Figure 5-57 *Outer loop of the sketch*

Figure 5-58 *Sketch after drawing the sketch of the inner cavity*

7. Set the value of the **Number** spinner in the **Step** area to **3** and then choose the **OK** button to create the circular pattern. This completes the sketch of the inner cavities, see Figure 5-59.

Figure 5-59 *Sketch after creating the circular pattern of the inner cavity*

Drawing the Sketch for the Holes

Next, you need to draw the sketch for the holes. Draw one of the circles and then add the dimension to it. Then you need to create a circular pattern of the circle.

1. Taking the center point of one of the smaller arcs of the outer loop, draw a circle. Add a diameter dimension to it so that the value of the diameter is forced to 10 mm.

    The circle turns black when you dimension it.

2. Select the circle and invoke the **Circular Pattern PropertyManager**.

3. Drag the center of the circular pattern to the center of the outer arc of 100 mm diameter.

4. Set the value of the **Number** spinner in the **Step** area to **6**. Choose **OK** to create the pattern. All instances in the pattern are displayed in black.

    This completes the sketch of the model. The final sketch of the model is shown in Figure 5-60.

Figure 5-60 *Final sketch of the model*

Extruding the Sketch

The next step after creating the sketch is to extrude it. The sketch is extruded using the **Extruded Boss/Base** tool.

1. Choose the down arrow available on the right of the **Features** button in the **CommandManager** to display a flyout. Choose the **Extruded Boss/Base** option from this flyout.

    The current view is changed to trimetric view and the **Extrude PropertyManager** is displayed. Also, the preview of the model, created using the default values, is displayed in the drawing area.

2. Set the value of the **Depth** spinner to **20** and then choose the **OK** button to extrude the sketch.

    Because the option to display shadow was turned on in the previous tutorial, the shadow is displayed in this tutorial also.

3. Press the SPACEBAR and then double-click on the **Isometric** option in the **Orientation** dialog box to change the current view to isometric view. The completed model for Tutorial 3 is shown in Figure 5-61.

Rotating the View

Before you start rotating the view of the model, it is recommended that you turn off the display of the shadow.

Figure 5-61 *Completed model for Tutorial 3*

1. Choose the **Shadows In Shaded Mode** button from the **View** toolbar to turn off the display of the shadow.

2. Now, choose the **Rotate View** button from the **View** toolbar; the arrow cursor is replaced by the rotate view cursor.

3. Press the left mouse button and drag the cursor in the drawing area to rotate the view.

4. Change the current view to isometric view using the **Orientation** dialog box.

Saving the Model

1. Choose the **Save** button from the **Standard** toolbar and save the model with the name given below.

    \My Documents\SolidWorks\c05\c05tut3.sldprt.

2. Choose **File > Close** from the menu bar to close the document.

SELF-EVALUATION TEST

Answer the following questions and then compare your answers with those given at the end of this chapter:

1. In SolidWorks, a sketch is revolved using the **Extrude PropertyManager**. (T/F)

2. You can also specify the depth of extrusion dynamically in the preview of the extruded feature. (T/F)

3. You can invoke the drawing display tools such as **Zoom to Fit** while the preview of a model is displayed on the screen. (T/F)

4. When you rotate the view with the current display mode set to **Shaded With Edges**, the hidden lines in the model are automatically displayed while the view is being rotated. (T/F)

5. _____ tool is used to display the perspective view of a model.

6. The **Cap ends** check box is displayed in the **Extrude PropertyManager** only when the sketch for the thin base feature is _____.

7. The _____ check box is used to create a feature with different values in both directions of the sketching plane.

8. The _____ check box is used to apply automatic fillets while creating a thin feature.

9. The _____ button is used to display the shadow in the shaded mode.

10. To resume rotating the view freely after you have completed rotating it around a selected vertex, edge, or face, _____ any where in the drawing area.

REVIEW QUESTIONS

Answer the following questions:

1. You can also invoke the **Rotate View** tool by choosing the **Rotate View** option from the _____ that is displayed when you right-click in the drawing area.

2. When you choose the **Wireframe** button, all _____ lines will be displayed along with the visible lines in the model.

3. You can also modify the parallel view to perspective view by choosing _____ from the menu bar.

4. When you invoke the **Extruded Boss/Base** tool or the **Revolved Boss/Base** tool, the view is automatically changed to a _____.

5. The thin revolved features can be created using a _____ or an _____ sketch.

6. Which of the following buttons is chosen to modify the orientation of the standard views?

   (a) **Update Standard Views**   (b) **Reset Standard Views**
   (c) None   (d) Both

7.   Which of the following buttons is not available in the **View** toolbar by default?

      (a) **Hidden Lines Removed**   (b) **Hidden Lines Visible**
      (c) **Shaded**   (d) **Perspective**

8.   Which of the following parameters is not displayed in the preview of the model?

      (a) Depth   (b) Draft angle
      (c) None   (d) Both

9.   If the sketch is open, it can be converted into

      (a) Thin feature   (b) Solid feature
      (c) None   (d) Both

10. In SolidWorks, which tool is used to make a sketch fully defined?

      (a) **Fully Define Sketch**   (b) **Smart Dimension**
      (c) None   (d) Both

EXERCISES

Exercise 1

Create the model shown in Figure 5-62. The sketch of the model is shown in Figure 5-63. Create the sketch and dimension it using the fully define sketch option. The extrusion depth of the model is 15 mm. After creating the model, rotate the view.   **(Expected time: 30 min)**

Figure 5-62 *Model for Exercise 1*

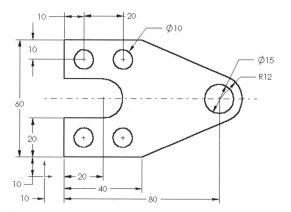

Figure 5-63 *Sketch of the model for Exercise 1*

Exercise 2

Create the model shown in Figure 5-64. The sketch of the model is shown in Figure 5-65. Create the sketch and dimension it using the fully define sketch option. The extrusion depth of the model is 25 mm. Modify the standard view such that the current front view of the model is displayed when you invoke the top view.   **(Expected time: 30 min)**

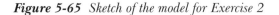

Figure 5-64 Model for Exercise 2   *Figure 5-65* Sketch of the model for Exercise 2

Answers to Self-Evaluation Test
1. F, **2.** T, **3.** T, **4.** F, **5. Perspective, 6.** closed, **7. Direction 2, 8. Auto-fillet corners, 9. Shadows In Shaded Mode, 10.** double-click

Chapter 6

Creating Reference Geometries

IMPORTANCE OF SKETCHING PLANES

In earlier chapters, you created basic models by extruding or revolving the sketches. All these models were created on a single sketching plane, the **Front Plane**. But most mechanical designs consist of multiple sketched features, referenced geometries, and placed features. These features are integrated together to complete a model. Most of these features lie on different planes. When you start a new SolidWorks document and try to invoke the sketching plane, you are prompted to select the plane on which you want to draw the sketch. On the basis of the design requirements, you can select any plane to create the base feature. To create additional sketched features, you need to select an existing plane or a planar surface, or you need to create a plane that will be used as a sketching plane. For example, consider the model shown in Figure 6-1.

Figure 6-1 *A multifeatured model*

The base feature of this model is shown in Figure 6-2. The sketch for the base feature is drawn on the **Top Plane**. After creating the base feature, you need to create the other sketched features, placed features, and referenced features, see Figure 6-3. The boss features and cut features are the sketched features that require sketching planes where you can draw the sketch of the features.

It is evident from Figure 6-3 that the features added to the base feature are not created on the same plane on which the sketch for the base feature is created. Therefore, to draw the sketches of other sketched features, you need to define other sketching planes.

REFERENCE GEOMETRY

The reference geometry features are those that are available only to assist you in creating models. The reference geometries in SolidWorks include planes, axes, points, and coordinate systems. These reference geometries act as a reference for drawing the sketches for sketched features, defining the sketch plane, and assembling the components. They also act as references for various placed features and sketched features. These features have no mass or volume. You must have a good understanding of these geometries because they are widely used in creating complex models.

Figure 6-2 Base feature for the model   *Figure 6-3* Model after adding other features

Reference Planes

Generally, all engineering components or designs are multifeatured models. Also, as discussed earlier, all features of a model are not created on the same plane on which the base feature is created. Therefore, you have to select one of the default planes or create a new plane that will be used as the sketching plane for the second feature. It is clear from the above discussion that you can use the default planes as the sketching plane or you can create a plane that can be used as a sketching plane. The default planes and the creation of a new plane are discussed next.

Default Planes

When you start a new SolidWorks part document, SolidWorks provides you with three default planes: **Front Plane**, **Top Plane**, and **Right Plane**.

The orientation of the component depends on the sketch of the base feature. Therefore, it is recommended that you carefully select the sketching plane for drawing the sketch for the base feature. The sketching plane for drawing the sketch of the base feature can be one of the three datum planes provided by default.

If you create the base feature and choose the **Sketch** tool to invoke the sketching environment, the three default planes will be automatically displayed in the drawing area. However, if you create an additional feature, these planes will not be displayed when you invoke the **Sketch** tool. You need to manually select the required plane.

To select a plane for an additional feature, choose the **Sketch** button; the **Edit Sketch PropertyManager** will be displayed. Whenever a **PropertyManager** is displayed, the **FeatureManager Design Tree** shifts to the drawing area. Click on the + sign located on the left of the part document name in the **FeatureManager Design Tree**, which is displayed in the drawing area. The tree view will expand and display the names of the planes. Select the required plane from the tree view.

Tip. *You can turn on the display of the default planes in the drawing area using the following procedure.*

*Press and hold the CTRL key down and one by one select the **Front Plane**, **Top Plane**, and **Right Plane** from the **FeatureManager Design Tree**. Right-click to display the shortcut menu and choose the **Show** option to display the planes in the drawing area. Choose the **Isometric** option from the **Standard Views** flyout.*

*By default, the reference planes are not shaded. To turn on the shade of the planes, choose **Tools** > **Options** from the menu bar to invoke the **System Options - General** dialog box. Select the **Display/Selection** option from the left of this dialog box; the name of the dialog box will be changed to **System Options - Display/Selection**. Select the **Display shaded planes** check box from this dialog box and choose the **OK** button.*

*When the planes are displayed in shaded, invoke the **Rotate View** tool and drag the rotate view cursor to rotate the shaded planes. You will observe that one side of the plane is displayed in reddish color and the other side is displayed in brownish color. The reddish side of the plane symbolizes the positive side and the brownish side symbolizes the negative side. This means that when you create an extruded feature, the depth of extrusion will be assigned to the positive side of the plane by default. When you create a cut feature, the depth of the cut feature will be assigned to the negative direction by default.*

Note
*You can also select a plane before choosing the **Sketch** button to invoke the sketching environment. In this case, the **Edit Sketch PropertyManager** is not displayed and you are not prompted to select a plane for sketching. The selected plane is automatically taken as the sketching plane.*

Creating New Planes

CommandManager:	Reference Geometry > Plane
Menu:	Insert > Reference Geometry > Plane
Toolbar:	Reference Geometry > Plane

Default planes or the reference planes are used to draw sketches for the sketched features. These planes are also used to create a placed feature such as holes, reference an entity or a feature, and so on. You can also select a planar face of a feature that will be used as a sketching plane. Generally, it is recommended that you use the planar faces of the features as the sketching planes. However, sometimes you have to create a sketch on a plane that is at some offset distance from a plane or a planar face. In this case, you have to create a new reference plane at an offset distance from a plane or a planar face.

Consider another case where you have to define a sketching plane tangent to a cylindrical face of a shaft. You have to create a plane tangent to the cylindrical face of the shaft and this plane will be used as a sketching plane. In SolidWorks, there are six methods of creating planes. To create planes, choose the **Plane** button from the **Reference Geometry CommandManager**;

the **Plane PropertyManager** will be displayed, as shown in Figure 6-4. The confirmation corner will also be displayed at the top right corner of the drawing area.

Figure 6-4 *The Plane PropertyManager*

The options available in the **Plane PropertyManager** to create new planes are discussed next.

Creating a Plane Passing Through Lines/Points

The **Through Lines/Points** option is used to create a plane that passes through an edge and a point, an axis and a point, or a sketch line and a point. Using this option, you can also create a plane that passes through three points. The selected point can be a sketched point or a vertex. To create a plane using this option, invoke the **Plane PropertyManager** and choose the **Through Lines/Points** button. Select the required entities from the drawing area. The name of the selected entities will be displayed in the **Reference Entities** selection box. Choose the **OK** button from the **Plane PropertyManager**. Figure 6-5 shows an edge and a vertex selected to create a plane. The resulting plane is displayed in Figure 6-6. The creation of a new plane by selecting three points is displayed in Figures 6-7 and 6-8.

Creating a Plane Parallel to an Existing Plane or Planar Face and Passing Through a Point

The **Parallel Plane at Point** option is used to create a plane that is parallel to another plane or a planar face and passes through a point. To create a plane using this option, invoke the **Plane PropertyManager** and then choose the **Parallel Plane at Point** button. Now, select a plane or a planar face to which the new plane will be parallel. Next, select a sketched point, an endpoint of an edge, or a midpoint of an edge. The new plane will pass through this point. Choose the **OK** option. Figure 6-9 shows a planar face and the point selected to create the parallel plane. Figure 6-10 shows the resulting plane.

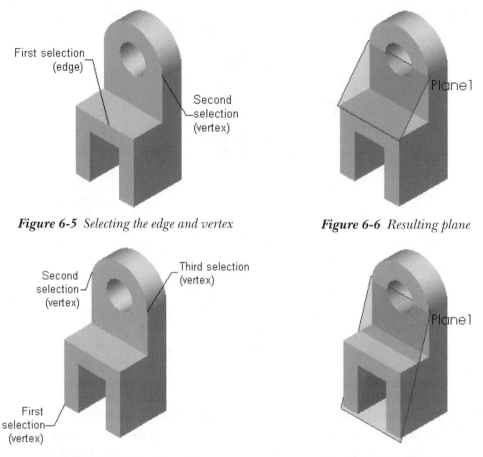

Figure 6-5 *Selecting the edge and vertex*

Figure 6-6 *Resulting plane*

Figure 6-7 *Selecting the vertices*

Figure 6-8 *Resulting plane*

Creating a Plane at an Angle to an Existing Plane or a Planar Face

The **At Angle** option is used to create a plane that is at an angle to the selected plane or a planar face and also passes through an edge, axis, or sketched line. To create a plane at an angle, choose the **At Angle** button from the **Plane PropertyManager**; the **Angle** spinner will be invoked. The **Reverse direction** check box and the **Number of Plane to Create** spinner will appear below the **Distance** spinner in the **Plane PropertyManager**, as shown in Figure 6-11. Now, select an edge, an axis, or a sketched line through which the plane will pass. Next, you have to select a planar face or a plane to define the angle. After selecting the plane or the planar face, set the angle value using the **Angle** spinner. You can reverse the direction of the plane creation by selecting the **Reverse direction** check box. You can also create multiple planes by increasing the value of the **Number of Planes to Create** spinner. Each plane will be incremented by the angle value defined in the **Angle** spinner. Figure 6-12 shows a planar face and an edge selected. Figure 6-13 shows the resulting plane created at an angle of 45-degrees to the selected plane.

Figure 6-9 Selecting a planar face and a vertex   *Figure 6-10 Resulting plane*

*Figure 6-11 The **Plane PropertyManager** with the **At Angle** option selected*

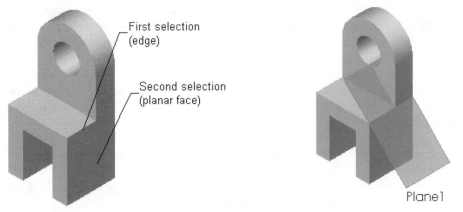

Figure 6-12 Selecting the edge and the planar face   *Figure 6-13 Resulting plane*

Creating a Plane at Some Offset From an Existing Plane or a Planar Face

The **Offset Distance** option is used to create a plane that is at some offset distance from a selected plane or planar face. To create a plane using this option, choose the **Offset Distance** button from the **Plane PropertyManager**. When you invoke this option, the **Distance** spinner will be invoked. Also, the **Reverse direction** check box and the **Number of Planes to Create** spinner will be displayed below the **Distance** spinner in the **Plane PropertyManager**. Select a plane or a planar face and set the value of the distance in the **Distance** spinner and choose the **OK** button from the **Planar PropertyManager**. You can reverse the direction of plane creation by selecting the **Reverse direction** check box. You can also create multiple planes by increasing the value of the **Number of Planes to Create** spinner. Each plane will be placed at the offset distance specified in the **Distance** spinner. Figure 6-14 shows a plane selected to create a parallel plane and Figure 6-15 shows the resulting plane created at the required offset.

Figure 6-14 Selecting the plane

Figure 6-15 Resulting plane

Creating a Plane Normal to Curve

This option is used to create a plane normal to a selected curve. The curve can be a sketched entity or an edge of a feature. To create a plane normal to a curve, choose the **Normal to Curve** button from the **Plane PropertyManager** and select a curve normal to which the new plane will be created. As soon as you select the curve, the preview of the plane will be displayed in the drawing area. This plane is displayed by default at the endpoint closest to the point from where you selected the curve. If you have selected the curve close to its midpoint, the plane will be displayed at the midpoint of the selected curve. If you want to place it at the other endpoint or at any other point on the curve, select that point. The preview of the plane will change accordingly. After selecting the plane and the point, choose the **OK** button to create the plane.

When you choose the **Normal to Curve** button from the **Plane PropertyManager**, the **Set origin on curve** check box will be displayed below this button. This check box is selected to set the origin of the plane on the curve. Figure 6-16 shows a curve to create the plane and Figure 6-17 shows the resulting plane created normal to the selected curve.

Creating a Plane On Surface

The **On Surface** option is used to create a plane passing through a point on the selected plane or planar surface. To create a plane on a surface, choose the **On Surface** button from the **Plane PropertyManager** and select the surface on which you want to create the plane. Next, select the sketched point. The preview of the plane will be displayed in the drawing area and you have to right-click to choose the **OK** option. If the sketch is created on a plane at an offset distance from the selected surface, the **Project to nearest location on surface** and **Project onto surface along sketch normal** radio buttons, and the **Other Solutions** button will be displayed on the **Plane**

> **Tip**. *You can also create the planes by dynamically dragging an existing plane. For creating a plane by dragging, you do not need to invoke the **Plane PropertyManager**. Using the left mouse button, select the plane from the **FeatureManager Design Tree** or the **drawing** area. Press and hold the CTRL key down and drag the cursor. You will notice that the value of the distance in the **Distance** spinner of the **Plane PropertyManager** is modified and the preview of the plane is displayed in the drawing area. After dragging the plane to a required location, release the left mouse button. Right-click and choose the **OK** option or choose the **OK** button from the **Plane PropertyManager**.*
>
> *You can also create a plane at an angle by dragging. To create a plane at an angle by dragging, select an edge or an axis and an existing plane. Now, hold the CTRL key and drag the mouse. Enter the angle value in the **Angle** spinner.*

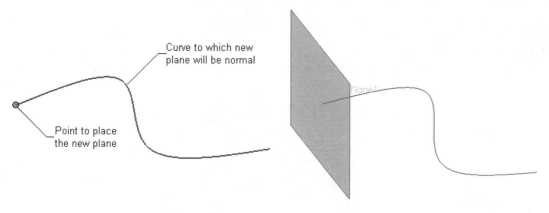

Figure 6-16 Edge to be selected   *Figure 6-17 Resulting plane*

PropertyManager. Select any of the radio buttons according to the requirement. You can also view the other solutions of the plane creation using the **Other Solutions** button from the **Plane PropertyManager**. Figure 6-18 shows the selection of references for the plane creation and Figure 6-19 shows the resulting plane created.

> **Tip**. *If you select an edge of a model or an existing curve and invoke the sketching environment, a reference plane will be automatically created normal to that edge or curve. Also, it will be selected as the sketching plane.*

Creating Reference Axes

CommandManager:	Reference Geometry > Axis
Menu:	Insert > Reference Geometry > Axis
Toolbar:	Reference Geometry > Axis

The **Reference Axis** option is used to create a reference axis or construction axis. These axes are the parametric lines passing through a model, feature, or reference entity. The reference axes are used to create reference planes, coordinate systems,

Figure 6-18 *References to be selected*   *Figure 6-19* *Resulting plane*

circular patterns, and for applying mates in the assembly. These are also used as reference while sketching or creating features. The reference axes are displayed in the model as well as in the **FeatureManager Design Tree**. When you choose the **Axis** button from the **Reference Geometry CommandManager** to create an axis, the **Axis PropertyManager** will be displayed, as shown in Figure 6-20.

Figure 6-20 *The Axis PropertyManager*

Tip. *If the axis is not displayed in the drawing area even after you have created it, choose* **View** > **Axes** *from the menu bar.*

The options available in the **Axis PropertyManager** are discussed next.

Creating a Reference Axis Using One Line/Edge/Axis

The **One Line/Edge/Axis** option is used to create a reference axis by selecting a sketched line or construction line, an edge, or a temporary axis. To use this option, invoke the **Axis**

PropertyManager and choose the **One Line/Edge/Axis** button. Select a sketched line, edge, or a temporary axis. The name of the selected entity will be displayed in the **Reference Entities** selection box and the preview of the reference axis will be displayed in the drawing area. Choose the **OK** button to create the reference axis. Figure 6-21 shows a construction line selected as a reference for creating an axis and Figure 6-22 shows an axis created using this option.

Figure 6-21 Line to be selected   *Figure 6-22* Resulting reference axis

Creating a Reference Axis Using Two Planes

Using the **Two Planes** option, you can create a reference axis at the intersection of two planes. To create a reference axis using this option, invoke the **Axis PropertyManager** and choose the **Two Planes** button. Now, select two planes, two planar faces, or a plane and a planar face you want to use to create the axis. The preview of the axis will be displayed in the drawing area. Choose the **OK** button from the **Axis PropertyManager**. Figure 6-23 shows two planes selected and Figure 6-24 shows the resulting reference axis created using this option.

Creating a Reference Axis Using Two Points or Vertices

Using the **Two Points/Vertices** option, you can create a reference axis that passes through two points or two vertices. To create a reference axis using this option, invoke the **Axis PropertyManager** and choose the **Two Points/Vertices** button. Now, select two points or two vertices through which you want the reference axis to pass. The preview of the reference axis will be displayed in the drawing area. Choose the **OK** button from the **Axis PropertyManager**. Figure 6-25 shows two vertices to be selected and Figure 6-26 shows the resulting reference axis created using this option.

Creating a Reference Axis Using a Cylindrical or a Conical Face

Using the **Cylindrical/Conical Face** option, you can create a reference axis that passes through the center of a cylindrical or a conical face. To create a reference axis using this option, invoke the **Axis PropertyManager** and choose the **Cylindrical/Conical Face** button. Now, select the cylindrical or the conical face through the center of which the axis needs to pass. The preview of the reference axis will be displayed in the drawing area. Choose the **OK** button from the **Axis PropertyManager**. Figure 6-27 shows a cylindrical face selected and

Figure 6-23 *Planes to be selected*   ***Figure 6-24*** *Resulting reference axis*

Figure 6-25 *Vertices to be selected*   ***Figure 6-26*** *Resulting reference axis*

Figure 6-28 shows the resulting reference axis created using this option.

Creating a Reference Axis on a Face/Plane Passing Through a Point

Using the **Point and Face/Plane** option you can create a reference axis that passes through a point and is normal to the selected face/plane. If the selected face is a nonplanar face, the selected point should be created on the face. To create a reference axis using this option, invoke the **Axis PropertyManager**. Select the **Point and Face/Plane** button from this **PropertyManager**. Now, select a point, vertex, or midpoint and then select a face or a plane. The preview of the axis will be displayed in the drawing area. Choose the **OK** button from the **Axis PropertyManager**. The newly created axis will be normal to the selected face or plane. Figure 6-29 shows the point and face selected and Figure 6-30 shows the resulting axis created using this option.

Note
*When you create a circular feature, a temporary axis is automatically created. You can display the temporary axis by choosing **View** > **Temporary Axis** from the menu bar.*

Cylindrical surface

Figure 6-27 Cylindrical face to be selected

Axis1

Figure 6-28 Resulting reference axis

Second selection
(planar surface)

First selection
(point)

Figure 6-29 Point and face to be selected

Axis1

Figure 6-30 Resulting reference axis

Creating Reference Points

CommandManager:	Reference Geometry > Point
Menu:	Insert > Reference Geometry > Point
Toolbar:	Reference Geometry > Point

Reference points are also created to assist you in designing. They work as an aid for creating another reference geometry or feature. To create a reference point, choose the **Point** button from the **Reference Geometry CommandManager**; the **Point PropertyManager** will be displayed, as shown in Figure 6-31.

This **PropertyManager** allows you to use five methods of creating reference points. These methods are discussed next.

Creating a Reference Point at the Center of an Arc or a Curved Edge

The **Arc Center** option is used to create a reference point at the center of a sketched arc or a curved edge. When you invoke the **Point PropertyManager** and choose the **Arc Center** button,

Figure 6-31 *The Point PropertyManager*

you will be prompted to select an arc or a circular edge to define the reference point. As soon as you select a sketched arc or circle, or a curved edge, the preview of the reference point will be displayed at its center. Choose **OK** to confirm the creation of the reference point. Figure 6-32 shows a curved edge selected to create the reference point and the preview of the resulting reference point.

Figure 6-32 *Reference point at the center of a curved edge*

Creating a Reference Point at the Center of a Face

The **Center Of Face** option allows you to create a reference point at the center of a face. When you choose this button, you will be prompted to select a face to define the reference point. You can select a planar or a curved face. The resulting point is automatically placed at the point of the center of gravity of the selected face.

Creating a Reference Point at the Intersection of Two Edges, Sketched Segments, or Reference Axes

The **Intersection** option allows you to create a reference point at the intersection of two edges, sketched segments, or reference axes.

Creating a Reference Point by Projecting an Existing Point

The **Projection** option allows you to create a reference point by projecting a point from some other plane to a specified plane. The point that you can project can be a sketched point, endpoints, or center points of sketched entities, or a reference point.

Creating Single or Multiple Reference Points Along the Distance of a Sketched Curve or an Edge

The **Along curve distance or multiple reference point** option allows you to create single or multiple reference points along the distance of a selected curve. When you choose this button, the **Selections** rollout of the **Point PropertyManager** will expand and provide additional options. These options are discussed next.

Enter the distance/percentage value according to distance

This spinner is used to specify the distance or the percentage value between the individual reference points along the selected curve.

Distance

This radio button is selected to define the gap between the individual points in terms of the distance value. If this radio button is selected, the value entered in the **Enter the distance/percentage value according to distance** spinner will be in terms of linear units of the current document.

Percentage

This radio button is selected to define the gap between the individual points in terms of the percentage of the length of the selected curve. If this radio button is selected, the total length of the selected curve will be taken as 100%. Now, the value entered in the **Enter the distance/percentage value according to distance** spinner will be in terms of the percentage of the selected curve.

Evenly Distribute

This radio button is selected to evenly distribute the specified number of reference points through the length of the selected curve. If this radio button is selected, the **Enter the distance/percentage value according to distance** spinner will not be available.

Enter number of reference points to be created along the selected entity

This spinner is used to specify the number of reference points to be created. The specified number of reference points will be placed with the gap defined in the **Enter the distance/percentage value according to distance** spinner along the selected curve.

Creating Reference Coordinate Systems

CommandManager:	Reference Geometry > Coordinate System
Menu:	Insert > Reference Geometry > Coordinate System
Toolbar:	Reference Geometry > Coordinate System

 In SolidWorks, you may need to define some reference coordinate systems other than the default coordinate system for creating features, analyzing the geometry, analyzing the assemblies, and so on. To create a user-defined coordinate system, choose the **Coordinate System** button from the **Reference Geometry CommandManager**; the **Coordinate System PropertyManager** will be displayed, as shown in Figure 6-33. Also, a coordinate system will be displayed at the origin of the current document.

*Figure 6-33 The **Coordinate System PropertyManager***

To create a new coordinate system, you need to select a point that will be selected as the origin for the new coordinate and then define the directions of the X and Y, Y and Z, or Z and X axes. This is the reason that when you invoke the **Coordinate System PropertyManager**, the **Origin** selection box will be highlighted. After selecting the origin, you can define the direction of any two axes. The direction of the third axis will be automatically determined. You can select edges, points, or reference axes to define these directions.

You can reverse the directions of the axes by choosing the buttons available on the right of their respective selection boxes.

OTHER BOSS/BASE OPTIONS

Some of the boss/base extrusion options were discussed in the previous chapter. In this chapter, the remaining boss/base extrusion options are discussed.

From

The **From** option available in the **Extrude PropertyManager** is a major enhancement in the recent releases of SolidWorks. Using this option, you can specify from where the sketch will start to extrude. The **From** rollout of the **Extrude PropertyManager** is shown in Figure 6-34. The options available in this rollout are discussed next.

*Figure 6-34 The **From** rollout of the **Extrude PropertyManager***

Sketch Plane

When you invoke the **Extrude PropertyManager**, the **Sketch Plane** option will be chosen by default in the **From** rollout. With this option chosen, the extrude feature starts from the sketching plane on which the sketch is drawn. This option is mostly used while creating the extrude features.

Surface/Face/Plane

The **Surface/Face/Plane** option is used to start the extrude feature from a selected surface, face, or a plane, instead of the plane on which the sketch is drawn. To do this, invoke the **Extrude PropertyManager** and select the **Surface/Face/Plane** option from the **Start Condition** drop-down list in the **From** rollout; the **Select A Surface/Face/Plane** selection box will be displayed in the **From** rollout. Select a surface, face, or plane from where you need start the extrude feature. Figure 6-35 shows the sketch to be extruded and the face selected as reference for starting the extrude feature. Figure 6-36 shows the resulting feature extruded from the selected face up to a specified depth.

Figure 6-35 Sketch to be extruded and a reference face to be selected

Figure 6-36 Resulting extruded feature

Vertex

The **Vertex** option is used to specify a vertex as the reference for starting the extrude feature. To do this, invoke the **Extrude PropertyManager** and select the **Vertex** option from the **Start Condition** drop-down list; the **Select A Vertex** selection box will be displayed. Select a vertex of an existing feature or an endpoint of an existing sketch. Figure 6-37 shows the sketch to be extruded and the vertex to be selected as reference to start the extrude feature. Figure 6-38 shows the resulting extruded feature from the selected vertex to the defined depth.

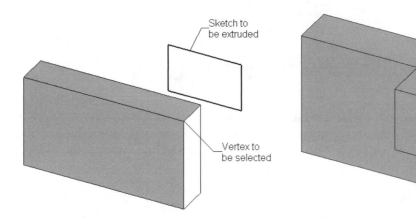

Figure 6-37 *Sketch to be extruded and a reference vertex to be selected*

Figure 6-38 *Resulting extruded feature*

Offset

The **Offset** option is used to start the extrude feature at an offset from the plane on which the sketch is drawn. To do this, select the **Offset** option from the **Start Condition** drop-down list; the **Enter Offset Value** spinner will be displayed. Set the value of the offset in this spinner. Figure 6-39 shows the preview of the sketch drawn on the **Front Plane** being extruded using the **Offset** option. Figure 6-40 shows the resulting extruded feature from an offset distance from the sketching plane to a defined depth.

Figure 6-39 *Sketch being extruded using the **Offset** option*

Figure 6-40 *Resulting extruded feature*

End Condition

The options available in the **End Condition** drop-down list are discussed next.

Through All

The **Through All** option is available in the **End condition** drop-down list only after you create a base feature. After creating a base feature, define a new sketching plane and create the sketch using the standard sketching tools. Now, choose the **Extruded Boss/Base** button from the **Features CommandManager** to invoke the **Extrude PropertyManager**. The preview of the extruded feature that will be created using the default settings will be displayed in temporary graphics in the drawing area. Select the **Through All** option from the **End Condition** drop-down list; the preview of the extruded feature will extend from the sketching plane through all existing geometric entities. You can also reverse the direction of extrusion using the **Reverse Direction** button available on the left of the **End Condition** drop-down list.

While creating an extruded feature using the **Through All** option, the sketch extrudes through all existing geometries. You will observe that the **Merge result** check box is displayed in the **Extrude PropertyManager**. This check box is selected by default. Therefore, the newly created extruded feature will merge with the base feature. If you clear this check box, this extruded feature will not merge with the existing base feature, resulting in the creation of another body. The creation of a new body can be confirmed by observing the **Solid Bodies** folder in the **FeatureManager Design Tree**. The value of the number of disjoint bodies in the model is displayed in parentheses on the right of the **Solid Bodies** folder. You can click on the + sign on the left of the **Solid Bodies** folder to expand the folder. To collapse the folder back, click on the - sign.

Figure 6-41 displays a sketch created on the sketching plane at an offset distance from the right planar face of the model. Figure 6-42 displays the feature created by extruding the sketch using the **Through All** option.

Figure 6-41 *A sketch drawn at an offset distance from the right planar surface*

Figure 6-42 *Sketch extruded using the **Through All** option*

Tip. *The feature created from multiple disjoint closed contours results in the creation of disjoint bodies.*

Note
*It is recommended that while creating additional features after the base feature, you should always select the **Merge results** check box in the **Feature PropertyManager**.*

Up To Next

The **Up To Next** option is used to extrude the sketch from the sketching plane to the next surface that intersects the feature. After creating a base feature, create a sketch by selecting or creating a sketching plane. Invoke the **Extrude PropertyManager**; the preview of the base feature will be displayed with the default options. Select the **Up To Next** option from the **End Condition** drop-down list. You can also reverse the direction of feature creation using the **Reverse Direction** button. The preview of the feature will be modified and the sketch will be displayed as extruded from the sketching plane to the next surface that intersects the feature geometry. Figure 6-43 shows the sketch that will be extruded using the **Up To Next** option and Figure 6-44 shows the resulting feature.

*Figure 6-43 A sketch drawn on the **Right Plane** as the sketching plane*

*Figure 6-44 Sketch extruded using the **Up To Next** option*

Up To Vertex

The **Up To Vertex** option is used to define the termination of the extruded feature at a virtual plane parallel to the sketching plane and passing through the selected vertex. You can also select a point on an edge, a sketched point, or a reference point. Figure 6-45 shows a sketch drawn on a plane at an offset distance and Figure 6-46 shows the model in which the sketch is extruded up to the selected vertex.

Up To Surface

The **Up To Surface** option is used to define the termination of the extruded feature using a selected surface or a face. To create an extruded feature using this option, draw a sketch using the normal sketching options and then invoke the **Extrude PropertyManager**. Select the

Figure 6-45 *Sketch drawn on a plane created at an offset distance and a vertex to be selected*

Figure 6-46 *Sketch extruded using the **Up To Vertex** option.*

Up To Surface option from the **End Condition** drop-down list; the **Face/Plane** selection box will be displayed and you will be prompted to select a face or a surface. Select a surface up to which you want to extrude the feature. Figure 6-47 shows the sketch drawn at an offset distance and the surface to be selected. Figure 6-48 shows the resulting feature extruded up to the selected surface.

Figure 6-47 *Sketch drawn on a plane created at an offset distance and a surface to be selected*

Figure 6-48 *Sketch extruded using the **Up To Surface** option.*

Offset From Surface

The **Offset From Surface** option is used to define the termination of the extruded feature on a virtual surface created at an offset distance from the selected surface. To create an extruded feature using the **Offset From Surface** option, create a sketch and invoke the **Extrude PropertyManager**. Select the **Offset From Surface** option from the **End Condition** drop-down list; the **Face/Plane** selection box will be displayed along with the **Offset Distance** spinner. You will be prompted to select a face or a surface. Select the surface and set the offset distance in the **Offset Distance** spinner. You can reverse the direction of the offset by selecting the **Reverse offset** check box from the **Direction 1** rollout. If the **Translate surface** check box is cleared, the virtual surface created for the termination of the extruded feature will have a concentric relation with the selected surface. Therefore, it reflects the true offset of the selected surface. If the **Translate surface** check box is selected, the virtual surface will be translated to the distance provided as the offset distance from the reference surface. Therefore, a virtual surface is created to define the termination of the extruded feature and it does not reflect the true offset of the selected surface. This concept will be more clear if you refer to Figure 6-49.

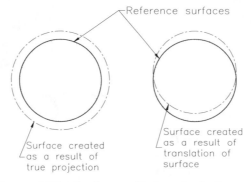

Figure 6-49 *Surfaces with true projection and translation*

Figure 6-50 shows the front view of the sketch extruded with termination at an offset distance from the selected cylindrical surface with the **Translate surface** check box cleared. Figure 6-51 shows the front view of the extruded feature with the **Translate surface** check box selected.

Figure 6-50 *Sketch extruded using the **Offset From Surface** option with the **Translate surface** check box cleared*

Figure 6-51 *Sketch extruded using the **Offset From Surface** option with the **Translate surface** check box selected*

Up To Body

The **Up To Body** option is used to define the termination of the extruded feature to another body. To create an extruded feature using the **Up To Body** option, invoke the **Extrude PropertyManager** and select the **Up To Body** option from the **End Condition** drop-down list;

the **Solid/Surface Body** selection box will be displayed. Select the body to terminate the feature and choose the **OK** button. Figure 6-52 shows the sketch for the extruded feature and a body up to which the sketch will be extruded. Figure 6-53 shows the resulting feature.

Figure 6-52 *Sketch to be extruded and the body to be selected for the extrude feature*

Figure 6-53 *Sketch extruded using the **Up To Body** option*

Direction of Extrusion

In SolidWorks 2006, you can define the direction for extruding the sketches. As mentioned in the previous chapter, the direction of extrusion is generally normal to the sketching plane. You can also define the direction of extrusion using a sketched line, an edge, or a reference axis. Note that the entity you want to use for defining the direction of extrusion should not be drawn on the sketch plane parallel to the plane on which the sketch to be extruded is drawn.

To define the direction of extrusion, click on the **Direction of Extrusion** selection box in the **Direction 1** area of the **Extrude PropertyManager**. Next, select an edge, a sketched line segment, or an axis. Figure 6-54 shows a sketch drawn on the top face of a rectangular block and a line sketched on the left face of the block to define the direction of extrusion. Figure 6-55 shows the resulting extruded feature.

MODELING USING THE CONTOUR SELECTION METHOD

Modeling using the contour selection method allows you to use partial sketches for creating the features. Using this method, you can draw sketches of the entire model in a single sketching environment and then manipulate the sketches by sharing them between various features. To understand this concept, consider the multifeatured solid model shown in Figure 6-56.

For a multifeatured model similar to the one shown in Figure 6-56, ideally you first need to draw the sketch for the base feature and convert it into the base feature. Next, you need to draw the sketch for the second sketched feature and so on. In other words, you have to draw the sketch for each sketched feature. But using the contour selection method, you can share the contour created using the sketch for creating features. Figure 6-57 shows the sketch to be drawn for modeling using the contour selection method.

Figure 6-54 *Sketch to be extruded and the direction of extrusion*

Figure 6-55 *Resulting extruded feature*

Figure 6-56 *Multifeatured solid model*

Figure 6-57 *Sketch for creating the model*

After drawing the entire sketch, right-click in the drawing area to invoke the shortcut menu. Make sure you are still in the sketching environment. Choose the **Contour Selection Tool** option from the shortcut menu. If this option is not displayed by default, choose the down arrows in the shortcut menu to expand it. This option will be displayed now. When you choose this option, the select cursor will be replaced by the contour selection cursor and contour selection confirmation corner will be displayed. Using the contour selection cursor, click between the two circles on the left. The area between the two circles will be selected, as shown in Figure 6-58. Invoke the **Extrude PropertyManager** and extrude the selected contour using the **Mid Plane** option, as shown in Figure 6-59.

Now, right-click in the drawing area and again choose the **Contour Selection Tool** option from the shortcut menu. Using the contour selection cursor, select any entity in the sketch and then select the middle contour of the sketch, as shown in Figure 6-60. Invoke the **Extrude PropertyManager** and extrude the selected contour using the **Mid Plane** option. Again, invoke the contour selection tool and select an entity in the sketch. Similarly, again invoke the contour selection tool and select any entity of the sketch. Next, specify a point between the two circles on

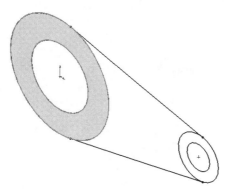

Figure 6-58 *Contour selected for creating the extruded feature*

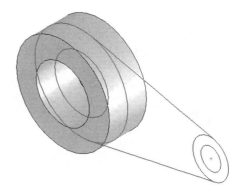

Figure 6-59 *Isometric view of the feature created by extruding the selected contour*

Tip. *When you move the contour selection cursor in the sketch, the areas where the contour selection is possible are dynamically highlighted.*

the right and extrude the same using the **Mid Plane** option.

After creating the model using this option, you will notice that the sketches are displayed in the model. This is the reason why you need to hide them. Click on the **+** sign located on the left of any of the extruded features to expand the tree view. Select the sketch icon and right-click to invoke the shortcut menu. Choose the **Hide** option. Figure 6-61 shows the model after creating all features using the contour selection method and after hiding the sketch.

Figure 6-60 *Contour selected for the second feature*

Figure 6-61 *Final model*

In SolidWorks 2006, you can also select the model edges as a part of the contour. For example, consider Figure 6-62. This figure shows a line drawn on the top face of a rectangular block. You can use the edges of the top face that form a contour with the line as a sketch to be extruded, see Figure 6-63.

Figure 6-62 *Line drawn on the top face of a rectangular model*

Figure 6-63 *Selecting the contour formed by the line and the model edges*

Figure 6-64 shows the resulting extruded feature.

Figure 6-64 *Extruded feature created using the model edges as a part of the contour*

Tip. *When you select the contour using the contour selection tool and invoke the **Extrude PropertyManager**, you can observe the name of the selected contour in the selection box of the **Contour Selection** rollout.*

You can select the contours for all sketched features such as revolve, cut, sweep, loft, and so on.

You can also select a single sketched entity from a sketch using the contour selection tool instead of selecting the contour for creating the sketched features.

Note
*If you click on the +sign to expand the extruded feature in the **FeatureManager Design Tree**, you will notice that instead of showing the icon of a simple sketch, it will show the icon of the contour selected sketch.*

CREATING CUT FEATURES

The cut is a material removal process. You can define a cut feature by extruding a sketch, revolving a sketch, sweeping a section along a path, lofting sections, or by using a surface. You will learn more about sweep, loft, and surface in later chapters. The cut feature can be created only if a base feature exists. The extruded and revolved cut features are discussed next.

Creating Extruded Cuts

CommandManager:	Features > Extruded Cut
Menu:	Insert > Cut > Extrude
Toolbar:	Features > Extruded Cut

To create an extruded cut feature, create a sketch for the cut feature and then choose the **Extruded Cut** button from the **Features CommandManager**. The **Cut-Extrude PropertyManager** will be displayed, as shown in Figure 6-65. Also, the preview of the cut feature with default options will be displayed in the drawing area.

Figure 6-65 The Cut-Extrude PropertyManager

Figure 6-66 shows the preview of the cut feature when you invoke the **Cut-Extrude PropertyManager** after creating a sketch. Remember that when you are creating a cut feature, the current view is not automatically changed to a 3D view. You need to change it manually. The material to be removed is displayed in temporary graphics. Figure 6-67 shows the model after creating the cut feature.

Figure 6-66 *The preview of the cut feature*   **Figure 6-67** *Cut feature added to the model*

The options available in the **Cut-Extrude PropertyManager** are discussed next.

From

In SolidWorks, you are provided with the options of specifying parameters at the start of the extruded cut. These options are available in the **From** rollout and are the same as those discussed earlier for the **Boss/Base** option. Figure 6-68 shows the sketch to be extruded using with the curved face selected as the reference face for the end condition for starting the extrusion. Figure 6-69 shows the resulting extruded cut feature.

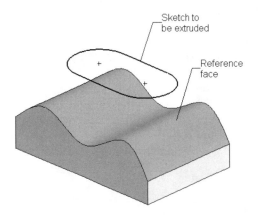

Figure 6-68 *Sketch to be extruded and the reference face*   **Figure 6-69** *Resulting extruded cut feature*

Direction 1

The **Direction 1** rollout is used to define the termination of the extrude in the first direction. The options available in the **Direction 1** rollout are discussed next.

End Condition

The **End Condition** drop-down list available in the **Direction 1** rollout is used to specify the type of termination option available. The feature termination options available in this drop-down list are **Blind**, **Through All**, **Up To Next**, **Up To Vertex**, **Up To Surface**, and **Mid Plane**. These options are the same as those discussed for the boss/base options. By default, the **Blind** option is selected in the **End Condition** drop-down list. Therefore, the **Distance** spinner is displayed to specify the depth. If you choose the **Through All** or the **Through Next** options, the spinner will not be displayed. The type of spinner or the selection box that is displayed depends on the option selected from the **End Condition** drop-down list. The **Reverse Direction** button is used to reverse the direction of the feature creation. If you choose the **Mid Plane** option from the **End Condition** drop-down list, the **Reverse Direction** button will not be available.

Flip side to cut

The **Flip side to cut** check box is selected to define the side of the material removal. By default, the **Flip side to cut** check box is cleared. Therefore, the material will be removed from inside the profile of the sketch drawn for the cut feature. If you select this check box, the material will be removed from outside the profile of the sketch. Figure 6-70 shows a cut feature with the **Flip side to cut** check box cleared and Figure 6-71 shows a cut feature with the **Flip side to cut** check box selected.

*Figure 6-70 Cut feature with the **Flip side to cut** check box cleared*

*Figure 6-71 Cut feature with the **Flip side to cut** check box selected*

Tip. *You can also reverse the direction of material removal by clicking on the arrow available on the sketch while creating the cut feature. This arrow is only available if you have selected or cleared the **Flip side to cut** check box once.*

Draft On/Off

The **Draft On/Off** button is used to apply the draft angle to the extruded cut feature. The **Draft Angle** spinner available on the right of the **Draft On/Off** button is used to set the value of the draft angle. By default, the **Draft outward** check box is cleared. Therefore, the draft is created inward with respect to the direction of feature creation. If you select this check box, the draft added to the cut feature will be created outward with respect to the direction of the feature creation. Figure 6-72 shows the draft added to the cut feature with the **Draft outward** check box cleared and Figure 6-73 shows the draft added to the cut feature with the **Draft outward** check box selected.

Figure 6-72 *Cut feature with the* ***Draft outward*** *check box cleared*

Figure 6-73 *Cut feature with the* ***Draft outward*** *check box selected*

The **Direction 2** rollout is used to specify the termination of the feature creation in the second direction. The options available in the **Direction 2** rollout are the same as those discussed for the **Direction 1** rollout.

The **Selected Contour** rollout is used to select specific contours from the current sketch.

Tip. *The sketch used for the cut feature can be a closed loop or an open sketch. Note that if the sketch is an open sketch, the sketch should completely divide the model into two or more parts.*

Thin Feature

The **Thin Feature** rollout is used to create a thin cut feature. When you create a cut feature, you have to apply the thickness to the sketch in addition to the end condition. This rollout is used to specify the parameters to create the thin feature. To create a thin cut feature, invoke the cut tool after creating the sketch and specify the end conditions in the **Direction 1** and **Direction 2** rollouts. Now, select the check box available in the **Thin Feature** rollout to activate the **Thin Feature** rollout. The options available in this rollout are the same as those discussed for the thin boss feature.

Handling Multiple Bodies in the Cut Feature

While creating the cut feature, sometimes because of the geometric conditions, feature termination, or end conditions, the cut feature results in the creation of multiple bodies. Figure 6-74 shows a sketch created on the top planar surface of the base feature to create a cut feature. Figure 6-75 shows the cut feature created with the end condition as **Through All**. Using this type of sketch and end condition, if you choose **OK** from the **Extrude-Cut PropertyManager**, the **Bodies to Keep** dialog box will be displayed. As multiple bodies are created while applying the cut feature, this dialog box is used to define which body do you want to keep.

The **Bodies to Keep** dialog box is displayed in Figure 6-76. By default, the **All Bodies** radio button is selected. Therefore, if you choose **OK** from this dialog box, all bodies created after the

Figure 6-74 *Sketch created for the cut feature*

Figure 6-75 *Multiple bodies created using the cut feature*

Figure 6-76 *The **Bodies to Keep** dialog box*

cut feature will remain in the model. If you want the cut feature to consume any of the bodies, select the **Selected bodies** radio button to expand the dialog box, as shown in Figure 6-77.

You can select the check box provided on the left of the name of the body to keep that body. The selected body is displayed in green in temporary graphics. Select the bodies to keep and choose the **OK** button from the **Bodies to Keep** dialog box. Figure 6-78 shows a sketch created for the cut feature. Figure 6-79 shows the cut feature created using the thin option and the **All bodies** option selected from the **Bodies to Keep** dialog box.

Note
You will learn more about configurations in the later chapters.

Figure 6-77 *The **Bodies to Keep** dialog box with the **Selected bodies** option selected*

Figure 6-78 *Sketch to create a cut feature using the thin option*

Figure 6-79 *A thin cut feature created with all the resulting bodies retained*

Creating Revolved Cuts

CommandManager:	Features > Revolved Cut
Menu:	Insert > Cut > Revolve
Toolbar:	Features > Revolved Cut

Revolved cuts are used to remove the material by revolving a sketch around a selected axis. Similar to revolved boss/base features, you can define the revolution axis using a centerline or using an edge in the sketch. When you invoke the **Revolved Cut** tool, the **Cut-Revolve PropertyManager** will be displayed, as shown in Figure 6-80.

Various options available in this **PropertyManager** are similar to those discussed earlier. Figure 6-81 shows a sketch for a revolved cut feature and Figure 6-82 shows the resulting cut feature. Note that in Figure 6-82, a texture is applied to the cut feature.

Figure 6-80 The Cut-Revolve PropertyManager

Figure 6-81 Sketch for the revolved cut feature

Figure 6-82 Resulting cut feature with a texture

Note

*You can also select the tool to create the feature first and then select the plane to create the sketch. This way, after you exit the sketching environment, the feature tool will be activated automatically and you can define the parameters in their respective rollouts. For example, you can choose the **Revolved Cut** tool without creating any sketch. In this case, the **Revolve PropertyManager** will be displayed and you will be prompted to select a plane or a planar face to create a sketch or to select a sketch. As soon as you exit the sketching environment after creating the sketch, the **Cut-Revolve PropertyManager** will be automatically displayed.*

CONCEPT OF THE FEATURE SCOPE

As discussed earlier, you can create different disjoint bodies in a single part file in SolidWorks. After creating two or more disjoint bodies, when you create another feature, the **Feature Scope** rollout will be displayed in the **PropertyManager**. This rollout is used to define the bodies that will be affected by the creation of the feature. The feature scope option is used with the Extrude boss and cut, Revolve boss and cut, Sweep boss and cut, Loft boss and cut, Boss cut and thicken, Surface cut, and Cavity features.

In the **Feature Scope** rollout, the **Selected bodies** radio button and the **Auto-select** check box are selected by default. With the **Auto-select** check box selected, all disjoint bodies are selected and are affected by the feature creation. If you clear the **Auto-select** check box, a selection box will be invoked. You can select the bodies that you want to be affected by the feature creation. The name of the selected body is displayed in the selection box. If you select the **All bodies** radio button, all bodies available in the part file will be selected and affected by the creation of the feature.

Tip. *You can invoke the previous command by pressing the ENTER key.*

TUTORIALS

Tutorial 1

In this tutorial, you will create the model shown in Figure 6-83 by drawing the sketch of the front view of the model and then select the contours to extrude them. As a result, you will learn the procedure of modeling using the contours selection method. The dimensions of the model are shown in Figure 6-84.   **(Expected time: 30 min)**

Figure 6-83 Solid model for Tutorial 1

Figure 6-84 *Dimensions and views for Tutorial 1*

It is clear from the figures that the given model is a multifeatured model. It consists of various extruded features. You first need to draw the sketch for each feature and then convert that sketch into a feature. In conventional methods, you create a separate sketch for each sketched feature. But in this tutorial, you use the contour selection method to draw a sketch and select the contours and share the same sketch for creating all the features.

The steps to be followed to complete this tutorial are listed next.

a.   Create the sketch on the default plane and apply the required relations and dimensions, refer to Figure 6-85.
b.   Invoke the extrude option and extrude the selected contour, refer to Figures 6-86 and 6-87.
c.   Select the second set of contours and extrude them to the required distance, refer to Figures 6-88 and 6-89.
d.   Select the third set of contours and extrude them to the required distance, refer to Figures 6-90 and 6-91.
e.   Save the document and then close the document.

Creating the Sketch of the Model

1.   Start a new SolidWorks part document using the **New SolidWorks Document** dialog box.

2.   Draw the sketch of the front view of the model on the **Front Plane**. Apply the required

relations and dimensions to the sketch, as shown in Figure 6-85. Make sure that you do not exit the sketching environment.

Selecting and Extruding the Contours of the Sketch

In this tutorial, you need to use the contour selection method to create the model. Therefore, you first need to select one of the contours from the given sketch and extrude it. For a better representation of the sketch, you also orient the sketch to isometric view.

1. Choose the **Isometric** option from the flyout that is displayed when you choose the **Standard Views** button from the **View** toolbar.

2. Right-click in the drawing area to invoke the shortcut menu and choose the **Contour Select Tool** option. The select cursor is replaced by the contour selection cursor and the selection confirmation corner is displayed.

3. Move the cursor to the lower rectangle of the sketch; the area of the rectangle is highlighted. This indicates that this rectangle is a closed profile.

4. Click at this location when the rectangular area is highlighted. Figure 6-86 shows the lower rectangle selected using the contour selection tool.

Figure 6-85 Fully defined sketch for creating the model

Figure 6-86 Lower rectangle selected as a contour

5. Choose the **Extruded Boss/Base** button from the **Features CommandManager**; the **Extrude PropertyManager** is invoked and the preview of the base feature is displayed in the drawing area in temporary graphics.

The name of the selected contour is displayed in the selection box of the **Selected Contours** rollout.

6. Right-click in the drawing area and choose the **Mid Plane** option from the shortcut menu. The preview of the feature is modified dynamically when you choose the **Mid Plane** option.

7. Set the value of the **Depth** spinner to **52** and choose the **OK** button from the **Extrude PropertyManager**. The base feature of the model by extruding the selected contour is shown in Figure 6-87.

8. Right-click in the drawing area and choose the **Contour Select Tool** option from the shortcut menu; the select cursor is replaced by the contour selection cursor.

9. Using the contour selection cursor, select any entity of the sketch to invoke the selection mode of the sketch.

10. Using the left mouse button, select the middle contour of the sketch, as shown in Figure 6-88. The selected region is highlighted.

Figure 6-87 *Base feature of the model*

Figure 6-88 *Middle contour is selected using the contour selection tool*

11. Invoke the **Extrude PropertyManager**. Right-click in the drawing area and choose the **Mid Plane** option from the shortcut menu.

12. Set the value of the **Depth** spinner to **40** and choose the **OK** button from the **Extrude PropertyManager**. The feature created by selecting the middle contour is shown in Figure 6-89.

13. Again invoke the **Contour Select Tool** and select a sketched entity. Next, select the right contour of the sketch. Press and hold the CTRL key down and select the left contour of the sketch, see Figure 6-90.

14. Invoke the **Extrude PropertyManager**. Right-click and choose the **Mid Plane** option from the shortcut menu.

15. Set the value of the **Depth** spinner to **8** and choose the **OK** button from the **Extrude PropertyManager**.

Figure 6-89 *Second feature created by extruding the middle contour*   *Figure 6-90* *The right and the left contours selected*

The model is completed, but the sketch is displayed in the model. Therefore, you need to hide the sketch.

16. Move the cursor to any of the sketched entities and when the entity turns red, select it. The selected sketched entity is displayed in green. Now, right-click and choose the **Hide** option from the shortcut menu.

The isometric view of the final model, with the visibility of the sketch turned off, is shown in Figure 6-91. The **FeatureManager Design Tree** of the model is shown in Figure 6-92.

Figure 6-91 *Final solid model*

Figure 6-92 The FeatureManager Design Tree

Saving the Model

1. Choose the **Save** button from the **Standard** toolbar and save the model with the name given below.

    \My Documents\SolidWorks\c06\c06tut1.sldprt

2. Choose **File** > **Close** from the menu bar to close the document.

Tutorial 2

In this tutorial, you will create the model shown in Figure 6-93. You will use a combination of the conventional modeling method and the contour selection method to create this model. The dimensions of the model are shown in Figure 6-94. **(Expected time: 30 min)**

Figure 6-93 Solid model for Tutorial 2

Figure 6-94 *Drawing views of the solid model*

The steps that will be used to complete the model are listed next.

a. Draw the sketch of the front view of the model, refer to Figure 6-95.
b. Extrude the selected contours, refer to Figures 6-96 through 6-98.
c. Add the recess feature to the model by drawing the sketch on the right planar face, refer to Figures 6-99 and 6-100.
d. Create four holes using the cut feature on the top face of the base feature, refer to Figures 6-101 and 6-102.
e. Save and close the document.

Drawing the Sketch for Contour Selection Modeling

1. Start a new SolidWorks part document. Draw the sketch of the front view of the model on the **Front Plane** using the standard sketching tools.

2. Apply the required relations and dimensions to fully define the sketch, see Figure 6-95.

    Orient the view to isometric view because it will help you in the selection of contours.

3. Change the current view to isometric view.

4. Right-click and choose the **Contour Select Tool** option from the shortcut menu; the select cursor is replaced by the contour selection cursor.

5. Using the contour selection cursor select the area enclosed by the lower rectangle, as shown in Figure 6-96.

Figure 6-95 *Fully defined sketch*   ***Figure 6-96*** *Lower rectangle selected as a contour*

6. Choose the **Extruded Boss/Base** button from the **Features CommandManager** to invoke the **Extrude PropertyManager**.

7. Set the value of the **Depth** spinner to **86** and choose the **OK** button from the **Extrude PropertyManager**. The base feature created after extruding the selected contour is shown in Figure 6-97.

8. Using the contour selection tool and the extrude tool create the other features and then hide the sketch. The model created after extruding all the contours and hiding the sketch is shown in Figure 6-98.

Figure 6-97 *Base feature created after extruding the selected contour*   ***Figure 6-98*** *Model created after extruding all contours*

Creating the Recess at the Base of the Model

After creating the extruded features of the model, you need to create the recess provided at the base of the model. The recess is created by a cut extrude feature created using a sketch drawn on the right planar face of the model.

1. Select the right planar face of the base feature as the sketching plane; the selected face is displayed in green.

2. Right-click in the drawing area and choose the **Insert Sketch** option from the shortcut menu to invoke the sketching environment.

   Now, you need to orient the view such that the selected face is normal to your eye view.

3. Choose the **Normal To** option from the flyout that is displayed when you choose the **Standard Views** button to orient the selected plane normal to the view.

4. Using the standard sketching tools, draw the sketch for the recess and apply the required relations and dimensions to it. The fully defined sketch for the cut feature is shown in Figure 6-99.

5. Choose the **Extruded Cut** button from the **Features CommandManager** to invoke the **Cut-Extrude PropertyManager**. The preview of the cut feature is displayed in the drawing area in temporary graphics.

6. Right-click in the drawing area and choose **Through All** from the shortcut menu.

7. Choose **OK** from the **Cut-Extrude PropertyManager** to complete the feature creation. The isometric view of the model after creating the cut feature is shown in Figure 6-100.

Figure 6-99 Sketch for the cut feature

Figure 6-100 Cut feature added to the model

Creating Holes

Next, you need to create the holes at the base of the model. These holes will be created as the extruded cut features. You need to draw the sketch of the hole feature on the top planar face of the base feature of the model. To draw the sketch of the holes, you need to first draw a circle and then using the **Linear Sketch Step and Repeat** option create the remaining circles.

1. Select the top planar face of the base feature as the sketching plane. Right-click and choose the **Insert Sketch** option from the shortcut menu.

2. Orient the current view normal to the viewing direction. Using the standard sketching tools, draw the sketch for the holes and apply the required relations and dimensions to fully define the sketch. You may need to apply the horizontal relations between the center points of the top circles to fully define the sketch. The fully defined sketch is shown in Figure 6-101.

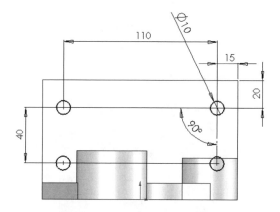

Figure 6-101 Holes sketched for the cut feature

3. Change the current view to isometric view and then choose the **Extruded Cut** button from the **Features CommandManager** to invoke the **Cut-Extrude PropertyManager**.

4. Right-click in the drawing area and choose the **Through All** option from the shortcut menu. Choose the **OK** button from the **Cut-Extrude PropertyManager**. The isometric view of the final model after hiding the sketch is shown in Figure 6-102. The **FeatureManager Design Tree** of the model is shown in Figure 6-103.

Saving the Model

1. Choose the **Save** button from the **Standard** toolbar and save the model with the name given below.

   \My Documents\SolidWorks\c06\c06tut2.sldprt

2. Choose **File > Close** from the menu bar to close the document.

Figure 6-102 *Final solid model*

Figure 6-103 *The FeatureManager Design Tree*

Tutorial 3

In this tutorial, you will create a model whose dimensions are shown in Figure 6-104. The solid model is shown in Figure 6-105.   **(Expected Time: 30 min)**

Section A—A

Figure 6-104 *Top view, sectioned front view, and sectioned right view of the model*

Figure 6-105 *Solid model for Tutorial 3*

The steps that will be followed to complete this tutorial are listed next.

a.   Create the base feature by extruding the sketch drawn on the **Front Plane**, refer to Figures 6-106 and 6-107.
b.   Extrude the sketch created on the **Top Plane** to create a cut feature, refer to Figures 6-108 through 6-110.
c.   Create a plane at an offset distance of 150 from the **Top Plane**.
d.   Draw a sketch on the newly created plane and extrude it to the selected surface, refer to Figures 6-111 and 6-112.
e.   Create a contour bore using the cut revolve option, refer to Figures 6-113 and 6-114.
f.   Create the holes using the cut feature, refer to Figures 6-115 and 6-116.
g.   Save the document and close it.

Creating the Base Feature

It is evident from the model that its base comprises a complex geometry. You need to create the base feature and then apply the cut feature to the base of the model to get the desired shape. You need to create the base feature on the **Front Plane** as the sketching plane. After drawing the sketch, you need to extrude it using the mid plane option to complete the feature creation.

1.   Start a new SolidWorks part document and invoke the sketching environment to draw the sketch for the base feature.

2.   Using the standard sketching tools, draw the sketch of the base feature and then apply the required relations and dimensions to the sketch, as shown in Figure 6-106.

3.   Invoke the **Extrude PropertyManager**. Right-click in the drawing area and choose the **Mid Plane** option from the shortcut menu.

4.   Set the value of the **Depth** spinner to **150** and choose the **OK** button from the **Extrude PropertyManager**. The isometric view of the base feature of the model is shown in Figure 6-107.

Figure 6-106 *Sketch of the base feature*   **Figure 6-107** *Base feature of the solid model*

Creating the Cut Feature

Now, you need to create a cut feature to get the required shape of the base feature. The sketch for this cut feature is created using a reference plane defined tangent to the curved face of the previous feature.

1. Choose the **Plane** button from the **Reference Geometry CommandManager** to display the **Plane PropertyManager**.

2. Select the upper curved face of the existing feature. The **On Surface** button is automatically chosen. Now, move the cursor close to the midpoint of the curved edge of the upper curved face; the point is highlighted in red, see Figure 6-108. Select this point; the preview of a plane tangent to the curved face and passing through the midpoint of the curved edge is displayed. Choose **OK** to create the reference plane.

3. Draw the sketch for the cut feature using the standard sketching tools and then apply the required relations and dimensions to the sketch, as shown in Figure 6-109.

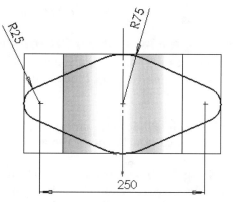

Figure 6-108 *Selecting the point to define the tangent plane*

Figure 6-109 *Fully dimensioned sketch for the cut feature*

4. Choose the **Extruded Cut** button from the **Features CommandManager** to invoke the **Cut-Extrude PropertyManager**. Change the current view to isometric view.

    You will also observe that the direction of the material removal is not in the required direction. Therefore, you need to flip its direction.

5. Select the **Flip side to cut** check box. You will observe that the direction of the material removal is also changed in the preview.

6. Right-click in the drawing area and choose the **Through All** option from the shortcut menu and choose the **OK** button from the **Cut-Extrude PropertyManager**.

    Because the reference plane is displayed in the drawing area, you need to hide it.

7. Right-click on **Plane1** in the drawing area and choose **Hide** from the shortcut menu; the display of the reference plane is turned off. The model, after creating the base feature, is shown in Figure 6-110.

Figure 6-110 *Cut feature added to the base feature*

Creating a Plane at an Offset Distance for the Extruded Feature

After creating the base of the model, you need to create a plane at an offset distance of 150 mm from the **Top Plane**. This newly created plane is used as a sketching plane for the next feature.

1. Choose the **Plane** button from the **Reference Geometry CommandManager** to invoke the **Plane PropertyManager**.

2. Choose the **Offset Distance** button from the **Plane PropertyManager**. The **Distance** spinner, the **Reverse direction** check box, and the **Number of Planes to Create** spinner are displayed in the **Plane PropertyManager**.

3. Click on the + sign located on the left of the **FeatureManager Design Tree**, which is now displayed in the drawing area. The tree view expands and the three default planes are now visible in the tree view.

4. Select the **Top Plane** from the **FeatureManager Design Tree**; the preview of the newly created plane at a default offset is displayed in the drawing area.

5. Set the value of the **Distance** spinner to **150** and choose the **OK** button from the **Plane PropertyManager**. The required plane is created.

Creating the Extruded Feature

After creating the plane at an offset distance from the **Top Plane**, you need to draw the sketch for the next feature.

1. Select the reference plane you just created if it is not selected, and invoke the sketching environment. Set the current view normal to the eye view.

2. Draw the sketch of the circle and apply the required relations to the sketch, as shown in Figure 6-111.

3. Change the current view to isometric view and invoke the **Extrude PropertyManager**. You will observe from the preview that the direction of the feature creation is opposite to the required direction. Therefore, you need to change the direction of the feature creation.

4. Choose the **Reverse Direction** button provided on the left of the **End Condition** drop-down list to reverse the direction of feature creation. The preview of the feature is changed when you reverse the direction of the feature creation.

5. Right-click in the drawing area and choose the **Up To Surface** option from the shortcut menu; you are prompted to select a face or a surface to complete the specification of the first direction. Also, the **Face/Plane** selection box is displayed under the **End Condition** drop-down list in the **Direction 1** rollout.

6. Select the upper curved surface of the model using the left mouse button. You will observe that the preview shows the feature extruded up to the selected surface.

7. Choose the **OK** button from the **Extrude PropertyManager**.

    Because the plane is displayed in the drawing area, you need to turn off its display.

8. Select **Plane2** from the **FeatureManager Design Tree** or from the drawing area and invoke the shortcut menu. Choose the **Hide** option from the shortcut menu. The model created after creating the extruded feature is shown in Figure 6-112.

Figure 6-111 *Sketch created on the newly created plane*

Figure 6-112 *Sketch extruded up to a selected surface*

Creating the Counterbore Hole

Next, you need to create the counterbore hole. It will be created as a revolved cut feature using a sketch drawn on the **Front Plane**.

1. Invoke the sketching environment by selecting the **Front Plane** as the sketching plane and orient the plane normal to the eye view.

2. Draw the sketch of the counterbore hole using the standard sketching tools. Add the required relations and then add the linear diameter dimensions, as shown in Figure 6-113.

3. Set the current view to isometric view and then choose the **Revolved Cut** button from the **Features CommandManager**; the **Cut-Revolve PropertyManager** is displayed.

   The preview of the cut feature is displayed in the drawing area in temporary graphics. The value of the angle in the **Angle** spinner is set to **360** by default. Therefore, you do not need to set the value of the **Angle** spinner.

4. Choose the **OK** button from the **Cut-Revolve PropertyManager**. Figure 6-114 shows the model after creating the revolve cut feature.

Figure 6-113   *Fully defined sketch for the counterbore hole*

Figure 6-114   *Cut feature added to the model*

Creating Holes

After creating all features, you need to create the holes using the extruded cut feature to complete the model. The sketch for the cut feature is to be drawn using the top planar surface of the base feature as the sketching plane.

1. Select the top planar surface of the base feature and invoke the sketching environment. Orient the model so that the selected face of the model is oriented normal to the eye view.

2. Draw the sketch using the standard sketching tools and apply the required relations and dimensions, as shown in Figure 6-115.

3. Change the current view to isometric view. Choose the **Extruded Cut** button from the **Features CommandManager** to invoke the **Cut-Extrude PropertyManager**.

4. Right-click and choose the **Through All** option from the shortcut menu and choose the **OK** button from the **Cut-Extrude PropertyManager**. The final model is shown in Figure 6-116.

Figure 6-115 *Fully defined sketch for the cut feature*   *Figure 6-116* *Final model*

The **FeatureManager Design Tree** of the model is shown in Figure 6-117.

Figure 6-117 *The FeatureManager Design Tree*

Saving the Model

1. Choose the **Save** button from the **Standard** toolbar and save the model with the name given next.

   \My Documents\SolidWorks\c06\c06tut3.sldprt

2. Choose **File** > **Close** from the menu bar to close the document.

SELF-EVALUATION TEST

Answer the following questions and then compare your answers with those given at the end of this chapter:

1. When you draw a sketch for the first time in the sketching environment, the sketch is drawn on the default plane, which is the **Front Plane**. (T/F)

2. When you start a new SolidWorks part document, SolidWorks provides you with two default planes. (T/F)

3. You can choose the **Plane** button from the **Reference Geometry CommandManager** to invoke the **Plane PropertyManager**. (T/F)

4. You cannot create a plane at an offset distance by dynamically dragging. (T/F)

5. When you create a circular feature, a temporary axis is automatically created. (T/F)

6. The _____ option is used to extrude a sketch from the sketching plane to the next surface that intersects the feature.

7. The _____ option available in the **End Condition** drop-down list is used to define the termination of the extruded feature up to another body.

8. The _____ check box is used to merge the newly created body with the parent body.

9. Using the _____ option, you can create a reference axis that passes through the center point of a cylindrical or a conical surface.

10. Sometimes multiple bodies are created while applying the cut feature. Therefore, the _____ dialog box is displayed, which allows you to define which body to keep.

REVIEW QUESTIONS

Answer the following questions:

1. If the _____ check box is cleared, the virtual surface created for the termination of the extruded feature will have a concentric relation with the selected surface.

2. The _____ option is selected from the shortcut menu to select the contours.

3. The _____ option is available in the **End condition** drop-down list only after you create the base feature.

4. The _____ check box is used to define the side of the material removal.

5. The _____ check box is used to create an outward draft in a cut feature.

6. Which check box is selected while creating any other feature in a single-body modeling?

   (a) **Combine results**   (b) **Fix bodies**
   (c) **Merge results**   (d) **Union results**

7. Which button is used to add a draft angle to a cut feature?

   (a) **Add Draft**   (b) **Create Draft**
   (c) **Draft On/Off**   (c) None of these

8. Which **PropertyManager** is invoked to create a cut feature by extruding a sketch?

   (a) **Extruded Cut**   (b) **Cut-Extrude**
   (c) **Extrude-Cut**   (d) **Cut**

9. Which of the following options is used to define the termination of feature creation at an offset distance to a selected surface?

   (a) **Distance To Surface**   (b) **Normal From Surface**
   (c) **Distance From Surface**   (d) **Offset From Surface**

10. Which of the following options is used to define the termination of feature creation to the selected surface?

   (a) **To Surface**   (b) **Selected Surface**
   (c) **Up To Surface**   (d) None of these

EXERCISES

Exercise 1

Create a model whose dimensions are shown in Figure 6-118. The solid model is shown in Figure 6-119.   **(Expected time: 30 min)**

Figure 6-118 *Dimensions of the model for Exercise 1*

Figure 6-119 *Model for Exercise 1*

Exercise 2

Create the model shown in Figure 6-120 . The dimensions of the model are given in Figure 6-121.

(Expected time: 30 min)

Figure 6-120 *Model for Exercise 2*

Figure 6-121 *Dimensions for Exercise 2*

Answers to Self-Evaluation Test
1. F, **2.** F, **3.** T, **4.** F, **5.** T, **6. Up To Next**, **7. Up To Body**, **8. Merge results,**
9. Cylindrical/Conical Surface, **10. Bodies to Keep**

Chapter 7

Advanced Modeling Tools-I

Learning Objectives

After completing this chapter, you will be able to:
- *Create holes using the Simple Hole option.*
- *Create standard holes using the Hole Wizard option.*
- *Apply simple and advanced fillets.*
- *Understand various selection methods.*
- *Chamfer the edges and vertices of the model.*
- *Create the Shell feature.*
- *Create the Wrap feature.*

ADVANCED MODELING TOOLS

This chapter discusses various advanced modeling tools available in SolidWorks that assist you in creating a better and accurate design by capturing the design intent in the model. For example, in the previous chapters you learned to create a hole using the cut option. In this chapter, you will create holes using the **Simple Hole** option and the **Hole Wizard** option. Using the hole wizard, you can create standard holes classified on the basis of the industrial standard, screw type, and size. The **Hole Wizard** tool of SolidWorks is one of the largest standard industrial virtual hole generation machines available in any CAD package. You will also learn about some other advanced modeling tools such as the fillet, chamfer, shell, and warp in this chapter.

Creating Simple Holes

CommandManager:	Features > Simple Hole	(Customize to Add)
Menu:	Insert > Features > Hole > Simple	
Toolbar:	Features > Simple Hole	(Customize to Add)

 The **Simple Hole** tool is used to create a simple hole feature. In the previous chapter you learned to create holes by sketching a circle and then using the cut option. But using the simple hole option, you do not need to draw a sketch of the hole. This is the reason why the holes created with this option act as a placed feature. To create a hole using this option, first you need to select the plane on which you want to place the hole feature. If you invoke this tool before selecting a plane, the **Hole PropertyManager** will be displayed, which will prompt you to select a placement plane. Now, choose the **Simple Hole** button from the **Features CommandManager** after customizing it; the **Hole PropertyManager** will be displayed, as shown in Figure 7-1.

Figure 7-1 The Hole PropertyManager

When you invoke the **Hole PropertyManager**, the preview of the hole feature will be displayed in the drawing area in temporary graphics with the default values. The preview of the hole feature with the default values is shown in Figure 7-2.

*Figure 7-2 Preview of the hole being created using the **Simple Hole** tool*

Tip. *It is recommended that before creating the hole feature, you create a point that will define its placement. While creating the hole feature, you can dynamically move it by selecting the center point of the sketch and dragging the cursor to the point sketched earlier. The cursor will snap to that point and the **Coincident** relation will be applied between the sketched point and the center point of the hole.*

Using the **End Condition** drop-down list, specify the termination type and set the value of the hole diameter in the **Hole Diameter** spinner. You can also specify the direction of extrusion using the **Direction of Extrusion** selection box. You can also specify a draft angle in the hole feature using the **Draft On/Off** button and set the value of the draft angle using the **Draft Angle** spinner. The preview of the draft angle is also displayed in the drawing area in temporary graphics. After setting all parameters, choose the **OK** button from the **Hole PropertyManager**.

The hole feature created using this option is placed on the selected plane but the placement of the hole is not yet defined. Therefore, select the hole feature from the **FeatureManager Design Tree** and right-click to display the shortcut menu. Choose the **Edit Sketch** option from the shortcut menu; the sketching environment will be invoked and you can apply the relations and dimensions to define the placement of the hole feature on the selected face and exit the sketching environment.

Creating Standard Holes Using the Hole Wizard

CommandManager:	Features > Hole Wizard
Menu:	Insert > Features > Hole > Wizard
Toolbar:	Features > Hole Wizard

The **Hole Wizard** tool is used to add standard holes, such as the standard counterbore, countersink, drilled, tapped, and pipe tap holes. You can also add a user-defined counterbored drilled hole, counter-drilled drilled hole, counterbored hole, counterdrilled hole, countersunk hole, countersunk drilled hole, simple hole, simple drilled hole, tapered hole, and tapered drilled hole. You can control all parameters of the holes, including the termination options. You can also modify the holes according to your requirement after placing them. Therefore, you can place the standard parametric holes using this tool. You can select a face or a plane to place the hole even before invoking this tool. The placement face can be a planar face or a curved face. After selecting the placement plane or face, choose the **Hole Wizard** button from the **Features CommandManager**. From this release of SolidWorks, the **Hole Specification PropertyManager** is displayed when you invoke this tool. This **PropertyManager** is shown in Figure 7-3.

Figure 7-3 *Partial view of the **Hole Specification PropertyManager***

When you preselect the placement plane and invoke the **Hole Specifications PropertyManager**, the preview of the hole feature will be displayed in the graphics area. If you modify the parameters of the hole or change its type, the preview of the hole will also be modified dynamically. The options in the **Hole Specification PropertyManager** are discussed next.

Hole Specification Rollout

The **Hole Specification** rollout (Figure 7-4) available in the **Type** tab of the **Hole Specifications PropertyManager** is used to define the type of standard hole to be created. You will notice that the **Counterbore** button is chosen by default. As a result, a counterbore hole will be created. The other options available in this rollout are discussed next.

Standard

The **Standard** drop-down list is used to specify the industrial dimensioning and hole standards. By default, the **Ansi Inch** standard is selected. Various other dimensioning standards are available in this drop-down list, such as **Ansi Metric**, **BSI**, **DIN**, **ISO**, **JIS**, **DME**, **Hasco Metric**, **PCS**, **Progressive**, and **Superior**.

Figure 7-4   The Hole Specification rollout

Type

The **Type** drop-down list is used to define the type of fastener to be inserted in the hole. The standard holes created using the **Hole Wizard** tool depend on the type of fastener to be inserted in that hole and the size of the fastener. You can select the screw type from the **Type** drop-down list. The types of screws available in the drop-down list depend on the standard selected from the **Standard** drop-down list.

Size

The **Size** drop-down is used to define the size of the fastener that will be inserted in the hole that is created using the **Hole Wizard** tool. The sizes of the fasteners available in the **Size** drop-down list depend on the standard selected from the **Standard** drop-down list.

Fit

The **Fit** drop-down list is used to specify the types of fits to be applied to the hole. You can apply the **Close**, **Normal**, or **Loose** fits to the hole.

Figure 7-5 shows the button available in the **Hole Specification** rollout. Each button is used to create a specific type of standard hole. The options used to create all the standard holes, except legacy holes, are the same as those discussed above.

Figure 7-5   Buttons available in the Hole Specification rollout

When you choose the **Legacy Hole** button, the preview of the hole is displayed in the preview area below the **Type** drop-down list. Also, the **Section Dimensions** rollout is displayed. Select the type of hole that you need to create using the **Type** drop-down list. The preview of the hole feature updates automatically. You can set the parameters of the hole by double-clicking on the fields in the **Value** column of the **Section Dimensions** rollout.

End Condition Rollout

The **End Condition** rollout, shown in Figure 7-6, is used to specify the hole termination options. By default, the **Through All** option is selected in this drop-down list. The hole termination options are similar to the other feature termination options discussed in earlier chapters. You can also flip the direction of the hole creation using the **Reverse Direction** button.

Reverse Direction   End Condition

*Figure 7-6 The **End Condition** rollout*

If you are creating a tapped hole or a pipe tapped hole, the additional options will be displayed to specify the termination conditions for threads.

Options Rollout

Options available in the **Options** rollout are used to define some of the additional parameters of the hole. These parameters are optional and are specified only if required. Figure 7-7 shows the **Options** rollout with all check boxes selected. All these options are discussed next.

Head clearance

The **Head clearance** check box is selected to specify the clearance distance between the head of the fastener and the placement plane of the hole feature. After you select this check box, the **Head Clearance** spinner is displayed. You can set the value of clearance using this spinner.

Near side countersink

The **Near side countersink** check box is selected to specify the diameter and the angle for the countersink on the upper face, which is the placement plane of the hole feature. After you select this check box, the **Near Side Countersink Diameter** and **Near Side Countersink Angle** spinners are displayed. You can set the values of the diameter and angle using their respective spinners.

*Figure 7-7 The **Options** rollout*

Under head countersink

The **Under head countersink** check box is selected to specify the diameter and the angle for the countersink to be applied at the end of the counterbore head. After you select this check box, the **Under Head Countersink Diameter** and the **Under Head Countersink Angle** spinners are displayed. You can set the values of the diameter and angle using these spinners.

Far side countersink

The **Far side countersink** check box is selected to specify the diameter and the angle for the countersink on the bottom face of the hole feature. After you select this check box, the **Far Side Countersink Diameter** and **Far Side Countersink Angle** spinners are displayed. You can set the values of the diameter and angle using their respective spinners.

If you are creating a user-defined hole using the **Legacy Hole** button, the **Options** rollout is not displayed. If you are creating a tapped hole, some additional options are displayed. These options are discussed next.

Cosmetic thread

The **Cosmetic thread** check box is selected to display cosmetic threads. When you select the check box, the **Cosmetic Thread** drop-down list is displayed. By default, the **With thread callout** option is selected in this drop-down list. Therefore, a callout will be attached to the cosmetic thread. You can also select the option of not displaying the callout.

Thread class

The **Thread class** check box is selected to specify the class of the thread. When you select this check box, the **Thread Class** drop-down list is displayed. You can select the type of class using this drop-down list.

Favorite

The **Favorite** rollout is used to add the frequently used holes to the favorite list. If you add a hole to the favorite list, you will not have to configure the same settings to add similar types of holes every time. The method of adding a hole setting to the favorite list is the same as that used to add dimensional settings. This procedure was discussed in Chapter 4.

Custom Sizing

The **Custom Sizing** rollout, shown in Figure 7-8, is used to specify the custom size to a standard hole. It is not recommended to change the size of the standard holes. The options available in the **Custom Sizing** rollout depend on the type of hole that you are creating.

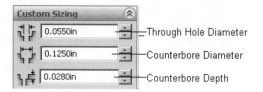

*Figure 7-8 The **Custom Sizing** rollout*

Defining the Position for Placing a Hole

As discussed earlier, the preview of the hole feature is dynamically updated in the drawing area while you are defining the parameters of the hole feature. This is because you have already selected the placement plane for the hole feature. If you do not select a placement plane, the preview of the hole feature will not be displayed in the drawing area. After configuring all parameters of the hole feature, you need to define its placement position. To define the placement of the hole, choose the **Positions** tab from the **Hole Specification PropertyManager**. On invoking this tab, you will notice that **Hole Specification PropertyManager** is changed to **Hole Position PropertyManager**, as shown in Figure 7-9.

Figure 7-9   The Hole Position PropertyManager

The message in the **Hole Position(s)** rollout informs you to use the dimension and other sketch tools to place the hole. The select cursor will be replaced by the placement cursor. Using the placement cursor, you can place more holes in the current hole features. As discussed earlier, if the placement plane is selected earlier, the hole will be placed on the selected placement plane. If the placement plane is not selected earlier, you can specify a point to place the hole feature. You can also constrain the placement of the placement point of the hole feature using the relations and dimensions. Choose the **OK** button to complete the feature creation.

Note
*If you create a pattern feature of a tapped hole feature, the thread graphic will not be displayed in the other instances of the pattern, except the parent instance. Therefore, to add the thread graphic in other pattern instances, use the **Texture PropertyManager**. You will learn more about patterns in later chapters.*

Figure 7-10 through 7-13 show the models with various types of holes placed using the **Hole Wizard** tool. Figure 7-14 shows a base plate on which various types of holes are applied using the **Hole Wizard** tool.

Figure 7-10 Counterbore holes   *Figure 7-11 Countersink holes*

Figure 7-12 *Drilled holes*   **Figure 7-13** *Tapped holes*

Figure 7-14 *Base Plate with holes created using the **Hole Wizard** option*

Creating Fillets

CommandManager:	Features > Fillet
Menu:	Insert > Features > Fillet/Round
Toolbar:	Features > Fillet

In SolidWorks, you can add fillets as a feature in the model manually or using the FilletXpert. Using the manual fillet, you can round an internal or external face or edge of a model. You can also use the advanced fillet options to add advanced fillets to the model. You can preselect the face, edge, or feature to which the fillet has to be applied. You can also select the entity to be filleted after invoking the fillet tool. To add a manual fillet, choose the **Fillet** button from the **Features CommandManager**; the **Fillet PropertyManager** is invoked. Choose the **Manual** tab to display the options to create manual fillets, as shown in Figure 7-15. The preview of the fillet feature will also be displayed in the drawing area if the entities to be filleted are selected and the **Full Preview** radio

Tip. *The hole feature created using the **Hole Wizard** tool consists of two sketches. The first sketch is the sketch of the placement point and the second sketch is the sketch of the profile of the hole feature. If you select the placement plane before invoking the **Hole Definition** dialog box, the resulting placement sketch will be a 2D sketch. Instead of preselecting the placement plane, if you select the placement point after invoking the **Placement Point** dialog box, the resulting placement sketch will be a 3D sketch. You will learn more about 3D sketches in the later chapters.*

In the modern modeling practice, the creation of threads is avoided in models because it results in the creation of a complex geometry. The views are generated from those models that contain complex geometry, which is difficult to understand. Therefore, it is a better practice to avoid the creation of threads in the model and add the cosmetic threads. Using the cosmetic threads, you will get the thread convention in the drawing views, which is recommended.

*If a cosmetic thread is added to a tapped hole, the cosmetic thread will also be displayed along with the placement and hole profile sketches. You can edit the cosmetic threads by selecting them from the **FeatureManager Design Tree** and right-clicking to display the shortcut menu. Choose the **Edit Definition** option to display the **Cosmetic Thread** dialog box. The **Cosmetic Thread** dialog box and the cosmetic threads are discussed in later chapters.*

You can also view the convention of the thread if the cosmetic thread is added to a tapped hole feature. Orient the model to the top view to observe the thread convention from the top view. Orient the model in the front view, back view, or any side view to observe the thread convention from the side views.

button will be selected by default. If preselection is not done, you will be prompted to select the edges, faces, features, or loops to add the fillet feature. Using the select cursor, select the entity to be filleted. A fillet callout will also be displayed along the preview of the fillet. Figure 7-16 shows the preview of the fillet feature with the fillet callout.

Using the fillet tool, you can create various types of fillets, which are given next.

1. Constant radius fillet
2. Variable radius fillet
3. Face Fillet
4. Full round fillet

The above-mentioned fillets are discussed next.

Constant Radius Fillet

The constant radius fillet option creates a fillet of a constant radius along the selected entity. This is the default option selected in the **Fillet Type** rollout. You can set the value of the fillet radius using the **Fillet** spinner provided in the **Items To Fillet** rollout or by clicking in the

Figure 7-15 The **Fillet PropertyManager**

Figure 7-16 Preview of the fillet feature

value area of the fillet callout. The value area of the callout will be replaced by the radius edit box. Enter the value of the radius and press the ENTER key on the keyboard. The preview of the fillet will be changed dynamically when the value of the radius of the fillet is changed. The names of the selected entities are displayed in the **Edges, Faces, Features, and Loops** selection box. The entities that you can select to add the fillet feature are faces, edges, features, and loops. Next, choose the **OK** button from the **Fillet PropertyManager**. Figures 7-17 through 7-22 show the selection of different entities and the resulting fillet creation from the selected entities.

Edges selected
to fillet

Figure 7-17 *Selecting the edges*

Figure 7-18 *Resulting fillet*

Face selected
to fillet

Figure 7-19 *Selecting the face*

Figure 7-20 *Resulting fillet*

Boss feature
selected to
fillet

Figure 7-21 *Selecting the feature*

Figure 7-22 *Resulting fillet*

Tip. *You can preselect a feature for creating a fillet feature or select the feature after invoking the* **Fillet** *tool. For post selection of the feature to be filleted, expand the* **FeatureManager Design Tree**, *which is displayed in the drawing area, and select the feature. You can also select the feature from the drawing area. The preview of the filleted feature will be displayed in the drawing area.*

Multiple Radius Fillet

Using the **Multiple radius fillet** option provided in the **Fillet PropertyManager**, you can specify a fillet of different radii to all the selected edges. For creating a fillet feature using the multiple radius option, preselect the edges, faces, or features or select them after invoking the **Fillet PropertyManager**. After invoking the **Fillet** tool, select the **Multiple radius fillet** check box. The preview of the fillet feature with the default value will be displayed in the drawing area. You will notice that you are provided with different callouts for each selected entity. Figure 7-23 shows the preview of the fillet feature with the **Multiple radius fillet** check box selected.

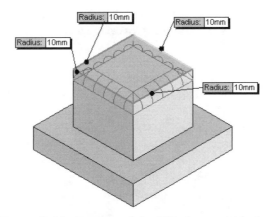

Figure 7-23 *Preview of the fillet feature with the* **Multiple radius fillet** *check box selected*

The names of the selected entities are displayed in the **Edges**, **Faces**, **Features and Loops** display box. The boundaries of the currently selected entity in the selection box are highlighted in green with a thick line. You can set the value of each selected entity by using the **Radius** spinner or by specifying the value of the fillet radius in the radius callout, as shown in Figure 7-24. As you modify the value of the radius, the preview of the fillet feature will be modified dynamically in the drawing area. Figure 7-25 shows the fillet created using the multiple radius fillet.

Fillet With and Without Tangent Propagation

In SolidWorks, you can add a fillet feature to a model with or without the tangent propagation. When you invoke the **Fillet PropertyManager**, you will observe that by default the **Tangent propagation** check box is selected. Therefore, if you select an edge, face, feature, or loop to fillet, it will automatically select other entities that are tangential to the selected entity. Thus, it will apply the fillet feature to all entities that are tangential to the selected one. If you clear

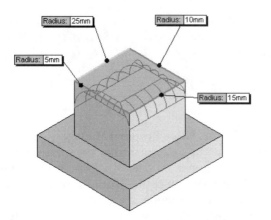

Figure 7-24 *Different radii specified in each radius callout*

Figure 7-25 *Resulting fillet*

the **Tangential propagation** check box, the fillet will be applied only to the selected entity. Figure 7-26 shows the entity to be selected to add a fillet feature. Figures 7-27 and 7-28 show the fillet feature created with the **Tangent propagation** check box cleared and selected respectively.

Figure 7-26 *Edge to be selected to apply the fillet feature*

Setback Fillets

The setback fillet is created where three or more edges are merged into a vertex. This type of fillet is used to smoothly blend transition surfaces generated from the edges to the fillet vertex. This smooth transition is created between all selected edges and the vertex selected for the setback type of fillet. To create a setback fillet, invoke the **Fillet PropertyManager** and select three or more edges to apply the fillet. Note that the edges should share the same vertex. The preview of the fillet will be displayed in the drawing area. Now, click on the black arrow in the **Setback Parameters** rollout to expand the rollout. The **Setback Parameters** rollout will be displayed, as shown in Figure 7-29. This rollout will be used to specify the setback parameters.

Tip. *The **Full preview** radio button available in the **Fillet PropertyManager** is used to preview the fillet feature before actually creating it. If you select the **Partial preview** radio button, you can view only the partial preview of the fillet feature. If you select a face to add a fillet feature and select the **Partial preview** radio button, you cannot preview the fillet feature created on all edges adjacent to the selected face. You can preview only the fillet on the single edge of the selected face. Press the A key on the keyboard to cycle the preview of the fillet feature on other edges of the selected face. If you select the **No preview** radio button, you cannot see the preview of the fillet feature.*

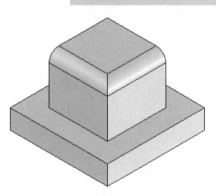

Figure 7-27 Fillet feature created with the ***Tangent propagation*** *check box cleared*

Figure 7-28 Fillet feature created with the ***Tangent propagation*** *check box selected*

*Figure 7-29 The **Setback Parameters** rollout*

Click once in the **Setback Vertices** selection box to invoke the setback vertex selection command. Now, select the vertex where the edges meet. Figure 7-30 shows the selected edges and the vertex to which the setback parameters are assigned.

When you select the vertex for the setback fillet, you will observe that callouts with unassigned setback distances are displayed in the drawing area. The name of the selected vertex will be displayed in the **Setback Vertices** selection box. The names of the selected edges will be displayed in the **Setback Distances** edit box. Select the name of the edge in the **Setback Distances** edit box to assign a setback distance to that edge; a magenta arrow will be displayed along that edge. Using the **Distance** spinner provided in the **Setback Parameters** rollout,

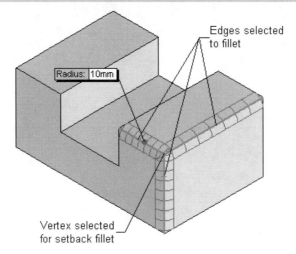

Figure 7-30 Edges and vertex to be selected to apply the setback fillet feature

assign a setback distance. Similarly, assign the setback distance to all edges. You can also assign the setback distance directly by specifying the value in the setback callouts displayed in the drawing area. As discussed earlier, the preview of the fillet will be updated automatically when you assign any value. The **Set Unassigned** button available in the **Setback Parameters** rollout is used to assign the setback distance displayed in the **Distance** spinner to all unassigned edges. The **Set All** button is used to assign the setback distance displayed in the **Distance** spinner to all edges. Figure 7-31 shows the preview of the setback fillet and Figure 7-32 shows a setback fillet on the right of the model and a normal fillet on the other side of the model.

Other Fillet Options

You are also provided with various other fillet options using which you can create an accurate and aesthetic design. The other fillet options available in the **Fillet PropertyManager** are **Keep features**, **Round corners**, **Controlling the Overflow type**, and so on. These options are discussed next.

Select through faces

This option allows you to select the edges hidden behind the faces of the model. This is a new feature introduced in this release of SolidWorks.

Keep feature

If you have boss or cut features in a model and the fillet created is large enough to consume them, it is recommended that you select the **Keep features** check box available

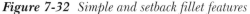

Figure 7-31 *Preview of the setback fillet*   *Figure 7-32* *Simple and setback fillet features*

in the **Fillet Options** rollout. This check box is selected by default, but you should confirm before creating any fillet feature. If you clear this check box, the fillet feature will consume the features that will obstruct its path. Note that the features that are consumed by the fillet feature are not deleted from the model. They disappear from the model because of some geometric inconsistency. When you rollback, suppress, or delete the fillet, the consumed features will reappear. You will learn more about rollback and suppress in later chapters. Figure 7-33 shows the model and the edge to be selected for fillet.

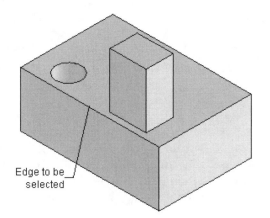

Figure 7-33 *Edge to be selected to apply the fillet feature*

Figure 7-34 shows the fillet feature with the **Keep features** check box selected and Figure 7-35 shows the fillet feature with the **Keep features** check box cleared.

Round corners
The **Round corners** option is used to round the edges at the corners of the fillet feature. To create a fillet feature with round corners, select the **Round corners** check box from the **Fillet Options** rollout after specifying all parameters of the fillet feature. Figure 7-36 shows a fillet feature created with the **Round corners** check box cleared and Figure 7-37 shows a fillet feature created with the **Round corners** check box selected.

Figure 7-34 *Fillet feature created with the* ***Keep features*** *check box selected*

Figure 7-35 *Fillet feature created with the* ***Keep features*** *check box cleared*

Figure 7-36 *Fillet feature created with the* ***Round corners*** *check box cleared*

Figure 7-37 *Fillet feature created with the* ***Round corners*** *check box selected*

Overflow type

The **Overflow type** area is used to specify the physical condition that the fillet feature should adopt when it extends beyond an area. By default, SolidWorks automatically adopts the best possible flow type to accommodate the fillet, depending on the geometric conditions. This is because the **Default** option is selected by default in the **Overflow type** area. The other two options available in this area are discussed next.

Keep edge

The **Keep edge** radio button is selected when the fillet feature extends beyond a specified area. Therefore, to accommodate the fillet feature this option will divide the fillet into multiple surfaces and the adjacent edges will not be disturbed. A dip is created at the top of the fillet feature. Figure 7-38 shows a fillet feature created with the **Keep edge** radio button selected from the **Overflow type** area.

Keep surface

The **Keep surface** radio button available in this area is selected to accommodate the fillet feature by trimming it. This will maintain the smooth rounded fillet surface but it will disturb the adjacent edges. As this option maintains the smooth fillet surface, it extends to the adjacent surface. Figure 7-39 shows a fillet feature created with the **Keep surface** radio button selected from the **Overflow type** area.

Figure 7-38 *Fillet feature created with the overflow type as **Keep edge***

Figure 7-39 *Fillet feature created with the overflow type as **Keep surface***

Variable Radius Fillet

The variable radius fillet is created by specifying different radii along the length of the selected edge at specified intervals. Depending on the options, you can create a smooth transition or a straight transition between the vertices to which the radii are applied. To create a variable radius fillet, invoke the **Fillet PropertyManager**. Select the **Variable radius** radio button from the **Fillet Type** rollout; the **Variable Radius Parameters** rollout will be automatically displayed in the **Fillet PropertyManager**, as shown in Figure 7-40.

Figure 7-40 *The **Variable Radius Parameters** rollout*

You will be prompted to select the edge to fillet. Using the left mouse button, select the edge or edges you want to fillet. The name of the selected edge will be displayed in the **Edges, Faces, Features and Loops** selection box. By default, the radius is applied at the start point and the endpoint. The variable radius callouts are displayed at the ends of the selected edge, as shown in Figure 7-41.

The names of the vertices on which the callouts are added are displayed in the **Attached Radii** display box. You will find three red points on the selected edge because the value of the control point in the **Number of Instances** spinner is set to **3**. You can create a number of control points using the **Number of Instances** spinner. These control points are also called movable points because you can change the position of these control points. The additional radii are specified on these points on the selected edge.

Using the left mouse button, select the three control points available on the selected edge. As you select the control point the **Radius and Position** callouts will be displayed for each control point, as shown in Figure 7-42. The name of the selected point will also be displayed in the **Attached Radii** display box.

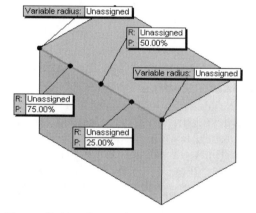

Figure 7-41 *Variable radius callouts displayed at the vertices of the selected edge*

Figure 7-42 *The **Radius and Position** callouts are displayed after selecting the control points*

You will observe that the position of the three points is described in terms of percentage. You can modify the position of the points by modifying the value of percentage in the **Position** area of the **Radius and Position** callout. By following this procedure, you can also modify the placement of the other points. You will observe that the radius value is not assigned to any of the callouts. Therefore, you need to specify the value of the radius in the callouts. Using the left mouse button, select the name of the vertex or point; the name of the selected item will be highlighted in yellow in its respective callout. Using the **Radius** spinner set the value of the radius for the selected item. You can also specify the value of the radius in the radius area of the callout. Set the value of each unassigned radius. You can also use the **Set Unassigned** button to assign the value displayed in the **Radius** spinner to all unassigned radii. The **Set All** button is used to assign the same value that is displayed in the **Radius** spinner to all radii. Figure 7-43 shows the preview of the fillet feature with modified positions of the control points with the radius values specified to all points and vertices. Figure 7-44 shows the resulting fillet feature.

Figure 7-43 *Preview of the variable radius fillet*

Figure 7-44 *Resulting fillet*

Smooth transition

When selected, the **Smooth transition** radio button creates a smooth transition by smoothly blending the points and vertices on which you have defined the radius on the selected edge.

Straight transition

The **Straight transition** radio button, when selected, creates a linear transition by blending the points and vertices on which you have defined the radius on the selected edge. In this case, the edge tangency is not maintained between one fillet radius and the adjacent face.

Figures 7-45 and 7-46 show the fillets created with the smooth and straight transition options, respectively.

Figure 7-45 *Variable radius fillet with smooth transition*

Figure 7-46 *Variable radius fillet with straight transition*

Face Fillet

Using the **Face Fillet**, you can add a fillet between two sets of faces. It blends the first set of faces with the second set of faces. It adds or removes the material according to the geometric conditions. It can also completely or partially remove the faces to accommodate the fillet feature. To create a face fillet feature, invoke the **Fillet PropertyManager** and select the **Face fillet** radio button from the **Fillet Type** rollout; the **Item To Fillet** rollout will be modified and provide the **Face Set 1** and **Face Set 2** selection boxes. The **Fillet PropertyManager** is shown in Figure 7-47 with the **Face fillet** radio button selected.

Figure 7-47 The ***Fillet PropertyManager*** *with the* ***Face fillet*** *radio button selected*

You will be prompted to select the faces to fillet for face set 1 and face set 2. Using the left mouse button, select the first set of faces. You can even select more than one face in a set. The name of the selected faces will be displayed in the **Face Set 1** display box and the selected faces will be displayed in green. The **Face Set 1** callout with radius will be displayed in the drawing area. Click in the **Face Set 2** selection box to invoke the selection tool and select the second set of faces. The second set of selected faces will be displayed in magenta and the **Face Set 2** callout will be displayed in the drawing area. Also, the preview of the face fillet will be displayed in the drawing area. Now, set the value of the radius in the **Radius** spinner. The **Tangent propagation** check box is used to create the face fillet tangent to the adjacent faces. This check box is selected by default. If you clear this check box, the fillet will not be forced to be tangent to the adjacent faces. Figure 7-48 shows the faces to be selected to apply the face fillet. Figure 7-49 displays the resulting fillet with three faces of the slot completely eliminated after applying the fillet.

Face Fillet Using the Hold Line
Using the face fillet created with the hold line you can specify the radius and the shape of the

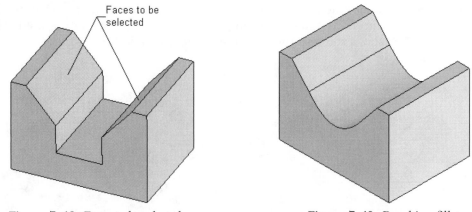

Figure 7-48 *Faces to be selected*   **Figure 7-49** *Resulting fillet*

fillet by determining a hold line. A hold line can be a set of edges, or a split line projected on a face. You will learn more about split lines in later chapters. The radius of the fillet is determined by the distance between the hold line and the edges or faces selected to be filleted. To create a face fillet using the hold line, invoke the **Fillet PropertyManager**. Using the left mouse button, click on the black arrow available at the top right corner of the **Fillet Options** rollout to display the rollout, as shown in Figure 7-50.

Figure 7-50 *The **Fillet Options** rollout*

The selection mode is active in the **Face Set 1** selection box and you are prompted to select the faces to be filleted for face set 1 and face set 2. Using the left mouse button, select the faces for the face set 1. The names of the selected faces will be displayed in the **Face Set 1** selection box and the selected faces will be displayed in green. Now, click in the **Face Set 2** selection box to activate the selection mode and select the faces to add in the face set 2. The selected faces will be displayed in magenta. The preview of the face fillet with the default settings will be displayed in the drawing area. By default, the **Tangent propagation** check box is selected. Therefore, you do not need to select the tangent faces in both face sets. This is because it will automatically select the faces tangent to the selected face. Now, using the left mouse button click on the **Hold line** display box and select the hold line or lines. The preview of the face fillet will be modified automatically. Now, choose the **OK** button from the **Fillet PropertyManager**. Figure 7-51 shows an example in which the faces and the hold line are selected. Figure 7-52 shows the resulting face fillet using the hold line.

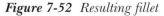

Figure 7-51 *Faces and hold line to be selected*   **Figure 7-52** *Resulting fillet*

Curvature Continuous in the Face Fillet With Hold Line

The **Curvature continuous** check box is selected to apply the face fillet feature with continuous curvature throughout the fillet feature. Note that fillet with continuous curvature is possible only by creating a face fillet feature with the hold line. You have to specify the hold lines on both sets of faces. Figure 7-53 shows a model in which a face fillet using the hold line is created on both the pillars. On the right pillar the face fillet is created with the **Curvature continuous** check box cleared and on the left pillar the face fillet is created with the **Curvature continuous** check box selected.

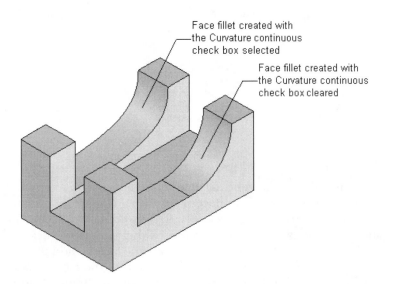

Figure 7-53 *Face fillet created with the* **Curvature continuous** *check box selected and cleared*

Constant Width

In the recent releases of SolidWorks, the **Fillet** tool is enhanced with the addition of the **Constant width** option. Consider a case in which you have applied a face fillet to the faces that are at an angle other than 90-degrees. You will notice that additional material is added to the fillet on the side that forms an acute angle with the other face, refer to Figure 7-54. If you select the **Constant width** check box from the **Fillet Options** rollout, a fillet of constant width will be applied between the selected face, refer to Figure 7-55.

Figure 7-54 *Face fillet with the* **Constant width** *check box cleared*

Figure 7-55 *Face fillet with the* **Constant width** *check box selected*

Full Round Fillet

The full round fillet is used to add a semicircular fillet feature. To create a full round fillet, invoke the **Fillet PropertyManager** and select the **Full round fillet** radio button; the **Items To Fillet** rollout will be modified, as shown in Figure 7-56. The selection mode is active in the **Side Face Set 1** selection box and you are prompted to select faces for the center and side face sets. Select the first face for the side face set 1. The selected face will be displayed in green. Now, click in the **Center Face** selection box and select the center face; the selected face will be displayed in blue. Next, click in the **Side Face Set 2** selection box and select the face for the side face set 2. The preview of the full round fillet will be displayed in the drawing area. Choose the **OK** button from the **Fillet PropertyManager**. Figure 7-57 shows the two faces being selected; the third face to be selected is the left face parallel to the first selected face. Figure 7-58 shows the resulting full round fillet.

Tip. *You can turn on or off the display of tangent edges of the model. To do so, choose* **Tools > Options** *from the menu bar to display the* **System Options - General** *dialog box. Choose the* **Display/Selection** *option from the area on the left and then the* **As visible** *or* **Removed** *radio buttons from the* **Part/Assembly tangent edge display** *area.*

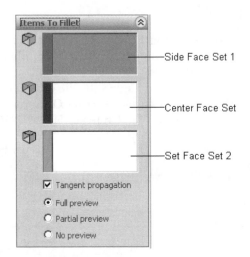

Figure 7-56 *The **Items To Fillet** rollout when the **Full round fillet** radio button is selected from the **Fillet Type** rollout*

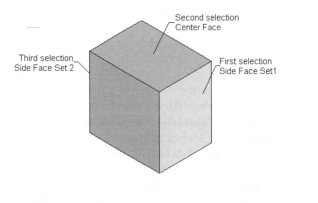

Figure 7-57 *Faces selected to create the full round fillet.*

Figure 7-58 *Resulting full round fillet*

Selection Methods

As you have learned about basic and advanced modeling tools, it is necessary for you to learn about some selection methods using which you can increase your productivity and speed of modeling. The selection methods that can increase your speed of creating fillets and chamfers are discussed next.

Select Other

One of the major enhancements in the selection options is the addition of the **Select Other** list box in the **Select Other** option. The **Select Other** option is the most common tool to cycle through the entities for selection. This option is used when the selection is difficult in a multifeatured complex model. Before invoking any other tool, select any entity and right-click to invoke the shortcut menu. Choose the **Select Other** option from the shortcut menu to display the **Select Other** list box, as shown in Figure 7-59, and the select cursor will be replaced by the select next cursor. The entities that are surrounding the selected entities will be listed in this list box. Also, the entities that are hidden behind the selected entity will be listed in this list box. When you move the cursor on the name of the entity, the entity will be highlighted in the drawing area. To select an entity using this list box, you just need to select the name of the entity in the list box; the resulting entity will be selected in the model and the **Select Other** list box will be closed.

*Figure 7-59   The **Select Other** list box*

If you select a face and invoke the **Select Other** list box, the display of the selected face will be turned off and you can easily select the face that is behind the selected face. The name of the hidden face will be displayed in the **Select Other** list box.

Select Loop

The **Select Loop** option is used to select the loops. Using this tool, you can also cycle through various loops before confirming the selection. This option is extremely useful when you are working with a complex model and you have to select a loop from that model. Using the select cursor, select any of the edges of the loop and right-click to invoke the shortcut menu. Choose the **Select Loop** option from the short cut menu. The loop that is possible by selecting that edge will be highlighted in green and an arrow will be displayed in yellow. Move the cursor on that arrow and when the arrow is highlighted in red, use the left mouse button to cycle through the loops. Repeat this until you select the required loop. Figure 7-60 shows a loop selected using the **Select Loop** option. Figure 7-61 shows the second loop selected when the left mouse button is used on the arrow to cycle through the loops.

*Figure 7-60 Loop selected using the **Select Loop** tool*

Figure 7-61 Second loop is selected while cycling through the loops

Select Partial Loop

Using this technique, you can select the partial loop created by joining two edges. To select a partial loop, select two edges, as shown in Figure 7-62. Invoke the shortcut menu and select the **Select Partial Loop** option from the shortcut menu. Generally, the selection point on second edge defines the major or minor partial loop selection. Figure 7-63 shows the resulting partial loop selected.

Figure 7-62 *Selecting edges to define the partial loop*

Figure 7-63 *Resulting partial loop that is selected*

Note
For a better visualization of the selected partial loop, the display of the model edges is turned off in Figures 7-62 and 7-63.

Tip. *The* **Select Midpoint** *option available in the shortcut menu is generally used in the sketching environment or while creating 3D sketches. You will learn more about 3D sketches in later chapters.*

Select Tangency

The **Select Tangency** option is used to automatically select the edges or faces that are tangent to the selected face. This option will be available in the shortcut menu only when a face or an edge is tangent to the selected face or edge. To use this option, select any face or edge using the select tool and right-click. Choose the **Select Tangency** option from the shortcut menu.

Creating Fillets Using the FilletXpert

CommandManager:	Features > Fillet
Menu:	Insert > Features > Fillet/Round
Toolbar:	Features > Fillet

The **FilletXpert** is a latest tool that allows you to create single or multiple fillets and reorder them, if required. To create fillets using the **FilletXpert**, invoke the **Fillet PropertyManager** and choose the **FilletXpert** button; the **FilletXpert** options will be displayed, as shown in Figure 7-64.

By default, the **Add** tab is chosen in the **FilletXpert**. This tab provides the options to create single or multiple fillets. These options are similar to those discussed while creating the fillets manually. To create multiple fillets, create the first fillet and then choose **Apply** from the **Items To Fillet** rollout. You can create multiple fillets using this procedure. Once a fillet

*Figure 7-64 The **FilletXpert** options in the*
Fillet PropertyManager

is created, it will be listed in the **Change** tab of the **PropertyManager**. You can select the
existing fillets from the **Existing Fillets** rollout of this tab and resize or remove them.

Creating Chamfers

CommandManager:	Features > Chamfer
Menu:	Insert > Features > Chamfer
Toolbar:	Features > Chamfer

Chamfering is defined as a process in which the sharp edges are beveled in order
to reduce the area of stress concentration. This process also eliminates the sharp
edges and corners that are not desirable. In SolidWorks, a chamfer is created
using the **Chamfer** tool. This tool is invoked by choosing the **Chamfer** button
available in the **Features CommandManager**. When you invoke the **Chamfer** tool, the
Chamfer PropertyManager will be displayed, as shown in Figure 7-65. Various types of
chamfers created using the **Chamfer PropertyManager** are discussed next.

Creating Edge Chamfer

The chamfers that are applied to the edges are known as the edge chamfer. To create an edge
chamfer, invoke the **Chamfer PropertyManager** and then select the edges to be chamfered.
When you select an edge to be chamfered, the preview of the chamfer feature with a distance
and angle callout will be displayed in the drawing area. The name of the selected edge will be

*Figure 7-65 The **Chamfer PropertyManager***

displayed in the **Edges and Faces or Vertex** selection box. Also, the selected entity will be highlighted in green and a yellow arrow will be displayed in the preview. The **Tangent propagation** check box is selected by default. Therefore, the edges tangent to the selected edge are selected automatically. By default, the **Partial preview** button is selected. You can select the **Full preview** button to display the full preview of the chamfer feature. Figure 7-66 shows the edge to be selected for chamfering and Figure 7-67 shows the full preview of the chamfer feature.

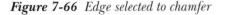

Figure 7-66 *Edge selected to chamfer*   **Figure 7-67** *Preview of the chamfer feature*

By default, the **Angle distance** radio button is selected. Therefore, the distance and angle callout is displayed in the drawing area. You can set the value of the distance and angle using the **Distance** and **Angle** spinners or you can enter their values directly in the **Distance** and **Angle** callouts. The **Flip direction** check box is used to specify the direction of the distance measurement. If you select the **Flip direction** check box, the arrow will also be flipped in the preview in the drawing area. You can also flip the direction by clicking on the arrow in the drawing area.

If you select the **Distance distance** radio button from the **Chamfer Parameters** rollout, the **Flip direction** check box will be replaced by the **Equal distance** check box. The **Angle** and **Distance** callouts will be replaced by **Distance 1** and **Distance 2** callouts. By default, the **Equal distance** check box is cleared. Set the value of the chamfer distance in the **Distance 1** spinner or specify the value in the callout. Now, set the value of distance 2 in the respective spinner or callout. If you need to specify the name distance for creating the chamfer, select the **Equal distance** check box. The **Distance 2** will spinner will disappear from the **Chamfer Parameters** rollout.

After specifying all parameters, choose the **OK** button from the **Chamfer PropertyManager**. Figure 7-68 shows the chamfer created on a model.

Figure 7-68 Chamfer created on a base plate

Tip. *You can also select the face for applying the chamfer feature. If you do so, the chamfer will be applied to all edges of the selected face.*

Creating Vertex Chamfer

Using the chamfer tool, you can also add a chamfer to a selected vertex. It will chop the selected vertex to the specified distance. To create the vertex chamfer, invoke the **Chamfer PropertyManager** and select the **Vertex** radio button from the **Chamfer Parameters** rollout. Select the vertex; the preview of the chamfer will be displayed in the drawing area with the **Distance** callouts. Figure 7-69 shows the vertex to be selected and Figure 7-70 shows the preview of the vertex chamfer.

Set the value of the chamfer distance along each edge in the **Distance 1**, **Distance 2**, and **Distance 3** spinners. You can also specify the value of the chamfer distance in the distance callouts. If you want to specify an equal distance to all edges, select the **Equal distance** check

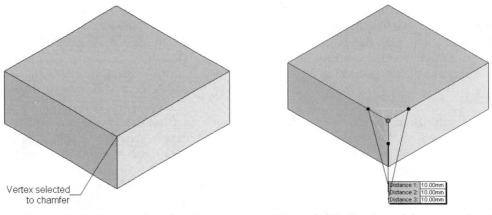

Figure 7-69 *Vertex to be selected*   **Figure 7-70** *Preview of the vertex chamfer*

box. After specifying all parameters, choose the **OK** button from the **Chamfer PropertyManager**. Figure 7-71 shows the vertex chamfer feature applied to the base feature.

Figure 7-71 *Vertex chamfer created on a base feature*

Chamfer With and Without Keep Feature Option

If you have boss or cut features in a model and the chamfer created is large enough to consume those features, it is recommended that you select the **Keep features** check box. If this check box is cleared, the chamfer feature will consume the features that will obstruct its path. Note that the features that are consumed by the chamfer feature are not deleted from the model. They are removed from the model because of some geometric inconsistency. When you rollback or delete the chamfer, the consumed features will reappear. Figure 7-72 shows the chamfer feature with the **Keep features** check box cleared and Figure 7-73 shows the chamfer feature with the **Keep features** check box selected.

Creating Shell Features

CommandManager:	Features > Shell
Menu:	Insert > Features > Shell
Toolbar:	Features > Shell

*Figure 7-72 Chamfer feature with the **Keep features** check box cleared*

*Figure 7-73 Chamfer feature with the **Keep features** check box selected*

 Shelling is defined as the process in which the material is scooped out from a model and the resulting model is hollowed from inside. The resulting model will be a hollow model with walls of a specified thickness and cavity inside. The selected face or faces of the model are also removed in this operation. If you do not select any face to be removed, a closed hollow model will be created. You can also specify multiple thicknesses to the walls. You can create a shell feature using the **Shell** tool. Use the **Shell** button from the **Features CommandManager** to invoke The **Shell1 PropertyManager**, as shown in Figure 7-74.

*Figure 7-74 The **Shell1 PropertyManager***

You will be prompted to select the faces to remove. Select the face or faces of the model that you want to remove. The selected faces will be highlighted in green and their names will be displayed in the **Faces to Remove** selection box. Set the value of the wall thickness in the

Thickness spinner and choose the **OK** button from the **Shell1 PropertyManager**. Figure 7-75 shows the face selected to remove and Figure 7-76 shows the resulting shell feature created.

Figure 7-75   *Face selected to be removed*   *Figure 7-76*   *Resulting shell feature*

If none of the faces are selected to be removed, the resulting model will be hollowed from inside with no face removed. Figure 7-77 shows a model in the **Hidden Line Visible** mode with a shell feature in which faces are not selected to be removed.

Figure 7-77   *Shell feature with no face selected to be removed*

The in-built artificial intelligence of the **Shell** command in SolidWorks enables the shell feature to decide how much quantity of material to be removed, depending on the geometric conditions. Figure 7-78 shows the shell feature whose wall thickness is small for uniform shelling of the entire model. Figure 7-79 shows the shell feature whose wall thickness is large because of which it cannot accommodate the uniform shelling of the entire model. Therefore, the shell feature will not remove the material from that area where the material removal is not possible.

The **Shell outward** check box is selected to create the shell feature on the outer side of the model. You can also display the preview of the shell feature by selecting the **Show preview** check box from the **Parameters** rollout of the **Shell1 PropertyManager**.

Figure 7-78 *Shell feature with smaller shell thickness*

Figure 7-79 *Shell feature with larger shell thickness*

Tip. *If the thickness of the shell feature is more than the radius of the fillet feature, the fillet will not be included in the shell feature. Therefore, it results in sharp edges after adding the fillet. The same is with the chamfer feature. The faces selected to be removed in the shell feature can be a planar face or a curved face. But creating a shell by removing a curved face depends on the geometry of the curved face to adopt the specified shell thickness and other geometric conditions.*

Creating Multithickness Shell

Using this option available in the **Shell** tool, you can specify different thickness values to the selected faces. To use this option, invoke the **Shell1 PropertyManager** and select the faces to be removed and then specify the uniform thickness in the **Thickness** spinner of the **Parameters** rollout. Click once in the **Multi-thickness(es) Faces** selection box to activate the selection mode. Select the faces to which you want to specify the special thickness. Set the value of the thickness using the **Multi-thickness(es)** spinner and choose the **OK** button. Figure 7-80 shows the faces to be selected to specify the multithickness shell and Figure 7-81 shows the resulting shell feature.

Figure 7-80 *Faces to be selected to apply multithickness shell*

Figure 7-81 *Resulting multithickness shell*

Error Diagnostics

This option activates automatically if the shell feature creation fails. With this option, you can figure out the possible reasons for the failure of the shell feature creation.

While creating the shell feature, specify all parameters in the **Shell1 PropertyManager** and choose the **OK** button. If the shell feature creation fails because of geometric inconsistency, the **What's Wrong** dialog box will be displayed, which will inform you about the possible errors due to which the feature creation failed. You will learn more about the **Rebuild Errors** dialog box later in this chapter. The **Error Diagnostics** rollout, shown in Figure 7-82, is displayed in the **Shell 1 PropertyManager**.

Figure 7-82 The **Error**
Diagnostics *rollout*

The radio buttons available in the **Diagnosis scope** area of the **Error Diagnostics** rollout are used to define the diagnosis to be done on the entire body or only on the faces that failed to be shelled. The **Check body/faces** button is used to run the diagnostic tool. When you choose this button, the areas of the model that are responsible for the feature creation failure will be highlighted using callouts. The **Display mesh** check box is used to display the surface curvature mesh. The **Display curvature** check box is selected to display the surface curvature.

Creating Wrap Features

CommandManager:	Features > Wrap *(Customize to Add)*
Menu:	Insert > Features > Wrap
Toolbar:	Features > Wrap *(Customize to Add)*

The **Wrap** tool is used to emboss, deboss, or scribe a closed multiloop sketch on a selected planar or curved face that is tangent to the plane on which the selected sketch is created. You can also create this type of geometry by extruding the sketch from a selected surface using the boss or cut option. There are two main differences between the emboss and deboss created using the **Wrap** tool and those created using the boss or cut tool. The first difference is in the method of projection. The projection of the geometry using the **Wrap** tool follows the rule of true length, which means the actual length of the geometry remains the same after projecting it on the surface. The projection of the geometry created using the **From** option of the boss or cut tool follows the rule of true projection. Therefore, the original size of the geometry is distorted. The second difference is the direction of the side faces of the geometry. The side faces of the geometry created using the **Wrap** tool are always normal to the reference surface, while those created using the **From** option of the cut or extrude tool are normal to the sketching plane or parallel to the direction vector.

To create a wrap feature, create a closed multiloop or a single loop sketch and then choose the **Wrap** button from the **Features CommandManager**. The **Message PropertyManager** will be displayed and you will be prompted to select a plane or face on which you need to create a closed counter or select an existing sketch. Select an existing sketch to display the **Wrap1 PropertyManager**, as shown in Figure 7-83.

Figure 7-83 The Wrap1 PropertyManager

You will notice that the **Emboss** radio button is selected by default. This radio button is selected to create an embossed wrap feature. Next, select the face on which you need to wrap the sketch. As soon as you select the face, the preview of the wrap feature that will be created with the default settings will be displayed in the drawing area. Set the value of the thickness using the **Thickness** spinner. Choose the **OK** button from the **Wrap1 PropertyManager**. Figure 7-84 shows the sketch and the face to be selected to create the wrap feature and Figure 7-85 shows the resulting embossed wrap feature.

Using the **Deboss** radio button available in the **Wrap Parameters** rollout you can engrave the sketch on a selected planar or curved face. Figure 7-86 shows a wrap feature created using the **Deboss** option. The **Scribe** radio button is selected to project the selected sketch on a planar or a curved face. The projected sketch will split the face on which it is projected. Using the **Pull Direction** rollout you can specify the normal direction in which you need to create the wrap feature. Figure 7-87 shows the wrap feature created using the **Scribe** option.

Figure 7-84 *Sketch and face selected to create the wrap feature*

Figure 7-85 *Resulting embossed wrap feature*

Figure 7-86 *Wrap feature created using the Deboss option*

Figure 7-87 *Wrap feature created using the Scribe option*

TUTORIALS

Tutorial 1

In this tutorial, you will create the model of the Plummer Block Casting shown in Figure 7-88. The dimensions of the model are shown in Figure 7-89.   **(Expected time: 30 min)**

Figure 7-88 *Solid model of the Plummer Block Casting*

Figure 7-89 *Dimensions of the Plummer Block Casting*

The steps to be followed to complete this tutorial are listed next.

a. Create the base feature of the model on the **Front Plane**, refer to Figures 7-90 and 7-91.
b. Create the second feature, which is a cut feature, on the top planar face of the base feature, refer to Figures 7-92 through 7-94.

c.   Create the rectangular recess as a cut feature at the bottom of the base, refer to Figure 7-95.

d.   Create the square cuts that will act as the recess for the head of the square head bolts, refer to Figure 7-95.

e.   Create a hole feature using the **Hole PropertyManager** and modify the placement of the hole feature, refer to Figure 7-96.

f.   Create the cut feature on the second top planar face of the base feature, refer to Figure 7-97.

g.   Add the fillet feature to the model, refer to Figures 7-98 and 7-99.

h.   Add chamfers to the model, refer to Figures 7-100 and 7-101.

Creating the Base Feature

1.   Start a new SolidWorks part document using the **New SolidWorks Document** dialog box.

2.   Invoke the **Extruded Boss/Base** tool and select the **Front Plane** as the sketching plane.

3.   Draw the sketch of the front view of the model using the automatic mirroring option to capture the design intent of the model.

4.   Add the required relations and dimensions to the sketch, as shown in Figure 7-90.

Figure 7-90 *Fully defined sketch of the base feature*

Note

*As shown in Figure 7-90, tolerances are applied to some dimensions. After adding the dimensions to the sketch, select the dimension and add the tolerance to the dimension using the **Dimension PropertyManager**, as discussed in the earlier chapters.*

*Using the **Dimension Properties** dialog box, change the radial dimension of the arc to the diameter dimension.*

You need to extrude the sketch to a distance of 46 mm using the **Mid Plane** option. You need to extrude the sketch using the **Mid Plane** option because it is recommended that parts that are to be assembled should have default planes in the center of the model.

5.   Exit the sketching environment to display the **Extrude PropertyManager**.

6. Right-click in the drawing area and select the **Mid Plane** option from the shortcut menu to extrude the sketch symmetrically to both sides of the sketching plane.

7. Set the value of the **Depth** spinner to **46** and choose the **OK** button from the **Extrude PropertyManager**.

8. Change the view orientation to isometric. The resulting base feature created after extruding the sketch to a given depth is shown in Figure 7-91.

Figure 7-91 *Isometric view of the base feature of the model*

Tip. *Sometimes, you may need to apply tolerance to the dimensions. For example, consider a case in which the depth of the extruded feature has a tolerance applied to it. In such cases, double-click on the extruded feature in the **FeatureManager Design Tree** or in the drawing area; all dimensions applied to the model are displayed. Select the dimension that reflects the depth of the extruded feature and apply the tolerance using the **Dimension PropertyManager**.*

Creating the Second Feature

The second feature of the model is a cut feature. The sketch of the cut-extrude feature is drawn on the top planar face of the base feature. This sketch is extruded up to the specified plane to create the resulting cut feature.

1. Invoke the **Extruded Cut** tool and select the top planar face of the base feature as the sketching plane.

2. Orient the model normal to the sketching plane and using the standard sketching tools, draw the sketch for the cut feature. Apply the required relations to the sketch.

    The sketch of the cut-extrude feature is shown in Figure 7-92.

3. Exit the sketching environment to display the **Cut-Extrude PropertyManager**.

    The preview of the cut feature is displayed in the drawing area with the default values of

Figure 7-92 Sketch of the second feature

the blind option. You need to extrude the cut feature up to the selected surface. Therefore, orient the model in the isometric view because the feature termination surface can be easily selected in this view.

4. Change the view orientation to isometric.

    You will observe that the preview of the cut feature is inside the model. You need to remove the outer part of the sketch profile. Therefore, you need to change the side of the cut feature.

5. Select the **Flip side to cut** check box; the preview of the cut feature is modified dynamically.

6. Right-click in the drawing area and select the **Up To Surface** option from the shortcut menu.

    You are prompted to select a face or a surface to complete the specification of direction 1.

7. Select the surface for the feature termination shown in Figure 7-93. Right-click and choose **OK** from the shortcut menu to exit the tool.

    The model, after creating the cut feature, is shown in Figure 7-94.

Figure 7-93 Surface to be selected for the cut feature

Figure 7-94 Model after creating the cut feature

Creating the Rectangular Recess

The third feature is the rectangular recess. This feature is created using a rectangular cut feature that will be created on the bottom face of the model.

1. Orient the model using the **Rotate View** tool and select the bottom face of the base feature as the sketching plane.

2. Invoke the **Extruded Cut** tool to invoke the sketching environment.

3. Using the standard sketching tools, draw a rectangle of 195 mm x 35 mm as the sketch of the rectangular recess. Apply the required relations and dimensions to the sketch.

4. Exit the sketching environment.

5. Set the value of the **Depth** spinner to **2** and choose **OK** from the **Cut-Extrude PropertyManager**.

Creating the Recess for the Head of Square-headed Bolt

It is evident from Figure 7-90 that the bolt to be inserted in the part will be a square-headed bolt. Therefore, you need to create the recess for the head of the square-headed bolt. A square of 26 mm length is used to create this recess.

1. Rotate the model and select the upper face of the recess created in the previous section as the sketching plane. Invoke the **Extruded Cut** tool and orient the model normal to the sketching plane.

2. Using the standard sketching tools, draw the sketch. The sketch includes two squares of 26 mm length and the distance between the centers of the squares is 78 mm, refer to Figure 7-89. Apply the required relations and dimensions.

3. Exit the sketching environment and extrude the sketch to a depth of 10 mm. Exit the tool. The rotated model, after adding this cut feature, is shown in Figure 7-95.

Figure 7-95 Model after creating recess for square-headed bolts

Creating the Hole Feature

After creating the recess for the head of the square-headed bolt, you need to create a hole using the **Hole** tool. To create the hole, you first need to place sketched points on the placement plane of the hole feature. After placing the sketched points, select the hole placement plane and invoke the **Hole** tool.

1. Invoke the sketching environment using the top right planar surface of the base feature as the sketching plane.

2. Create two sketched points on the right and the left top planar faces of the base feature.

   Next, you need to define the placement of these sketched point. It is evident from Figure 7-90 that the center point of the hole is coincident with the center point of the square recess feature. Therefore, you need to coincide the sketched points with the center of the squares. First you have to change the model view display from **Shaded** to **Hidden Lines Visible** so that the square recess feature is visible.

3. Orient the view normal to the viewing direction and choose the **Hidden Lines Visible** button from the **View** toolbar.

4. Invoke the **Centerline** tool from the **Sketch CommandManager** and move the cursor to the lower left corner of the left square. When a red dot is displayed along with the cursor, specify the start point of the line. Move the cursor to the upper right corner of the square and when the red dot is displayed, specify the endpoint of the line.

5. Right-click in the drawing area and choose the **Select** option from the shortcut menu. This will end the line creation and also exit the **Line** tool. A centerline is drawn as a diagonal of the square.

6. Press and hold the CTRL key down and select the centerline created earlier. Now, select the left sketched point.

   The **Properties PropertyManager** is displayed. Using this, add the relation between the left sketched point and the centerline. The centerline is drawn as the diagonal of the square and it is a general geometric fundamental that the midpoint of the diagonal of a square or a rectangle lies at its center. Therefore, you need to add a relation such that the sketched point is placed at the midpoint of the diagonal.

7. Choose the **Midpoint** button from the **Add Relations** rollout of the **Properties PropertyManager** and then choose the **OK** button from the **Properties PropertyManager**.

8. Similarly, draw the diagonal centerline for the right square. Add the midpoint relation between this centerline and the right sketched point.

9. Exit the sketching environment and change the model display mode to shaded. Select the right top planar surface of the base feature as the placement plane for the hole feature.

10. Choose **Insert > Features >Hole > Simple** from the menu bar to invoke the **Hole PropertyManager**. The preview of the hole feature with the default settings is displayed in the drawing area.

11. Right-click in the drawing area and choose the **Through All** option from the shortcut menu to define the feature termination.

12. Set the value of the **Hole Diameter** spinner to **12**.

13. Select the center point of the hole and drag the cursor to the right sketched point. Release the left mouse button when the cursor snaps to the sketched point. Now, choose the **OK** button from the **Hole PropertyManager**

14. Using the same procedure, create the second hole feature on the left of the model. The model, after creating both hole features, is displayed in Figure 7-96.

15. Similarly, create the cut feature on the second top planar face of the base feature, refer to Figure 7-89 for the dimensions of the sketch.

Note that the dimension of 162 mm between the cut on the left and the cut on the right is given from the center of the sketches. To get this dimension, you need to create vertical centerlines in both sketches. Using the dimensions and relations, you need to make sure that the centerlines pass through the center of the sketches. Now, add the dimension between these two vertical centerlines. The model, after creating the cut feature, is shown in Figure 7-97.

Figure 7-96 *Model after adding the hole features*   **Figure 7-97** *Model after adding the cut features*

Adding a Fillet to the Model

After creating all other features, you now need to add the fillet feature to the model.

1. Choose the **Fillet** button from the **Features CommandManager** to invoke the **Fillet PropertyManager**.

After invoking the **Fillet PropertyManager**, you are prompted to selected edges, faces, features, or loops to be filleted. As evident from the model, you need to select only the edges to apply the fillet feature.

2. Select the edges shown in Figure 7-98.

    As soon as you select the edges, the preview of the fillet feature with the default values is shown in the drawing area. A radius callout is also displayed along the selected edge. Now, you need to modify the default radius value of the fillet feature.

Note

*If the preview of the fillet feature is not displayed in the drawing area, select the **Full Preview** radio button available in the **Items To Fillet** rollout of the **Fillet PropertyManager**.*

3. Set the value of the **Radius** spinner to **8** and choose the **OK** button from the **Fillet PropertyManager**.

    The model, after adding the fillet, is shown in Figure 7-99.

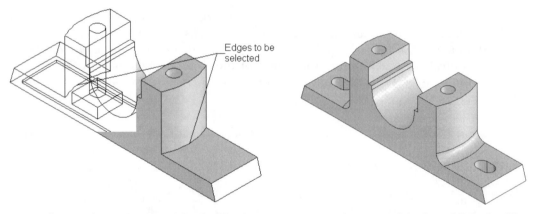

Figure 7-98 Edges to be selected for the fillet feature   *Figure 7-99 Model after adding the fillet*

Adding a Chamfer to the Model

The next feature that you need to add to this model is the chamfer.

1. Choose the **Chamfer** button from the **Features CommandManager** to invoke the **Chamfer PropertyManager**.

2. Select the edges of the cut features as shown in Figure 7-100. The edges that are tangent to the selected edges are selected automatically because the selection mode of the chamfer feature uses tangent propagation by default.

    As soon as you select the edges, the preview of the chamfer feature is displayed in the drawing area with the default values. The angle and distance callouts are also displayed. Now, you need to set the required value of the chamfer.

The required values of the chamfer parameters are 1 mm and 45-degrees. The **Angle distance** radio button is selected by default in the **Chamfer Parameters** rollout. The value of the angle in the **Angle** spinner is set as 45-degrees. Therefore, you do not need to modify this value. You need to set only the value of the distance in the **Distance** spinner.

3. Set the value of the distance in the **Distance** spinner to **1** and choose the **OK** button from the **Chamfer PropertyManager**.

4. Following the same procedure, add a chamfer to the semicircular edges on the front and back faces of the base feature. Refer to Figure 7-89 for the parameters of the chamfer feature. The final solid model is shown in Figure 7-101.

Figure 7-100 *Edges to be selected*   *Figure 7-101* *Final solid model*

Saving the Model

Next, you need to save the document.

1. Choose the **Save** button from the **Standard** toolbar and save the document with the name given below.

    \My Documents\SolidWorks\c07\c07tut1.sldprt.

2. Choose **File > Close** from the menu bar to close the document.

Tutorial 2

In this tutorial, you will create the model shown in Figure 7-102. For a better understanding, the section view of the model is shown in Figure 7-103. The dimensions of the model are shown in Figure 7-104.   **(Expected time: 30 min)**

Figure 7-102 *Solid model for Tutorial 2*

Figure 7-103 *Section view of the model*

Figure 7-104 *Top view, front section view, and right-side view with dimensions*

The steps to be followed to complete this tutorial are listed next.

a. Create the base feature of the model by extruding a rectangle of 100 mm x 70 mm to a distance of 20 mm.
b. Add a fillet to the base feature, refer to Figures 7-105 through 7-108.
c. Create the shell feature to create a thin-walled part and remove some of the faces, refer to Figures 7-109 and 7-110.
d. Create a reference plane at an offset distance from the top planar face of the base feature and extrude the sketch created on the new plane, refer to Figure 7-111.
e. Using the **Hole Wizard** tool, add the countersink hole to the model, refer to Figure 7-112.
f. Add a fillet to the extruded feature, refer to Figures 7-113 and 7-114.
g. Create the lip of the component by extruding the sketch, refer to Figure 7-115.

Creating the Base Feature

The base feature of the model is created by extruding a rectangle of 100 mm x 70 mm to a distance of 20 mm. It is evident from the model that the sketch of the base feature is created on the **Top Plane**. Therefore, you have to select the **Top Plane** as the sketching plane.

1. Start a new SolidWorks part document and invoke the **Extruded Boss/Base** tool. Select the **Top Plane** from the **FeatureManager Design Tree**.

2. Orient the sketch plane normal to the viewing direction.

3. Using the **Rectangle** tool, draw a rectangle and force it to a dimension of 100 mm x 70 mm. Add the other required dimensions to fully define the sketch.

4. Exit the sketching environment and extrude the rectangle to a depth of 20 mm.

Creating the Fillet Features

After creating the base feature, you need to add fillets to the model. In this model, you need to add three fillet features. Two fillet features will be added at this stage of the design process and the remaining one will be added at a later stage of the design process.

1. Choose the **Fillet** button from the **Features CommandManager** to invoke the **Fillet PropertyManager**.

2. Select the edges of the model, as shown in Figure 7-105.

As soon as you select the edges of the model, the preview of the fillet with the default values and the radius callout are displayed in the drawing area.

3. Set the value of the **Radius** spinner to **15** and choose the **OK** button from the **Fillet PropertyManager**.

Figure 7-106 shows the model, after adding the first fillet feature.

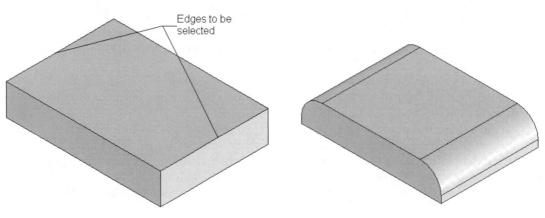

Figure 7-105 *Edges to be selected*   **Figure 7-106** *Fillet added to the base feature*

Now, add the second fillet feature to the model.

4. Invoke the **Fillet PropertyManager** and set the value of the **Radius** spinner to **5**.

5. Select the edges of the model, as shown in Figure 7-107. Right-click and choose **OK** from the shortcut menu to complete the feature creation. The model, after adding the second fillet feature, is shown in Figure 7-108.

Figure 7-107 *Edges to be selected*   **Figure 7-108** *Second fillet added to the model*

Tip. *The edges tangent to the selected edges are filleted automatically because by default, the **Tangent propagation** check box is selected in the **Fillet PropertyManager**.*

Creating the Shell Feature

It is evident from Figures 7-102 and 7-103 that a shell feature is required to create a thin-walled structure. As discussed earlier, the shell feature is used to scoop out the material from the model, leaving behind a thin-walled hollow part.

1. Choose the **Shell** button from the **Features CommandManager** to invoke the **Shell1 PropertyManager**; you are prompted to select the faces to remove.

2. Rotate the model and select the faces to be removed, as shown in Figure 7-109. The names of the selected faces are displayed in the **Faces to Remove** selection box.

3. Set the value of the **Thickness** spinner to **2** and choose the **OK** button from the **Shell1 PropertyManager**.

    The model, after creating the shell feature, is shown in Figure 7-110.

Figure 7-109 *Faces to be selected to remove*

Figure 7-110 *Model after creating the shell feature*

Creating the Extruded Feature

The next feature that you are going to create is an extruded feature. But, before creating this feature, you need to create a reference plane at an offset distance from the top planar face of the base feature.

1. Invoke the **Plane PropertyManager** and create a plane at an offset distance of 15 mm from the top planar face of the base feature. You have to select the **Reverse direction** check box from the **Plane PropertyManager** to create the plane.

2. Invoke the **Extruded Boss/Base** tool and select the newly created plane as the sketching plane and create the sketch using the standard sketching tools. The sketch consists of two circles of 6 mm diameter. For other dimensions, refer to Figure 7-104.

3. Exit the sketching environment and extrude the sketch using the **Up To Next** option and add an outward draft of 5-degrees. Hide the reference plane.

    Figure 7-111 shows the rotated model after creating the extruded feature with draft.

Adding the Countersink Hole Using the Hole Wizard Tool

The next feature that you are going to create is a **M3.5 Flat Head Machine Screw**

Figure 7-111 *Model after creating the extruded feature*

countersink hole, refer to Figure 7-104. In SolidWorks, you are provided with one of the largest standard hole-generating techniques known as **Hole Wizard**. Using the **Hole Wizard** tool, you can create the standard holes to the model that can accommodate standard fasteners.

1. Rotate the model and select the top planar face of the base feature and then choose the **Hole Wizard** button from the **Features CommandManager**.

   The **Hole Specification PropertyManager** is displayed and the preview of the hole feature on the selected face with the default values is shown in the drawing area.

   Tip. *If you select the placement plane for the placement of the hole feature before invoking the **Hole Definition** dialog box, the placement sketch will be a 2D sketch. If you select the placement plane after invoking the **Hole Definition** dialog box, the hole placement sketch will be a 3D sketch. You will learn more about 3D sketches in the later chapters.*

2. Choose the **Countersink** button from the **Hole Specification** rollout.

   Now, set the parameters to define the standard hole. The preview of the standard hole is modified dynamically as you set the parameters for the hole feature.

3. Select the **Ansi Metric** option from the **Standard** drop-down list.

4. Select the **Flat Head Screw - ANSI B18.6.7M** option from the **Type** drop-down list.

5. Select the **M3.5** option from the **Size** drop-down list and choose the **Through All** option from the **End Condition** drop-down list.

6. Choose the **Position** tab from the **Hole Specification PropertyManager**; you will be

prompted to use the dimensions and other sketching tools to position the hole. Also, the select cursor is replaced by the point cursor.

7. Using the point cursor, specify another point anywhere on the top planar face of the base feature to create another hole.

    Because both placement points are not properly placed, you need to add the required relations and dimensions to define the proper location of these placement points. Before doing that, you need to change the model display from **Shaded With Edges** to **Hidden Lines Visible** for a better display.

8. Choose the **Hidden Lines Visible** button from the **View** toolbar to display the model with the hidden lines visible.

9. Press the ESC key to invoke the select cursor.

10. Right-click in the drawing area and choose the **Add Relation** option from the shortcut menu to display the **Add Relations PropertyManager**.

11. Select the left placement point and then select the upper left hidden circle. Choose the **Concentric** button from the **Add Relations** rollout.

12. Right-click in the drawing area and choose **Clear Selections** from the shortcut menu. Select the right placement point and the upper right hidden circle. Now, choose the **OK** option from the confirmation corner.

13. Choose the **OK** button from the **Hole Specification PropertyManager** and choose the **Shaded With Edges** button from the **View** toolbar.

    The isometric view of the model, after adding the hole feature, is shown in Figure 7-112.

Figure 7-112 *Model after adding the hole feature using the **Hole Wizard** tool*

Adding a Fillet to the Model

Now, you need to add a fillet to the edges of the extruded feature with the draft that was created earlier.

1. Rotate the model and invoke the **Fillet PropertyManager**. Select the edges of the model, as shown in Figure 7-113.

2. Set the value of the **Radius** spinner to **1** and choose the **OK** button to end the feature creation. The model, after adding the fillet, is shown in Figure 7-114.

Figure 7-113 Edges to be selected   *Figure 7-114 Model after adding the fillet*

Adding a Lip to the Model

The last feature you need to add to the model is a lip. It is created by extruding an open sketch using the thin option.

1. Invoke the **Extrude Boss/Base** tool and select the bottom face of the base feature as the sketching plane and invoke the sketching environment.

2. Using the select tool, select any one of the inner edges of the model on the current sketching plane and right-click to display the shortcut menu. Now, choose the **Select Tangency** option from the shortcut menu.

3. Choose the **Convert Entities** button from the **Sketch CommandManager**; the selected edges are converted into sketched entities.

4. Exit the sketching environment; the **Extrude PropertyManager** is displayed and the **Thin Feature** rollout is invoked automatically because you are extruding an open sketch.

5. Set the value of the **Distance** spinner in the **Direction 1** rollout to **1** and set the value of the **Thickness** spinner in the **Thin Feature** rollout to **1**.

6. Choose the **OK** button from the **Extrude PropertyManager**. The rotated view of the final model is shown in Figure 7-115.

Figure 7-115 Final model rotated to display the maximum features

Saving the Model

1. Choose the **Save** button from the **Standard** toolbar and save the part document with the name given below.

   \My Documents\SolidWorks\c07\c07tut2.sldprt

2. Choose **File** > **Close** from the menu bar to close the document.

SELF-EVALUATION TEST

Answer the following questions and then compare your answers with those given at the end of this chapter:

1. Using the **Hole PropertyManager**, you can create counterbore, countersink, and tapped holes. (T/F)

2. The hole features created using the **Hole Wizard** tool and the **Hole PropertyManager** are not parametric. (T/F)

3. You cannot define a user-defined hole using the **Hole Wizard** tool. (T/F)

4. You cannot preselect the edges or faces for creating a fillet feature. (T/F)

5. In SolidWorks, you can create a multithickness shell feature. (T/F)

6. The _____ check box is selected to create the shell feature on the outer side of the model.

7. The _____ is created by specifying different radii along the length of the selected edge at specified intervals.

8. The names of the faces to be removed in the shell features are displayed in the _____ selection box.

9. If you want to specify different distances while creating the chamfer, clear the _____ check box.

10. The _____ check box is selected to apply the face fillet feature with continuous curvature throughout the fillet feature.

REVIEW QUESTIONS

Answer the following questions:

1. The _____ option is used to add standard holes to the model.

2. After specifying all parameters of a hole feature using the **Hole Specification PropertyManager**, the _____ tab is chosen to specify the placement of the hole feature.

3. The _____ radio button is selected to create a smooth transition by smoothly blending the points and vertices on which you have defined the radius on the selected edge.

4. The _____ button is chosen from the **Hole Specifications** rollout to define a standard drilled hole.

5. By default, the _____ radio button is selected in the **Chamfer PropertyManager**.

6. If you preselect the placement surface for creating a hole feature using the **Hole Wizard** tool, the resulting placement sketch will be a

    (a) 2D sketch   (b) Planar sketch
    (c) Bezier spline   (d) 3D sketch

7. Which one of the following options, when selected, does not require a radius to create a fillet feature?

    (a) Face fillet with hold line   (b) Constant radius fillet
    (c) Variable radius fillet   (d) Full round fillet

8. Which radio button in the **Variable Radius Parameters** rollout is used to create a smooth transition while creating a variable radius fillet?

(a) **Straight transition**   (b) **Parametric transition**
(c) **Smooth transition**   (d) **Surface transition**

9. If you do not select any face to be removed while creating a shell feature, what will be the resulting model?

(a) Remains complete solid model   (b) Thin walled hollow model
(c) Automatically removed one face   (d) None of these

10. Which **PropertyManager** is displayed by default when you choose the **Hole Wizard** button from the **Features CommandManager**?

(a) **Hole**   (b) **Hole Definition**
(c) **Hole Wizard**   (d) **Hole Specification**

EXERCISES

Exercise 1

Create the model shown in Figure 7-116. The dimensions of the model are shown in Figure 7-117.   **(Expected time: 30 min)**

Figure 7-116 Solid model for Exercise 1

Figure 7-117 Views and dimensions of the model for Exercise 1

Exercise 2

Create the model shown in Figure 7-118. The dimensions of the model are shown in Figure 7-119.   **(Expected time: 30 min)**

Figure 7-118 Solid model for Exercise 2

Figure 7-119 *Views and dimensions of the model for Exercise 2*

Answers to Self-Evaluation Test
1. F, 2. F, 3. F, 4. F, 5. T, 6. Shell outward, 7. Variable radius fillet, 8. Faces to Remove, 9. Equal distance, 10. Curvature continuous

Chapter 8

Advanced Modeling Tools-II

Learning Objectives

After completing this chapter, you will be able to:
- *Mirror features, faces, and bodies.*
- *Create linear patterns.*
- *Create circular patterns.*
- *Create sketch-driven patterns.*
- *Create curve-driven patterns.*
- *Create table-driven patterns.*
- *Create rib features.*
- *Display the section view of the model.*

ADVANCED MODELING TOOLS

Some of the advanced modeling options were discussed in Chapter 7, Advanced Modeling Tools-I. In this chapter, you will learn about more advanced modeling tools that you can use to capture the design intent of the model. The rest of the advanced modeling tools are discussed in later chapters.

Creating Mirror Features

CommandManager:	Features > Mirror
Menu:	Insert > Pattern/Mirror > Mirror
Toolbar:	Features > Mirror

The **Mirror** tool is used to copy or mirror the selected feature, face, or body about a specified mirror plane, which can be a reference plane or a planar face. To use this tool, choose the **Mirror** button from the **Features CommandManager**, or choose **Insert > Pattern/Mirror > Mirror** to invoke the **Mirror PropertyManager**, as displayed in Figure 8-1. The confirmation corner is also displayed in the drawing area. The options that are used to mirror features, faces, and bodies are discussed next.

*Figure 8-1 The **Mirror PropertyManager***

Mirroring Features

You can mirror the selected feature along the specified mirror plane or face by using this feature. To do so, invoke the **Mirror PropertyManager**. You are prompted to select a plane or a planar face about which to mirror, followed by the features to be mirrored. Select a plane or a planar face that will act as a mirror plane or mirror face. After selecting the mirror plane or face, the selection mode of the **Features to Mirror** selection box is invoked and you are prompted to select the features to mirror. Select the feature or features from the drawing area or from the **FeatureManager Design Tree** which is displayed in the drawing area. When you select the features to be mirrored, the preview of the mirrored image is displayed in the drawing area. After selecting all the required features, choose the **OK** button from the **Mirror PropertyManager**. Figure 8-2 shows the mirror plane and features to be mirrored and Figure 8-3 shows the resulting mirrored features.

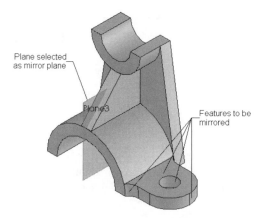

Figure 8-2 *Mirror plane and the features to be mirrored*

Figure 8-3 *The resulting mirror feature*

Tip. *You can also preselect the mirror plane or mirror face and the features to be mirrored before invoking the **Mirror PropertyManager**.*

Mirroring with and without Geometric Pattern

When you create a mirror feature, you are provided with the **Geometry Pattern** option. This option is available in the **Options** rollout shown in Figure 8-4.

Figure 8-4 *The **Options** rollout*

By default, the **Geometry Pattern** check box is cleared. Therefore, if you mirror a feature that is related to some other entity, the same relationship will be applied to the mirrored feature. Consider a case in which an extruded cut is created using the **Offset From Surface** option. If you mirror the cut feature along a plane, the same relationship will be applied to the mirrored cut feature. The mirrored cut feature will be created with the same end condition of feature termination. Figure 8-5 shows a hole feature created on the right and mirrored along **Plane 1**, with the **Geometry Pattern** check box cleared.

If you select the **Geometry Pattern** check box, the mirror feature created will not depend on the relational references. It will just create a replica of the selected geometry. Figure 8-6 shows the mirror feature created with the **Geometry Pattern** check box selected.

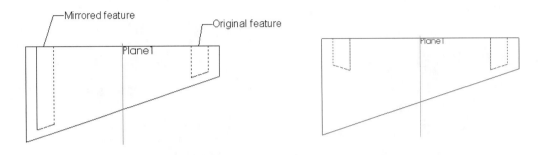

Figure 8-5 Mirror feature created with the Geometry Pattern check box cleared

Figure 8-6 Mirror feature created with the Geometry Pattern check box selected

Propagating Visual Properties While Mirroring

With this release of SolidWorks, the **Propagate Visual Properties** check box is provided in the **Options** rollout. This check box is selected by default and is used to transfer the visual properties assigned to the feature or parent body to the mirrored instance. Note that the visual properties will be visible only after you exit this tool. These visual properties include colors and textures applied to the features or part bodies. If you clear this check box, the color or texture applied on faces, features, or bodies will be reflected in the resulting mirrored instance. Figure 8-7 shows the mirrored feature with the **Propagating Visual Properties** check box selected and Figure 8-8 shows the mirrored features with this check box cleared.

*Figure 8-7 Mirror feature with the **Propagating Visual Properties** check box selected*

*Figure 8-8 Mirror feature with the **Propagating Visual Properties** check box cleared*

Mirroring Faces

Using this option, you can mirror faces about a mirror plane or mirror face. To use this option, invoke the **Mirror PropertyManager**. You are prompted to select a plane or a planar face about which to mirror. Select the planar face or a plane about which the selected faces will be mirrored. Now, click once in the **Faces to Mirror** selection box to invoke the selection mode, and select the faces to be mirrored. The selected faces must form a closed body. Else, the feature creation is not possible. Use the **OK** button from the **Mirror PropertyManager** to end the feature creation. Figure 8-9 shows the faces and the mirror plane to be selected. Figure 8-10 shows the resulting mirror feature created.

Figure 8-9 *Mirror plane and faces selected to mirror*   *Figure 8-10* *The resulting mirror created*

Note

The following are some of the factors that should be considered while creating a mirror feature by mirroring the faces along the selected plane or planar face:

1. If the replica of the faces is not coincident to the parent part body, SolidWorks will give an error while creating the mirror feature.

2. If the replica of the faces exists on faces other than the original face, SolidWorks will give an error while creating the mirror feature.

3. If the selected faces form a complex geometry, SolidWorks will give an error while creating the mirror feature.

4. If the mirrored faces exist on more than one face, SolidWorks will give an error while creating the mirror feature.

5. The selected faces should form a closed body. If the selected faces do not form a closed body, SolidWorks will give an error while creating the mirror feature.

Mirroring Bodies

As discussed in the earlier chapters, SolidWorks supports the multibodies environment. Therefore, using the **Mirror** tool, you can also mirror the disjoint bodies. To mirror a body along a plane, invoke the **Mirror PropertyManager** and select a plane or a planar face that will act as a mirror plane. Invoke the **Bodies to Mirror** rollout and select the body from the drawing area. Alternatively, you can expand the **FeatureManager Design Tree** flyout and select the body to be mirrored from the **Solid Bodies** folder. The name of the selected body is displayed in the **Solid/Surface Bodies to Mirror** selection box. The preview of the mirrored body is displayed in the drawing area. Choose the **OK** button from the **Mirror PropertyManager**. Figure 8-11 shows the plane and the body selected to be mirrored. Figure 8-12 shows the resulting mirrored feature.

Figure 8-11 *Selecting the mirror plane and body to*   ***Figure 8-12*** *Resulting mirrored feature*
be mirrored

The options available in the **Options** rollout while mirroring the bodies are discussed next. The **Options** rollout with these options, is displayed in Figure 8-13.

Figure 8-13 *The **Options** rollout*

Merge solids

The **Merge solids** option is used to merge the mirrored body with the parent body. Consider a case, in which you mirror a body along a selected plane or a planar face of the same body and the resulting mirrored body is joined to the parent body. In this case, if you select the **Merge solids** check box, the resulting mirrored body will merge with the parent body to become a single body. If the **Merge solids** check box is cleared, the resulting body will be joined with the parent body, but it will not merge with it. Therefore, it will result in two separate bodies.

Knit surfaces

If you mirror a surface body, the **Knit Surface** check box is selected to knit the mirrored and the parent body together.

> **Tip**. *As discussed earlier, the design intent is captured in the model using the mirror option. Therefore, if you modify the parent feature, face, or body the same will be reflected on the mirrored feature, face, or body.*
>
> *If you want to mirror all the features of the model using the **Features to Mirror** option, you need to select all the features. But for using **Bodies to Mirror** option, you need to select the body from the **Solid Bodies** folder. By selecting the body, all the features are added to the mirror image.*

Creating Linear Pattern Features

CommandManager:	Features > Linear Pattern
Menu:	Insert > Pattern/Mirror > Linear Pattern
Toolbar:	Features > Linear Pattern

As discussed in the previous chapters, you can arrange the sketched entities in a particular arrangement or pattern. In the same manner, you can also arrange the features, faces, and bodies in a particular pattern. In SolidWorks, you are provided with various types of patterns such as linear patterns, circular patterns, sketch-driven patterns, curve-driven patterns, and table-driven patterns.

In this section, you will learn to create linear patterns. The other type of patterns are discussed later in this chapter.

To create a linear pattern, choose the **Linear Pattern** button from the **Features CommandManager**, or choose **Insert > Pattern/Mirror > Linear Pattern** from the menu bar. The **Linear Pattern PropertyManager** is invoked, and the confirmation corner is also displayed. A partial view of the **Linear Pattern PropertyManager** is displayed in Figure 8-14. Various options available in the **Linear Pattern PropertyManager** are discussed next.

Linear Pattern in One Direction

When you invoke the **Linear Pattern PropertyManager**, the **Direction 1** rollout and the **Features** rollout are invoked by default. Also, you are prompted to select an edge or axis for direction reference and face of the feature for pattern features. Therefore, first you need to select an edge or axis as a direction reference. Select an edge or axis as the direction reference. The name of the selected reference will be displayed in the **Pattern Direction** selection box of the **Direction 1** rollout. The selected reference is displayed in green and the **Direction 1** callout is attached to it. The **Direction 1** callout has two edit boxes to define the number of instances and spacing. You are also provided with the **Reverse Direction** arrow along with the selected reference. Now, select a face of the feature to be patterned. The name of the selected feature will be displayed in the **Features to pattern** area of the **Features to Pattern** rollout. The preview of the pattern is displayed in the drawing area with the default values. Set the value of the center to center spacing between the pattern instances in the **Spacing** spinner. Set the value of the number of instances to be patterned in the **Number of**

Reverse Direction ———— [Linear Pattern panel] ———— Pattern Direction
———— Spacing
———— Number of Instances
———— Features to Pattern

Figure 8-14 *Partial view of the **Linear Pattern PropertyManager***

Instances spinner. You can also set these values in the **Direction 1** callout. Using the **Reverse Direction** button from the **PropertyManager** or the **Reverse Direction** arrow from the drawing area, you can reverse the direction of the pattern feature creation. Figure 8-15 shows the feature and edge to be selected for directional reference and Figure 8-16 shows the model after the pattern creation.

Figure 8-15 *Feature and the edge to be selected*   **Figure 8-16** *Linear pattern created using the* ***Direction 1*** *option*

Linear Pattern in Two Directions

As discussed earlier, you can create a linear pattern of features, faces, and bodies by defining

Tip. *When you select the feature to be patterned, its dimensions are also displayed in the drawing area. You can also select the dimensions as the directional reference.*

As discussed earlier, you can mirror the faces and bodies. In addition you can also pattern them. It should be noted that the selected faces must form a closed body, otherwise the patterning of faces will give an error.

a single direction using the **Direction 1** rollout. You can also define the parameters in the **Direction 2** rollout to define the pattern in the second direction. The **Direction 2** rollout is shown in Figure 8-17. When you define the pattern in the second direction, the entire row created by specifying the parameters in the first direction is patterned in the second direction.

*Figure 8-17 The **Direction 2** rollout*

To create a pattern by specifying the parameters in both the directions, select the feature to be patterned, and invoke the **Linear Pattern PropertyManager**. Select the first directional reference. Next, specify the parameters in the **Direction 1** rollout. Now, select the second directional reference. If the **Direction 2** rollout is not invoked by default in the **Linear Pattern PropertyManager**, use the blue arrow in the **Direction 2** callout to invoke it. The options available in the **Direction 2** rollout are the same as those discussed in the **Direction 1** rollout. Figure 8-18 shows the directional references and the feature to be selected. Figure 8-19 shows the linear pattern created using the **Direction 1** and **Direction 2** rollouts.

Figure 8-18 References and feature to be selected

Figure 8-19 Linear pattern created using the **Direction 1** *and* **Direction 2** *rollouts*

By default, all rows of the instances created in the first direction are patterned in the second direction also. This is because the **Pattern seed only** check box in the **Direction 2** rollout is cleared. You can select this check box to pattern only the original selected feature (also called seed feature) in the second direction. Figure 8-20 shows the pattern created with the **Pattern seed only** check box selected.

Original item
(seed feature)

*Figure 8-20 Linear pattern created with the **Pattern seed only** check box selected*

Instances to Skip

Using the **Instances to Skip** option, you can skip some of the instances from the pattern. These instances are not actually deleted. These only disappear from the pattern feature and you can resume them at any time of your design cycle. To skip the pattern instances, invoke the **Instances to Skip** rollout from the **Linear Pattern PropertyManager**. The **Instances to Skip** rollout is displayed in Figure 8-21.

Instances to Skip

*Figure 8-21 The **Instances to Skip** rollout*

As soon as you invoke this rollout, pink dots are displayed at the center of all pattern instances except the parent instance. Therefore, you cannot skip the parent instance. Now, move the cursor to the pink dot of the instance to be skipped. The cursor will be replaced by the instance to skip the cursor and the position of that instance, in the form of a matrix, is displayed in the tooltip below this cursor. Use the left mouse button to skip that instance. The pink dot will be replaced by a red dot and the preview of that instance will disappear from the pattern. The position of the skipped instance is displayed in the **Instances to Skip** selection box of the **Instances to Skip** rollout. Figure 8-22 shows a pattern created with some instances skipped. You can resume the skipped instances by deleting the position of the instance from the **Instances to Skip** selection box or selecting the red dot from the drawing area.

Pattern Using a Varying Sketch

The **Vary sketch** option in the **Options** rollout is used in a pattern where the shape and size of

Figure 8-22 *Linear pattern created with some instances skipped*

each pattern instance is controlled by the relations and dimensions of the sketch of that feature. In this type of pattern, the dimension of the sketch of the feature is selected as the directional reference, which then drives the shape and size of the sketch of the feature to be patterned. In Figure 8-23 a cut feature is created on the base feature. Figure 8-24 shows the linear pattern created using the varying sketch option. For creating this type of pattern, the sketch of the feature to be patterned should be in relation with the geometry along which it will vary. The dimensions of the sketch should allow it to change the shape and size easily. You should also provide a linear dimension that will drive the entire sketch and will also be the directional reference. From the **FeatureManager Design Tree** select the feature to be patterned and then invoke the **Linear Pattern PropertyManager**. Now, select the dimension to specify the directional reference and set the value of spacing and the number of instances. In this case, the horizontal dimension that measures 5 is selected as the dimensional reference. Next, invoke the **Options** rollout and select the **Vary sketch** check box; the preview of the pattern disappears from the drawing area. Choose the **OK** button from the **Linear Pattern PropertyManager** to end the feature creation. In this case, the lower edge of the cut feature is constrained to the bottom face of the model and top edge varies along the curved edge of the model. Therefore, the pattern features will be created such that their height varies along with the curved edge of the model.

Figure 8-23 *Cut feature created on the base feature*

Figure 8-24 *Linear pattern created with the **Vary sketch** check box selected*

The **Geometry pattern** option available in the **Options** rollout of the **Linear Pattern PropertyManager** is the same as that discussed earlier in the **Mirror PropertyManager**.

Propagating Visual Properties While Patterning

With this release of SolidWorks, the **Propagate Visual Properties** check box is provided in the **Options** rollout. This check box is selected by default and is used to transfer the visual properties assigned to the feature or parent body to the patterned instances. These visual properties includes colors and textures applied to the features or part bodies after you exit this tool. If you clear this check box, then the color or texture applied on faces, features, or bodies will be not be reflected in the resulting mirrored instance.

Creating Circular Pattern Features

CommandManager:	Features > Circular Pattern
Menu:	Insert > Pattern/Mirror > Circular Pattern
Toolbar:	Features > Circular Pattern

As discussed in the previous chapters, you can arrange the sketched entities in a circular pattern using the **Circular Sketch Step and Repeat** option. In this section, you will learn to create the circular pattern of a feature, face, or body by using the **Circular Pattern** tool. To invoke this tool, choose the **Circular Pattern** button from the **Features CommandManager** or choose **Insert > Pattern/Mirror > Circular Pattern** from the menu bar; the **Circular Pattern PropertyManager** is invoked and the confirmation corner is displayed. The partial view of the **Circular Pattern PropertyManager** is shown in Figure 8-25.

*Figure 8-25 Partial view of the **Circular Pattern PropertyManager***

After invoking the **Circular Pattern PropertyManager**, you are prompted to select an edge or axis for the direction reference, and a face of the feature to be patterned. If the base feature of the model is a circular feature, the temporary axis is created automatically at the center of the model. Choose **View > Temporary Axes** from the menu bar to display the temporary axis. Else, before invoking the **Circular Pattern** tool, you need to create an axis. Now, select the axis that will act as the pattern axis, and the feature to be patterned; the preview of the pattern feature with the default values is displayed in the drawing area. The **Direction 1** callout is also displayed with the **Reverse Direction** arrow in the drawing area. By default, the **Equal Spacing** check box is cleared. Therefore, you need to set the value of the incremental angle between the instances in the **Total Angle** spinner. Set the value of number of instances to pattern in the **Number of Instances** spinner. If you select the **Equal Spacing** check box, you need to enter the value of the total angle, along which all the instances of the pattern will be placed. The angular spacing between the instances will be automatically calculated.

The **Reverse Direction** button available on the left of the **Pattern Axis s**election box is used to change the direction of rotation. By default, the direction of the pattern creation is clockwise. If you choose this button then the resulting pattern will be created in the counterclockwise direction. You can also change the direction of the pattern creation using the **Reverse Direction** arrow from the drawing area. Figure 8-26 shows the feature and the temporary axis being selected. Figure 8-27 shows the resulting pattern feature.

Figure 8-26 *The reference to be selected for creating a circular pattern*

Figure 8-27 *The resulting circular pattern*

Circular Pattern Using a Dimensional Reference

You can also create a circular pattern by selecting an angular dimension. To create a pattern using this option, you need to create an angular dimension in the sketch of the feature that is to be patterned. Invoke the **Circular Pattern PropertyManager** and select the feature to be patterned. The dimensions of the feature to be patterned will be displayed in the drawing area, as shown in Figure 8-28. Now, select the angular dimension and set the value of the total angle and spacing in the **Circular Pattern PropertyManager**. Figure 8-29 shows the pattern created by selecting the angular dimension as the angular reference. The other options available in the **Circular Pattern PropertyManager** are the same as those discussed earlier for the **Linear Pattern PropertyManager**.

Tip. *In SolidWorks you can pattern a patterned feature. You can also pattern a mirrored feature. The mirror of the pattern feature is also possible in SolidWorks.*

Figure 8-28 *Dimensions displayed after selecting the feature to be patterned*

Figure 8-29 *Circular pattern created by selecting the angular dimension as the angular reference*

Tip. *Instead of setting the value of the angle and the number of instances in the respective spinners, you can also set the values in the callout. Entering values in the callout is a better option and a timesaving practice.*

*It is always a good practice to create patterns of features instead of creating complex sketches or repeatedly creating the same feature again and again. It also helps in capturing the design intent of the model. The patterns created in the **Part** mode are very useful in assembly modeling. You will learn more about assemblies in later chapters.*

Creating Sketch-driven Patterns

CommandManager:	Features > Sketch Driven Pattern	*(Customize to Add)*
Menu:	Insert > Pattern/Mirror > Sketch Driven Pattern	
Toolbar:	Features > Sketch Driven Pattern	*(Customize to Add)*

A sketch-driven pattern is created when the features, faces, or bodies are to be arranged in a nonuniform manner, which is neither rectangular nor circular. For creating a sketch-driven pattern, first you have to create an arrangement of the sketch points in a single sketch. This arrangement of sketch points will drive the instances in the pattern feature. After creating the feature to be patterned and placing the points in the sketch, invoke the **Sketch Driven Pattern PropertyManager**, as shown in Figure 8-30. You are prompted to select a sketch for pattern layout, and the face of the feature to be patterned. Select the feature or features to be patterned. Now, click in the **Reference Sketch** display box in the **Selections** rollout and select any one of the sketched points from the drawing area. You can also select the sketch from the **FeatureManager Design Tree** flyout. Choose the **OK** button from the **Sketch Driven Pattern PropertyManager**.

Figure 8-31 shows the feature and the sketch point to be selected and Figure 8-32 shows the resulting pattern feature.

The options available in the **Sketch Driven Pattern PropertyManager** are discussed next.

Figure 8-30 *The **Sketch Driven Pattern** PropertyManager*

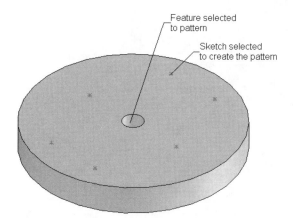

Figure 8-31 *The feature and the sketch point to be selected*

Figure 8-32 *The resulting pattern feature*

Sketch Driven Pattern Using a Centroid

When you invoke the **Sketch Driven Pattern PropertyManager**, the **Centroid** radio button is selected by default in the **Reference Point** area of the **Selections** rollout. Therefore, the pattern created is with reference to the centroid.

Sketch Driven Pattern Using a Selected Point

If you select the **Selected point** radio button from the **Reference Point** area of the **Selections** rollout, the pattern created is with reference to the selected point. When you select this radio button, a **Reference Vertex** selection box is displayed. Select a vertex; the pattern will be created in reference to that vertex.

With this release of SolidWorks, you can also propagate the visual properties to the resulting patterned instances by keeping the **Propagate Visual Properties** check box in the **Options** rollout selected.

Creating Curve-driven Patterns

CommandManager:	Features > Curve Driven Pattern	*(Customize to Add)*
Menu:	Insert > Pattern/Mirror > Curve Driven Pattern	
Toolbar:	Features > Curve Driven Pattern	*(Customize to Add)*

The **Curve Driven Pattern** option is used to pattern the features, faces, or bodies along a selected reference curve. The reference curve can be a sketched entity or an edge, or an open profile, or a closed loop. To create a pattern using this option, choose the **Curve Driven Pattern** button from the **Features CommandManager** or choose **Insert > Pattern/Mirror > Curve Driven Pattern** from the menu bar. When you choose this button, the **Curve Driven Pattern PropertyManager** is displayed, as shown in Figure 8-33. Figure 8-34 shows the feature and the curve that will be used to create the pattern. Figure 8-35 shows the resulting curve-driven pattern.

*Figure 8-33 Partial view of the **Curve Driven Pattern PropertyManager***

After invoking the **Curve Driven Pattern PropertyManager**, you are prompted to select an edge, curve, or sketch segment for pattern layout and select a face of feature to be patterned. Select the reference curve along which the feature, face, or body is to be patterned. From this

Figure 8-34 *The feature and curve to be used*
to create the curve-driven pattern

Figure 8-35 *The resulting pattern feature*

release of SolidWorks, you can also select 3D curves or sketches as the reference curve. You will learn more about 3D curves and sketches in later chapters. When you select the reference curve, its name is displayed in the **Pattern Direction** selection box and the **Direction 1** callout is also displayed. As discussed earlier, the **Direction 1** callout is divided in two areas. Select the feature to be patterned; the preview of the pattern is displayed in the drawing area. Set the various parameters available in the **Direction 1** rollout and choose the **OK** button from the **Curve Driven Pattern PropertyManager**.

The options available in the **Direction 1** rollout are discussed next.

Equal Spacing

The **Equal Spacing** check box is used to accommodate all the instances of the pattern along the selected curve. By default, this check box is cleared. Therefore, you have to specify the distance between the instances and the total number of instances to be created along the selected curve. When you select this check box, the **Spacing** spinner is not available and you have to specify only the total number of instances. The distance between the instances is calculated automatically.

Curve method and Alignment method

The **Curve method** area of the **Direction 1** rollout is used to specify the type of curve method to be followed while creating patterns. The two options available in this area are in the form of the **Transform curve** and **Offset curve** radio buttons. The **Alignment method** area of the **Direction 1** rollout is used to specify the type of alignment method to be applied. The two alignment methods are the **Tangent to curve** method and the **Align to seed** method. Figure 8-36 shows the curve-driven pattern created with selected **Transform curve** and the **Tangent to curve** radio buttons. Figure 8-37 shows the curve-driven pattern created with the **Transform curve** and **Align to seed** radio buttons selected.

Figure 8-38 shows the curve-driven pattern created with the **Offset curve** and the **Tangent to curve** radio buttons selected. Figure 8-39 shows the curve-driven pattern created with the **Offset curve** and **Align to seed** radio buttons selected.

Figure 8-36 *Pattern created with **Transform curve** and **Tangent to curve** radio buttons selected*

Figure 8-37 *Pattern created with **Transform curve** and **Align to seed** radio buttons selected*

Figure 8-38 *Pattern created with **Offset curve** and **Tangent to curve** radio buttons selected*

Figure 8-39 *Pattern created with **Offset curve** and **Align to seed** radio buttons selected*

Other options available in the **Curve Driven PropertyManager** are the same as those discussed earlier for the mirror and other pattern features. By selecting the check box available in the **Direction 2** rollout, you can also specify the parameters in the second direction. Figure 8-40 shows the curve-driven pattern feature created with the pattern defined in the first and second direction.

Figure 8-40 *A curve-driven pattern created by specifying parameters in both the directions*

Creating Table-driven Patterns

CommandManager:	Features > Table Driven Pattern	*(Customize to Add)*
Menu:	Insert > Pattern/Mirror > Table Driven Pattern	
Toolbar:	Features > Table Driven Pattern	*(Customize to Add)*

The table driven pattern is created by specifying the X and Y coordinates with reference to a coordinate system. The instances of the selected features, faces, or bodies are created at the points specified using the X and Y coordinates. For creating this pattern, you first need to create a coordinate system using the **Coordinate System** button from the **Reference Geometry** toolbar. The coordinate system defines the direction along which the selected feature will be patterned. Choose the **Table Driven Pattern** button from the **Features CommandManager** or choose **Insert > Pattern/Mirror > Table Driven Pattern** from the menu bar. The **Table Driven Pattern** dialog box is displayed, as shown in Figure 8-41.

*Figure 8-41 The **Table Driven Pattern** dialog box*

Select the feature to be patterned and the coordinate system, from the drawing area or from the **FeatureManager Design Tree**. Enter the coordinates for creating the instances in the **Coordinate points** area of the **Table Driven Pattern** dialog box. As you enter the coordinates for the instances, the preview of the pattern is displayed in the drawing area. After entering all the coordinate points, choose the **OK** button from the **Table Driven Pattern** dialog box. Figure 8-42 shows the

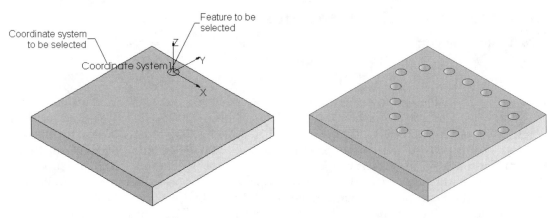

Figure 8-42 *Feature and the coordinate system to be selected for creating a table-driven pattern*

Figure 8-43 *The resulting pattern after specifying the coordinate points*

feature and the coordinate system to be selected. Figure 8-43 shows the table-driven pattern created after entering the coordinate values in the **Table Driven Pattern** dialog box.

You can also save the table-driven pattern file and retrieve the same coordinates by simply browsing the saved file using the **Browse** button from the **Table Driven Pattern** dialog box. You can also write the coordinates in a text file and browse the same file while creating a table-driven pattern. The other options available in this dialog box are the same as those discussed earlier.

Creating Rib Features

CommandManager:	Features > Rib
Menu:	Insert > Features > Rib
Toolbar:	Features > Rib

Ribs are defined as the thin walled structures that are used to increase the strength of the entire structure of the component so that it does not fail under an increased load. In SolidWorks, the ribs are created using an open sketch as well as a closed sketch. To create a rib feature, invoke the **Rib PropertyManager** and select the plane on which you need to draw the sketch for creating the rib feature. Draw the sketch and exit the sketching environment. Specify the rib parameters in the **Rib PropertyManager** and view the detailed preview using the **Detailed Preview** button. The **Rib** tool is invoked by choosing the **Rib** button from the **Features CommandManager** or by choosing **Insert > Features > Rib** from the menu bar. After invoking the **Rib** tool, draw the sketch and exit the sketching environment; the **Rib PropertyManager** is displayed, as shown in Figure 8-44.

The preview of the rib feature with the direction arrow and the confirmation corner is displayed in the drawing area. Figure 8-45 shows the sketch drawn for the rib feature and Figure 8-46 shows the resulting rib feature.

The options available in the **Rib PropertyManager** are discussed next.

*Figure 8-44 The **Rib PropertyManager***

Figure 8-45 Sketch for the rib feature

Figure 8-46 The resulting rib feature

Tip. *You can also create the rib feature by first drawing the sketch and then invoking the **Rib** tool within the sketching environment. If you exit the sketching environment after creating the sketch for a rib feature, invoke the **Rib** tool and select the sketch from the drawing area.*

Thickness

The **Thickness** area of the **Parameters** rollout is used to specify the side of the rib thickness and the thickness of the rib feature. The buttons available in this area are used to control the side on which you want to add the rib thickness. By default, the **Both Sides** button is chosen. Therefore, the rib is created on both sides of the sketch. You can choose the **First Side** or **Second Side** button to create ribs on either side of the sketch. The **Rib Thickness** spinner in this area of the **Parameters** rollout is used to specify the rib thickness.

Extrusion direction

The **Extrusion direction** area of the **Parameters** rollout is used to specify the method of extruding the closed or open sketch. When you invoke the **Rib PropertyManager**, by default the option that is suitable for creating the rib feature will be active, depending on the geometric conditions. The options available in this area are discussed next.

Parallel to Sketch

The **Parallel to Sketch** option is used to extrude the sketch in a direction that is parallel to both the sketch and sketching plane. When you invoke the **Rib PropertyManager** and the sketch created for the rib feature is a continuous single entity open sketch, this option is selected by default. Figure 8-47 shows an open sketch suitable for creating a rib using the **Parallel to Sketch** option. Figure 8-48 shows the rib feature created using the sketch.

Figure 8-47 *An open sketch for the rib feature*   **Figure 8-48** *The resulting rib feature*

Normal to Sketch

The **Normal to Sketch** option is used to create a rib feature when the sketch of the rib feature is a closed loop sketch, or it consists of multiple sketched entities. The sketch with multiple entities can be closed loops or open profiles. If you draw a sketch with a closed loop or with multiple sketched entities and invoke the **Rib** tool, the **Normal to Sketch** button will be selected by default. You can also choose the **Normal to Sketch** button from the **Extrusion Direction** area to use this option. Figure 8-49 shows a multiple entity sketch for the rib feature. Figure 8-50 shows the resulting rib feature.

When this option is selected, the **Type** area is displayed under the **Draft Angle** spinner. The options available in the **Type** area are discussed next.

Type

The **Type** area is available only when you choose the **Normal to Sketch** button from the **Extrusion direction** area of the **Parameters** rollout. The **Type** area is provided with two radio buttons, **Linear** and **Natural**. These radio buttons are used if the endpoints of the open sketch for the rib are not coincident with the faces of the existing feature. If the **Linear Radio** button is selected, the rib is created by extending the sketch normal to

Figure 8-49 *Multiple entities for the rib feature*   **Figure 8-50** *The resulting rib feature*

Tip. *You will observe that the endpoints of the sketched lines drawn in Figure 8-47 do not merge with the model edges. However, the rib created using this sketch merges with the model edges. This is because while creating the sketch for the rib feature, you do not have to create a complete sketch. The ends of the rib feature automatically extend to the next surface.*

the sketched entity direction. The sketch will be extended up to a point where it meets the boundary.

On the other hand, if the **Natural** radio button is selected, the rib feature is created by extending the sketch along the direction of the sketched entities. For example, consider the sketch shown in Figure 8-51 which shows a multiple entity sketch created for the rib feature.

Figure 8-51 *Sketch for the rib feature*

Figure 8-52 shows a rib feature created by extending the sketch normal to the arc and the line. This is because the **Linear** radio button is selected. Similarly, in Figure 8-53, the feature is created by extending the sketch along the line and arc using the **Natural** radio button. This is the reason a circular feature is created at the end where the sketch has the arc.

Figure 8-52 *Rib feature created with the* ***Linear*** *radio button selected from the* ***Type*** *area of the* ***Rib PropertyManager***

Figure 8-53 *Rib feature created with the* ***Natural*** *radio button selected from the* ***Type*** *area of the* ***Rib PropertyManager***

Flip material side

The **Flip material side** check box is selected to reverse the direction of material addition, while creating the rib feature. You can also reverse the direction of material addition using the **Flip material side** arrow available in the drawing area.

Draft On/Off

The **Draft On/Off** button is used to add the taper to the faces of the rib feature. When you choose the **Draft On/Off** button, the **Draft Angle** spinner is invoked. If you are creating a rib feature using multiple sketched entities, you can add only a simple draft to it. Figure 8-54 shows the draft angle added to the rib feature. By default, the draft is added inwards to the rib feature.

Figure 8-54 *Draft angle added to the rib feature*

Using the **Draft outward** check box you can add the draft outwards. If the rib feature to be created consists of a single continuous sketch and if you choose the **Draft On/Off** button, the **Next Reference** button is displayed below the **Draft Angle** spinner. A reference arrow is also displayed in the drawing area. Using the **Next Reference** button, you can cycle through the reference along which you want to add the draft angle.

Figure 8-55 shows the preview of the rib feature and Figure 8-56 shows the resulting rib feature with the **Draft outward** check box selected.

Figure 8-55 *Preview of the rib feature*

Figure 8-56 *The resulting rib feature with the **Draft outward** check box selected*

Figure 8-57 shows the preview of the rib feature and Figure 8-58 shows the resulting rib feature with the **Draft outward** check box cleared.

Figure 8-57 *Sketch selected to create a rib feature with an inward draft*

Figure 8-58 *The resulting rib feature*

Displaying the Section View of the Model

CommandManager:	View > Section View *(Customize to Add)*
Menu:	View > Display > Section View
Toolbar:	View > Section View

The **Section View** tool is used to display the section view of the model by cutting it using a plane or face. You can also save the section view with a name and then generate this section view directly on the drawing sheet in the drawing mode. To display the section view of a model, choose the **Section View** button from the **View CommandManager** or choose **View > Display > Section View** from the menu bar. You need to invoke the **View CommandManager**, if it not is not available by default. Move the cursor on any one of the buttons available in **CommandManager** and right-click to invoke the shortcut menu.

Choose the **Customize CommandManager** option from it. The **Customizing CommandManager** menu is displayed. Select the **View** check box to display the **View CommandManager** and click once anywhere in the drawing area. On invoking this tool, the **Section View PropertyManager** is displayed, as shown in Figure 8-59.

Figure 8-59 The Section View PropertyManager

By default, the **Front Plane** is automatically selected in the **Section View PropertyManager** and the section view of the model, created using the **Front Plane** as the section plane, is displayed in the drawing area. A drag handle is provided in the drawing area to dynamically adjust the offset distance of the section plane, as shown in Figure 8-60.

If you need to select the **Right Plane** or **Top Plane** as the section plane, choose the respective buttons available in the **Section 1** rollout. You can also select a face or a user-defined plane as the section plane. You can also specify the offset distance using the **Offset Distance** spinner. You will observe that as you modify the offset distance, the preview of the section view is automatically modified. You can also rotate the section plane along the X axis and the Y axis using the **X Rotation** and **Y Rotation** spinners respectively.

The **Edit Color** button is used to modify the color of the preview of the section cap. This color is displayed only when the **Section View PropertyManager** is active. When you exit the **PropertyManager**, the color is not displayed in the section view.

To create a half section view, you need to invoke the **Section 2** rollout and specify the section plane in it. You can also specify the offset distance and the rotation of the plane, as discussed earlier for **Section 1**. After setting all the parameters, choose the **OK** button from the **Section View PropertyManager**. Figure 8-61 shows the preview of the model after defining the section plane.

Figure 8-60 *Drag handle for dynamic offset*

Figure 8-61 *Section preview after selecting the second section plane*

You can also define the third section plane using the **Section 3** rollout. This rollout is displayed only after you invoke the **Section 2** rollout.

The options available in the **Options** rollout are used to save the section view as a named view. You can retrieve the saved section view from the **Orientation** dialog box at any stage of your design cycle. To save a named view, choose the **Save View** button from the **Options** rollout. The **Named View** dialog box is displayed; specify the name of the view and choose the **OK** button from this dialog box. Using the **Reset** button, you can reset the section view setting to the default settings. The **Show section cap** check box is selected by default. If you clear this check box, the preview of the section view is not capped. Figure 8-62 shows the section view of a model.

Figure 8-62 *Section view of a model*

Tip. *You can also rotate the section plane dynamically by moving the cursor on the edge of the section plane. The cursor will be replaced by the rotate cursor. Drag the cursor to dynamically rotate the section plane.*

To switch back to the full view mode, you need to choose the **Section View** *button from the* **View CommandManager**. *You can also select any face of the sectioned model and then right-click to invoke the shortcut menu. Choose the* **Section View** *option from the shortcut menu.*

To modify the section view, select any face of the sectioned model and invoke the shortcut menu. Choose the **Section View Properties** *option from it. The* **Section View PropertyManager** *is displayed and you can modify the section view.*

TUTORIALS

Tutorial 1

In this tutorial, you will create the model shown in Figure 8-63. The dimensions of the model are shown in Figure 8-64.   **(Expected time: 30 min)**

Figure 8-63 Solid model for Tutorial 1

The steps to be followed to complete this tutorial are discussed next.

a. Create the base feature of the model by extruding a rectangle of 69 mm x 45 mm, created on the **Right Plane** to a depth of 10 mm, refer to Figure 8-65.
b. Create the second feature, which is created by extruding the sketch created on the back face of the base feature, refer to Figure 8-66.
c. The third feature of the model is a circular feature, refer to Figure 8-67.

Figure 8-64 *Views and dimensions of the model for Tutorial 1*

d.   Create a hole feature placed concentric to the circular feature.
e.   Create the hole on the specified BCD and pattern the hole feature using the circular pattern option.
f.   Create the hole feature on the base feature, refer to Figure 8-68.
g.   Create a fillet feature to add the required fillets, refer to Figures 8-69 and 8-70.
h.   Create the rib feature, refer to Figures 8-71 and 8-72.

Creating the Base Feature

1.   Start SolidWorks and then start a new part document from the **New SolidWorks Document** dialog box.

It is evident from the model that the sketch of its base feature is drawn on the **Right Plane**. Therefore, you need to select the **Right Plane** from the **FeatureManager Design Tree** to create the base feature.

2.   Select the **Right Plane** from the **FeatureManager Design Tree** and choose the **Extruded Boss/Base** button from the **Features CommandManager**. The sketching environment is invoked and the **Right Plane** is oriented normal to the view.

3. Draw the sketch of the base feature of the model, which consists of a rectangle of dimensions 69 mm x 45 mm.

4. Add the required relations and dimensions to the sketch. Exit the sketching environment.

5. Set the value of the **Depth** spinner to 10 mm and exit the **Extrude PropertyManager**. The base feature of the model is shown in Figure 8-65.

Figure 8-65 *Base feature of the model*

Creating the Second Feature of the Model

The second feature of the model is also an extruded feature. Draw the sketch for the second feature on its back face, and extrude this sketch to the given depth.

1. Select the back face of the base feature as the sketching plane and invoke the **Extruded Boss/Base** tool.

2. Draw the sketch of the second feature and add the required relations and dimensions.

3. Exit the sketching environment and select the **Reverse Direction** button from the **PropertyManager**.

4. Set the value of the **Depth** spinner to **38** and end the feature creation.

The model, after creating the second feature, is shown in Figure 8-66.

Note
You can also create the first and second features using the contour selection method.

Creating the Third Feature

The third feature of this model is a circular extruded feature, which is created by extruding a circular sketch on both sides of the sketching plane. The sketch for this feature is drawn on the right planar face of the second feature.

1. Select the right planar face of the second feature as the sketching plane and invoke the **Extruded Boss/Base** tool.

2. Draw the sketch using the **Circle** tool. Add the required relations and dimensions to it.

3. Exit the sketching environment and set the value of the **Depth** spinner available in the **Direction 1** rollout to **12**. Since you have to extrude the sketch in both the directions with variable values, therefore, you need to invoke the **Direction 2** rollout. Set the value of the **Depth** spinner available in the **Direction 2** rollout to **13** and end the feature creation.

    Figure 8-67 shows the model, after adding the third feature.

Figure 8-66 *Second feature added to the model*   ***Figure 8-67*** *Third feature added to the model*

Creating the Fourth Feature

The fourth feature of this model is a hole feature. You will create a hole using the **Simple Hole** option on the right face of the third feature. To create a hole using this option, you need to place a point on which the hole will be placed.

1. Select the right face of the third feature as the sketching plane for placing the sketch point and invoke the sketching environment. The center point of the hole to be created, using the **Hole PropertyManager**, will be placed coincident to this sketched point.

2. Place a point on the right face of the circular feature.

3. Add the **Concentric** relation between the sketched point and the circular edge of the third feature and exit the sketching environment.

4. Now, select the face on which the point is placed. Choose the **Simple Hole** button from the **Features CommandManager**, or choose **Insert > Features > Hole > Simple** from the menu bar to invoke the **Hole PropertyManager**.

5. Choose the **Through All** option from the **End Condition** drop-down list and set the value of the **Hole Diameter** spinner to **16**.

6. Select the center point of the hole feature and drag the cursor to the sketched point drawn earlier. Release the left mouse button when the cursor snaps the sketched point.

7. Choose the **OK** button from the **Hole PropertyManager**.

Creating the Fifth Feature

1. Using the procedure given in the previous section, create the fifth feature, which is also a hole feature placed on the same placement plane. The hole feature is created using the **Through All** option, with the diameter of the hole as **4**. Next, define the placement of the feature by adding the required relations and dimensions.

Patterning the Hole Feature

After creating the fifth feature, which is a hole feature, you will pattern it using the **Circular Pattern** tool.

1. In case all the buttons of the **CommandManager** are not visible, select the black arrow; a flyout appears. Choose the **Circular Pattern** button from the **CommandManager** flyout.

    The **Circular Pattern PropertyManager** is invoked and you are prompted to select an edge or axis for direction reference; select a face of the feature for pattern features.

    To create a circular pattern, you need an edge or axis that will be used as the central axis. As discussed in the earlier chapters, when you create a circular feature, a temporary axis is automatically created passing through its center. In this tutorial, the feature to be patterned is created on a circular feature. Therefore, you will display the temporary axis of the circular feature which will be used as the central axis.

2. Choose **View > Temporary Axes** from the menu bar to display the temporary axis; the temporary axes are displayed in the model.

3. Select the temporary axis that passes through the center of the first hole feature; the **Direction 1** callout is displayed and is attached to the selected axis.

4. Click in the **Features to Pattern** selection box to invoke the selection mode.

5. Select the smaller hole from the drawing area, or expand the **FeatureManager Design Tree**, which is displayed in the drawing area, and select the **Hole2** feature; the preview of the pattern feature is displayed with the default settings.

6. Select the **Equal spacing** check box, if cleared and set the value of the **Number of Instances** spinner to **6**. Choose the **OK** button from the **PropertyManager**.

7. Choose **View** > **Temporary Axes** to hide the temporary axes.

Creating the Seventh Feature

1. The seventh feature of this model is a hole feature. You will create this hole feature using the procedure given to create the fourth feature. This hole feature will be placed on the right planar face of the base feature. Therefore, after selecting the right planar face of the base feature, place the hole feature. Next, define the placement of the hole feature by adding the required relations and dimensions. Figure 8-68 shows the model after adding the hole features.

Figure 8-68 *Model after adding all the hole features*

Creating the Fillet Feature

Next, you need to create the fillet feature. It is evident from the model that the fillets to be added to the model are of different radii. In SolidWorks, you can specify different radii to individual selected edges, faces, or loops in a single fillet feature.

1. Choose the **Fillet** button from the **Features CommandManager** to invoke the **Fillet PropertyManager**; you are prompted to select edges, faces, features, or loops to be filleted.

2. Select the **Multiple radius fillet** check box from the **Items To Fillet** rollout of the **Fillet PropertyManager**.

3. Select the edges to fillet, as shown in Figure 8-69. As the **Multiple radius fillet** check box is selected, therefore, each selected edge has a separate **Radius** callout.

4. Modify the value of the radii, as required in the respective **Radius** callouts.

5. Choose the **OK** button from the **Fillet PropertyManager**.

The isometric view of the model, after adding the fillet feature, is shown in Figure 8-70.

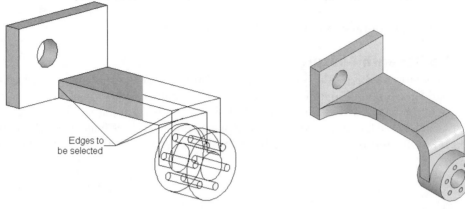

Figure 8-69 *Edges to be selected*   *Figure 8-70* *Model after adding the fillet feature*

Creating the Rib Feature

The next feature that you need to create is a rib feature. The sketch of the rib feature needs to be drawn on a sketching plane at an offset distance from the back planar face of the model. Therefore, first you need to create a reference plane at an offset distance from the back planar face of the model.

1. Invoke the **Plane PropertyManager**.

2. Rotate the model and select its back planar face. Choose the **Reverse direction** check box under the **Distance** spinner and set the value of the **Distance** spinner to **19**.

3. Choose the **OK** button from the **Plane PropertyManager** to end the feature creation; a new plane is created at an offset distance from the back planar face of the model.

4. Choose the **Rib** button from the **Features CommandManager**.

5. Create the sketch for the rib feature on the newly created plane and add the required relations and dimensions to the sketch, as shown in Figure 8-71.

6. Exit the sketching environment; the **Rib PropertyManager** is displayed.

The preview of the rib feature is displayed in the drawing area and you will observe that the direction of material addition is displayed by an arrow in the drawing area. The direction of material addition is opposite to the required direction. Therefore, you need to flip its direction.

7. Select the **Flip material side** check box to flip the direction of the material addition.

Figure 8-71 Sketch for the rib feature

The default value of the rib thickness is 10, which is the required value, and so you do not need to change it.

8.   Choose **OK** from the **Rib PropertyManager**. Also, hide the newly created plane.

The last feature of the model is the fillet feature. Add the fillet feature on the left edge of the rib using the **Fillet** tool. Figure 8-72 shows the isometric view of the final model.

Figure 8-72 The final solid model

Saving the Model

1.   Create a *c08* folder in the *SolidWorks* folder and choose the **Save** button from the **Standard** toolbar. Save the model with the name given below.

\My Documents\SolidWorks\c08\c08tut1.sldprt

2.   Choose **File** > **Close** from the menu bar to close the document.

Tutorial 2

In this tutorial, you will create the model shown in Figure 8-73. The dimensions of the model are shown in Figure 8-74.   **(Expected time: 30 min)**

Figure 8-73 *Model for Tutorial 2*

Figure 8-74 *Front view and aligned section view with dimensions*

The steps to be followed to complete this tutorial are discussed next.

a. Create the base feature of the model by revolving the sketch along a centerline, refer to Figures 8-75 and 8-76.
b. Create the second feature, which is on the outer periphery of the base feature, by extruding the sketch from the sketch plane to a selected surface, refer to Figures 8-77 and 8-78.
c. Place a counterbore hole feature on the top face of the second feature using the hole wizard.
d. Pattern the second and third features along the temporary axis using the **Circular Pattern** tool, refer to Figure 8-79.
e. Create the rib feature, refer to Figure 8-80.
f. Pattern the rib feature along a temporary axis using the **Circular Pattern** tool, refer to Figure 8-81.

Creating the Base Feature

Start a new SolidWorks part document. First you need to create the base feature of the model by revolving the sketch along the axis of revolution. The axis of revolution will be a centerline and the sketch for the base feature will be drawn on the **Right Plane**.

1. Invoke the **Revolved Boss/Base** tool and select the **Right Plane** as the sketching plane.

2. Create the sketch for the base feature and add the required relations and dimensions to the sketch, as shown in Figure 8-75.

Figure 8-75 Sketch for the base feature

3. Exit the sketching environment and set the value of the **Angle** spinner to **360**.

4. Choose the **OK** button from the **Revolve PropertyManager**. The base feature created after revolving the sketch is shown in Figure 8-76.

Figure 8-76 Base feature of the model

Creating the Second Feature

The second feature is created by extruding a sketch up to the selected surface.

1. Invoke the **Extruded Boss/Base** tool and select the face shown in Figure 8-77 as the sketching plane.

2. Create the sketch of the second feature and add the required relations and dimensions to the sketch.

3. Exit the sketching environment. Use the **Up To Surface** option to extrude the sketch. The surface to be selected is shown in Figure 8-78.

Figure 8-77 Face to be selected   *Figure 8-78 Surface to be selected*

4. Choose the **OK** button from the **Extrude PropertyManager**.

Creating the Hole Feature

It is evident from Figure 8-74 that a counterbore hole needs to be added to the model by using the **Hole Wizard**. Before invoking this tool, select the placement plane for the hole feature.

1. Select the top face of the second feature as the placement plane for the hole feature.

2. Choose the **Hole Wizard** button from the **Features CommandManager** to invoke the **Hole Specification PropertyManager**.

    The preview of the hole feature with the default settings in the **Hole Specification PropertyManager** is displayed in the drawing area.

3. Choose the **Counterbore** button from the **Hole Specification** rollout, if it is not chosen by default. Select the **Ansi Metric** option from the **Standard** drop-down list.

4. Select the **Socket Button Head Cap Screw - ANSI B18.3.4M** option from the **Type** drop-down list to specify the type of screw.

5. Select the **M3** option from the **Size** drop-down list to specify the size of the fastener to be used in the hole.

6. Choose the **Positions** tab from the **Hole Specification PropertyManager**; you will be prompted to use dimensions and other sketching tools to position the center of the holes.

7. Invoke the **Add Relations PropertyManager** and apply a concentric relation between the center point of the hole feature and the circular edge of the second feature.

8. Choose the **OK** button from the **Hole Specification PropertyManager** to end the feature creation.

Patterning the Features

After creating the second and third feature, you need to pattern them about the temporary axis using the **Circular Pattern** tool.

1. Choose the **Circular Pattern** button from the **Features CommandManager** to invoke the **Circular Pattern PropertyManager**.

    You need to define an axis as the direction reference to create a circular pattern. Therefore, display the temporary axes by choosing **View > Temporary Axes** from the menu bar.

2. Select the temporary axis that passes through the center of the model and invoke the selection mode in the **Features to Pattern** area; the **Direction 1** callout is displayed.

3. Select the second and third features from the drawing area or from the **FeatureManager Design Tree** that is displayed in the drawing area.

4. Set the value of the **Number of Instances** spinner to **3** and make sure the **Equal spacing** check box is selected. Clear the **Geometry pattern** check box from the **Options** rollout, if it is selected.

5. Choose the **OK** button from the **Circular Pattern PropertyManager**.

6.   Hide the temporary axes. The model, after patterning the features, is shown in Figure 8-79.

Creating the Rib Feature

The next feature is a rib. The sketch for the rib feature will be created on the **Front Plane**.

1.   Choose the **Rib** button from the **Features CommandManager** and select the **Front Plane** from the **FeatureManager Design Tree**.

2.   Set the display model to wireframe, create the sketch for the rib feature, and add the required relations, as shown in Figure 8-80.

Figure 8-79 *Model after patterning the features*   **Figure 8-80** *Sketch for the rib feature*

3.   Exit the sketching environment and set the value of the **Rib Thickness** spinner to **2**. Leave all the other default options as they are and choose the **OK** button from the **Rib PropertyManager**.

4.   Change the model display mode to shaded.

5.   Using the **Circular Pattern** tool, create six instances of the rib feature. The final model, after creating all the features, is shown in Figure 8-81.

Saving the Model

1.   Choose the **Save** button from the **Standard** toolbar and save the model in the *c08* folder with the name given below.

     \My Documents\SolidWorks\c08\c08tut2.sldprt

2.   Choose **File > Close** from the menu bar to close the document.

Figure 8-81 *Final solid model*

Tutorial 3

In this tutorial, you will create the cylinder head of a two-stroke automobile engine shown in Figure 8-82. The dimensions of the model are shown in Figure 8-83. You will also create a section view of the model using the **Section View** tool.

(Expected time: 1 hr)

Figure 8-82 *Model for Tutorial 3*

Figure 8-83 *Top view and the section front view with dimensions*

The steps to be followed to complete this tutorial are discussed next.

a. Create the base feature of the model by extruding a polygon to the given depth, refer to Figure 8-84.
b. Add the fillet to the base feature.
c. Create a circular feature at the bottom face of the base feature.
d. Create the revolve cut feature to create the dome of the cylinder head, refer to Figures 8-85 and 8-86.
e. Create the left fin of the cylinder head by extruding the sketch. The sketch for this feature should be carefully dimensioned and defined, refer to Figure 8-87.
f. Use the **Vary sketch** option to pattern the fins, refer to Figure 8-88.
g. Create other cut and extrude features to complete the model, refer to Figure 8-89.
h. Create a tap hole using the hole wizard, refer to Figure 8-90.
i. Create the section view of the model, refer to Figure 8-91.

Creating the Base Feature

1. Create a new SolidWorks part document.

   The base feature of the model will be created by extruding the sketch created on the **Top** plane.

2. Invoke the **Extruded Boss/Base** tool and select the **Top Plane** as the sketching plane.

3. Create the sketch for the base feature and add the required relations and dimensions to the sketch, as shown in Figure 8-84.

Figure 8-84 *Sketch for the base feature*

4. Exit the sketching environment and extrude the sketch to a depth of 4 mm.

Creating the Second Feature

The second feature of the model is the fillet feature. You need to fillet all the vertical edges of the base feature using the given radius.

1. Invoke the **Fillet** tool and set the value of the **Radius** spinner to **15**. Select all the vertical edges of the base feature to add the fillet feature.

2. Choose the **OK** button from the **Fillet PropertyManager**.

Creating the Third Feature

After creating the base and adding fillet at its vertical edges, you will create the third feature of the model, which is a circular extruded feature. The sketch of the feature will be drawn on the bottom face of the base feature and it will be extruded to the given depth.

1. Invoke the **Extruded Boss/Base** tool and select the bottom face of the base feature as the sketching plane.

2. Create a circle of 55 mm diameter with its center point at the origin.

3. Exit the sketching environment and extrude the sketch to a depth of 4 mm.

Creating the Fourth Feature

The fourth feature is a revolved cut feature whose sketch will be drawn on the **Front Plane**. After drawing the sketch, apply the required relations and dimensions to it.

1. Invoke the **Revolved Cut** tool and select the **Front Plane** from the **FeatureManager Design Tree**.

2. Draw the sketch for the revolved cut feature and add the required relations and dimensions, as shown in Figure 8-85. You need to apply the vertical relation between the center point of the arc and the origin to fully define it.

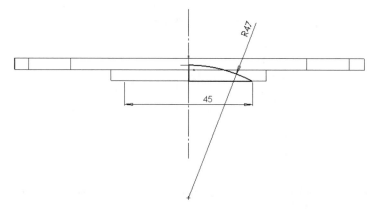

Figure 8-85 *Sketch for the revolve cut feature*

Note
When you draw a sketch for the revolved cut feature for this tutorial, draw a horizontal centerline, such that the start point of the centerline is merged with the upper endpoint of the arc. Also, ensure a tangent relation between the arc and the centerline exists to maintain the tangency of the arc.

3. Select the vertical centerline and exit the sketching environment. Make sure that the **Angle** spinner value is **360**.

4. Choose the **OK** button from the **Cut-Revolve PropertyManager**.

    The rotated model, after creating the fourth feature, is shown in Figure 8-86.

Figure 8-86 *Cut revolve feature added to the model*

Creating the Fifth Feature

Next, you will create the left fin of the cylinder head. It will be created by extruding a sketch to both the directions using the **Through All** option. The sketch of this feature, drawn on the **Front Plane**, will be dimensioned and defined such that the length of the fin is driven by a construction arc and a horizontal dimension. The detailed step by step procedure of drawing, dimensioning, and defining the sketch is discussed next.

1. Invoke the **Extruded Boss/Base** tool and select the **Front Plane** from the **FeatureManager Design Tree**.

2. Using the **Line** tool draw the triangle and then draw a vertical centerline that passes through the upper vertex to the triangle, refer to Figure 8-87.

3. Invoke the **3 Pt Arc** tool and draw the arc, as shown in Figure 8-87. Select the arc and select the **For Construction** check box from the **Options** rollout of the **Arc PropertyManager**.

4. Invoke the **Add Relations PropertyManager** and add the coincident relation between the upper vertex of the triangle and the centerline.

5. Add the midpoint relation between the lower endpoint of the centerline and the horizontal line of the triangle. Make sure that the **Coincident** relation between the upper vertex of the triangle and the centerline exists. Also, add the vertical relation to the centerline, if it is missing.

6. Add the coincident relation between the upper vertex of the triangle and the arc.

7. Add the required dimensions and relations to fully define the sketch, as shown in Figure 8-87.

8. Exit the sketching environment and extrude the sketch in both the directions using the

Figure 8-87 Sketch for the fin of the cylinder head

Tip. *It is evident from Figure 8-87 that one of the horizontal dimensions has a value of 6.155. By default, the primary unit precision is set to two decimal places. Therefore, for defining a dimension value with more number of decimal places, you need to select the dimension and set the precision value to the required decimal places from the **Primary Unit Precision** drop-down list from the **Dimension PropertyManager**.*

Through All option. You will notice that the fin extends out of the base feature at both the ends. You will learn how to remove the unwanted material of the fin later in this tutorial.

Patterning the Fifth Feature

You will pattern the fin using the **Vary Sketch** option from the **Linear Pattern** tool. Using the **Vary sketch** option, the geometry of each instance of the pattern varies according to the driven dimension and the relation added to the sketch of the feature to be patterned.

1. Select the fifth feature, if it is not already selected and choose the **Linear Pattern** button from the **Features CommandManager** to invoke the **Linear Pattern PropertyManager**.

    You are prompted to select the directional reference.

2. Select the horizontal dimension with the value of **6.155** as the directional reference in the **Pattern Direction** selection box of the **Direction 1** rollout.

3. Set the value of the **Spacing** spinner to **9**. Set the value of the **Number of Instances** spinner to **13**. Choose the **Reverse Direction** button.

4. Invoke the **Options** rollout and select the **Vary Sketch** check box from this rollout; the

preview of the pattern is not displayed in the drawing area.

5. Choose the **OK** button from the **Linear Pattern PropertyManager**.

The model, after adding the pattern feature, is shown in Figure 8-88.

Figure 8-88 *Model after patterning the fin of the cylinder head*

Creating the Cut Feature

The next feature that you will create is a cut feature. Using the **Rotate View** tool, rotate the solid model and you will observe that the fins of the cylinder head that you patterned in the last feature extend beyond the boundary of the base feature. Therefore, to trim the extended portion of the fins, you will create a cut feature.

1. Invoke the **Extruded Cut** tool and select the top planar face of the base feature as the sketching plane.

2. Draw the sketch using the standard sketch tools. The sketch for this feature will be the outer profile of the base feature.

Tip. *You can draw the sketch using the outer profile of the base feature using the **Convert Entities** tool. Select the lower flat face of the base feature and choose the **Convert Entities** button from the **Sketch** toolbar. You will notice that the sketch similar to the outer boundary of the base feature will be placed on the sketching plane.*

3. Exit the sketching environment and choose the **Reverse Direction** button from the **Direction 1** rollout and select the **Through All** option from the **End Condition** drop-down list.

Since the direction of the side from which the material is to be removed is opposite to the required direction, therefore, you need to flip the direction of material removal.

4. Select the **Flip side to cut** the check box from the **Direction 1** rollout and choose the **OK** button from the **Cut-Extrude PropertyManager**.

5. Using the standard modeling tools shape the model, as shown in Figure 8-89.

Figure 8-89 *Model after adding other extrude and cut features*

Patterning the Remaining Features

After creating all the features, you need to pattern the cut, extrude, and hole features created at the lower left corner of the model.

1. Invoke the **Linear Pattern PropertyManager** and select the cut, extrude, and hole features, created on the lower left corner of the model.

2. Select the two directional references to pattern the features in both the directions and set the values of the distances between the instances and the number of instances, refer to Figure 8-83.

Tip. *The sketch sharing option is also available in SolidWorks. This allows you to use a sketch used earlier in creating a sketch feature. For sharing the sketch, select it from the FeatureManager Design Tree, after invoking the feature tool. You need to expand the created sketched feature to select the sketch for sharing from the FeatureManager Design Tree.*

3. Choose the **OK** button from the **Linear PropertyManager**.

Creating a Tapped Hole

The last feature of the model is a hole feature. You will create a tapped hole using the **Hole Wizard** and then define the placement of the hole.

1. Select the top face of the middle circular extrude feature as the placement plane for the hole feature.

2. Invoke the **Hole Specification PropertyManager** by choosing the **Hole Wizard** button from the **Features CommandManager**. Choose the **Tap** button from the **Hole Specification** rollout. Select **ANSI Metric** from the **Standard** drop-down list.

3. Select the **M18x1.5** option from the **Size** drop-down list to define the size of the tap hole.

4. Select the **Through All** option from the **End Condition** drop-down list in the **End Condition** rollout. Also, select the **Through All** option from the **Thread Type** drop-down list.

5. Choose the **Cosmetic thread** button from the **Options** rollout. Also, select the **With thread callout** check box.

6. Choose the **Position** tab from the **Hole Specification PropertyManager**.

   The tapped hole will be placed by default on the placement plane. This default location is not the required position to place the hole. You need to define the placement of the tapped hole concentric with the center circular feature.

6. Invoke the **Add Relations PropertyManager** and add the **Concentric** relation between the center point of the tapped hole and the circular extruded feature of diameter 55 mm.

7. Choose the **OK** button from the **Hole Specification PropertyManager** to end the tapped hole feature creation. The rotated final model is shown in Figure 8-90.

Figure 8-90 *Final solid model*

Displaying the Section View of the Model

Next, you will display the section view of the model. The section view of the model is created using the **Section View PropertyManager**.

1.   Orient the model in the isometric view.

2.   Choose the **Section View** button from the **View CommandManager**.

The **Front** view is selected as the section plane in the **Section View PropertyManager** by default. The preview of the section view, using the **Front Plane** as the section plane, is displayed in the drawing area.

3.   Choose the **OK** button from the **Section View PropertyManager** to view the section of the model.

The section view of the model is shown in Figure 8-91.

4.   Choose the **Section View** button again from the **View CommandManager** to return to the full view mode.

Saving the Model

When you choose the **Save** button from the **Standard** toolbar, the **Save As** dialog box will be displayed because the document has not been saved until now. You can enter the name of the document in this dialog box.

1.   Choose the **Save** button from the **Standard** toolbar and save the model in the *c08* folder with the name given below.

\My Documents\SolidWorks\c08\c08tut3.sldprt

2.   Choose **File > Close** from the menu bar to close the document.

Figure 8-91 *Section view of the model*

SELF-EVALUATION TEST

Answer the following questions and then compare your answers with those given at the end of this chapter:

1. To invoke the **Mirror PropertyManager**, choose **View** > **Pattern/Mirror** > **Mirror** from the menu bar. (T/F)

2. If you modify the parent feature, then the same change will not reflect on the mirrored feature. (T/F)

3. You cannot preselect the mirror plane and the feature to be patterned before invoking the **Mirror** tool. (T/F)

4. You can mirror a single face using the **Mirror** tool. (T/F)

5. You can also pattern a pattern feature. (T/F)

6. The _____ **PropertyManager** is used to view the section view.

7. A _____ is provided in the drawing area to dynamically adjust the offset distance of the section plane.

8. The _____ option is used to create a pattern by specifying the coordinates.

9. The _____ option is used to create a pattern with respect to the sketched points.

10. Using the _____ rollout, you can delete the pattern instances.

REVIEW QUESTIONS

Answer the following questions:

1. The _____ check box is used to accommodate all the instances of a pattern along the selected curve.

2. Enter the coordinates for creating the instances in the _____ area of the **Table Driven Pattern** dialog box.

3. You need to invoke _____ to create a rib feature.

4. The _____ check box is used to transfer the visual properties assigned to the feature or parent body to the mirrored instance.

5. Using _____ check box from the **Section View PropertyManager**, you can create a section using an invisible plane normal to the eye view as the section plane.

6. When you choose the **Mirror** button from the **Features** tool, which **PropertyManager** is displayed?

   (a) **Mirror Feature PropertyManager**   (b) **Mirror All PropertyManager**
   (c) **Mirror PropertyManager**   (d) **Copy/Mirror PropertyManager**

7. Which option is used to mirror the exact geometry of the feature independent of the relationships between the geometries?

   (a) **Same Mirror**   (b) **Geometry Pattern**
   (c) **Geometry Copy**   (d) **Copy Geometry**

8. Which pattern is created along the sketched lines, arcs, or splines?

   (a) Curve-driven pattern   (b) Sketch-driven pattern
   (c) Geometry-driven pattern   (d) Linear pattern

9. Which dialog box is invoked to create a pattern by specifying the coordinate points?

   (a) **Sketch Driven Pattern**   (b) **Table Driven Pattern**
   (c) **Mirror**   (d) None of these

10. Which plane is selected by default when you invoke the **Section View PropertyManager** to view a section of the model?

   (a) **Right**   (b) **Top**
   (c) **Front**   (d) **Plane 1**

EXERCISES

Exercise 1

Create the model shown in Figure 8-92. The dimensions of the model are shown in Figure 8-93.

(Expected time: 1 hr)

Figure 8-92 *Solid model for Exercise 1*

Figure 8-93 *Views and dimensions of the model for Exercise 1*

Exercise 2

Create the model shown in Figure 8-94. The dimensions of the model are shown in Figure 8-95.

(Expected time: 1 hr)

Figure 8-94 *Solid model for Exercise 2*

Figure 8-95 *Views and dimensions of the model for Exercise 2*

Exercise 3

Create the model shown in Figure 8-96. Next, create the section view of the model using the **Right Plane**. Figure 8-97 shows the section view of the model whose dimensions are shown in Figure 8-98.   **(Expected time: 45 min)**

Figure 8-96 *Solid model for Exercise 3*

Figure 8-97 *Section view of the model*

Figure 8-98 *Views and dimensions of the model for Exercise 3*

Answers to Self-Evaluation Test

1. F, **2.** F, **3.** F, **4.** F, **5.** T, **6. Section View**, **7.** drag handle, **8. Table Driven Pattern**, **9. Sketch Driven Pattern**, **10. Instances to Skip**

Chapter 9

Editing Features

Learning Objectives

After completing this chapter, you will be able to:
- *Edit features.*
- *Edit sketches of the sketched features.*
- *Edit the sketch plane of the sketched features.*
- *Edit using the Move/Size Features option.*
- *Cut, copy, and paste features and sketches.*
- *Copy features using the drag and drop method.*
- *Delete features.*
- *Delete bodies.*
- *Suppress and unsuppress features.*
- *Move or copy bodies.*
- *Reorder features.*
- *Roll back the model.*
- *Rename features.*
- *Create folders.*
- *Use the What's Wrong functionality.*

EDITING FEATURES OF THE MODEL

Editing is one of the most important aspects of the product design cycle. Almost all designs require editing during or after their creation. As discussed earlier, SolidWorks is a feature-based parametric software. Therefore, the design created in SolidWorks is a combination of individual features integrated together to form a solid model. All these features can be edited individually. For example, Figure 9-1 shows a base plate with some holes.

Now, to replace the four inner holes with four counterbore holes, you need to perform one editing operation. Using the editing operation, you will change the drilled holes to the counterbore holes. For editing the holes, you need to select the hole feature and right-click to invoke the shortcut menu. Next, choose the **Edit Feature** option from the shortcut menu to invoke the **Hole Definition** dialog box. Finally, set the new parameters and end the feature creation. The drilled holes will be automatically replaced by counterbore holes. Figure 9-2 shows the base plate with drilled holes modified to the counterbore holes.

Figure 9-1 *Base plate with drilled holes*   *Figure 9-2* *Modified base plate*

Similarly, you can also edit the reference geometry and the sketches of the sketched features. The feature created using the reference geometry also modifies automatically, when you modify the reference geometry. For example, if you create a feature on a plane at some angle and then edit the angle of the plane, the resulting feature is automatically modified. In SolidWorks, you can perform editing tasks using various methods, which are discussed next.

Editing Using the Edit Feature Option

Editing, using the **Edit Feature** option, is the most common method in SolidWorks. To edit any feature of the model using this option, select that feature from the **FeatureManager Design Tree** or from the drawing area. Next, right-click on it to invoke the shortcut menu and choose the **Edit Feature** option, as shown in Figure 9-3. Depending on the feature selected, the **PropertyManager** or dialog box will be invoked, and you can modify the parameters of that feature. The **PropertyManager** will also have the sequence number of the feature. The **Extrude PropertyManager** is displayed in Figure 9-4 with the sequence number 1. After editing

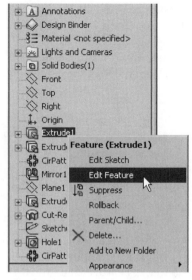

Figure 9-3 *Choosing the **Edit Feature** option from the shortcut menu*

Figure 9-4 *The **Extrude PropertyManager***

the parameters, choose the **OK** button to complete the feature creation. The feature will be modified automatically.

Editing Sketches of the Sketched Features

In SolidWorks, you can also edit the sketches of the sketched features using the **Edit Sketch** option. Select the feature from the **FeatureManager Design Tree** or from the drawing area and right-click to invoke the shortcut menu. Choose the **Edit Sketch** option from it and you will enter the sketching environment. Using the standard sketching tools, edit the sketch of the sketched feature and exit the sketching environment. Choose CTRL+B to rebuild the model. You can also select the **Rebuild** button from the **Standard** toolbar to exit the sketching environment and rebuild the model.

Tip. *You can also use the + sign available on the left of the sketched feature to expand the sketched feature in the **FeatureManager Design Tree**. The sketch icon will be displayed when you expand the sketched feature. Select the sketch icon and invoke the shortcut menu. Select the **Edit Sketch** option from it to enter the sketching environment to edit the sketch.*

Changing the Sketch Plane of Sketches

You can also change the sketch plane of the sketches of the sketched features. To edit the sketch plane, expand the sketched feature by clicking on the + sign on its left in the **FeatureManager Design Tree**. Select the sketch icon in the **FeatureManager Design Tree**. Right-click to invoke the shortcut menu and choose the **Edit Sketch Plane** option from it. Figure 9-5 shows the **Edit Sketch Plane** option chosen from the shortcut menu.

*Figure 9-5 The **Edit Sketch Plane**
option being chosen*

The **Sketch Plane PropertyManager** will be displayed, as shown in Figure 9-6. The name of the current sketch plane is displayed in the **Sketch Plane/Face** selection box. Now, select any other plane or face as the sketching plane. Next, choose the **OK** button from the **Sketch Plane PropertyManager**.

Figure 9-6 The Sketch Plane PropertyManager

 Tip. *If you select a sketch plane on which the relations and dimensions do not find any reference to be placed, the **What's Wrong** dialog box will be displayed. You, will need to undo the last step using the **Undo** button from the **Standard** toolbar. After this, invoke the **Sketch Plane PropertyManager** again and select the appropriate plane. You will learn more about the **What's Wrong** dialog box later in this chapter.*

Editing by Double-clicking on Entities and Features

You can also edit a feature, reference geometry, or a sketch by double-clicking the feature either from the **FeatureManager Design Tree** or from the drawing area. For example, if you double-click on the extrude feature, all its dimensions, and those of the sketch used to create it are displayed in the drawing area. Remember that the dimensions of the sketch will be displayed in black and the dimensions of the feature will be displayed in blue. Double-click the dimension that you need to modify; the **Modify** dialog box is invoked. Set the new value in the **Modify** dialog box and press the ENTER key on the keyboard or choose the **Save the current value and exit the dialog** button from the dialog box. You will notice that the value of the dimension is modified but the model is not modified relative to the modified value. Therefore, you need to rebuild the model using the **Rebuild** option. To rebuild the model, choose the **Rebuild** button from the **Standard** toolbar or choose CTRL+B on the keyboard.

Editing Using the Move/Size Features Tool

| **CommandManager:** | Features > Move/Size Features | *(Customize to Add)* |
| **Toolbar:** | Features > Move/Size Features | *(Customize to Add)* |

You can dynamically modify the feature and the sketch of the sketched feature without invoking the sketching environment by using this option. To edit the feature or sketch, choose the **Move/Size Features** button from the **Features CommandManager**. You will notice that the **Move/Size Features** button is chosen in it. Select any face of the feature to modify. The selected face will be highlighted in green and if the selected feature is a sketched feature then its sketch will also be highlighted in green. You will be provided with the resize handle, rotate handle, and the move handle. Figure 9-7 shows the move handle, resize handle, and the rotate handle provided for the selected feature.

To resize the feature, move the cursor to the resize handle; the select cursor will be replaced by the resize cursor with its name displayed as the tooltip. Press and hold down the left mouse button at this location and drag the cursor to resize the feature. The feature will be resized with an increment of 10. Release the left mouse button when you have resized it. You will notice that

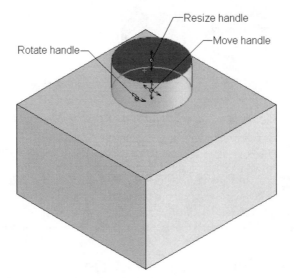

Figure 9-7 *Feature selected with the* ***Move/Size Features*** *button selected*

the feature will be dynamically resized. Figure 9-8 shows the cursor being dragged to resize the feature. Figure 9-9 shows the resulting modified feature.

Figure 9-8 *Dragging the resize handle to resize the feature*

Figure 9-9 *Resulting modified feature*

The rotate handle is used to rotate the selected feature. To rotate the feature using the rotate handle, move the cursor to the rotate handle, press and hold down the left mouse button. Drag the cursor to rotate the feature. You can drag the feature clockwise or counterclockwise. The preview of the feature will be displayed in the drawing area. The feature will be rotated with an increment of 10-degrees. Release the left mouse button, after rotating the feature to a specified location.

Note
*If you rotate a sketched feature whose sketch is fully or partially defined using relations and dimensions, the **Move Confirmation** dialog box will be displayed, as shown in Figure 9-10. This dialog box informs you that the external constraints in the feature are being moved, and prompts whether you want to delete those constraints or keep them by recalculating or make them dangling. The relations or dimensions that do not find the external reference after the placement are made dangling.*

Figure 9-10 *The **Move Confirmation** dialog box*

After rotating the feature, if you invoke the **Move Confirmation** dialog box, you need to choose either the **Delete** or the **Keep** button, based on the geometric and dimensional conditions. Figure 9-11 shows the preview of the rotating feature. Figure 9-12 shows the resulting rotated feature.

Figure 9-11 *Preview of the feature being rotated*   **Figure 9-12** *Resulting rotated feature*

To move a feature using the move handle, select a face of the feature and move the cursor to the move handle. Press and hold down the left mouse button, drag the cursor to move the feature to the desired position and then release the left mouse button. If the dimensions or relations of the feature do not remain defined after moving, the **Move Confirmation** dialog box will be displayed. Choose the options available in this dialog box. Using these options, you can also change the placement plane or the sketch plane of the feature. Figure 9-13 shows the feature being moved to another face. Figure 9-14 shows the resulting moved feature.

Figure 9-13 *The feature being moved*   **Figure 9-14** *Resulting moved feature*

You can also modify the sketches of the sketched feature using this option. To modify the sketch, move the cursor to the sketch highlighted in light green color. The symbol of the geometry, close to which the cursor is moved, appears on the right of the cursor. Press and hold down the left mouse button and drag the cursor. After modifying the sketch to the required size, release the left mouse button. Figure 9-15 shows the preview of the sketch being modified. Figure 9-16 shows the resulting modified model.

Figure 9-15 *Preview of the sketch being modified*   **Figure 9-16** *Resulting modified model*

Editing Sketches With the Move/Size Features Tool Active

When the **Move/Size Features** tool is active, and you choose the **Edit Sketch** option to edit the sketch of the sketched feature, you will enter the sketching environment. The feature whose sketch you need to modify will be displayed in transparent yellow temporary graphics, as shown in Figure 9-17.

Now, modify the sketch according to the requirement. Consider a case in which two circles are added to the model and the height of the inclined line is increased. The model shown in temporary graphics will be modified dynamically in the sketching environment. Therefore, you

Figure 9-17 *Preview of the sketch being modified*

can have a better understanding of how the model will be displayed after modifying the sketch. Note that the temporary graphics will show the preview of the feature created by the section you add only if you drag one of the entities in the sketch. Otherwise, the new addition will not be displayed as a preview in the temporary graphics. It is recommended that you invoke the **Modify/ Size Features** button before modifying the sketch. After modifying the sketch, exit the sketching environment. If the sketch of the model is dimensioned, you can modify it by modifying the dimension. Figure 9-18 shows two circles added to the model and the length of the inclined line being increased. Figure 9-19 shows the resulting modified model in the sketching environment.

Editing Features and Sketches by Cut, Copy, and Paste

SolidWorks allows you to adapt the windows functionality of cut, copy, and paste to copy and paste the features and sketches. The method of using this functionality is the same as used in other windows-based applications. Select the feature or sketch to cut or copy. To cut the selected

Figure 9-18 *Sketch being modified*   **Figure 9-19** *Resulting modified model in the sketching environment*

item, choose **Edit > Cut** from the menu bar or use the shortcut key, CTRL+X. The **Confirm Delete** dialog box is displayed, because when you cut the selected item, it is deleted from the document. Choose the **Yes** button from this dialog box. You will learn more about deleting later in this chapter. After you cut an item, select the placement plane or placement reference where you want to place the feature. Choose **Edit > Paste** from the menu bar or use the shortcut key CTRL+V on the keyboard. Sometimes the **Copy Confirmation** dialog box is displayed, as shown in Figure 9-20, in which you are prompted to delete the external constraints or leave them dangling. This dialog box is displayed only when the item to paste has some external references in the form of relations and dimensions. The feature will be pasted on the selected reference.

Figure 9-20 *The **Copy Confirmation** dialog box*

 Tip. *For pasting a selected sketch, you need to select a plane or a planar face as the reference. For pasting a sketched feature, a simple hole, or a hole created using the hole wizard, you have to select a plane or a planar face as the reference. For pasting chamfers and fillets, you have to select an edge, edges, or face as the references.*

If you copy and paste an item, the selected item will remain at its position and its copy will be pasted on the selected reference. To copy an item, select the feature or sketch. Choose **Edit > Copy** from the menu bar, or press CTRL+C on the keyboard. Select the reference where you want to paste the selected item and choose **Edit > Paste** from the menu bar, or press CTRL+V on the keyboard to paste. You can paste the selected item any number of times. If you select another item and copy it on the clipboard, the last copied item will be deleted from the memory of the clipboard.

Cutting, Copying, and Pasting Features and Sketches from One Document to the Other

You can also cut or copy the features and sketches from one document and paste them in another document. For example, you need to copy a sketch created in the current document and paste it in a new document. You need to select the sketch and use CTRL+C on the keyboard to copy the item to the clipboard. Create a new document in the **Part** mode and select the plane on which you want to paste the sketch. Press CTRL+V on the keyboard to paste the sketch on the selected plane. Using the same procedure, you can also copy features from one document to the other.

Copying Features Using Drag and Drop

SolidWorks also provides you with the drag and drop functionality of windows to copy and paste the item within the document. Press and hold down the CTRL key on the keyboard. Next, select and drag that item from the drawing area or from the **FeatureManager Design Tree**. Drag the cursor to a location where you want to paste the item and release the left mouse button. If the item to be pasted is defined using the dimensions or relations, the **Copy Confirmation** dialog box will be displayed to delete or make those constraints dangle. Figure 9-21 shows the feature being dragged. Figure 9-22 shows the resulting pasted feature.

Figure 9-21 *Feature being dragged*   *Figure 9-22* *Resulting pasted feature*

Dragging and Dropping Features from One Document to the Other

You can also drag and drop features and sketches from one document to the other. For pasting the items from one document to the other, you should open both the documents in the SolidWorks session. Choose **Windows > Tile Vertical/Tile Horizontal** from the menu bar. Display both the documents at the same time in the SolidWorks window. Press and hold down the CTRL key on the keyboard. Select and drag the feature or sketch to the other document, and place it on the required reference. Figure 9-23 shows the fillet feature being dragged to be applied on the edge of the model in the second document.

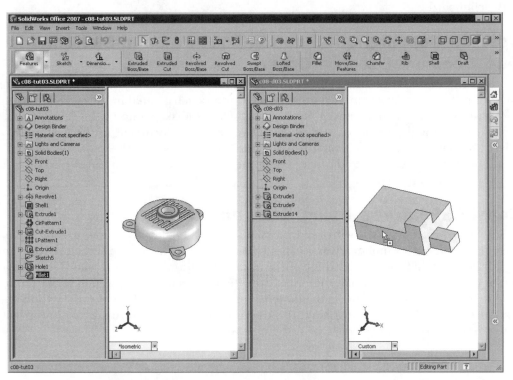

Figure 9-23 *Fillet feature being dragged to be pasted in the second document*

Deleting Features

You can delete the unwanted features from the model by selecting the feature from the **FeatureManager Design Tree** or from the drawing area. After selecting the feature to be deleted, choose the DELETE key on the keyboard, or right-click to invoke the shortcut menu and choose the **Feature** option from the **Feature** area. When you delete a feature, the **Confirm Delete** dialog box is displayed, as shown in Figure 9-24. The features that are dependent on the feature to be deleted are also displayed in the **Confirm Delete** dialog box, which informs you that all the dependent features to the parent feature will also be deleted. You are provided with the **Also delete all child features** check box. If this check box is selected, all the child features related to the parent feature are also deleted. When you delete a sketched feature, the sketches related to it will not be deleted. These sketches are known as absorbed features. To delete the absorbed features along with the parent feature, select the **Also delete absorbed features** check box from the **Confirm Delete** dialog box. Choose the **Yes** button to delete the selected features, or else choose the **No** button to cancel the delete operation. You can also delete a selected feature by choosing **Edit > Delete** from the menu bar.

Figure 9-24 *The **Confirm Delete** dialog box*

Deleting Bodies

CommandManager:	Features > Delete Solid/Surface	*(Customize to Add)*
Menu:	Insert > Features > Delete Body	
Toolbar:	Features > Delete Solid/Surface	*(Customize to Add)*

As discussed earlier, the multibody environment is supported in SolidWorks. Therefore, you can create multiple disjoint bodies in SolidWorks. You can also delete the unwanted bodies. The bodies to be deleted can be solid bodies or surface bodies. To delete a body, choose **Insert > Features > Delete Body** from the menu bar. You can invoke this tool by selecting the **Delete Solid/Surface** button from the **Features CommandManager** after customizing the **CommandManager**. The **Delete Body PropertyManager** is invoked, as shown in Figure 9-25. You are prompted to select the solid and/or surface bodies to be deleted.

Figure 9-25 *The **Delete Body** **PropertyManager***

Select the body or bodies to be deleted from the drawing area or from the **Solid Bodies** folder available in the **FeatureManager Design Tree**, which is displayed in the drawing area. The selected body is displayed in green and its name is displayed in the **Bodies to Delete** selection box. Choose the **OK** button from the **Delete Body PropertyManager**. A new item with the name **Body-Delete1** appears in the **FeatureManager Design Tree**. This item stores the deleted bodies. Therefore, at any point of your design cycle, you can delete or suppress this item to resume the deleted body back in your design. You will learn more about suppressing the feature later in this chapter.

Tip. *You can also choose the **Delete Body** option from the shortcut menu. To delete a body using the shortcut menu, select the body and right-click to invoke the shortcut menu. Choose the **Delete** option from **the Body** area of the shortcut menu; the **Delete Body PropertyManager** will be displayed. Choose the **OK** button from the **Delete Body PropertyManager** to delete the body.*

Suppressing Features

CommandManager:	Features > Suppress *(Customize to Add)*
Menu:	Edit > Suppress > This Configuration
Toolbar:	Features > Suppress *(Customize to Add)*

Sometimes, you do not want a feature to be displayed in the model or in its drawing views. Instead of deleting those features, they can be suppressed. When you suppress a feature, it is neither visible in the model nor in the drawing views. If you create an assembly using that model, the suppressed feature will not be displayed even in the assembly. You can resume the feature anytime by unsuppressing it. When you suppress a feature, the features that are dependent on it are also suppressed. To suppress a feature, select it from the **FeatureManager Design Tree** or from the drawing area. Choose the **Suppress** button from the **Features CommandManager** after customizing it, or right-click and choose the **Suppress** option from the shortcut menu. The suppressed feature will be removed from the display of the model, and the icon of the feature will be displayed in gray in the **FeatureManager Design Tree**. When you suppress a feature, then all the features dependent on that feature are also suppressed.

Unsuppressing the Suppressed Features

CommandManager:	Features > Unsuppress *(Customize to Add)*
Menu:	Edit > Unsuppress > This Configuration
Toolbar:	Features > Unsuppress *(Customize to Add)*

The suppressed features can be unsuppressed using this option. To resume the suppressed feature, select the suppressed feature from the **FeatureManager Design Tree** and choose the **Unsuppress** button from the **Features CommandManager**. You can also choose this option from the shortcut menu, after selecting the suppressed feature. As discussed earlier, when you suppress a feature, the dependent features are also suppressed. But when you resume a suppressed feature, the dependent features remain suppressed. Therefore, you need to unsuppress all the features independently. The method of resuming the parent feature and the dependent features using a single option is discussed next.

Unsuppressing Features With Dependents

CommandManager:	Features > Unsuppress with Dependents *(Customize to Add)*
Menu:	Edit > Unsuppress with Dependents > This Configuration
Toolbar:	Features > Unsuppress with Dependents *(Customize to Add)*

Using this option, you can resume the suppressed feature along with the dependents of the suppressed parent feature. To resume the suppressed feature using this option, select the suppressed feature from the **FeatureManager Design Tree**. Choose **Unsuppress with Dependents** button from the **Features** toolbar. You will observe that the dependent suppressed features are also unsuppressed.

Hiding Bodies

While working in the multibody environment, you can also hide the bodies. The hidden body is not displayed in the model, assembly, or in the drawing views. The display of the dependent bodies is not turned off when you hide a body. To hide a body, expand the **Solid Bodies** folder available in the **FeatureManager Design Tree,** and select the body to be hidden. Right-click to invoke the shortcut menu and choose the **Hide Solid Body** option from it. The selected body will disappear from the drawing area. The icon of the hidden body is displayed in wireframe in the **Solid Bodies** folder. Select the hidden body from that folder and choose the **Show Solid Body** option from the shortcut menu to turn on the display of the hidden body.

Moving and Copying Bodies

CommandManager:	Features > Move/Copy Bodies	*(Customize to Add)*
Menu:	Insert > Features > Move/Copy Bodies	
Toolbar:	Features > Move/Copy Bodies	*(Customize to Add)*

In SolidWorks, you can also move or copy the bodies by choosing the **Move/Copy Bodies** button from the **Features CommandManager** after customizing it, or choosing **Insert > Features > Move/Copy Bodies** from the menu bar. The **Move/Copy Body PropertyManager** will be displayed. By default, it shows the **Mates Settings** rollout. Choose the **Translate/Rotate** button below the **Options** rollout; the **Translate** and **Rotate** rollouts will be displayed, as shown in Figure 9-26.

Figure 9-26 The Move/Copy Body PropertyManager

You will notice a 3D triad is displayed at the centroid of the selected body. It is used to dynamically rotate or move the selected body. The three arrows of this triad are the X, Y, and Z axes along which the body can be moved. The triad also has three rings around which the body can be rotated, see Figure 9-27.

Figure 9-27 *3D triad to move and rotate the body*

To move a body dynamically, move the cursor close to any one of the arrows of the triad; the arrow is highlighted and the select cursor is replaced by the move cursor. Press and hold the left mouse button and drag the cursor to move the body. You can also move the cursor on the plane between two arrows to move the body in that plane.

To rotate the body, move the cursor over one of the rings; the ring will be highlighted and the cursor will be replaced by the rotate cursor. Press and hold the left mouse button and drag the cursor to rotate the body.

You can also move the body freely in 3D space. To do so, move the cursor on the spherical ball where the three arrows meet. The cursor is replaced by the move cursor. Drag it to move the body to a desired location in the 3D space
.

Various options available in the **Move/Copy Body PropertyManager** are discussed next.

Bodies to Move/Copy

The **Bodies to Move/Copy** rollout is used to define the body to copy or move. On invoking the **Move/Copy Body PropertyManager**, you are prompted to select the bodies to move/copy and set the options. Move the cursor on the body to be selected; the cursor will be replaced by the body selection cursor and the edges of the body will be highlighted in red. The name of the body is also displayed in the tooltip. Select the body; it will be highlighted in green. The name of body is displayed in the **Solid and Surface or Graphics Bodies to Move/Copy** selection box. You can also select the body from the **Solid Bodies** folder after invoking the **FeatureManager Design Tree** flyout.

Copy

The **Copy** check box is cleared by default. If you select the **Copy** check box, you can create the copies of the selected body. When you select this check box, the **Number of Copies** spinner is displayed below the **Copy** check box. Set the number of copies using this spinner.

Translate

The **Translate** rollout available in the **Move/Copy Body PropertyManager** is used to define the translational parameters to move the selected body. Set the value of the destination in the **Delta X**, **Delta Y**, and **Delta Z** spinners. When you set the value, the preview of the moved body is displayed in temporary graphics in the drawing area. You can also move or copy the selected body between points. To move or copy a body by specifying two points, select the **Translation Reference (Linear Entity, Coordinate System, Vertex)** selection box. The selection mode in this area is active. Select the vertex from which you want the translation to start. When you select the first vertex as the translation reference, the **Delta X**, **Delta Y**, and **Delta Z** spinners are replaced by the **To Vertex** selection box. The selection mode in the **To Vertex** selection box is active. Select the second translation reference. You will observe the preview of the body move between the two selected vertices. The placement of the body also depends on the sequence of selection of the vertices. Therefore, you need to be very careful, while selecting the two vertices. Figure 9-28 shows the sequence for the selection of references and Figure 9-29 shows the resulting copied body.

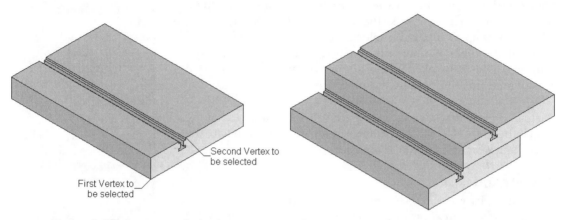

Figure 9-28 *Sequence of selection*   *Figure 9-29* *Resulting copied body*

Rotate

The **Rotate** spinner available in the **Move/Copy Body PropertyManager** is used to define the parameters to rotate the body. To open this rollout, click once on the black arrow provided at the right of this rollout. The **Rotate** rollout is shown in Figure 9-30.

Figure 9-30 *The **Rotate** rollout*

As discussed earlier, a filled square is placed at the origin when you invoke the **Move/Copy PropertyManager**. It is clearly visible, when you hide the origin by choosing **View** > **Origin** from the menu bar. It indicates the origin along which the selected body will be rotated. You can adjust the position of this temporary moveable origin using the **X Rotation Origin** spinner, **Y**

Rotation Origin spinner, and **Z Rotation Origin** spinner. The **X Rotation Angle** spinner is used to set the value of the angular increment to rotate or copy the body along the X axis, the **Y Rotation Angle** spinner is used to rotate or copy the body along the Y axis, and the **Z Rotation Angle** spinner is used to rotate or copy the body along the Z axis.

To rotate or copy the selected body along an edge, click once in the **Rotation Reference (Linear Entity, Coordinate System, Vertex)** selection box to invoke the selection. Select the edge along which you want to rotate the selected body. When you select an edge, all the other spinners disappear from the rollout, and the **Angle** spinner is invoked in the **Rotate** rollout. Set the value of the angular increment in this spinner.

Instead of selecting an edge, you can also select a vertex along which the body will rotate or copy. Then you need to specify the axis along which you want to rotate it.

Constraint
In SolidWorks, you can apply mates between the multiple bodies to place them at an appropriate location. Choose the **Constraint** button from the **Move/Copy Body PropertyManager**; the **Bodies to Move** and the **Mate Settings** rollouts are displayed, as shown in Figure 9-31. You need to select the body that you need to move. The **Mate Setting** rollout helps you to position the selected body by applying mates. You will learn more about mates in later chapters.

Figure   9-31   The PropertyManager after choosing the Constraints button

Reordering Features
Reordering the features is defined as a process of changing the position of the features created in the model. Sometimes, after creating a model, it may be required to change the order in which its features were created. For reordering the features, the features are dragged and placed before or after another feature in the **FeatureManager Design Tree**.

For reordering the features, select the feature in the **FeatureManager Design Tree,** and drag it to the required position. When you drag the feature to reorder them, the bend arrow pointer is displayed, which suggests that feature dragging is possible. If you drag the child feature above the parent feature, the reorder error pointer will be displayed. If you drag a child feature above a parent feature, the **SolidWorks** warning box will be displayed, as shown in Figure 9-32. Choose **OK** from this warning box.

Consider a case, in which you have created a rectangular block and a pattern of through holes created on the base feature, as shown in Figure 9-33. Now, if you create a shell feature and remove the top face, the front face, and the right face of the model, it will appear, as shown in Figure 9-34.

Figure 9-32 The *SolidWorks* warning box

Figure 9-33 Model created with a pattern of through holes on the base feature

Figure 9-34 Shell feature added to the model

But this was not the desired result. Therefore, you need to reorder the shell feature before the holes. Select the shell feature in the **FeatureManager Design Tree** and drag it above the holes. All the features will be automatically adjusted in the new order, as shown in Figure 9-35.

Figure 9-35 Model after reordering the features

Rolling Back the Model

Rolling back the model is defined as a process, in which you rollback the model to an earlier stage. When you rollback a feature or features, those features are suppressed, and you can add new features when the model is in the rollback state. The newly added features are added before the features that are rolled back. While working with a multifeatured model, if you want to edit a feature that was created at the starting of the design cycle of the model, it is recommended that you should rollback the model up to that feature. This is because after each editing operation, the time of regeneration will be minimized. Rolling back is done using the **Rollback Bar** available in the **FeatureManager Design Tree,** as shown in Figure 9-36.

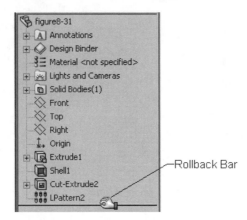

Figure 9-36 The rollback bar of the
FeatureManager Design Tree

Using the select tool, select the **Rollback Bar**; after selection it will be changed to blue and the select cursor will be replaced by the hand pointer. Drag the hand pointer to the feature up to which you want to rollback the model, and then release it. To resume or roll the model, drag the **Rollback Bar** to the last feature of the model. You can also rollback using the menu bar. Select the feature up to which you want to rollback the model and choose **Edit > Rollback** from the menu bar. You will have to customize the **Edit** menu to add this option.

> **Tip**. *If you want to rollback the model to the previous step, choose **Edit > Roll to Previous** from the menu bar. To rollback the entire model to its original position, choose **Edit > Roll to End** from the menu bar.*
>
> *You can also choose the **Roll Forward**, **Roll Previous**, **Roll End** options from the shortcut menus invoked by selecting the features placed below the **Rollback Bar**. These options are used to control the roll and rollback of the model.*
>
> *You can also rollback the model using the keyboard, by selecting the **Rollback Bar** and using the CTRL+ALT+Up Arrow key to roll forward. Use the CTRL+ALT+Down Arrow key to roll backward.*

Renaming Features

The names of the features are displayed in the **FeatureManager Design Tree**. By default, the naming of the features is done according to the sequence in which they are created. You can also rename the features, according to your convenience, by selecting the feature from the **FeatureManager Design Tree** and then clicking once on the selected feature. An edit box will be displayed in the **FeatureManager Design Tree**. Enter the name of the feature and press the ENTER key or click anywhere on the screen.

Creating Folders in the FeatureManager Design Tree

You can also add the folders in the **FeatureManager Design Tree** and the features displayed in the **FeatureManager Design Tree** are added in the folder. This is done to reduce the length of the **FeatureManager**. Consider a case, in which the base of the model consists of more than one feature. You can add a folder named Base Feature, and add all the features used to create the base in that folder. To add a folder in the **FeatureManager Design Tree,** select any feature, right-click to invoke the shortcut menu, and choose the **Create New Folder** option. A new folder is created above the selected feature. Specify the name of the folder and click anywhere on the screen. Now, you can drag and drop the features to the newly created folder. You can also rename the folder by selecting it and then clicking on it once. Now, enter the name in the edit box and press the ENTER key.

To add the selected feature in a new folder, choose **Add to New Folder** from the shortcut menu. A new folder will be created in the **FeatureManager Design Tree,** and the selected feature will be added to the newly created folder. You can also delete the folder by selecting the folder, and invoking the shortcut menu, and selecting the **Delete** option from it. Using the options in this shortcut menu, you can also rollback and suppress the features available in the selected folder.

What's Wrong Functionality

Sometimes, a model may not be rebuilt properly after you modify a sketch or a feature because of the errors resulting from the modification. Therefore, you are provided with a **What's Wrong** dialog box shown in Figure 9-37. The possible errors in the feature are displayed in this dialog box along with their detailed description.

Figure 9-37 The *What's Wrong* dialog box

The **Show errors** check box is selected by default to display the errors in the **What's Wrong** dialog box. The **Show warnings** check box is selected by default to display the warnings messages. The **Display What's Wrong during rebuild** check box is selected by default and is used to display the errors at every rebuild of the model unless the error is fixed. After reading the description of the errors from this dialog box, choose the **Close** button to exit it. The errors are also displayed in the **FeatureManager Design Tree**. The **FeatureManager Design Tree,** with an error in a feature, is displayed in Figure 9-38.

Down arrow error symbol displayed at the left of the document name indicates error in the part or assembly

Cross symbol indicates the features responsible for the error

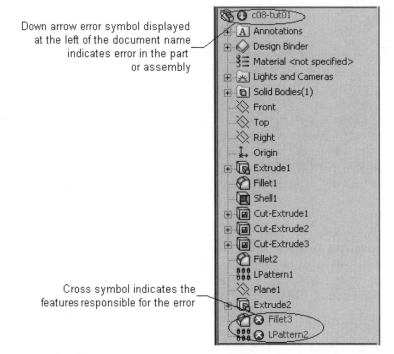

Figure 9-38 *The **FeatureManager Design Tree** with a feature having errors*

If there is an error in a model or in an assembly, the down arrow symbol appears on the left of the name of the model or assembly in the **FeatureManager Design Tree**. If a feature has an error, then the cross symbol appears on the left of the feature in the **FeatureManager Design Tree**. If there is an error in the child feature, the error symbol appears on the left of the parent feature and also on the name of the document in the **FeatureManager Design Tree**. If a warning message appears for a feature, then a triangle with an exclamation mark appears on the left of that feature in the **FeatureManager Design Tree**.

Tip. *You can also invoke the **What's Wrong** dialog box by selecting the feature having errors from the **FeatureManager Design Tree** and choosing the **What's Wrong?** option from the shortcut menu.*

TUTORIALS

Tutorial 1

In this tutorial, you will create the model shown in Figure 9-39. After creating some of its features, you will dynamically modify it, and then undo the modification. The dimensions of the model are shown in Figure 9-40. **(Expected time: 30 min)**

Figure 9-39 *Model for Tutorial 1*

Figure 9-40 *Views and dimensions of the model for Tutorial 1*

The steps to be followed to create the model are listed next.

a. Create the base feature of the model by extruding the profile to a given distance, refer to Figures 9-41 and 9-42.
b. Add the fillets to the base feature, refer to Figures 9-43 and 9-44.
c. Add the shell feature to the model and remove the top face of the base feature, refer to Figures 9-45 and 9-46.
d. Dynamically modify the model, refer to Figures 9-47 through 9-48.
e. Create the cuts on the sides of the model, refer to Figure 9-50.
f. Create the slots on the lower part of the base and add the fillet to the slots feature, refer to Figure 9-50.
g. Pattern the slots and the fillet feature, refer to Figure 9-50.
h. Create a plane at an offset distance from the **Top Plane**.
i. Create the standoffs using the extrude and **Fillet** tool, and pattern the standoffs, refer to Figure 9-51.

Creating the Base Feature

You will draw the sketch of the base feature on the **Front Plane** and extrude it using the **Mid Plane** option.

1. Start SolidWorks and start a new SolidWorks Part document using the **New SolidWorks Document** dialog box.

2. Invoke the **Extruded Boss/Base** tool and draw the sketch of the base feature on the **Front Plane**. Add the required relations and dimensions to the sketch, as shown in Figure 9-41.

Figure 9-41 *Sketch for the base feature*

3. Extrude the sketch to a distance of 35 mm using the **Mid Plane** option.

    The base feature of the model is shown in Figure 9-42.

Figure 9-42 *Base feature of the model*

Adding Fillet to the Base Feature

After creating the base feature, you will fillet its lower edges.

1. Invoke the **Fillet PropertyManager**, rotate the model, and select the edges of the base feature, as shown in Figure 9-43.

2. Set the value of the **Radius** spinner to **2.5** and choose the **OK** button from the **Fillet PropertyManager**.

    The model, after adding fillet to its edges, is shown in Figure 9-44.

Adding Shell to the Model

After creating the fillet feature, you need to shell the model using the **Shell** tool.

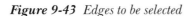

Figure 9-43 *Edges to be selected*   **Figure 9-44** *Fillet added to the model*

1. Orient the model in the isometric view and invoke the **Shell1 PropertyManager**.

2. Select the top planar face of the model, as shown in Figure 9-45.

3. Set the value of the **Thickness** spinner to **1,** and choose the **OK** button from the **Shell PropertyManager**.

    The model, after adding the shell feature, is shown in Figure 9-46.

Figure 9-45 *Face to be selected*   **Figure 9-46** *Shell feature added to the model*

Dynamically Editing the Features

After creating and adding the shell to the base of the model you will learn how to edit the features dynamically using the **Move/Size Features** tool.

1. Choose the **Move/Size Features** button from the **Features CommandManager** after customizing it to invoke the dynamic dragging tool.

2. Select the right planar face of the base feature from the drawing area, refer to Figure 9-47. The selected face will be highlighted in green. The sketch of the selected feature is also

displayed in the drawing area, along with various editing handles, as shown in Figure 9-47.

Rotate handle

Move handle

Resize handle

Figure 9-47 *Editing handles for editing the base feature*

Tip. *You can also select the feature to be edited from the **FeatureManager Design Tree**.*

*To edit the sketches using the **Move/Size Features** tool, you need to select the **Override Dimension** option by choosing **Tools > Sketch Settings > Override Dims on Drag/Move** from the menu bar. The check mark displayed on the left of this option in the menu bar means that the option is already chosen.*

3. Select the **Resize** handle from the drawing area and drag the cursor to resize the feature.

    The preview of the resized feature and its dimensions are displayed in the drawing area. As you drag the cursor, the preview and the dimensions update automatically.

4. Release the left mouse button after dragging the feature to some distance. Figure 9-48 shows the preview of the dragged feature and Figure 9-49 shows the edited feature.

5. Select the **Move/Size Features** button again to disable the dynamic editing tool and click anywhere in the drawing area to clear all the selections from the selection set.

    You have edited the model by dynamically dragging, but the original depth value of the feature was 35 mm. To bring the base feature back to its original size, you need to edit the feature.

6. Double-click on the base feature in the **FeatureManager Design Tree** or from the drawing area. All dimensions of the feature are displayed in it.

7. Double-click on the dimension that reflects the depth of the base feature that appears in blue.

Figure 9-48 *Dragging the **Resize** handle*   *Figure 9-49* *Resulting edited feature*

8.   The **Modify** dialog box will be displayed. Set the value of the **Dimension** spinner to **35** and press the ENTER key on the keyboard.

9.   Choose the **Rebuild** button from the **Standard** toolbar or CTRL+B on the keyboard to rebuild the model.

10. Using the **Extruded Cut**, **Fillet**, and **Linear Pattern** tools, create the remaining features of the model. The model, after creating the features using these tools, is displayed in Figure 9-50.

Creating the Standoffs

Now, you need to create the standoffs for the model. It is created by extruding a sketch drawn on a sketch plane at an offset distance from the **Top Plane**. You also need to specify a draft angle, while creating this feature.

1.   Create a reference plane at an offset distance of 10.5 mm from the **Top Plane**. You need to select the **Reverse direction** check box from the **Plane PropertyManager**.

2.   Select the newly created sketching plane, draw the sketch of the standoff, and apply the required relations and dimensions. The sketch consists of a circle of diameter 1 mm. For more dimensions, refer to Figure 9-40.

3.   Extrude the sketch using the **Up To Next** option with an outward draft angle of 10-degrees. Hide the newly created plane.

     This creates the standoffs of the model.

4.   Rotate the model and add a fillet of radius 0.25 to the base of the standoff.

     The rotated and zoom view of the complete standoff is displayed in Figure 9-51.

5.   Pattern the filleted standoff feature using the **Linear Pattern** tool. The isometric view of the final model is shown in Figure 9-52.

Figure 9-50 *Model after creating other features*

Figure 9-51 *Rotated and zoom view of the model to show the standoff*

Figure 9-52 *Final model*

Saving the Model

1. Choose the **Save** button from the **Standard** toolbar and save the model with the name given below.

   \My Documents\SolidWorks\c09\c09tut1.sldprt

2. Choose **File > Close** from the menu bar to close the document.

Tutorial 2

In this tutorial, you will create the model, shown in Figure 9-53, and then edit it with the **Move/Size Features** option selected. The views and dimensions of the model are shown in the same figure.   **(Expected time: 45 min)**

Figure 9-53 *Views and dimensions of the model for Tutorial 2*

The steps to be followed to complete this tutorial are listed next.

a. Create the base feature of the model by revolving the sketch along the central axis of the sketch, refer to Figures 9-54 and 9-55.
b. Draw the sketch of the second feature on the top face of the base feature and extrude it to a given dimension, refer to Figures 9-56 and 9-57.
c. Create the revolve cut feature, refer to Figures 9-58 and 9-59.
d. Create the hole using the **Simple Hole** tool, and then pattern it using the **Circular Pattern** tool, refer to Figure 9-59.
e. Create a drilled hole feature using the **Hole Wizard** tool, refer to Figure 9-59.
f. Mirror the hole feature along the **Right Plane**, refer to Figure 9-59.
g. Apply the fillet, refer to Figure 9-59.
h. Edit the model using the **Move/Size Features** tool, refer to Figures 9-60 through 9-62.

Creating the Base Feature

First, you will create the base feature of the model by revolving the sketch created on the **Front Plane**.

1. Start a new SolidWorks Part document using the **New SolidWorks Document** dialog box.

2. Invoke the **Revolved Boss/Base** tool and draw the sketch of the base feature on the **Front Plane**. Add the required relations and dimensions to the sketch, as shown in Figure 9-54.

3. Exit the sketching environment.

    You do not need to set any parameters in the **Revolve PropertyManager** because the default value in the **Angle** spinner is 360-degrees, as required.

4. Choose the **OK** button from the **Revolve PropertyManager**.

    The base feature created, after revolving the sketch, is shown in Figure 9-55.

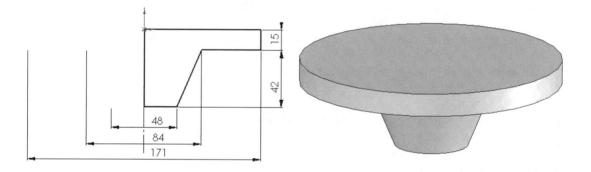

Figure 9-54 *Sketch for the base feature*   **Figure 9-55** *Dimetric view of the base feature*

Creating the Second Feature

The second feature of this model is an extruded feature. It is created by extruding a sketch created on the top planar face of the base feature.

1. Invoke the **Extruded Boss/Base** tool and select the top planar face of the base feature as the sketching plane.

2. Draw the sketch of the second feature and apply the required relations and dimensions to it, as shown in Figure 9-56. Make sure that the sketch is symmetrical about the centerline. If it is not, the sketch will not be properly mirrored.

3. Extrude the sketch to a distance of 75 mm.

The isometric view of the model, after creating the second feature, is displayed in Figure 9-57.

Figure 9-56 *Sketch for the second feature*   *Figure 9-57* *Second feature added to the model*

Creating the Third Feature

The third feature of the model is created by revolving a sketch using the cut option. The sketch for this feature will be created on the **Front Plane**.

1. Invoke the **Revolved Cut** tool and select the **Front Plane** as the sketching plane.

2. Draw the sketch for the revolved cut feature and apply the required relations and dimensions to it, as shown in Figure 9-58.

3. Exit the sketching environment, and create a revolved cut feature with a default angle value of 360-degrees.

Creating the Remaining Features

1. Create the other features of the model by referring to Figure 9-53 and using the **Simple Hole**, **Hole Wizard**, and **Mirror** tools.

    The isometric view of the model, after creating all the other features, is displayed in Figure 9-59.

Editing the Sketch of the Model With the Move/Size Features tool

After creating the model, you will edit the sketch of the second feature with the **Move/Size Features** tool. Therefore, before proceeding further you need to invoke this option.

1. Choose the **Move/Size Features** button from the **Features CommandManager** to invoke the **Move/Size Features** tool.

2. Select the second feature from the drawing area, and right-click to invoke the shortcut menu.

3. Choose the **Edit Sketch** option from the shortcut menu.

Figure 9-58 *Sketch for the revolve cut feature*

Figure 9-59 *Isometric view of the final model*

The sketch of the second feature with the preview of the feature in temporary graphics is displayed in the drawing area, as shown in Figure 9-60.

Figure 9-60 *Sketch and the preview of the second feature*

Now, you will modify the sketch by dragging the sketched entities. You will observe that the preview of the second feature displayed in temporary graphics is also modified.

4. Choose the **Tools > Sketch Settings > Override Dims on Drag/Move** option from the menu bar, if it is not selected.

5. Select the center point of the right arc of the sketch and drag the cursor toward the right. As you drag the cursor, the preview of the feature is also modified dynamically. Release the left mouse button. The new dimensions appear on the sketch. Continue this process until the value of the distance between the center of the right and left arcs shows a value close to 135.

Figure 9-61 shows the sketch being dragged. Figure 9-62 shows the final dragged sketch.

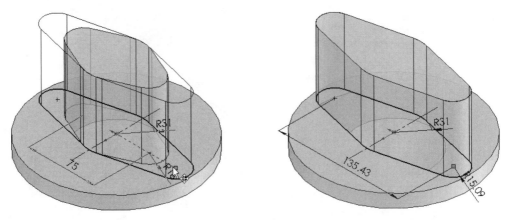

Figure 9-61 *Dragging the center point of the*   ***Figure 9-62*** *Sketch after dragging*
right arc

After modifying the sketch by dragging, you need to change the modified dimensions back to the original dimensions.

6. Double-click the linear dimension value between the center points of the right and left arcs, enter **75** in the **Modify** edit box, and press the ENTER key.

    Similarly, edit the other two dimensions using the **Modify** edit box, if necessary.

7. Use CTRL+B on the keyboard to rebuild the model.

Saving the Model

Now, you need to save the model.

1. Choose the **Save** button from the **Standard** toolbar and save the model with the name given below.

    \My Documents\SolidWorks\c09\c09tut2.sldprt.

2. Choose **File > Close** from the menu bar to close the document.

Tutorial 3

In this tutorial, you will create the model shown in Figure 9-63. While creating it, you will also perform some editing operations on it. The views and dimensions of the model are displayed in Figure 9-64.   **(Expected time: 45min)**

Figure 9-63 *Model for Tutorial 3*

Figure 9-64 *Views and dimensions of the model for Tutorial 3*

The steps to be followed to complete this tutorial are listed next.

a. Create a base feature of the model by revolving the sketch drawn on the **Front Plane**, refer to Figures 9-65 and 9-66.
b. Shell the model using the **Shell** tool, refer to Figure 9-67.
c. Draw the sketch on the **Top Plane** and extrude it to the given distance, refer to Figure 9-68.
d. Pattern the extrude feature using the **Circular Pattern** tool, refer to Figure 9-69.
e. Edit the circular pattern, refer to Figure 9-70.
f. Create a cut feature on the top planar face of the base feature, refer to Figure 9-71.
g. Pattern the cut feature using the **Linear Pattern** tool, refer to Figure 9-72.
h. Unsuppress the suppressed features and create the remaining features of the model, refer to Figures 9-73 and 9-74.

Creating the Base Feature

First, you need to create the base feature of the model by revolving the sketch created on the **Front Plane**.

1. Start a new SolidWorks Part document using the **New SolidWorks Document** dialog box.

2. Invoke the **Revolved Boss/Base** tool and draw the sketch of the base feature on the **Front Plane**. Add the required relations and dimensions to it, as shown in Figure 9-65.

3. Exit the sketching environment and create the base feature of the model, as shown in Figure 9-66.

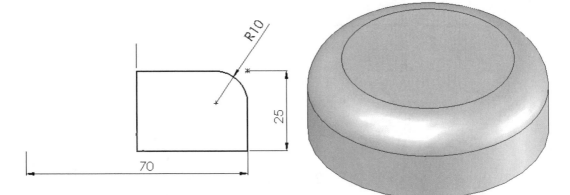

Figure 9-65 *Sketch for the base feature*   **Figure 9-66** *Base feature of the model*

Shelling the Base Feature

After creating the base feature, you need to shell the model using the **Shell** tool. You will also remove the bottom face of the base feature, leaving behind a thin walled model.

1. Invoke the **Shell1 PropertyManager** and set the value of the **Thickness** spinner to **2.5**.

2. Rotate the model and select its bottom face to remove it.

3. Choose the **OK** button from the **Shell1 PropertyManager**. The model, after adding the shell feature, is displayed in Figure 9-67.

Figure 9-67 Shell feature added to the model

Creating the Third Feature

After adding the shell feature to the model, you need to create its third feature, which is an extruded feature. The sketch for this feature will be drawn on the **Top Plane**.

1. Invoke the **Extruded Boss/Base** tool and select the **Top Plane** as the sketching plane.

2. Orient the model in the top view.

3. Draw the sketch of the third feature and add the required relations and dimensions to the sketch, as shown in Figure 9-68.

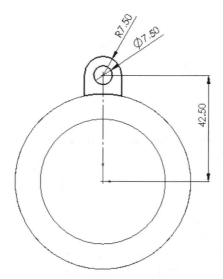

Figure 9-68 Sketch of the third feature

4. Exit the sketching environment and extrude the sketch to a depth of 5 mm.

Patterning the Third Feature

You need to pattern the third feature after creating it. This feature will be patterned using the **Circular Pattern** tool. Before proceeding further you need to display the temporary axes. The temporary axis of the base feature will be selected as the central axis to create the circular pattern.

1. Choose **View > Temporary Axes** from the menu bar to display the temporary axes.

2. Invoke the **Circular Pattern PropertyManager** and select the temporary axis of the base feature as the central axis.

3. Select the third feature, created earlier from the drawing area, if not selected in the **Features to Pattern** selection box. The preview of the pattern feature is displayed in the drawing area.

4. Set the value of the **Number of Instances** spinner to **5** and choose **OK** from the **Circular Pattern PropertyManager**.

5. Choose **View > Temporary Axes** from the menu bar to remove the temporary axes from the current display.

The model, after creating the pattern feature, is displayed in Figure 9-69.

Editing the Pattern Feature

The pattern created is not the same as required, refer to Figure 9-63. As a result, you need to edit it.

1. Select **CirPattern1** from the **FeatureManager Design Tree** or any one of the pattern instances other than the parent instance from the drawing area. Right-click and choose the **Edit Feature** option from the shortcut menu.

    The **CirPattern1 PropertyManager** is displayed. Presently, the number of instances in the pattern feature is 5, but the required number of instances is 3. Therefore, you will edit the number of instances.

2. Set the value of the **Number of Instances** spinner to **3** and choose the **OK** button from the **FeatureManager Design Tree**.

    The model, after editing the features, is shown in Figure 9-70.

Suppressing the Features

As discussed earlier, sometimes you may need to suppress some features to reduce the complications in the model. The suppressed features are actually not deleted; their display is turned off. When you suppress a feature, the child features associated with that feature are also suppressed.

Figure 9-69 *Pattern feature added to the model*   **Figure 9-70** *The edited pattern feature*

1.   Select the **Extrude1** feature, which is the third feature of the model, from the **FeatureManager Design Tree**. Right-click and choose the **Suppress** option from the shortcut menu.

The circular pattern feature is the child feature of the extrude feature. Therefore, it is also suppressed. Both features are not displayed in the drawing area. The **Extrude1** and the **CirPattern1** features are displayed in gray in the **FeatureManager Design Tree**, indicating that both of them are suppressed.

Creating the Cut Feature

The next feature that you are going to create is a cut feature. The sketch for this feature will be drawn on the top planar face of the base feature.

1.   Invoke the **Extruded Cut** tool and select the top planar face of the base feature as the sketching plane.

2.   Draw the sketch of the cut feature and add the required relations and dimensions to the sketch, as shown in Figure 9-71.

3.   Exit the sketching environment and specify the end condition as **Through All** from the **Cut-Extrude PropertyManager**.

4.   Choose the **OK** button from the **Cut-Extrude PropertyManager**.

5.   Now, using the **Linear Pattern** tool, create a linear pattern of the cut feature. You can select the dimension 18 as the directional reference. The model, after creating the linear pattern, is shown in Figure 9-72.

6.   Create the other features of the model. For dimensions, refer to Figure 9-64. The model, after creating the other features, is shown in Figure 9-73.

Figure 9-71 *Sketch for the cut feature*   **Figure 9-72** *Model after patterning the cut feature*

Figure 9-73 *Model after creating other features.*

Unsuppressing the Features

After completing the model, you need to unsuppress the features that you suppressed earlier.

1. Press and hold down the CTRL key on the keyboard, and select all the suppressed features from the **FeatureManager Design Tree**.

Note

On selecting only the parent suppressed feature and unsuppressing it, the child feature will not be unsuppressed. Therefore, you have to select the parent feature and the suppressed child features.

*Instead of selecting all the parent and child suppressed features from the **FeatureManager Design Tree,** select only the parent feature, and choose **Edit > Unsuppress with Dependents > All Configurations** from the menu bar. You will learn more about the configurations in the later chapters.*

On unsuppressing the child feature, the parent feature will be unsuppressed automatically.

2. Right-click and choose the **Unsuppress** option from the shortcut menu.

   The suppressed features will be restored in the model. The final model, after unsuppressing the features, is shown in Figure 9-74.

Figure 9-74 *The final model*

Saving the Model

1. Choose the **Save** button from the **Standard** toolbar and save the model with the name given below.

   \My Documents\SolidWorks\c09\c09tut3.sldprt

2. Choose **File** > **Close** from the menu bar to close the document.

SELF-EVALUATION TEST

Answer the following questions and then compare your answers with those given at the end of this chapter:

1. You cannot edit the sketch of a sketched feature. (T/F)

2. The **Edit Feature** option is used to edit any feature. (T/F)

3. You cannot rename the feature in the **FeatureManager Design Tree**. (T/F)

4. You cannot edit the sketch plane of the sketch of a sketched feature. (T/F)

5. You cannot edit the sketches using the **Move/ Size Features** option. (T/F)

6. The _____ dialog box is displayed when you edit a dimension.

7. The process of changing the position of a feature in the **FeatureManager Design Tree** is known as _____.

8. Using _____ **PropertyManager** you can delete the bodies.

9. The _____ **PropertyManager** is used to move or copy the bodies.

10. The _____ dialog box is displayed when there is any error in a feature.

REVIEW QUESTIONS

Answer the following questions:

1. The _____ **PropertyManager** is invoked to delete a body.

2. You can rotate a body using _____ **PropertyManager**.

3. The _____ key is used to copy a feature or a sketch.

4. The _____ key is used to cut a feature or a sketch.

5. When _____ tool is active, the preview of the feature is displayed in temporary graphics while editing the sketches.

6. The _____ **PropertyManager** is displayed to edit the sketch plane of a sketch.

7. To add the selected feature in a new folder, choose **Add to New Folder** from the shortcut menu. (T/F)

8. For reordering the features, select the feature in the **FeatureManager Design Tree** and drag it to the required position. (T/F)

9. The **Modify** dialog box is invoked, using a single click on the dimension to modify it. (T/F)

10. If you want to modify the sketch by dragging the fully or partially defined sketch, the **Override Dims on Drag/Move** option should be selected. (T/F)

EXERCISES

Exercise 1

Create the model that is sectioned and shown in Figure 9-75. The other views and dimensions of the model are also given in the same figure. The complete model is shown in Figure 9-76.

(Expected time: 45 min)

Figure 9-75 *Views and dimensions of the model for Exercise 1*

Figure 9-76 *Model for Exercise 1*

Exercise 2

Create the model shown in Figure 9-77. Its dimensions are shown in Figure 9-78.

(Expected time: 30 min)

Figure 9-77 *Model for Exercise 2*

Figure 9-78 *Views and dimensions of the model for Exercise 2*

Answers to Self-Evaluation Test

1. F, **2.** T, **3.** F, **4.** F, **5.** F, **6. Modify**, **7.** Reordering, **8. Delete Body**, **9. Move/Copy Body**,
10. Rebuild Errors

Chapter 10

Advanced Modeling Tools-III

Learning Objectives

After completing this chapter, you will be able to:
- *Create sweep features.*
- *Create loft features.*
- *Create 3D sketches.*
- *Edit 3D sketches.*
- *Create various types of curves.*
- *Extrude 3D sketches.*
- *Create draft features using the manual method and using the DraftXpert.*

ADVANCED MODELING TOOLS

Some of the advanced modeling tools were discussed in earlier chapters. In this chapter, you will learn about some more advanced modeling tools, such as sweep, loft, draft, curves, 3D sketches, and so on.

Creating Sweep Features

CommandManager:	Features > Swept Boss/Base
Menu:	Insert > Boss/Base > Sweep
Toolbar:	Features > Swept Boss/Base

 One of the most important advanced modeling tools is the **Swept Boss/Base** tool. This tool is used to extrude a closed profile along an open or a closed path. Therefore, you need a profile and a path to create a sweep feature. A profile is a section for the sweep feature and a path is the course taken by the profile while creating the sweep feature. The profile has to be a sketch, but the path can be a sketch, edge, or a curve. You will learn more about how to create the curves later in this chapter. An example of the profile and path for creating the sweep feature is shown in Figure 10-1.

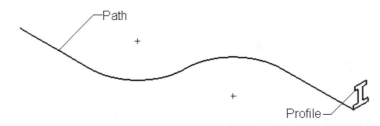

Figure 10-1 *Profile and path to create a sweep feature*

Choose the **Swept Boss/Base** button from the **Features CommandManager** to invoke the **Sweep PropertyManager**, as shown in Figure 10-2.

After invoking the **Sweep PropertyManager**, you are prompted to select the sweep profile. Select the sketch that is drawn as the profile from the drawing area; the sketch is highlighted in green and the **Profile** callout is displayed. Now, you are prompted to select the path for the sweep feature. Select the sketch or an edge to be used as the path; it is highlighted in magenta and the **Path** callout is displayed. The sweep feature is also displayed in temporary graphics in the drawing area. Choose the **OK** button from the **Sweep PropertyManager** to end the feature creation. Figure 10-3 shows a sweep feature.

 Tip. *You can also use the **Contour Select Tool** to select a contour as the section for the sweep feature.*

You can also use a shared sketch as the section of the sweep feature.

Figure 10-2 *The **Sweep PropertyManager***

Figure 10-3 *Sweep feature*

It is not necessary that the sketch drawn for the profile of the sweep feature intersects its path. However, the plane on which the profile is drawn should lie at one of the endpoints of the path. Figure 10-4 shows the nonintersecting sketches of the profile and the path. Figure 10-5 shows the resulting sweep feature. Figure 10-6 shows a sketch of a profile and a closed path. Remember, the plane on which the profile is drawn should intersect the closed path. Figure 10-7 shows the resulting sweep feature.

Figure 10-4 *Nonintersecting sketches of profile and path*

Figure 10-5 *The resulting sweep feature*

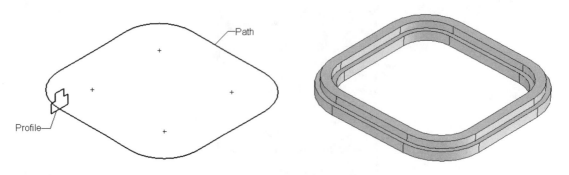

Figure 10-6 *Sketch of a profile and a closed path*   **Figure 10-7** *The resulting sweep feature*

Various other options available in the **Sweep PropertyManager** to create advanced sweep features are discussed next.

Sweep Using the Follow Path and Keep Normal Constant Options

While creating a sweep feature, the **Follow Path** option is selected by default in the **Orientation/twist type** drop-down list available in the **Options** rollout. The **Options** rollout is displayed in Figure 10-8. The **Path alignment type** drop-down list is also displayed. Using this drop-down list, you can set the options to create an even sweep feature when the curvature along the path fluctuates unevenly.

Figure 10-8 *The **Options** rollout*

While creating a sweep feature using the **Follow Path** option, the section will follow the path to create it. If you select the **Keep normal constant** option from the **Orientation/twist type** drop-down list, the section will be swept along the path with a normal constraint and will not change its orientation along the sweep path. Therefore, the starting and the end face of the sweep feature will be parallel. Figure 10-9 shows the sketches of the path and profile for the sweep feature. Figure 10-10 shows the sweep feature created using the **Follow Path** option. Figure 10-11 shows the sweep feature created using the **Keep normal constant** option. The other options available in the **Orientation/twist type** drop-down list are discussed later in this chapter.

Merge tangent faces

The **Merge tangent faces** check box, available in the **Options** rollout, is used to merge the tangent faces of the profile throughout the swept feature.

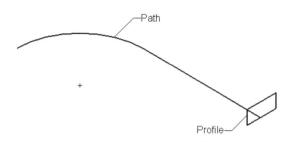

Figure 10-9 *Sketches for the sweep feature*

Figure 10-10 *Sweep feature with the **Follow Path** option selected from the **Orientation/twist type** drop-down list*

Figure 10-11 *Sweep feature with the **Keep normal constant** option selected from the **Orientation/twist type** drop-down list*

Show preview

The **Show preview** check box, available in the **Options** rollout, is used to display the preview of the sweep feature in the drawing area. This check box is selected by default. If you clear it, the preview of the sweep feature will not be displayed in the drawing area.

Merge result

The **Merge result** check box, selected by default, is available only when you have at least one feature in the current document. If you clear the check box, it will result in the creation of the sweep feature as a separate body.

Tip. *On selecting a model edge as the sweep path, the **Tangent Propagation** check box is displayed in the **Options** rollout. If this check box is selected, the edges tangent to the selected edge are selected automatically as the path of the sweep feature.*

Align with end faces

The **Align with end faces** check box is available in the **Options** rollout only when at least one feature has already been created in the current document. When this option is selected, the sweep feature is extended or trimmed to align with the end faces. Figure 10-12 shows the profile and path for creating the sweep feature. Figure 10-13 shows the resulting sweep feature created with the **Align with end faces** check box cleared. Figure 10-14 shows the resulting sweep feature created with the **Align with end faces** check box selected.

Note
If the sweep feature does not merge, you need to reduce the size of the profile.

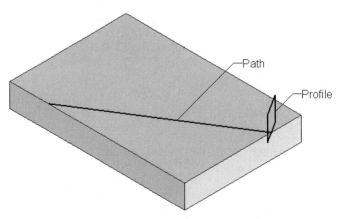

Figure 10-12 *Sketches for the sweep feature*

Figure 10-13 *Resulting sweep feature with the* **Align with end faces** *check box cleared*

Figure 10-14 *Resulting sweep feature with the* **Align with end faces** *check box selected*

Applying Twist to the Sweep Feature

While creating a sweep feature, you can also apply a twist to it by choosing the **Twist Along Path** option from the **Orientation/twist type** drop-down list. The **Defined by** drop-down list and the **Twist Angle** spinner is displayed below the **Orientation/twist type** drop-down list, as shown in Figure 10-15.

Figure 10-15 *The* **Options** *rollout*

Using the option available in this area, you can apply a twist to the swept feature. By default, the **Degrees** option is selected in the drop-down list provided in this area. With this option selected, you need to specify the twist angle in the **Twist Angle** spinner. You can reverse the direction of twist using the **Reverse Direction** spinner. You can also specify the amount of twist in terms of radians and turns using the options available in the **Defined by** drop-down list. Figure 10-16 shows the sweep feature using the **Follow Path** option and Figure 10-17 shows the sweep feature after applying the twist.

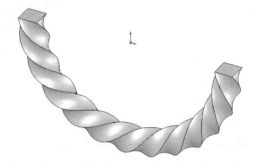

Figure 10-16 *Sweep feature created using the* *Follow Path* *option*

Figure 10-17 *Sweep feature after applying twist*

Applying Twist Along the Path Keeping the Normal Constant

You can also apply a twist to the swept feature keeping its end face parallel to the profile and the entire transition normal to the sweep path. To apply this type of twist, choose the **Twist Along Path With Normal Constant** option from the **Orientation/twist type** drop-down list and then set the twist parameters. Figure 10-18 shows the twist applied using the **Twist Along Path** option and Figure 10-19 shows the twist applied using the **Twist Along Path With Normal Constant** option.

Figure 10-18 *Twist applied using the* *Twist* *Along Path* *option*

Figure 10-19 *Twist applied using the* *Twist* *Along Path With Normal Constant* *option*

Sweep with Guide Curves

The sweep with guide curves is the most important option in the advanced modeling tools. In this sweep feature, the section of the sweep profile varies according to the guide curves along the sweep path. To create this type of feature, you need a profile, path, and the guide curves. After drawing the sketch of the profile, path, and guide curve, apply the coincident relation between the guide curves and the profile. You need to make sure that the guide curves intersects the profile. Now, invoke the **Sweep PropertyManager**. Select the profile and the path; the preview of the sweep feature is displayed in the drawing area. Click on the blue arrow on the right of the **Guide Curves** rollout to invoke this rollout. The **Guide Curves** rollout is shown in Figure 10-20.

*Figure 10-20 The **Guide Curves** rollout*

Select the sketch of the guide curve; the selected guide curve is displayed in purple with a **Guide Curve** callout. The preview of the sweep feature is also displayed in the drawing area. Choose the **OK** button from the **Sweep PropertyManager**. Figure 10-21 shows the sketch for the sweep feature with the guide curve. Figure 10-22 shows the resulting sweep feature creation.

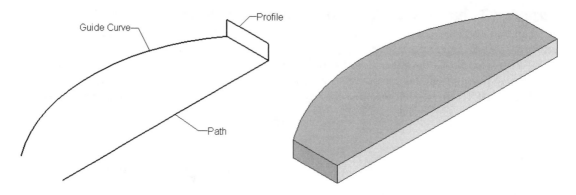

Figure 10-21 Sketches for the sweep feature with guide curves

Figure 10-22 Resulting sweep feature

In the previous case, the path of the sweep feature was a straight line and the guide curve was an arc. In the next case, an arc is selected as the path of the sweep feature and a straight line is selected as the guide curve. Figure 10-23 shows the sketches for the sweep feature. Figure 10-24 shows the resulting sweep feature.

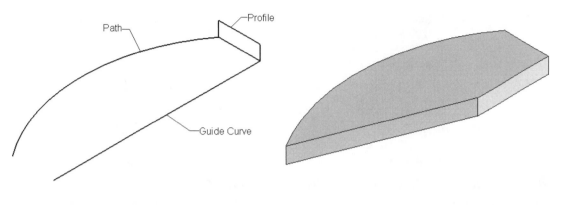

Figure 10-23 *Sketches for the sweep feature*   *Figure 10-24* *Resulting sweep feature*

Move Up and Move Down

The **Move Up** button and the **Move Down** button available on the left of the **Guide Curves** selection box are used to change the sequence of the selected guide curve.

Merge smooth faces

The **Merge smooth faces** check box available in the **Guide Curves** rollout is selected by default. This option is used to merge all the smooth faces together, resulting in a smooth sweep feature. After creating the sweep feature, when you edit it and clear the **Merge smooth faces** check box, the **Sweep Preview Warning** dialog box is displayed, as shown in Figure 10-25. In this dialog box, you are prompted that the feature you are creating may fail because of change in the smooth face option. Choose the **Yes** button from this dialog box to accept the change option. When you create a sweep feature with guide curves and this option is clear, the resulting feature will not merge the smooth faces together. This results in a sweep feature with a noncontinuous curvature surface. Figure 10-26 shows a sweep feature created with the **Merge smooth faces** check box selected. Figure 10-27 shows the same sweep feature with the **Merge smooth faces** check box cleared.

Figure 10-25 *The **Sweep Preview Warning** dialog box*

Note
*Remember that if you create the sweep feature with the **Merge smooth faces** check box cleared, the resulting feature will be generated faster and the adjacent faces and edges will be easily merged. Also, the lines and arcs in the guide curve will match accurately.*

Figure 10-26 *Sweep feature with the* **Merge smooth faces** *check box selected*

Figure 10-27 *Sweep feature with the* **Merge smooth faces** *check box cleared*

Show Sections

The **Show Sections** button available in the **Guide Curves** rollout is used to display the intermediate sections, while creating the sweep feature with guide curves. To display the intermediate profiles or sections along the sweep path, choose the **Show Section** button from the **Guide Curves** rollout. The **Section Number** spinner is invoked. Using this spinner, you can view the sections of the profile along the sweep path. The maximum value of the spinner goes up to the number of sections that fit inside the sweep feature. Figure 10-28 shows a section being displayed using the **Show Section** option and constrained by the guide curves.

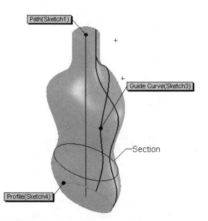

Figure 10-28 *Section being displayed using the* **Show Section** *option*

Sweep Feature Using the Follow path and 1st guide curve Option

When you create a sweep feature with a guide curve using the **Follow path and 1st guide curve** option from the **Options** rollout, the profile follows the path and the first guide curve to create the feature. For creating a sweep feature using this option, invoke the **Sweep PropertyManager** and select the profile, path, and guide curve(s). By default, the **Follow path** option is selected in the **Orientation/twist type** drop-down list of the **Options** rollout. Select the **Follow path and 1st guide curve** option from the **Orientation/twist type** drop-down list. Choose the **OK** button from the **Sweep PropertyManager** to end the creation of the feature.

Sweep Feature Using the Follow 1st and 2nd guide curves Option

Using this option, the profile of the sweep feature follows the first and second guide curves to create the resulting sweep feature. For creating this type of sweep feature, select the **Follow 1st and 2nd guide curves** option from the **Orientation/twist type** drop-down list from the **Options** rollout. Choose the **OK** button from the **Sweep PropertyManager** to end the creation of the feature.

Figure 10-29 shows the sketches of the profile, path, and guide curves for creating a sweep feature. Figure 10-30 shows the sweep feature created using the **Follow path and 1st guide curve** option. Figure 10-31 shows the sweep feature created using the **Follow 1st and 2nd guide curves** option.

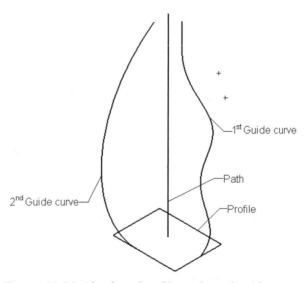

Figure 10-29 *Sketches of profile, path, and guide curves*

Start/End Tangency

The **Start/End Tangency** rollout available in the **Sweep PropertyManager** is used to define the tangency conditions at the start and end of the feature. Invoke the **Start/End Tangency** rollout, as shown in Figure 10-32. The various options available in the **Start/End Tangency** rollout are discussed next.

Start tangency type

The **Start tangency type** drop-down list is used to specify the options to define the tangency at the start of the sweep feature. The various options available in this drop-down list are discussed next.

Figure 10-30 Sweep feature using the **Follow path and 1st guide curve** option

Figure 10-31 Sweep feature using the **Follow 1st and 2nd guide curves** option

Figure 10-32 The **Start/End Tangency** rollout

None
The **None** option is selected by default and is used to create a sweep feature without applying any start tangency.

Path Tangent
The **Path Tangent** option is used to maintain the sweep feature normal to the path at the start.

Direction Vector
When you use the **Direction Vector** option, the starting of the sweep feature will be tangent to a virtual normal created from the selected entity. When you select this option, the **Direction Vector** selection box is also displayed and you need to select a linear edge, axis, planar face, or plane.

All Faces
The **All Faces** option is used to sweep the feature tangent to the adjoining faces of the existing geometry at the start.

The options available in the **End tangency type** drop-down list are the same as those discussed above except the **All Faces** option. The only difference is that the options in this drop-down list are applied to the end of the sweep feature. Figure 10-33 shows the sketches and the references to create the sweep feature with the start and end

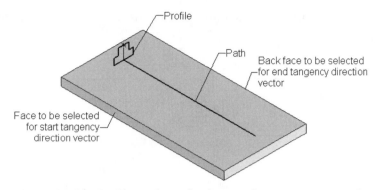

Figure 10-33 *Profile, path, and references for tangency using the* **Direction Vector** *option*

tangency, using the **Direction Vector** option. Figure 10-34 shows the resulting sweep feature.

Figure 10-34 *Resulting sweep feature*

Creating a Thin Sweep Feature

You can also create a thin sweep feature by specifying the thickness using the **Thin Feature** rollout, which is invoked by selecting the check box provided at the left of the **Thin Feature** rollout. The **Thin Feature** rollout is shown in Figure 10-35.

Figure 10-35 *The* **Thin Feature** *rollout*

The options available in this rollout are the same as those discussed in the earlier chapters, where extruding and revolving of thin features were discussed. Figure 10-36 shows a thin sweep feature.

Figure 10-36 Thin sweep feature

Creating Cut Sweep Features

CommandManager:	Features > Swept Cut	(Customize to Add)
Menu:	Insert > Cut > Sweep	
Toolbar:	Features > Swept Cut	(Customize to Add)

You can also remove material from an existing feature or model by creating a cut-sweep feature. To create it, choose the **Swept Cut** button from the **Features CommandManager** after customizing, as shown in Figure 10-37. The options available in the **Cut-Sweep PropertyManager** are the same as those discussed in the **Sweep PropertyManager**, with the only difference being that the options in this case are meant for the cut operation. Figure 10-38 shows the profile and the path. Figure 10-39 shows the resulting cut-sweep feature created using the **Swept Cut** tool.

Figure 10-37 The **Cut-Sweep PropertyManager**

Figure 10-38 *Profile and path for the cut sweep feature*

Figure 10-39 *Resulting cut-sweep feature*

Creating Loft Features

CommandManager:	Features > Lofted Boss/Base
Menu:	Insert > Boss/Base > Loft
Toolbar:	Features > Lofted Boss/Base

The lofted features are created by blending more than one similar or dissimilar sections together to get a free form shape. These similar or dissimilar sections may or may not be parallel to each other. Note that the sections for the solid lofts should be closed sketches.

To create a loft feature, invoke the **Loft PropertyManager** by choosing the **Lofted Boss/Base** button from the **Features CommandManager**. A partial view of the **Loft PropertyManager** is shown in Figure 10-40.

On invoking the **Loft PropertyManager**, after drawing the sketches, you are prompted to select at least two profiles. Select the profiles from the drawing area; the preview of the loft feature, along with a connector, is displayed in it. Choose the **OK** button from the **Loft PropertyManager** to end the creation of the feature. Figure 10-41 shows the preview of the loft feature along with the connector and Figure 10-42 shows the resulting loft feature. Note that by default, a mesh is displayed in the preview of the loft feature. You can turn off this mesh by right-clicking on the preview and choosing **Mesh Preview > Clear All Meshed Faces** from the shortcut menu. In this book, the mesh from all faces is removed for a better display.

The loft feature can be reshaped using the handles of the connector that appear in cyan in the preview it. Press and hold down the left mouse button on a handle; the handle appears red. Drag the cursor to specify a new location and release the left mouse button to place the connector on it. The process of controlling the loft shape using connectors is known as **Loft Synchronization**.

Tip. *You can also use the **Contour Select Tool** to select a contour that will be used as the profile to create the loft feature. You can also use a shared sketch as a profile that is currently in use by some other sketched feature.*

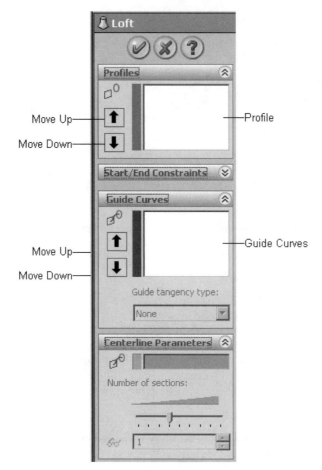

Figure 10-40 *Partial view of the **Loft PropertyManager***

Figure 10-41 *Preview of the loft feature*   **Figure 10-42** *Resulting loft feature*

Figure 10-43 shows the preview of the loft feature, after modifying the location of the handle of the connector. Figure 10-44 shows the resulting loft feature.

Figure 10-43 *Preview of the loft feature after modifying the location of the connector*

Figure 10-44 *Resulting loft feature*

Note
The reshaping or twisting using the default connector, available while creating the loft feature, is known as global twisting. Global twisting means if you change the location of one connecting point of the profile, other connecting points of the profile automatically change their positions with respect to the modified connecting point.

In global twisting of non-tangent profiles, the handles of the connectors move only from vertex to vertex.

To display all connectors, right-click and choose the **Show All Connectors** option from the shortcut menu. The number of connectors displayed using this option depends on the maximum number of vertices in the start or end loft section. If the start and end loft sections are circular, elliptical, or a closed spline section, then only one controller is displayed.

You can also add additional connectors to manipulate the loft feature. Connectors can be added to straight profiles or curved profiles. To add a connector, right-click on the location in the sketch, where you need to add the connector to invoke the shortcut menu. Choose the **Add Connector** option from the shortcut menu. A connector will be added to the loft feature. You can also add more connectors using this option. You can also modify them by dragging their handles. Figure 10-45 shows the preview of the loft feature after modifying all additional connectors and Figure 10-46 shows the resulting loft feature.

Note
Reshaping or twisting using additional connectors is known as local twisting, because the twisting using one connector does not affect the other connecting points of the profile. Therefore, you can independently modify all connectors simply by dragging the handles along the profile.

Start/End Constraints
The **Start/End Constraints** rollout available in the **Loft PropertyManager** is used to define the constraints at the start and end sections of the loft feature. You can define normal, tangency, or continuity constraints to the loft feature. Invoke this rollout to define the tangency. By default,

Figure 10-45 *Preview after adding all connectors*   **Figure 10-46** *Resulting loft feature*

Tip. *Invoke the shortcut menu and choose **Hide All Connectors** to hide all connectors. The connectors are not displayed in the preview, but the settings made by them remain in the loft feature. To hide a specific connector, select it and invoke the shortcut menu. Then choose the **Hide Connector** option.*

*If you choose the **Reset Connectors** option from the shortcut menu, all connectors and the settings related to them are deleted from the memory of the feature. Also, the default connector is displayed with the default connection points lying between the profiles of the loft feature.*

the **None** option is selected in the **Start constraint** and the **End constraint** drop-down lists. This implies that no constraint is applied to the loft feature. The other options available in these drop-down lists are discussed next.

Normal to Profile

The **Normal to Profile** option is used to define the tangency normal to the profile. When you select this option from the **Start constraints** and **End constraints** drop-down lists, an arrow is displayed at the start and end sections. Also, some additional options are displayed in the **Start/End Constraints** rollout, as shown in Figure 10-47. You can set the length of tangency using the tangency arrows attached to the sections. You can also set the values of the length of tangency using the **Start Tangency Length** and the **End Tangency Length** spinners provided in this rollout. You can also specify a draft angle using the **Draft angle** spinners. You will notice that the **Apply to all** check boxes are selected by default, implying that the tangency is applied evenly to all the vertices of the sections. However, if on clearing these check boxes, you can apply values of tangencies individually to all the vertices. Figure 10-48 shows the preview of the loft feature with the tangency arrows attached to the end sections of the loft feature. Figure 10-49 shows the tangency arrows attached to all vertices of the end sections of the loft feature. Figure 10-50 shows the resulting loft feature, after specifying the length of tangency.

Figure 10-47 The *Start/End Constraints* rollout with the *Normal to Profile* option selected

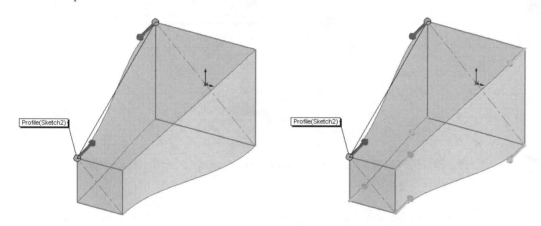

Figure 10-48 Two arrows attached to the sections   *Figure 10-49* Arrows attached to all vertices

Direction Vector

The **Direction Vector** option is used to define the tangency at the start and end of the loft feature by defining a direction vector. On invoking this option, you are provided with the **Direction Vector** selection box and the spinners to define the length of tangents and the draft angle. You need to select the direction vectors to specify the tangent at the start and end of the loft feature. You can also specify the length of the tangents, using the spinners provided in the **Start/End Constraints** rollout. The **Start/End Constraints** rollout, with the **Direction Vector** option selected, is displayed in Figure 10-51.

Figure 10-50 *Resulting loft feature*

Figure 10-51 *The **Start/End Constraints** rollout with the **Direction Vector** option selected*

Figure 10-52 shows the sections for the loft feature. Figure 10-53 shows the initial preview of the loft feature. Figure 10-54 shows the preview of the loft feature with tangent at the start of the loft and Figure 10-55 shows the tangent at the start and at the end of the loft. Figure 10-56 shows the final loft feature.

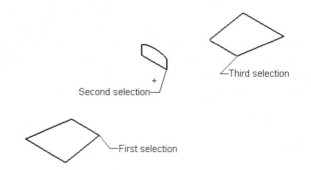

Figure 10-52 *Sections, selection points, and sequence of selection*

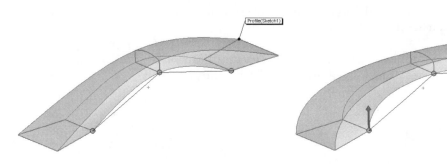

Figure 10-53 *Initial preview of the loft feature*   **Figure 10-54** *Tangent applied at the start section*

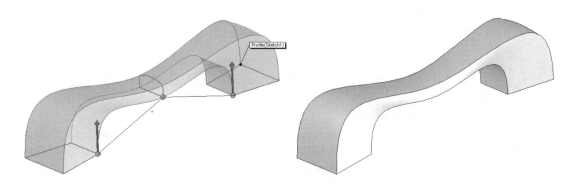

Figure 10-55 *Tangent applied at start and end of the loft feature*   **Figure 10-56** *The final loft feature*

Tangency To Face

If you select the **Tangent To Face** option from the **Start constraint** or **End constraint** drop-down lists, the resulting loft feature will maintain the tangency along the adjacent curved faces. The face, along which the tangency will be maintained, is highlighted in green. You can also switch between the faces along which you need to maintain the tangency using the **Next Face** button. You can also specify the lengths at the start and end tangencies, using the spinners available below it.

Curvature To Face

If you select the **Curvature To Face** option from the **Start constraint** or **End constraint** drop-down lists, the resulting loft feature will maintain the curvature along the adjacent curved faces. The face, along which the curvature will be maintained, is highlighted in green. You can also switch between the faces along which you need to maintain the tangency, using the **Next Face** button.

Guide Curves

SolidWorks enables you to specify the guide curves between the profiles of the loft feature to define the path of transition of the loft feature. The sketches drawn for the guide curve must coincide with the sketches that define the loft sections.

Figure 10-57 shows the profiles and the guide curves for creating a loft feature with guide curves. Figure 10-58 shows the resulting loft feature created using the guide curves.

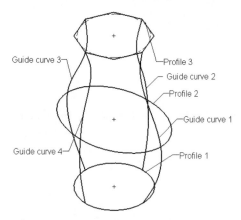

Figure 10-57 *Profiles and guide curves*

Figure 10-58 *Resulting loft feature*

Centerline Parameters

The **Centerline Parameters** rollout is used to create a loft feature by blending two or more than two sections along a specified path. The path that specifies the transition is called the centerline. From this release of SolidWorks, you can also define guide curves to the loft feature created by using the centerline. The options available in this rollout are discussed next.

Centerline

You need to specify the centerline after invoking the **Centerline Parameters** rollout. Therefore, select the sketch that defines the centerline for the loft feature; the name of the sketch will be displayed in the **Centerline** selection box.

Number of sections

The **Number of sections** slider bar provided in the **Centerline Parameters** rollout is used to define the number of intermediate sections, which further define the accuracy and the smoothness of the loft feature.

The **Show Sections** button and the **Section Number** spinner available in the **Centerline Parameters** rollout are used to display the intermediate sections, as discussed earlier. Figure 10-59 shows the sketches of the profiles and the centerline used to create the loft feature. Figure 10-60 shows the resulting loft feature.

Sketch Tools

The **Sketch Tools** rollout is used to select 3D sketches as the profile or the guide curves for the loft feature. Additionally, the tools in this rollout can be used when you want to select the sketches or the guide curves from the same sketch. By default, the **Sketch** button is chosen. As a result, you can select only the sketched entities. To select the 3D sketches, you can use the

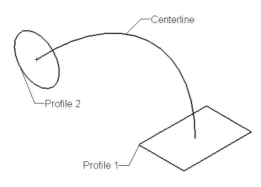

Figure 10-59 *Profiles and centerline*

Figure 10-60 *Resulting loft feature*

Chain Contour Select or the **Single Contour Select** buttons. The **Join** button is chosen when you want to select multiple intersecting contours. Choosing this button will form a single contour from all the selected entities. Choosing the **Drag Sketch** button allows you to drag the 3D sketch later on while editing the loft feature. The **Undo sketch drag** button undoes the dragging of the 3D sketch. You will learn more about the 3D sketches later in this chapter.

Options

The **Options** rollout of the **Loft PropertyManager** is provided with the options to improve the creation of the loft feature. These options are the same as those discussed in the sweep option. An additional option available with this rollout is discussed next.

Close Loft

A closed loft feature is one in which the end and start of the loft features are joined together. The **Close loft** check box is selected to create a closed loft feature. Figure 10-61 shows a loft feature created with the **Close loft** check box cleared. Figure 10-62 shows the loft feature created with the **Close loft** check box selected.

Figure 10-61 *Loft feature with the* **Close Loft** *check box cleared*

Figure 10-62 *Loft feature with the* **Close loft** *check box selected*

You can also create a thin loft feature by defining the thin parameters using the **Thin Feature** rollout. The options available in this rollout are the same as those discussed in the earlier chapters. Figure 10-63 shows a thin loft feature created using the **Thin Features** rollout available in the **Loft PropertyManager**.

Figure 10-63 A thin loft feature

 Tip. *To create a smooth loft feature between a circle and a polygon, it is a good practice to split the circle into a number of arcs. The number of arcs that form the circle should be the same as the number of sides of the polygon. Now, when you create the loft feature the number of connecting points in both the sections are predefined, which results in a smoother loft feature.*

Add a Section in the Loft Feature

After creating a loft feature, you can also add a section to it by selecting one of the side faces of the loft feature and right-clicking to invoke the shortcut menu. Choose the **Add Loft Section** option from it; the **Add Loft Section PropertyManager** is displayed. You are provided with a plane that can be moved or rotated dynamically. To move the plane, place the cursor on the arrows provided on it. The arrows turn red in color. Press and hold down the left mouse button and drag the cursor to move the plane. To rotate the plane, select one of its edges and drag the cursor. Set the position of the plane by dynamically moving and rotating it to define the position to add the sketch. Figures 10-64 and 10-65 show the plane being moved and rotated. After specifying the position of the plane, choose the **OK** button from the **Add Loft Section PropertyManager**. Figure 10-66 shows the section added in the model. This is a closed section created using a spline.

Tip. *From this release of SolidWorks, you can also display a mesh in the preview of the loft feature by right-clicking to invoke the shortcut menu and choosing **Mesh Preview > Mesh All Faces**. The mesh preview will only be displayed on the non-planar faces and not on the planar faces. To display a mesh preview on all faces of the loft preview, you need to change the planar faces to non-planar faces by manipulating the connectors.*

Expand the **Loft1** feature and select the sketch that is added using the **Add Loft Section** tool. Right-click and choose the **Edit Sketch** option from the shortcut menu. Edit the sketch, as shown in Figure 10-67 and rebuild the part. Figure 10-68 shows the resulting modified loft feature.

Figure 10-64 Moving the plane

Figure 10-65 Rotating the plane

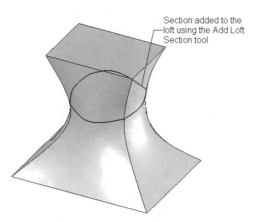

Figure 10-66 Resulting section added to loft feature

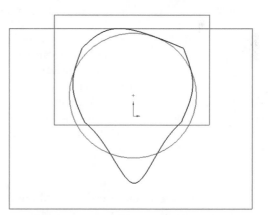

Figure 10-67 Modified loft section

Creating Lofted Cuts

CommandManager:	Features > Lofted Cut
Menu:	Insert > Cut > Loft
Toolbar:	Features > Lofted cut

Figure 10-68 *Resulting loft feature*

The **Cut Loft PropertyManager** is used to create a cut loft feature. This option is invoked by choosing **Insert** > **Cut** > **Loft** from the menu bar.

Creating 3D Sketches

CommandManager:	Sketch > 3D Sketch
Menu:	Insert > 3D Sketch
Toolbar:	Sketch > 3D Sketch

In earlier chapters, you learned to draw 2D sketches in the sketching environment. In this chapter, you will learn to draw 3D sketches. The 3D sketches are mostly used to create 3D paths for the sweep features, 3D curves, and so on. Figure 10-69 shows a chair frame created by sweeping a profile along a 3D path.

To draw a 3D sketch, choose the **3D Sketch** button from the **Sketch CommandManager**. On choosing this option, the 3D sketching environment is invoked and the origin is displayed in red color. You do not need to select a sketching plane for drawing a 3D sketch. When you invoke the 3D sketching environment, some of the sketching tools are activated in the **Sketch CommandManager**. These tools can be used in the 3D sketching environment and are discussed next.

Figure 10-69 *A chair frame created by sweeping a profile along a 3D path*

Line

It is better to orient the view to isometric for drawing lines in the 3D sketching environment. Choose the **Line** button from the **Sketch CommandManager** to invoke the **Line** tool; the **Insert Line PropertyManager** is displayed. The **As sketched** radio button is selected in the **Orientation** rollout, while the other options are frozen. The select cursor is replaced by the line cursor with **XY** displayed at it bottom. This implies that by default, the sketch will be drawn in the XY plane. The coordinate system is also displayed in the current plane. You can toggle between the default planes using the TAB key on the keyboard. On doing so, the orientation of the coordinate system also modifies with respect to the current plane. Move the cursor to the location from where you want to start sketching. On specifying the start point of the line, you are provided with a space handle.

You can also toggle the plane after specifying the start point of the line. The coordinate system will also change with respect to the current plane. Move the cursor to specify the endpoint of the line. Its length is displayed above the line cursor. Specify the endpoint of the line at this location. You will notice that a rubber-band line segment is attached to the cursor. Toggle the plane using the TAB key, if required. Move the cursor to draw another line and specify its endpoint at the desired location. Right-click to invoke the shortcut menu and select the **Select** option to end drawing the line. Figures 10-70 through 10-72 show sketching in different planes in the 3D sketching environment. Figure 10-73 shows an example of a 3D sketch.

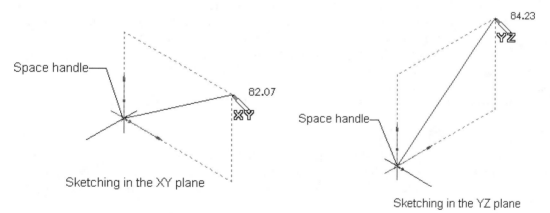

Figure 10-70 Sketching in the XY plane   *Figure 10-71 Sketching in the YZ plane*

Spline

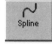

You can also draw a spline in the 3D sketching environment by choosing the **Spline** button from the **Sketch CommandManager**. The select cursor will be replaced by the spline cursor. Move it to the desired location to start the sketch. Specify the start point of the spline; the space handle is displayed. You can toggle between the default planes using the TAB key. Move the cursor and specify the second point of the spline. Follow the same procedure to continue drawing the spline. To end the spline creation, right-click and select the **Select** or **End Spline** option from the shortcut menu.

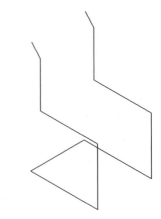

Figure 10-72 *Sketching in the ZX plane*   **Figure 10-73** *3D sketch created using the **Line** tool*

Point

Choose the **Point** button from the **Sketch CommandManager** to invoke the **Point** tool. The select cursor will be replaced by the point cursor. Use the left mouse button to draw the points.

Centerline

You can also draw centerlines in the 3D sketching environment. Invoke the 3D sketching environment and orient the view to isometric view. Choose the **Centerline** button from the **Sketch CommandManager** to draw a centerline; the select cursor is replaced by the line cursor. The procedure of drawing the centerline is the same as that discussed for drawing lines in the 3D sketching environment.

The dimensioning of 3D sketches is the same as the dimensioning of 2D sketches.

Editing 3D Sketches

You can perform a number of editing operations on 3D sketches including **Convert Entities**, **Sketch Chamfer**, **Trim Entities**, **Fit Spline**, **Sketch Fillet**, **Extend Entities**, **Construction Geometry**, and **Split Entities**. All these tools have been discussed in the previous chapters.

Creating Curves

You can also create various types of curves in SolidWorks. These curves are mostly used to create complex shapes generally using the **Swept Boss/Base** and **Lofted Boss/Base** tools. The types of curves that can be created in SolidWorks are discussed next.

Creating a Projection Curve

CommandManager:	Curves > Project Curve	*(Customize to Add)*
Menu:	Insert > Curve > Projected	
Toolbar:	Curves > Project Curve	*(Customize to Add)*

This option allows you to project a single closed/open sketched entity on one or more than one planar or curved faces. You can also project a sketched entity on another sketched entity to create a 3D curve. To create a projected curve, draw at least two sketches or a single sketch and at least one feature. Next, choose the **Project Curve** button from the **Curves CommandManager**, after customizing it. On choosing the **Project Curve** button, the **Projected Curve PropertyManager** is displayed, as shown in Figure 10-74. The confirmation corner is also displayed in the drawing area. The two different options to create projected curves are discussed next.

*Figure 10-74 The **Projected Curve PropertyManager***

Sketch onto Sketch

On invoking the **Projected Curve PropertyManager**, you will find the **Sketch onto Sketch** option selected by default in the **Projection Type** drop-down list. You are prompted to select two sketches to project onto one another. Select two sketches that do not lie on the same plane. When you select the sketches, their names are displayed in the **Sketches to Project** selection box. The preview of the projected curve is also displayed in the drawing area. Choose the **OK** button from the **Projected Curve PropertyManager** or choose **OK** from the confirmation corner. Figure 10-75 shows the two sketches selected to create a projected curve. Figure 10-76 shows the preview of the projected curve. Figure 10-77 shows the resulting projected curve.

Sketches onto Face(s)

The **Sketches onto Face(s)** option is available in the **Projection Type** drop-down list and is used to project a sketch on a planar or curved face(s). On choosing this option, the **Sketch to Project** and the **Projection Faces** selection box are displayed in the **Selections** rollout. You are also provided with the **Reverse Projection** check box The **Projected Curve PropertyManager** with the **Sketches onto Face(s)** option selected is displayed in Figure 10-78. Next, select the sketch from the drawing area and the face or faces on which you want to project the sketch. The selected sketch is highlighted in green and the selected face is highlighted in magenta. The arrow provided in the drawing area is used to reverse the direction of the projection. You can also reverse the direction of projection using the

Figure 10-75 *Sketches to be selected*   **Figure 10-76** *Preview of the projected curve*

Figure 10-77 *Resulting projected curve*

Figure 10-78 *The **Projected Curve PropertyManager**
with the **Sketches onto Face(s)** option selected*

Reverse Projection check box. Choose the **OK** button from the **Projected Curve PropertyManager** or choose **OK** from the confirmation corner. Figure 10-79 shows the sketch to be selected for projection and also the face to be selected on which the sketch will be projected. Figure 10-80 shows the resulting projected sketch.

Figure 10-79 *Sketch and the face to be selected*   **Figure 10-80** *Resulting projected curve*

Creating Split Lines

CommandManager:	Curves > Split Line	*(Customize to Add)*
Menu:	Insert > Curve > Split Line	
Toolbar:	Curves > Split Line	*(Customize to Add)*

The **Split Line** tool is generally used to project a sketch on a planar or curved face, which in turn it splits or divides the single face into two or more than two faces. Invoke the **Split Line PropertyManager**. Choose the **Split Line** button from the **Curves CommandManager**, after customizing it to invoke the **Split Line PropertyManager**, as shown in Figure 10-81. The two methods to create a split line are discussed next.

Silhouette

You can split a curved face by creating a silhouette line at the intersection of the projection of direction entity and the curved face. Invoke the **Split Line PropertyManager**; the **Silhouette** option available in the **Type of Split** rollout is selected by default. Change the type of split, or select the direction of pull and the faces to be split. You need to select an edge, line, or a plane that defines the direction of pull. Select the direction of pull; the selected entity will be highlighted in magenta color. Next, select the curved face; the selected face will be highlighted in green color. Choose the **OK** button from the **Split Line PropertyManager** or choose the **OK** option from the confirmation corner. The curved face

Tip. *You can also use the **Contour Select Tool** to select the contours for creating a projected curve or a split line. You will learn more about split lines later in this chapter.*

*Figure 10-81 The **Split Line PropertyManager***

will be divided in two or more faces. The **Angle** spinner in the **Selections** rollout is provided to define the draft angle for creating the silhouette line. By default, the value of this spinner is set to 0-degree.

Consider a case, in which you need to split a circular face, using this option. The plane will be selected to define the direction of pull. Figure 10-82 shows the plane and the face to be selected. Figure 10-83 shows the resulting split line created to split the selected face.

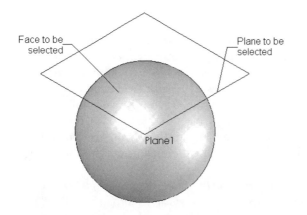

Figure 10-82 *Plane and the face to be selected*

Figure 10-83 *Resulting split line*

Projection

You can project a sketched entity onto a planar or curved face to create a split line on it. The split line splits the selected face on which the sketch is projected. To use this option, invoke the **Split Line PropertyManager**, and choose the **Projection** option from the **Type of Split** rollout. The **Split Line PropertyManager**, with the **Projection** option selected, is shown in Figure 10-84.

*Figure 10-84 The **Split Line PropertyManager** with the **Projection** option selected*

You are prompted to change the type of split, or select the sketch to project, direction, and faces to be split. Select the sketch and it will be displayed in magenta. Next, select the face to be split; the selected face will be displayed in green. Choose the **OK** button from the **Split Line PropertyManager**. The selected face will be split into two or more than two faces, depending on the sketch that is used to project it. Figure 10-85 shows the sketch and the face to be selected. Figure 10-86 shows the resulting split line created to split the selected face.

The other options available in the **Selections** rollout of the **Split Line PropertyManager** are discussed next.

Single direction

If the sketching plane on which the sketch is created lies within the model, the split line on a cylindrical face will be created on its two sides. The **Single direction** check box available in the **Selections** rollout is used to create the split line only in one direction.

Figure 10-85 *Sketch and the face to be selected*

Figure 10-86 *Resulting split line*

Reverse direction

The **Reverse direction** check box is available only if the **Single direction** check box is selected and is used to reverse the direction of the created split line. Figure 10-87 shows the split line created on both sides of the model. Figure 10-88 shows the split line created on a single side of the model.

Figure 10-87 *Split line created on both sides*

Figure 10-88 *Split line created on single side*

Intersection

The **Intersection** option is used to split the selected bodies or faces using tool bodies, face, or planes. Invoke the **Split Line PropertyManager** and select the **Intersection** radio button from the **Type of Split** rollout; the selection mode in the **Splitting Bodies/Faces/Planes** selection box is active. Select bodies, faces, or planes that will be used as tool bodies. Next, click in the **Faces/Bodies to Split** selection box and select the bodies to be split.

The **Split all** check box provided in the **Surface Split Options** rollout is used to split almost all areas of surfaces using the current selection set. You can also select the **Natural** or **Linear** radio button to define the shape of the split. Figure 10-89 shows the plane to be selected as a split tool and also faces to be split. Figure 10-90 shows the resulting split faces.

Figure 10-89   Plane and faces to be split   *Figure 10-90   Resulting split faces*

Creating a Composite Curve

CommandManager:	Curves > Composite Curve
Menu:	Insert > Curve > Composite
Toolbar:	Curves > Composite Curve

The **Composite Curve** option is used to create a curve by combining 2D or 3D curves, sketched entities, and part edges into a single curve. You need to ensure that the selected entities form a continuous chain. The composite curve is mainly used while creating a sweep or a loft feature. To create it, invoke the **Composite Curve PropertyManager**. Choose the **Composite Curve** button from the **Curves CommandManager** to invoke the **Composite Curve PropertyManager**. The **Composite Curve PropertyManager** is shown in Figure 10-91.

Figure 10-91 The Composite Curve PropertyManager

On invoking the **Composite Curve PropertyManager**, you are prompted to select a continuous set of sketches, edges, and/or curves. Select the continuous edges, curves, or sketched entities to create a composite curve. Choose the **OK** button to end its creation.

Creating a Curve Through XYZ Points

CommandManager:	Curves > Curve Through XYZ Points
Menu:	Insert > Curve > Curve Through XYZ Points
Toolbar:	Curves > Curve Through XYZ Points

 The **Curve Through XYZ Points** option is used to create a curve by specifying the coordinate points. To create a curve using this option, choose the **Curve Through XYZ Points** button from the **Curves CommandManager**. The **Curve File** dialog box is displayed, as shown in Figure 10-92. Double-click in the cell under the **X** column to enter the X coordinate as the start point for the curve. Similarly, double-click in the **Y** cell and **Z** cell to enter the respective Y and Z coordinates of the start point of the curve. Double-click in the cell below the first cell to enter the coordinates for the second point for creating the curve. Similarly, specify the coordinates of the other points of the curve, as shown in Figure 10-93. When you enter the coordinates of the points, the preview of the curve is displayed in the drawing area. Choose the **OK** button from the **Curve File** dialog box to complete the creation of the feature, as shown in Figure 10-94.

Figure 10-92 The **Curve File** dialog box

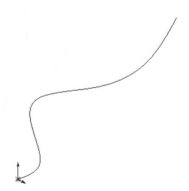

Figure 10-93 Coordinates entered in the **Curve File** dialog box

Figure 10-94 Resulting 3D curve

Tip. *You can select a row and use the DELETE key on the keyboard to delete it completely. Use the SHIFT key the select the entire row and use the **Insert** button, to add a new row between any two rows.*

You can also save the current set of coordinates using the **Save** button available in the **Curve File** dialog box. When choosing this button, the **Save As** dialog box is displayed. Browse the folder to save the coordinates, enter the name of the file in the **File name** edit box and choose the **Save** button. The curve file is saved with the *.sldcrv* extension. Using the **Save As** button, you can save the current set of coordinates in a file with some other name.

You can use the **Browse** button to open an existing curve file; the **Open** dialog box is displayed. You can browse the previously saved curve file to specify the coordinate points. You can also write the coordinates in a text (notepad) file and save it. In the **Open** dialog box, choose the **Text Files (*.txt)** option from the **Files of type** drop-down list and browse the text file to specify the coordinates.

Creating a Curve Through Reference Points

CommandManager:	Curves > Curve Through Reference Points
Menu:	Insert > Curve > Curve Through Reference Points
Toolbar:	Curves > Curve Through Reference Points

The **Curve Through Reference Points** option enables you to create a curve by selecting the sketched points, vertices, origin, endpoints, or center points. To create a curve through reference points, you have to invoke the **Curve Through Reference Points PropertyManager**. Choose the **Curve Through Reference Points** button from the **Curves CommandManager** to invoke the **Curve Through Reference Points PropertyManager**, as shown in Figure 10-95.

*Figure 10-95 The **Curve Through Reference Points** PropertyManager*

On invoking this tool, you are prompted to select the vertices to define the through points for the curve. Select the points to define the curve. On defining the points, the preview of the resulting curve created using the selected points, is displayed in the drawing area. After specifying all the points, choose the **OK** button. You can select the **Closed curve** check box to create a closed curve. Figure 10-96 shows the vertices to be selected to create the curve through reference points. Figure 10-97 shows the resulting curve.

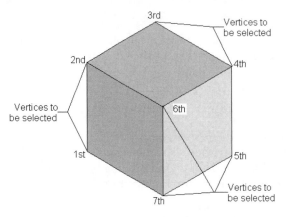

Figure 10-96 Vertices to be selected

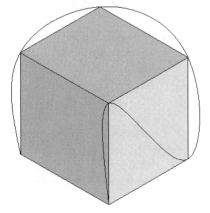

Figure 10-97 Resulting 3D curve

Creating a Helical/Spiral Curve

CommandManager:	Curves > Helix and Spiral
Menu:	Insert > Curve > Helix/Spiral
Toolbar:	Curves > Helix and Spiral

The **Helix and Spiral** tool is used to create a helical curve or a spiral curve. This curve is generally used as the sweep path to create springs, threads, spiral coils, and so on. Figure 10-98 shows a spring created by sweeping a circular profile along a helical path. Figure 10-99 shows a spiral coil created by sweeping a rectangular profile along a spiral path.

Figure 10-98 Spring   *Figure 10-99 Spiral coil*

To create a helix, choose the **Helix and Spiral** button from the **Curves CommandManager**. The **Helix/Spiral PropertyManager**, is displayed and you are prompted to select a plane, a planar face, or an edge to sketch a circle to define the helix cross-section, or a sketch that contains a single circle. The circle will define the diameter of the spring. If you are creating a spiral, the sketch will define the starting diameter of the spiral curve. The **Helix/Spiral PropertyManager** disappears on selecting a plane and you enter the sketching environment to draw the cross-section sketch for the helix or spiral. Exit the sketching environment after drawing the sketch. The **Helix/Spiral PropertyManager** will appear again, as shown in Figure 10-100.

Figure 10-100 The Helix/Spiral PropertyManager

Two arrows are displayed, one emerging from the center of the circle, and defining the direction of the helix. The second arrow is tangent to the circle and defines the rotation of the helix, either clockwise or counterclockwise. The preview of the helix curve, with the default values, is displayed in the drawing area. The various methods to specify the parameters of the helical curve are discussed next.

Pitch and Revolution

The **Pitch and Revolution** option, selected by default in the **Type** drop-down list of the **Defined By** rollout, is used to specify the pitch of the helical curve and the number of revolutions. When this option is selected, the **Pitch** spinner and the **Revolution** spinner are available in the **Parameters** rollout to define the value of pitch and the number of revolutions. You can also select the **Reverse direction** check box, available in the **Parameters** rollout, to reverse the direction of the helix creation. You can specify the start angle of the helical curve using the **Start angle** spinner The **Clockwise** and **Counterclockwise** radio buttons, available in this rollout, are used to define the direction of rotation of the helix.

Height and Revolution

The **Height and Revolution** option available in the **Type** drop-down list is used to define the parameters of the helix curve in the form of the total helix height and the number of revolutions. On choosing this option, the **Height** and **Revolutions** spinners are displayed in the **Parameters** rollout, along with the other options to specify the required parameters.

Height and Pitch

The **Height and Pitch** option available in the **Type** drop-down list is used to define the parameters of the helix curve in terms of the height and the pitch of the helix. When you select this option, the **Height** and **Pitch** spinners are displayed in the **Parameters** rollout, along with other options to specify the required parameters.

When you specify the parameters to create the helix curve, the preview in the drawing area modifies automatically. Figure 10-101 shows a helix curve.

Figure 10-101 *Helix Curve*

You can also create a tapered helix using the **Taper Helix** rollout The procedure for this is discussed next.

Taper Helix

Invoke the **Taper Helix** rollout by selecting the **Taper Helix** check box available in the **Taper Helix** rollout. The **Taper Angle** spinner and the **Taper outward** check boxes are enabled. Using the **Taper Angle** spinner, you can specify the value of the angle between the central axis of the helix and the periphery of the helix. The **Taper outward** check box is selected by default and is used to create an outward taper. When you specify the parameters to create a tapered helical curve, its preview of the helical curve updates automatically in the drawing area. Figure 10-102 shows a tapered helical curve. Figure 10-103 shows a tapered helical curve created with the **Taper outward** check box selected.

By default, the helical curve is created in the clockwise direction. Therefore, the **Clockwise** radio button is selected in the **Parameters** rollout of the **Helix/Spiral PropertyManager**. Select the **Counterclockwise** radio button to create the helical curve in the counterclockwise direction. After setting the parameters, choose the **OK** button from the **Helix/Spiral PropertyManager**.

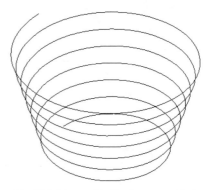

Figure 10-102 *Tapered helical curve*   ***Figure 10-103*** *Tapered helical curve with the **Taper outward** option selected*

Creating a Spiral Curve

For creating a spiral curve, select the **Spiral** option from the **Type** drop-down list available in the **Defined By** rollout. The preview of the spiral curve will be displayed in the drawing area. You can define the pitch and the number of revolutions in the **Pitch** and **Revolutions** spinners, respectively. The other options in the **Parameters** rollout are the same as those discussed earlier. After specifying all the required parameters, choose the **OK** button. Figure 10-104 shows a spiral curve.

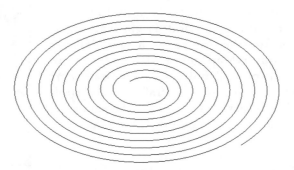

Figure 10-104 *Spiral curve*

Extruding a 3D Sketch

You can also extrude a 3D sketch drawn on the 3D sketching environment. A 3D sketch is always extruded along a direction vector, which can be a line, edge, planar face, or a plane. Invoke the **Extrude PropertyManager** and select the 3D sketch that you need to extrude. You also need to select a direction vector along which the sketch will be extruded. Set the parameters at the start of the extrude feature, using the **From** rollout. Now, set the value of the depth of the extrude feature and choose the **OK** button from the **Extrude PropertyManager**. Figure 10-105 shows a 3D sketch and the direction vector along which it will be extruded. Figure 10-106 shows the resulting extruded feature.

Figure 10-105 *3D sketch and the direction vector*   *Figure 10-106* *Resulting extruded feature*

Creating Draft Features

CommandManager:	Features > Draft
Menu:	Insert > Features > Draft
Toolbar:	Features > Draft

The **Draft** tool is used to add taper to the selected faces of the model. One of the main applications of creating the draft feature is in the models that are to be molded or casted so that it is easier to remove them from the mold or die. Invoke the **Draft PropertyManager**. Choose the **Draft** button from the **Features CommandManager** to invoke the **Draft PropertyManager**. With this release of SolidWorks, you can create manual drafts or use the **DraftXpert** to create the draft. When you invoke the **Draft** tool, the **Draft PropertyManager** will be displayed. The process of creating the draft using the manual method and the **DraftXpert** is discussed next.

To create a manual draft, choose the **Manual** tab, as shown in Figure 10-107; you are prompted to select a neutral plane and the faces to add the draft. You will notice that the **Neutral Plane** option is selected by default in the **Type of Draft** drop-down list in the **Type of Draft** rollout. Therefore, you need to select a neutral plane for creating the draft feature. Select a planar face or a plane that acts as a neutral plane. The selected entity will appear in magenta, along with the **Neutral Plane** callout. The **Reverse Direction** arrow is also displayed in the drawing area. The selection mode in the **Faces to Draft** selection box of the **Faces to Draft** rollout is activated. Select the faces to apply the draft. The selected faces will be displayed in green with the **Draft Face** callout. Next, set the value of the draft angle in the **Draft Angle** spinner available in the **Draft Angle** rollout. Choose the **OK** button from the **Draft PropertyManager** or choose **OK** from the confirmation corner.

Figure 10-107 *The Draft PropertyManager*

Figure 10-108 shows the neutral face and the faces to be selected to add the draft. Figure 10-109 shows the resulting draft feature. The other options in the **Draft PropertyManager** are discussed next.

Figure 10-108 *Faces to be selected*   *Figure 10-109* *Resulting draft feature*

Reverse Direction

The **Reverse Direction** button, available on the left of the **Neutral Plane** selection box in the **Neutral Plane** rollout, is used to reverse the direction of creation of the draft. You can also reverse the direction of the draft creation by selecting the **Reverse Direction** arrow from the drawing area.

Face propagation

The options available in the **Face propagation** drop-down list in the **Faces to Draft** rollout are used to extend the draft feature to the other faces. The options available in this drop-down list are discussed next.

None

The **None** option is selected by default. This option is used when you do not need to apply any type of face propagation.

Along Tangent

The **Along Tangent** option is used to apply the draft to the faces tangent to the selected face.

All Faces

The **All Faces** option is used to apply the draft to all the faces attached to the neutral plane or face.

Inner Faces

This option is used to draft all the faces inside the model that are attached to the neutral plane or face.

Outer Faces

This option is used to draft all the outside faces of the model that are attached to the neutral plane or face.

To create the draft using the **DraftXpert**, choose this tab; the related options will be displayed, as shown in Figure 10-110. Using the **DraftXpert**, you can create or modify an existing draft feature. Most of the options to create the draft feature are the same as those discussed in the manual draft. The options in the **Draft Analysis** rollout are different and are discussed next.

Auto paint

Selecting the **Auto paint** check box enables the draft analysis options. These options are discussed next.

Show/hide faces with positive draft

This is the first button below the **Auto paint** check box. If this button is chosen, the faces with the positive draft are highlighted with the color shown in the color box on the right of this button. Note that the faces will be highlighted only after you select the faces to add the draft and choose the **Apply** button from the **Items to Draft** rollout.

Show/hide faces requiring draft

While analyzing the draft, SolidWorks highlights the faces that require a draft. These faces are highlighted if this button is chosen.

Show/hide faces with negative draft

Choose this button to highlight the faces with the negative draft with the color shown in the color box on the right of this button. Note that the faces will be highlighted only after you select the faces to add the draft and choose the **Apply** button from the **Items to Draft** rollout.

Figure 10-110 The DraftXpert in the Draft PropertyManager

Tip. *After choosing the **Apply** button, when you move the cursor over any face of the model other than the neutral plane, the draft angle of that face is displayed dynamically above the cursor.*

TUTORIALS

Tutorial 1

In this tutorial, you will create the model shown in Figure 10-111. The dimensions of the model are shown in the same figure. The hidden lines in the top and side views are suppressed for clarity.   **(Expected time: 45 min)**

Figure 10-111 *Views and dimensions of the model for Tutorial 1*

The steps to be followed to complete this tutorial are listed next.

a. The base feature of the model is a sweep feature. First, you need to create the path for the sweep feature on the **Front Plane**. Next, you need to create a plane normal to this path. Select the newly created plane as the sketching plane and create the profile for the sweep feature. You will create a thin sweep feature because the base feature of the model is a hollow feature, refer to Figures 10-112 through 10-114.

b. Create the extrude features on both ends of the sweep feature, refer to Figure 10-115.

c. Create a plane at an offset distance from the right face of the model. Create the circular feature by extruding it using the **Up To Next** option.

d. Create the hole using the **Simple Hole** tool, refer to Figure 10-115.

e. Create the pattern of the hole feature, refer to Figure 10-115.

f. Create the counterbore hole using the cut revolve option, refer to Figure 10-115.

Creating the Path for the Sweep Feature

As discussed earlier, the base feature of the model is a sweep feature. To create the sweep feature, you first need to create its path. This path will be created on the **Front Plane**.

1. Start a new SolidWorks Part document using the **New SolidWorks Document** dialog box.

2. Draw the sketch of the path for the sweep feature on the **Front Plane** and add the required relations and dimensions to the sketch, as shown in Figure 10-112. Exit the sketching environment and change the view to isometric.

Creating the Profile for the Sweep Feature

After creating the path for the sweep feature, you will create its profile. For creating the profile, first you need to create a reference plane normal to the path. The newly created plane will be selected as the sketching plane for creating the profile for the sweep feature.

1. Invoke the **Plane PropertyManager** and using the **Normal to Curve** option, create a plane normal to the path, as shown in Figure 10-113.

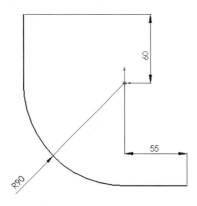

Figure 10-112 *Sketch of the path*

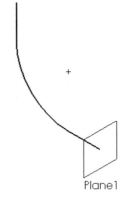

Figure 10-113 *Plane created normal to path*

2. Invoke the sketching environment by selecting the newly created plane as the sketching plane.

3. Draw the sketch of the profile of the sweep feature using the **Circle** tool. The center of the circle is at the origin and the diameter of the circle is 97 mm.

4. Exit the sketching environment after drawing the profile for the sweep feature.

Creating the Sweep Feature

The sweep feature that you are going to create is a thin sweep feature. You will use the **Thin Feature** rollout to specify its parameters.

1. Choose the **Swept Boss/Base** button from the **Features CommandManager**. The **Sweep PropertyManager** is invoked and you are prompted to select the sweep profile.

2. Select the profile for the sweep feature. The selected profile will be highlighted in green and the **Profile** callout will also be displayed.

You are prompted to select the sweep path after selecting the profile.

3. Select the path for the sweep feature. The selected path will be highlighted in magenta and the **Path** callout is also displayed. The preview of the sweep feature is also displayed in the drawing area.

4. Select the **Thin Feature** check box available on the left of the **Thin Feature** rollout; the **Thin Feature** rollout is invoked.

5. Set the value of thickness in the **Thickness** spinner to **16**.

Since the wall thickness added to the model is reverse to the required direction, therefore, you need to reverse the direction of the creation of thin feature.

6. Choose the **Reverse Direction** button from the **Thin Features** rollout. Choose the **OK** button from the **Sweep PropertyManager**, or choose **OK** from the confirmation corner.

The base feature created by sweeping a profile along a path is shown in Figure 10-114.

Tip. *Instead of creating a thin sweep feature, you can also create a solid sweep feature and then add a shell feature to hollow the base feature.*

Creating the Remaining Features

1. Create the remaining join features of the model using the extrude option.

2. Using the **Simple Hole PropertyManager**, create the holes and pattern them using the **Circular Pattern** tool. Create the counterbore hole using the **Hole Wizard** or the revolve cut option.

The final solid model of Tutorial 1 is shown in Figure 10-115.

Saving the Model

1. Choose the **Save** button from the **Standard** toolbar and save the model with the name given below

\My Documents\SolidWorks\c10\c10tut1.sldprt

2. Choose **File** > **Close** from the menu bar to close the file.

Figure 10-114 *Base feature of the model*

Figure 10-115 *Final model of Tutorial 1*

Tutorial 2

In this tutorial, you will create the chair frame shown in Figure 10-116. The dimensions of the chair frame are also shown in the same figure. **(Expected time: 30 min)**

Figure 10-116 *Views and dimensions of the model for Tutorial 2*

The steps to be followed to complete this tutorial are listed next.

a.   The chair frame is created by sweeping a profile along a 3D path. The 3D path will be created in the 3D sketching environment. Therefore, you need to invoke the 3D sketching environment and then draw the sketch of the 3D path. You will create only the left half of the 3D path in the 3D sketching environment, refer to Figure 10-117.

b.   Create a plane normal to the 3D path. Select the newly created plane as the sketching plane and draw the sketch of the profile.

c.   Sweep the profile along the 3D path using the **Thin Feature** option, refer to Figure 10-118.

d.   Mirror the sweep feature using the **Front Plane**, refer to Figure 10-119.

Creating the Path of Sweep Feature Using 3D Sketching Environment

It is evident from Figure 10-116 that the model is created by sweeping a profile along a 3D path. Therefore, you need to create a path of the sweep feature in the 3D sketching environment.

1.   Start a new SolidWorks part document.

2.   Create a plane at an offset distance of 40 mm from the **Front Plane**.

3.   Change the current view to isometric.

4.   Choose **Insert > 3D Sketch** from the menu bar to invoke the 3D sketching environment. You can also use the **3D Sketch** button from the **Sketch CommandManager** to invoke the 3D sketching environment.

The 3D sketching environment is invoked and the sketch origin is displayed in red. You are also provided with the confirmation corner on the top right of the drawing area. The sketching tools that can be used in the 3D sketching environment are also invoked.

5.   Invoke the **Line** tool; the select cursor is replaced by the line cursor. The **XY** symbol displayed below the line cursor suggests that by default, the line will be sketched in the XY plane.

You need to draw the first line in the ZX plane. Therefore, you will toggle the plane before you start creating the sketch.

6.   Press the TAB key on the keyboard twice to switch to the ZX plane.

7.   Move the line cursor to the origin. When a red dot is displayed, specify the start point of the line.

8.   Move the cursor in the positive Z direction of the triad. A small triad with Z appears below the cursor indicating that you are drawing the line in the **Z** direction. Specify the end point of the line, when a value close to 40 is displayed above the cursor; a rubber-band line is displayed attached to the cursor.

9.   Move the cursor toward the right along the infinite line indicating the X axis. Specify the end point of the line when a value close to 100 is displayed above the cursor.

10. Press the TAB key to switch over to the XY plane. Move the cursor vertically upwards.

11. Specify the end point of the line when the value above the cursor shows a value close to 85.

12. Similarly, draw the remaining sketch and add the required relations and dimensions to it. The final sketch is displayed in Figure 10-117.

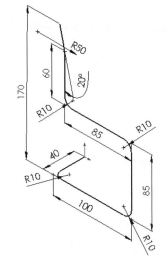

Figure 10-117 Sketch of the 3D path

13. Add the **On Surface** relation between the upper endpoint of the 3D sketch and **Plane1**.

14. Exit the 3D sketching environment using the confirmation corner.

Creating the Profile of the Sweep Feature

As discussed earlier, the sweep feature will be created by sweeping the profile along a 3D path. After creating the path, you need to create the profile for the sweep feature.

1.   Select the **Front Plane** as the sketching plane and invoke the sketching environment.

You do not need to create a reference plane, because the **Front Plane** is normal to the 3D path.

2.   Draw a circle of diameter 5 mm that will be used as the sketch of the profile of the sweep feature, refer to Figure 10-118.

3.   Exit the sketching environment.

Sweeping the Profile Along the 3D Path

After creating the 3D path and the profile for the sweep feature, you need to sweep the profile along the 3D path using the **Swept Boss/Base** tool.

1. Choose the **Swept Boss/Base** button from the **Features CommandManager**. The **Sweep PropertyManager** is invoked.

2. Make sure that the sketch of the profile is selected. The selected profile will be displayed in green. The profile callout will also be displayed.

   You are prompted to select the path for the sweep feature.

3. Select the path for the sweep feature. The path will be displayed in magenta color. The path callout will also be displayed. The preview of the sweep feature will also be displayed in the drawing area.

   As evident from Figure 10-116, the frame of the chair is made from a hollow pipe. Therefore, you need to create a thin sweep feature to create a hollow chair frame.

4. Invoke the **Thin Feature** rollout and set the value of the **Thickness** spinner to **1**.

5. Choose the **Reverse Direction** button from the **Thin Features** rollout to reverse the direction of the thin feature creation.

6. Choose the **OK** button from the **Sweep PropertyManager** to end the creation of the feature.

   The model, after creating the sweep feature, is displayed in Figure 10-118.

7. Mirror the sweep feature about the **Front Plane** using the **Mirror** tool. The model, after mirroring, is shown in Figure 10-119.

Saving the Model

1. Choose the **Save** button from the **Standard** toolbar and save the model with the name given below.

   \My Documents\SolidWorks\c10\c10tut2.sldprt

2. Close the document.

Figure 10-118 *Sweep feature created by sweeping a profile along a 3D path*

Figure 10-119 *The final model*

Tutorial 3

In this tutorial, you will create the spring shown in Figure 10-120. The dimensions of the spring are shown in Figure 10-121.   **(Expected time: 45 min)**

Figure 10-120 *Model for Tutorial 3*

Spring Data:
Height = 72.5mm
Pitch = 10mm
Diameter of Spring= 50mm
Diameter of Coil= 7mm

Figure 10-121 Views and dimensions of the model for Tutorial 3

The steps to be followed to complete this tutorial are listed next.

a. Create the helical path of the spring, refer to Figure 10-122.
b. Create the end clips of the spring, refer to Figure 10-125.
c. Combine the end clips and the helical curve to create a single curve using the **Composite Curve** option, refer to Figure 10-126.
d. Create the profile on the plane normal to the curve and sweep it along the curve, refer to Figures 10-127 and 10-128.

Creating the Helical Curve

For creating this model, you first need to create the helical curve of the spring. For creating the helical curve, you first need to create a circular sketch. This sketch will define the diameter of the spring.

1. Start a new SolidWorks Part document.

2. Choose the **Helix and Spiral** button from the **Curves CommandManager** and select the **Front Plane** as the sketching plane.

3. Draw a circle of diameter 50. Change the view to isometric view and exit the sketching environment.

The **Helix/Spiral Curve PropertyManager** is displayed and the preview of the helical curve with the default values is displayed in the drawing area.

4. Select the **Height and Pitch** option from the **Type** drop-down list available in the **Defined By** rollout.

5. Set the value of the **Height** spinner to **72.5** and the value of the **Pitch** spinner to **10**.

   You will observe that the preview of the helical curve is updated automatically when you modify the values in the spinners.

6. Set the value of the **Starting angle** spinner to **0** and choose the **OK** button from the **Helix/ Spiral PropertyManager**.

   The helical curve, created using the above steps, is shown in Figure 10-122.

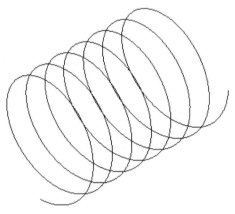

Figure 10-122 *Helical curve*

Drawing the Sketch of the End Clips of the Spring

After creating the helical curve, you need to draw the sketch that defines the path of the end clips. There are two end clips in this spring, and each end clip is created using two sketches. First, you will create the right end-clip and then the left end-clip.

1. Select the **Front Plane** as the sketching plane and invoke the sketching environment.

   The first sketch of the right end-clip consists of two arcs. The first arc will be drawn using the **Centerpoint Arc** tool and the second arc will be drawn using the **3 Point Arc** tool.

2. Choose the **Centerpoint Arc** button from the **Sketch CommandManager** and specify the centerpoint of the arc at the origin.

3. Move the cursor toward the right and specify the start point of the arc when the radius of the reference circle shows a value close to **25**.

4.   Move the cursor in the counterclockwise direction. Specify the endpoint of the arc when the value of the angle above the cursor shows a value close to **75**.

5.   Choose the **3 Point Arc** button from the **Sketch CommandManager**. Specify the start point of the arc on the upper endpoint of the previous arc. Create the arc, as shown in Figure 10-123.

6.   Add the **Pierce** relation between the lower endpoint of the first arc and the helical curve. Add the other relations and the dimensions to fully define the sketch. The fully defined sketch is shown in Figure 10-123.

7.   Exit the sketching environment.

     After drawing the first sketch of the right end-clip, you need to draw the second sketch of the right end-clip. The second sketch of the right end-clip will be drawn on the **Right Plane**.

8.   Select the **Right Plane** and invoke the sketching environment.

9.   Draw the sketch as shown in Figure 10-124. You need to apply the **Pierce** relation between the upper arc and the previous sketch and the left end point of the left arc of the current sketch.

10. Add a **Tangent** relation between the left arc of the current sketch and the upper arc of the sketch previously drawn. Add the required relations and dimensions to the current sketch. The sketch, after applying all the relations and dimensions, is shown in Figure 10-124.

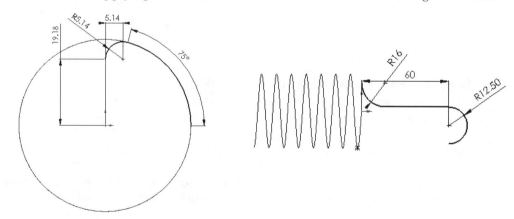

Figure 10-123 *First sketch of right end-clip*   ***Figure 10-124*** *Second sketch of right end-clip*

11. Similarly, draw the sketch of the left end-clip. Figure 10-125 shows the path of the spring after creating the helical curve, right end-clip, and the left end-clip.

Creating the Composite Curve

After creating all the required sketches and the helical curve, you need to combine them so that they form a single curve. This is done because the path of the sweep feature has to be a single curve or sketch.

1. Choose the **Composite Curve** button from the **Curves CommandManager** or choose **Insert > Curve > Composite** from the menu bar. The **Composite Curve PropertyManager** is displayed and the confirmation corner is also available.

2. Select both the end-clips and the helical curve from the drawing area or from the **FeatureManager Design Tree**.

3. Choose the **OK** button from the **Composite Curve PropertyManager** or choose **OK** from the confirmation corner.

    The composite curve is created and is displayed in Figure 10-126.

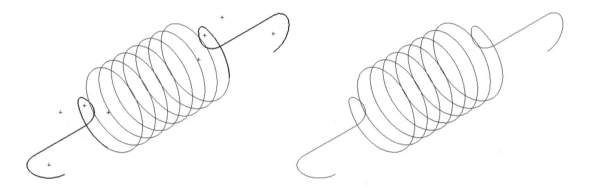

Figure 10-125   *Path for the spring*   *Figure 10-126*   *Composite curve*

Creating the Profile for the Sweep Feature

Next, you need to create the profile for the sweep feature. The sketch of the profile will be drawn on a plane normal to the curve on the endpoint of the right end-clip.

1. Create a plane normal to the path and at the endpoint of the right end-clip.

2. Draw the profile of the sweep feature and add the **Pierce** relation between the center of the circle and the composite curve. Add the required dimensions to the sketch.

3. Exit the sketching environment. Figure 10-127 shows the profile and the path for the sweep feature.

Creating the Sweep Feature

You will create a sweep feature to complete the creation of the spring.

1. Invoke the **Sweep PropertyManager** and you are prompted to select the sweep profile.

2. Select the sweep profile from the drawing area.

    You are prompted to select the sweep path.

3. Select the path and choose the **OK** button from the **Sweep PropertyManager**.

    The spring created, after sweeping the profile along the path, is shown in Figure 10-128.

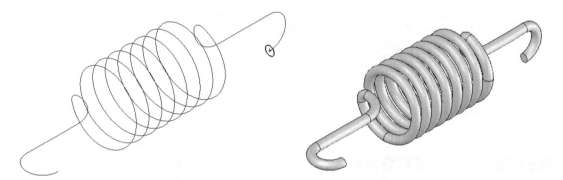

Figure 10-127 Profile and path of the sweep fea-   *Figure 10-128 Final model*

Saving the Model

1. Choose the **Save** button from the **Standard** toolbar and save the model with the name given below.

    \My Documents\SolidWorks\c10\c10tut3.sldprt

2. Close the document.

SELF-EVALUATION TEST

Answer the following questions and then compare your answers with those given at the end of this chapter:

1. You need a profile and a path to create a sweep feature. (T/F)

2. At least two sections are required to create a loft feature. (T/F)

3. You cannot sweep a closed profile along a closed path. (T/F)

4. You cannot create a thin sweep feature. (T/F)

5. You can also create a loft feature using open sections. (T/F)

6. The _____ **PropertyManager** is used to create a loft feature.

7. The _____ option is used to create a single curve by joining the continuous chain of existing sketches, edges, or curves.

8. You need to apply _____ relation between the sketch and the guide curve, while sweeping a profile along a path using guide curves.

9. _____ option is used to create a curve by defining the coordinates.

10. _____ **PropertyManager** is invoked to create a cut-sweep feature.

REVIEW QUESTIONS

Answer the following questions:

1. Using the _____ rollout, you can define the tangency at the start and end in the sweep feature.

2. The _____ rollout is used to create a thin loft feature.

3. You need to invoke _____ dialog box to create a spiral curve.

4. The _____ **PropertyManager** is invoked to create a curve projected on a surface.

5. The _____ dialog box is used to specify the coordinates to create the curve.

6. Which button is selected to invoke the 3D sketching environment?

    (a) **2D Sketch**   (b) **3D Sketching Environment**
    (c) **3D Sketch**   (d) **Sketch**

7. Which rollout, available in the **Sweep PropertyManager**, is used to define the tangency?

    (a) **Start/End Tangency**   (b) **Tangency**
    (c) **Options**   (d) None of these

8. Which button, available in the **Features PropertyManager**, is used to invoke the **Draft PropertyManager**?

    (a) **Draft**   (b) **Taper Angle**
    (c) **Draft Feature**   (c) **Draft Angle**

9. In which rollout would you define the pull direction, while creating a draft feature using the parting line option?

    (a) **Pull Direction**   (b) **Direction of Pull**
    (c) **Reference Direction**   (d) **Options**

10. Which button available in the **Guide Curves** rollout is used to display the sections, while creating the sweep feature with guide curves?

    (a) **Preview Sections**   (b) **Show Sections**
    (c) **Sections**   (d) **Preview**

EXERCISE

Exercise 1

Create the model of the Upper Housing shown in Figure 10-129. The dimensions of the model are shown in Figure 10-130. **(Expected time: 1 hr)**

Figure 10-129 *Model of the Upper Housing*

Figure 10-130 *Dimensions of the Upper Housing*

Tip. *This model is divided in three major parts. The first part is the base and is created by extruding the sketch to a distance of 80 mm using the **Mid Plane** option.*

*The second part of this model is the right portion of the discharge venturi and is created using the sweep feature. The path of the sweep feature will be created on the **Right Plane**. You need to create a plane at the left endpoint of the path and normal to the path.*

The third part of this model is the left portion of the discharge venturi created using the loft feature. You need to create the first section of the loft feature on the planar face of the sweep feature created earlier. The second section will be created on a plane at an offset distance from the planar face of the sweep feature created earlier. Create a loft feature using the two sections created earlier. The other features needed to complete the model are fillets, hole, circular pattern, and so on.

Answers to Self-Evaluation Test

1. T, 2. T, 3. F, 4. F, 5. T, 6. Loft, 7. Composite Curve, 8. Coincident, 9. Curve Through Free Points, 10. Cut-Sweep

Chapter 11

Advanced Modeling Tools-IV

Learning Objectives

After completing this chapter, you will be able to:
- *Create dome features.*
- *Create shape features.*
- *Create indent features.*
- *Create deform features.*
- *Create flex features.*
- *Create fastening features.*
- *Create freeform features.*

ADVANCED MODELING TOOLS

Some of the advanced modeling options were discussed in Chapters 7, 8, and 10. In this chapter, you will learn about more advanced modeling tools that you can use to enhance your ability to style your concept of product designing.

Creating Dome Features

CommandManager:	Features > Dome	(Customize to Add)
Menu:	Insert > Features > Dome	
Toolbar:	Features > Dome	(Customize to Add)

Using the **Dome** tool, you can create a dome feature on the selected face. Depending upon the feature creation direction, a dome can be of a convex or concave shape. To create a dome feature, choose the **Dome** button from the **Features CommandManager**, or choose **Insert >Features > Dome** from the menu bar. When you choose this button, the **Dome PropertyManager** is displayed, as shown in Figure 11-1.

*Figure 11-1 The **Dome PropertyManager***

After invoking the **Dome PropertyManager**, you are prompted to select a face or faces on which you want to add the dome feature. The face to be selected can be a planar or curved face. Select the face on which you need to create the dome feature; the name of the selected face will be displayed in the **Faces to Dome** selection box. The selected face can be a planar face or a curved face. The preview of the dome feature, with the default values, is displayed in the drawing area. Using the **Distance** spinner, you can set the height of the dome feature. You can also move the cursor on the thumbwheel available below the **Distance** spinner and drag the cursor to modify the value. Dragging the thumbwheel to the right will increase the value and dragging it to the left will decrease the value. The preview of the dome feature modifies dynamically when you modify the height using the **Distance** spinner. The height of the dome feature is calculated from the centroid of the selected face to the top of the dome feature. After specifying the height of the dome feature, choose the **OK** button from the **Dome PropertyManager**. Figure 11-2 shows the planar face to be selected for the dome feature. Figure 11-3 shows the resulting dome feature.

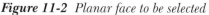
Figure 11-2 *Planar face to be selected*

Figure 11-3 *Resulting dome feature*

If the selected planar face belongs to a circular or an elliptical feature, the **Elliptical dome** check box is displayed in the **Dome PropertyManager**. You can create an elliptical dome by selecting this check box. Figure 11-4 shows a circular dome created by selecting a circular planar face. Figure 11-5 shows an elliptical dome created by first selecting the **Elliptical dome** check box and then a circular planar face.

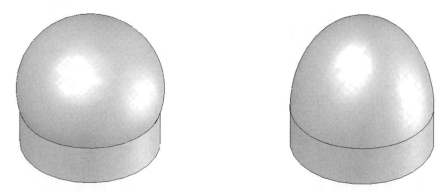

Figure 11-4 *Circular dome*   *Figure 11-5* *Elliptical dome*

The **Reverse direction** button in the **Dome PropertyManager** is used to create a concave dome. A concave dome is one in which the material is removed by creating a cavity in the form of a dome. For removing the material using the dome feature, select the **Reverse direction** button. Figure 11-6 shows the dome feature created with the **Reverse direction** button selected.

Other options available in the **Dome PropertyManager** are discussed next.

Constraint Point or Sketch

The **Constraint Point or Sketch** option is provided in the **Dome PropertyManager** to constraint the dome creation to the selected reference. The selected reference can be a point, sketched

Figure 11-6 *A dome feature created with the **Reverse** **direction** button selected*

point, or the endpoint of an entity. To create a dome feature using the **Constraint Point or Sketch** option, invoke the **Dome PropertyManager** and select the face on which you need to add the dome feature. Now, click once in the **Constraint Point or Sketch** selection box and select the constraint point from the drawing area and choose the **OK** button from the **Dome PropertyManager**. Figure 11-7 shows the face on which you need to add the dome feature and the point to be selected as the constraint point. Figure 11-8 shows the resulting dome feature.

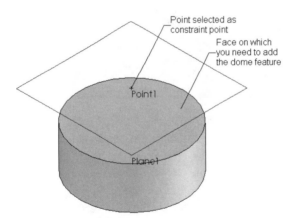

Figure 11-7 *Face and the point to be selected*

Figure 11-8 *Resulting dome feature*

Note
The dome feature will be created depending on the height of the dome and the position of the constraint point.

Direction

The **Direction** option in the **Dome PropertyManager** is used to specify the direction vector, in which you need to create the dome feature. For creating the dome feature by defining the direction vector, invoke the **Dome PropertyManager**. Select the face on which you need to create the dome feature. Now, click once in the **Direction** selection box and select an edge as the directional reference from the drawing area. The selected edge will be displayed in cyan. Set the value of the height of the dome and choose the **OK** button from the **Dome PropertyManager**. Figure 11-9 shows the faces on which you need to add the dome and the edge to be selected as the direction vector. Figure 11-10 shows the resulting dome.

Figure 11-9 Face and direction to be selected   *Figure 11-10 Resulting dome feature*

Creating Shape Features

CommandManager:	Features > Shape	*(Customize to Add)*
Menu:	Insert > Features > Shape	
Toolbar:	Features > Shape	*(Customize to Add)*

SolidWorks provides you with a free form styling tool named the **Shape** tool that you can use to create free form shapes by manipulating the faces of the models. This free form styling tool is named as the **Shape** tool. On using the **Shape** tool, the selected face acts like a rubber membrane on which pressure is applied. As a result, the face inflates or deflates like a balloon. You can also adjust the shape of the membrane by changing its stretch and bend characteristics. To create a shape feature, choose **Insert > Features > Shape** from the menu bar, or select the **Shape** button from the **Features CommandManager** after customizing it. When you invoke this tool, the **Shape Feature** dialog box is displayed, as shown in Figure 11-11.

After invoking the **Shape Feature** dialog box, select the face that you need to manipulate. The selected face will be highlighted in green and its name will be displayed in the **Face to shape** selection box. You can also constrain the selected face along a curve, sketch, or an edge. To select the constraining curve, click once in the **Constrain to** selection box and select the constraining reference from the drawing area. The **Maintain boundary tangents** check box is selected by default and is used to maintain the tangency between the shape feature and the boundary of the selected face. Choose the **Preview** button to display the preview of the shape feature. The preview of the shape feature in the form of a surface mesh will be displayed in the drawing area. Figure 11-12 shows the face to be manipulated and the sketch that will constrain the shape feature. Figure 11-13 shows the preview in the form of a mesh.

Figure 11-11 *The **Shape Feature** dialog box*

Figure 11-12 *Face to be manipulated and the sketch to constrain the shape feature*

Figure 11-13 *Preview in the form of a mesh*

Tip. *The constraint that will constrain the shape feature can be a point, sketch point, endpoint, vertex, sketch, edge, or a curve. The constrain can be created on the same face or another face at an offset, or angle.*

Next, you need to set the controls to manipulate the shape feature. Choose the **Control** tab to set its parameters. The options available in the **Control** tab are discussed next.

Gains

The **Gains** area of the **Control** tab is used to set the pressure and value of the curve influence, while creating the shape feature. These options are discussed next.

Pressure

The **Pressure** slider available in the **Gains** area is used to specify the pressure on the selected face. By default the slider is set at **0**. The positive pressure inflates and the negative pressure deflates it.

Curve Influence

The **Curve Influence** slider is used to specify the percentage of the influence of the constraining curve on the shape feature creation.

Characteristics

The **Characteristics** area is provided with the options, such as stretch and bend, that are used to adjust the smoothness of the shape feature.

Advanced controls

The **Advanced controls** area is used to set the resolution of the mesh. Using the **Resolution** slider available in the **Advanced controls** area, you can set the value of the resolution. The higher the resolution, the better will be the shape of the feature and more the time it will take to rebuild.

Figure 11-14 shows the model with the top face manipulated using the shape feature.

Figure 11-14 Shape feature added on the top face of the model

Creating Indents

CommandManager:	Features > Indent	*(Customize to Add)*
Menu:	Insert > Features > Indent	
Toolbar:	Features > Indent	*(Customize to Add)*

The **Indent** tool is extremely useful for the packaging industry, industrial designers, and product designers. You will learn about its benefits, while going through the examples in this section. The **Indent** tool is used to add or scoop out material, defined by the geometry of a body, from a target body. The body that is used to add or scoop out material is known as the tool body. Depending on the geometry, the tool is used to add or scoop out material from the target body.

To use this tool, choose the **Indent** button from the **Features CommandManager**; the **Indent PropertyManager** is displayed, as shown in Figure 11-15. The options available in this dialog box are discussed next.

Selections

The options available in the **Selections** rollout are used to select the target body, tool body, and set some parameters. These option are discussed next.

*Figure 11-15 The **Indent PropertyManager***

Target Body

After invoking the **Indent PropertyManager**, you need to select the body that will be deformed using this tool. This selected body is known as the target body. The name of the selected body is displayed in the **Target Body** selection box.

Tool Body Region

After selecting the target body, you need to select a body that will be used as the tool for deforming the target body. This body is known as the tool body. Select the body that needs to be defined as the tool body. The selected portion of the body is highlighted and its name is displayed in the **Tool Body Region** selection box. You will notice that by default, the **Keep Selections** radio button is selected. Therefore, the selected portion of the tool body will be retained and the other portion will be removed. If you select the **Remove Selections** radio button, the selected portion of the tool body will be removed and the remaining portion will be retained.

Cut

The **Cut** check box is selected to create a cut in the target body. This cut is defined by the geometry of the tool body.

Parameters

The **Parameters** rollout is used to define the value of clearance and thickness in the **Clearance** and **Thickness** spinners, respectively. Refer to Figure 11-16 to understand more about clearance and thickness. On selecting the **Cut** check box from the **Selections** rollout, the **Thickness** spinner is frozen.

Figure 11-16 *The **Indent PropertyManager***

Figure 11-17 shows two different bodies, with the smaller rectangular body placed inside the main body. Figure 11-18 shows the target body and the portion of the tool body to be selected.

Figure 11-17 *Two separate bodies*

Figure 11-18 *Bodies to be selected*

Figure 11-19 shows the resulting body, after removing the material using the **Indent** tool. In this figure, the display of the tool body is turned off. To turn off the display of a body, select it and invoke the shortcut menu. Choose the **Hide** option from the **Body** area of the shortcut menu. You will learn more about toggling the display of the bodies in the later chapters. Figure 11-20 shows the resulting body after rotating the view of the model.

Figure 11-19 *Resulting body*

Figure 11-20 *Resulting body after rotating its view*

Figure 11-21 shows the target body and the tool body to be selected. Figure 11-22 shows the resulting body created using the **Indent** tool with the **Cut** check box selected. The display of the tool body is turned off in this figure.

Figure 11-21 Bodies to be selected   *Figure 11-22 Resulting body created using the **Indent** tool with the **Cut** check box selected*

Figure 11-23 shows the eggs created by revolving the sketch, and then patterned using the **Linear Pattern** tool. Figure 11-24 shows the base plate created for the egg tray as a separate body and placed with the eggs. In this example, the base plate is selected as the target body and all eggs are selected from the bottom portion as tool bodies. Figure 11-25 shows the egg tray created using the **Indent** tool using the **Remove selections** radio button. The display of all eggs is turned off in this figure.

*Figure 11-23 Eggs patterned using the **Linear Pattern** tool*   *Figure 11-24 Base plate for creating the egg tray*

Figure 11-25 *Resulting egg tray*

Creating Deform Features

CommandManager:	Features > Deform	*(Customize to Add)*
Menu:	Insert > Features > Deform	
Toolbar:	Features > Deform	*(Customize to Add)*

The **Deform** tool is used to create free-style designs by manipulating the shape of the entire model or a particular portion of it. Choose the **Deform** button from the **Features CommandManager**, after customizing it; the **Deform PropertyManager** is invoked. Its partial view is shown in Figure 11-26. There are three methods of creating a deform feature and these are discussed next.

Creating the Deform Feature Using the Curve to curve Method

To create a deform feature using the **Curve to curve** method, invoke the **Deform PropertyManager**. Select the **Curve to curve** radio button, if it is not selected by default. The options available to create the deform feature using this method are discussed next.

Deform Curves

The **Deform Curves** rollout is used to define the curves that are used to deform the shape of the model. On invoking this tool, you are prompted to select the geometry to define the deformation and the fixed geometry for

Figure 11-26 *The **Deform PropertyManager***

the deform operation. You first need to select the initial curve. The initial curve defines the reference from where the deformation will start. Select an edge, or a chain of edges, or curves to define the initial curve. Next, you need to select the target curves. Click once in the **Target curves** selection box and select the target curve, which can be a sketch, an edge, or a curve. The profile of the target curve will define the shape of the deform feature, refer to Figure 11-27 and 11-28.

When you select the initial curve and the target curve, a connector connecting both curves is displayed. You can position the connector by using the handles provided at its sides. To define additional connectors, invoke the shortcut menu and choose the **Add Connector** option from it.

Deform Region

The **Deform Region** rollout is used to define the options to deform a specific area of the model. By default, the entire model is deformed, when you specify the initial curves and the target curves. The **Fixed edges** check box is selected by default. Therefore, the **Fixed Curves/Edges/Faces** selection box is invoked. Using this selection box, you can select the curves, edges, or faces that you need to keep fixed while creating the deform feature. The **Additional Faces to be Deformed** selection box is used to specify the additional faces that you need to deform. If you clear the **Fixed edges** check box, the **Fixed Curves/Edges/Faces** and **Additional Faces to be Deformed** selection boxes are not displayed.

The **Uniform** check box available in the **Deform Region** rollout is used to uniformly deform the model. If you clear the **Fixed edges** check box and select the **Uniform** check box from the **Deform Region** rollout, the **Deform radius** spinner is displayed. The **Bodies to be Deformed** selection box is used to define the bodies that you need to deform. This option is used in a multibody model.

Shape Options

The options available in this rollout are used to define the intensity of stiffness, shape, accuracy, and intensity of weight along the fixed reference or moving reference.

Note

*The **Weight** slider bar is available in the **Shape Options** rollout if the **Uniform** check box available in the **Deform Region** rollout is cleared.*

Figure 11-27 shows the references to be selected and Figure 11-28 shows the resulting preview of the deform feature.

After setting all the parameters, choose the **OK** button from the **Deform PropertyManager**. Figure 11-29 shows the resulting deform feature.

Figure 11-27 *References to be selected*   Figure 11-28 *Preview of the deform feature*

Figure 11-29 *Resulting deform feature*

Creating the Deform Feature Using the Point Method

To create the deform feature using the **Point** method, select the **Point** radio button from the **Deform Type** rollout, as shown in Figure 11-30. You are prompted to select the geometry to define the region, deformation point, and fixed geometry for the deform operation. Also, select a point on the model face, vertex, or edge from where you need to deform the model. On selecting any of the above-mentioned entities from the model, the model will be deformed at the selected point, using the default value of the deform distance and deform radius. You can set the value of the deform distance and the deform radius using the **Deform distance** and **Deform radius** spinners from the **Deform Point** and **Deform Region** rollouts, respectively. You can reverse the direction of the deform feature by using the **Reverse deform direction** button in the **Deform Point** rollout.

You can also specify a deform direction to create a deform feature by clicking once in the **Deform Direction** selection box and selecting the direction to create the deform feature. By default, the entire model is deformed using this tool. You can also specify a particular portion by selecting the **Deform region** check box. The options available to specify a region for deformation are the same as those discussed earlier.

*Figure 11-30 The **Deform PropertyManager***

Figure 11-31 shows the point where you need to select the face of the model. Figure 11-32 shows the resulting deform feature. Figure 11-33 shows the deform feature created using the **Point** option and the **Deform region** check box selected. Figure 11-34 shows the deform feature with the **Deform region** check box selected and the front face of the base feature selected as the additional faces to be deformed.

Figure 11-31 References to be selected   *Figure 11-32 Resulting preview of the deform feature*

Figure 11-33 *Deform feature with the* **Point** *option and the* **Deform region** *check box selected*

Figure 11-34 *Deform feature with front face selected as the additional face to be deformed*

You can also define the deform axis for deforming the entire model by specifying it in the **Deform axis** selection box available in the **Shape Options** rollout. Other options available are the same as those discussed earlier.

Creating the Deform Feature Using the Surface push Method

Using this option, you can deform the selected body or bodies by pushing the tool bodies inside them. To deform a body using this option, invoke the **Deform PropertyManager** and select the **Surface push** radio button from the **Deform Type** rollout. The partial view of the resulting **PropertyManager** is shown in Figure 11-35.

A 3D triad, along with the axes rings, is displayed placed coincident to the part origin. A transparent spherical ball is also displayed placed coincident to the 3D triad. This spherical ball is the default tool using which the selected bodies will be deformed. You can also use the other types of geometries as the tool body using the options available in the **Tool Body** drop-down list. Other types of geometries that can be used as the tool body are ellipse, ellipsoid, polygon, and rectangle. You can also select a separately created body as the tool body by choosing the **Select Body** option from the **Tool Body** drop-down list and selecting the body required as the tool body. You will notice that with each type of a default tool body, a callout is displayed, using which you can modify the size of the geometry of the tool body.

Figure 11-35 *The* **Deform PropertyManager** *with the* **Surface push** *radio button selected*

Next, you need to select the direction in which you need to push the target body. Select an edge, sketched line, or a face to define the push direction reference. Choose the **Reverse Direction** button to flip the default push direction, if required.

Click once in the **Bodies to be deformed** selection box and select the body or bodies to be deformed. The preview of the resulting deformed body is displayed in the drawing area.

You can modify the position of the tool body using the triad. To modify the location of the tool body, move the cursor close to any of the arrows of the cursor along which you need to move or rotate the tool body. The cursor will be replaced by the modify cursor. Press and hold down the left mouse button and drag the cursor in the direction pointing toward the arrow to move the tool body. Press and hold down the right mouse button and drag the cursor along the direction of the arrow of the triad to rotate the tool body. You can also use the options available in the **Tool Body Position** rollout to modify the position of the tool body.

The **Deform deviation** spinner provided in the **Deform Region** rollout is used to define the fillet radius where the tool body intersects the face of the target body. Figure 11-36 shows a deformed body with the lower value of deviation and Figure 11-37 shows a deformed body with a higher value of deviation.

Figure 11-36 *Deform feature with lower value of deviation*

Figure 11-37 *Deform feature with higher value of deviation*

Creating Flex Features

CommandManager:	Features > Flex	(Customize to Add)
Menu:	Insert > Features > Flex	
Toolbar:	Features > Flex	(Customize to Add)

The most awaited enhancement in the **Part** mode of SolidWorks is made in this release of the software. This enhancement is the **Flex** tool, which enables you to perform free form bending, twisting, tapering, and stretching of a selected body. The portion of the bodies to be deformed is defined by two planes that are known as trimming planes. You will learn more about these planes later in this chapter. To deform a body using this tool, choose the **Flex** button from the **Features CommandManager**; the **Flex PropertyManager** is displayed. The partial view of the **Flex PropertyManager** is shown in Figure 11-38.

The **Bending** radio button is selected by default in the **Flex Input** rollout and you are prompted

*Figure 11-38 The **Flex PropertyManager***

to select the bodies for flex and set the options. Select the body from the drawing area. You will notice that the selected body is displayed in transparent and two trimming planes are displayed at its extremes. A bending axis is also displayed passing through the selected body along which the body will be bent. A 3D triad, along with the axes rings, is displayed placed coincident to the part origin. Figure 11-39 shows the selected body along with the trimming planes, 3D triad, axes rings, and the bending axis.

You can modify the position and location of the trimming planes and the bending axis using the 3D triad and the axes rings. Move the cursor on the triad arrow along which you need to move the bending axis or the ring about which you need to rotate the trimming planes. The select cursor is replaced by the move or rotate cursor. Press and hold the left mouse button on the arrow to move the location of the bending axis. Figure 11-40 shows the preview of the flex feature, after modifying the value of the bending axis and the trimming planes.

You can also modify the location of the 3D triad. To do this, move the cursor to the origin of the triad, press and hold down the left mouse button and drag the cursor to change the location of the triad. You can also use the **Triad** rollout to modify the position of the triad and rotation angle of the bending axis and trimming planes.

As discussed earlier, by default the 3D triad is placed coincident to the part origin. Therefore, the body is deformed about the part origin. If you need to fix a face of the body while deforming it, move the cursor to the origin of the triad and press and hold down the left mouse button. Drag the cursor and place it on the face that you need to fix. Release the left mouse button when

Figure 11-39 *Selected body along with the trimming planes, 3D triad, and the bending axis*

Figure 11-40 *Body after modifying the bending axis and the trimming planes*

the boundary of the face on which the cursor moves is displayed in red. You can also set the position of the triad using the **Triad** rollout. Note that you can coincide the origin of the triad with an existing geometry such as a vertex, an edge, or a sketched entity.

The **Trim Plane 1** and the **Trim Plane 2** rollouts are used to specify an offset value of the current trimming planes. You can modify the gap between the trimming planes by dragging them using the arrows attached to them. The **Select a reference entity for Trim Plane 1** and the **Select a reference entity for Trim Plane 2** areas are used to select a vertex along which you need to align the trimming planes. The slider bar provided in the **Flex Options** rollout is used to increase the accuracy of the flex tool.

Next, move the cursor on the boundary of any of the trimming planes; the select cursor is replaced by a double-sided arrow cursor. Drag the cursor to dynamically define the bending angle and radius of the bend. You can also define them using the **Angle** and **Radius** spinners, respectively. Figure 11-41 shows the preview of a body being bent and Figure 11-42 shows the body after bending using the **Flex** tool.

Twisting a Body

To twist a body using the **Flex** tool, invoke the **Flex PropertyManager** and select the **Twist** radio button from the **Flex Input** rollout. Select the body or bodies that you need twist; the 3D triad and the trimming planes are displayed. Set the location of the trimming planes and the triad, if required. Move the cursor on the boundary of any of the trimming planes. The select cursor is replaced by the twist cursor. Drag the cursor to dynamically twist the selected body, or set the value of the twisting angle in the **Angle** spinner provided. Figure 11-43 shows the body being twisted with the triad placed coincident to the left face of the body and Figure 11-44 shows the resulting twisted body.

Tip. *While creating a flex feature, you can right-click and choose **Reset Flex** from the shortcut menu to restore the original shape of the model.*

Figure 11-41 *Body being bent dynamically*

Figure 11-42 *Body after bending*

Figure 11-43 *Body being twisted*

Figure 11-44 *The resulting twisted body*

Tapering a Body

To taper a body using the **Flex** tool, invoke the **Flex PropertyManager**, and select the **Taper** radio button from the **Flex Input** rollout. Select the body and set the position of the 3D triad and the trimming planes, if required. Move the cursor close to the boundary of any of the trimming planes. The select cursor is replaced by the taper cursor. Drag the cursor to specify the taper factor. You can also set the taper factor using the **Taper factor** spinner provided in the **Flex Input** rollout. Figure 11-45 shows the body being tapered and Figure 11-46 shows the resulting tapered body.

Stretching a Body

You can also stretch a selected body using the **Flex** tool. To do this, invoke the **Flex PropertyManager** and select the **Stretching** radio button from it. Select the body and move the cursor on the boundary of any one of the trimming planes. The select cursor is replaced by the stretch cursor. Drag the cursor to specify the stretching distance. You can also specify it using the **Stretch distance** spinner. Figure 11-47 shows the body being stretched and Figure 11-48 shows the resulting stretched body.

Figure 11-45 *Body being tapered*   **Figure 11-46** *Resulting tapered body*

Figure 11-47 *Body being stretched*   **Figure 11-48** *Resulting stretched body*

CREATING FASTENING FEATURES

One of the latest enhancements in the recent releases of SolidWorks is the introduction of fastening features. SolidWorks allows you to create four types of fastening features. These are discussed next.

Creating the Mounting Boss

CommandManager:	Fastening Features > Mounting Boss	*(Customize to Add)*
Menu:	Insert > Fastening Features > Mounting Boss	
Toolbar:	Fastening Features > Mounting Boss	*(Customize to Add)*

The **Mounting Boss** tool allows you to create mounting boss features, which are used in the plastic components to accommodate fasteners while assembling them. Figure 11-49 shows mounting boss features created on a component. In a mounting boss, the central cylindrical feature is termed as boss and the side features are termed as fins.

Figure 11-49 *Component with the mounting boss*

When you invoke this tool, the **Mounting Boss PropertyManager** is displayed. The options available in this **PropertyManager** are discussed next.

Position Rollout

The options available in this rollout (Figure 11-50) are used to specify the location of the mounting boss. When you invoke the **Mounting Boss PropertyManager**, the **Select a face or a 3D point** selection box is highlighted in this area. The face that you select will be taken as the placement face for the mounting boss and the preview of the mounting boss, created with the default parameters, will be displayed. If the mounting boss is being placed at a face that has a circular or filleted edge, you can use it to make the center of the mounting boss concentric with that edge. To do so, click once in the **Select circular edge to**

Figure 11-50 *The Position rollout*

position the mounting boss selection box and then select the circular edge; the preview of the mounting boss will be repositioned such that it is concentric with the circular edge.

When you specify the location of the mounting boss, a 3D point is placed at that point. After creating the mounting boss, you can edit the 3D point to define its exact location using dimensions.

Boss Rollout

The options available in this rollout (Figure 11-51) are used to specify the dimensions of the cylindrical feature (boss) in the mounting boss. Using the spinners in this rollout, you can set the values of the diameter, height, and the draft angle of the outer cylindrical face of the boss. By default, the **Enter boss height** radio button is selected in this area. As a result, you can specify the value of the height. If you select the **Select mating face** radio button, the **Select mating face** selection box will be displayed below this radio button. This selection box allows you to select a mating face that will determine the height of the boss.

Figure 11-51 *The Boss rollout*

Fins Rollout

The options available in this rollout (Figure 11-52) are used to specify the dimensions of the fins in the mounting boss.

Figure 11-52 *The* **Fins** *rollout*

The selection box in this area allows you to select a vector to define the orientation of the fins. Using the spinners in this rollout, you can specify the height, width, length, and the draft angle of the fin. You can also specify the number of fins using the last spinner in this area. Figures 11-53 and 11-54 show the mounting boss with different numbers of fins and with different boss and fins parameters.

Figure 11-53 *Mounting boss with 4 fins*

Figure 11-54 *Mounting boss with 6 fins*

Mounting Hole/Pin Rollout

The options available in this rollout (Figure 11-55) are used to specify the dimensions of the hole or the pin on top of the boss. The **Pin** and **Hole** radio buttons allows you to specify whether you want to create a hole or a pin in the boss. Figure 11-56 shows the mounting boss with a hole and Figure 11-57 shows the mounting boss with a pin.

If the **Enter diameter** radio button is selected in this rollout, you can specify the diameter, length, and the draft angle of the hole or pin using their respective spinners. However, if the **Select mating edge** radio button is selected, you can specify an existing edge to determine the

*Figure 11-55 The **Mounting Hole/Pin** rollout*

Figure 11-56 Mounting boss with hole in the boss

Figure 11-57 Mounting boss with pin in the boss

diameter of the hole or pin. The height and draft of the hole or pin in this case also can be specified using their respective spinners.

Creating Snap Hooks

CommandManager:	Fastening Features > Snap Hook	*(Customize to Add)*
Menu:	Insert > Fastening Features > Snap Hook	
Toolbar:	Fastening Features > Snap Hook	*(Customize to Add)*

Snap hooks are generally created in small plastic boxes to create a push fit type arrangement to close and open the box. Figure 11-58 shows a plastic box with the snap hook. When you invoke this tool, the **Snap Hook PropertyManager** is displayed. The options available in this **PropertyManager** are discussed next.

Tip. *After placing the snap hook, you can edit its sketch to modify its location on the placement face.*

Figure 11-58 *Box with a snap hook*

Snap Hook Selections Rollout

The options available in this rollout (Figure 11-59) are used to specify the location and orientation of the snap hook. These options are discussed next.

Select a position for the location of the hook

This selection box is active by default when you invoke the **Snap Hook PropertyManager**. You can select a face or an edge to define the location of the snap hook. On selecting the location, the preview of the snap hook, created using the default values, will be displayed.

Define the vertical direction of the hook

This selection box is used to define the vertical direction of the hook. You can select a planar face or an edge to define the direction. You can select the **Reverse direction** check box below this selection box to reverse the vertical direction of the hook.

Figure 11-59 *The Snap Hook Selections rollout*

Define the direction of the hook

This selection box is used to define the direction of the hook. The front face of the body of the snap hook will be made parallel to the face that you select. You can select the **Reverse direction** check box available below this selection box to reverse the direction of the hook.

Select a face to mate the body of the hook

This selection box is used to select a face that will mate with the front face of the body of the snap hook.

Enter body height

This radio button is selected to specify the height of the body of the snap hook. If this radio button is selected, the **Body height** spinner is enabled and you can specify the height in it.

Select mating face

This radio button is used to select a face that will mate with the bottom face of the hook to define the height of the snap hook. When you select this radio button, the **Select mating face** selection box will be displayed. You can use this selection box to specify the mating face; the snap hook will be resized such that the bottom face of the hook mates with the selected face.

Snap Hook Data Rollout

The options available in this rollout (Figure 11-60) are used to specify the parameters of the snap hook. As you modify these values, you can dynamically view the changes in the snap hook. These options are discussed next.

Figure 11-60 The Snap Hook Data rollout

Total width

This spinner is used to specify the total width of the top edge of the snap hook. Note that the width of the bottom edge of the snap hook is determined by the draft angle, which is also specified using the **Top draft angle** spinner in this rollout.

Depth at the base of the hook

This spinner is used to specify the total thickness of the snap hook at its base. Note that the base of the hook is the face that is aligned with the face that you selected as a position for the location of the hook using the first selection box in the **Snap Hook Selections** rollout.

Depth at the top of the hook

This spinner is used to specify the total thickness of the snap hook at its top. Note that the depth at the top should always be equal to or less than that at the bottom. If the depth at the top is less than that at the bottom, the back face of the snap hook will be tapered.

Top draft angle

This spinner is used to specify the draft angle from the top of the hook. This angle will determine the width of the hook at its bottom.

Hook height

This spinner is used to specify the height of the hook.

Hook overhang

This spinner is used to specify the distance by which the hook overhangs from the front face of the body of the snap hook.

Hook lip height

This spinner is used to specify the height of the lip of the hook. By default, this value is 0. This value should always be less than that of the hook height. Figure 11-61 shows a snap hook without a lip and Figure 11-62 shows the snap hook with a lip.

Figure 11-61 Snap hook without a lip   *Figure 11-62* Snap hook with lip

Creating Snap Hook Grooves

CommandManager:	Fastening Features > Snap Hook Groove *(Customize to Add)*
Menu:	Insert > Fastening Features > Snap Hook Groove
Toolbar:	Fastening Features > Snap Hook Groove *(Customize to Add)*

Snap hook grooves are cut features that are created to accommodate the snap hook in order to create push fit type arrangement to close and open the box. Note that this feature works only in case of multibody models. This is because you need to take reference from the snap hook created in one of the bodies to create the snap hook groove in the other body. Figure 11-63 shows the cap of a plastic box with the snap hook groove. Note that to create the snap hook groove, the two bodies should be placed such that the snap hook intersects with the body in which you want to create the snap hook groove. In Figure 11-63, the display of the body with the snap hook is turned off to make the snap hook groove visible.

Figure 11-63 Box with a snap hook groove

When you invoke this tool, the **Snap Hook Groove PropertyManager** will be displayed, as shown in Figure 11-64. This **PropertyManager** has the options to create a snap hook groove in the **Feature and Body Selections** rollout. These options are discussed next.

Select a snap hook feature from the feature tree

This selection box is active by default when you invoke the **Snap Hook Groove** tool and is used to select a snap hook from another body. The resulting groove will be used to accommodate the selected snap hook.

Select a body

This selection box is used to select the body in which the snap hook groove will be created.

Figure 11-64 The Snap Hook Groove PropertyManager

Offset height from Snap Hook

This spinner is used to specify the offset height between the top face of the snap hook and the top face of the snap hook groove when the hook is inserted inside the groove.

Offset width from Snap Hook

This spinner is used to specify the offset width between the side face of the snap hook and the side face of the groove when the hook is inserted inside the groove.

Groove Clearance

This spinner is used to specify the clearance between the snap and the groove.

Gap Distance

This spinner is used to specify the distance between the body of the snap hook and the groove.

Gap Height

This spinner is used to specify the gap height of the snap hook groove.

Creating Vents

CommandManager:	Fastening Features > Vent	*(Customize to Add)*
Menu:	Insert > Fastening Features > Vent	
Toolbar:	Fastening Features > Vent	*(Customize to Add)*

The **Vent** tool is used to create vents in existing models. This tool uses a closed sketch as the boundary of the vent and the open or closed sketched segments inside the closed sketch as the ribs and spars of the vent. Figure 11-65 shows a sketch created at an offset plane and the parameters required to create a vent and Figure 11-66 shows the resulting vent. When you invoke this tool, the **Vent PropertyManager** is displayed. The options in this **PropertyManager** are discussed next.

Figure 11-65 *Parameters required to create a vent*

Figure 11-66 *Resulting vent*

Boundary Rollout

The selection box in this rollout allows you to select a closed sketch that will act as the boundary of the vent. You need to individually select the segments of the sketch to make sure the result is a closed loop.

Geometry Properties Rollout

The options in this rollout (Figure 11-67) are used to specify the face on which the vent will be created and the draft angle for the ribs and spars in the vent. These options are discussed next.

Select a face on which to place the vent

This selection box is used to specify the face on which you want to create the vent. In Figure 11-66, the cylindrical face was selected as the face to place the vent. After selecting the boundary, as soon as you select the face, the preview of the vent will be displayed.

Figure 11-67 The Geometry Properties rollout

Draft On/Off

This button is chosen to add a draft angle to the ribs and spars. Note that before adding the draft angle, you need to select the segments to define the ribs and spars. When you choose this button, the **Draft Angle** spinner on the right of this button is enabled. You can specify the draft angle in this spinner.

Neutral Plane

This selection box is displayed below the **Draft Angle** spinner when you choose the **Draft On/Off** button. Note that this selection box will be available only after you select a face for placing the vent. This selection box allows you to select the neutral plane to define the draft angle direction.

Draft inward

This check box is used to reverse the direction of the draft.

Radius for the fillets

This spinner is used to add fillets between the boundary, ribs, and spars in the vent. Figure 11-68 shows a vent without a fillet and Figure 11-69 shows it with a fillet.

Figure 11-68 Vent without fillet

Figure 11-69 Vent with fillet

Show preview

If this check box is selected, the preview of the vent will be displayed while it is being created. The changes made in the parameters are also dynamically reflected in the preview.

Note

*If you have selected the **Show preview** check box and still the preview of the vent is not displayed, this suggests there is an error in the selection or in the dimensions of the ribs and spars. You will have to modify these values to create the vent.*

Flow Area Rollout

This rollout displays the total area of the vent and the open area in it. As you increase the number of ribs and spars, the open area in the vent reduces.

Ribs Rollout

The options in this rollout (Figure 11-70) are used to specify the segments that define the ribs, and the dimensional and offset values of ribs. These options are discussed next.

*Figure 11-70 The **Ribs** rollout*

Select 2D sketch segments that represent ribs of the vent

This selection box is used to select the sketch segments that will create ribs in the vent. If you have selected the options to show the preview and you select the segments for the ribs, you will be able to dynamically see the preview of the vent with the ribs.

Enter the depth of the ribs

This spinner is used to specify the depth of the ribs in the vent. Figures 11-71 and 11-72 show the ribs with different depths.

Figure 11-71 Depth of rib less than the thickness of the component

Figure 11-72 Depth of rib equal to the thickness of the component

Enter the width of the ribs

This spinner is used to specify the width of the ribs in the vent.

Enter the offset of the ribs from the surface

This spinner is used to specify the value by which the ribs will be offset from the face on which the vent will be created. Figure 11-73 shows the ribs of a vent created at an offset. You can reverse the offset direction by choosing the **Select Direction** button, as shown in Figure 11-74.

Figure 11-73 *Ribs created at an offset*

Figure 11-74 *After reversing the offset direction*

Spars Rollout

The options in this rollout (Figure 11-75) are used to specify the segments that define the spars, and the dimensional and offset values of spars. These options are discussed next.

Select 2D sketch segments that represent spars of the vent

This selection box is used to select the sketch segments that will create spars in the vent. If you have selected the options to show the preview and you select the segments for spars, you will be able to dynamically see the preview of the vent with the spars.

Figure 11-75 *The Spars rollout*

Enter the depth of the spars

This spinner is used to specify the depth of spars in the vent.

Enter the width of the spars

This spinner is used to specify the width of spars in the vent.

Enter the offset of the spars from the surface

This spinner is used to specify the value by which the spars will be offset from the face on which the vent will be created. Figure 11-76 shows a model with a vent with the ribs and spars. Note that in this model, the spars are created at an offset. You can reverse the offset direction by choosing the **Select Direction** button.

Figure 11-76 *Vent with ribs and spars*

Fill-In Boundary Rollout

The options in this rollout are used to specify a support boundary for the vent. These options are discussed next.

Select 2D sketch segments that form a closed profile to define a support boundary for the vent

This selection box is used to select the sketch segments that will create a filled feature inside the vent. Note that at least one segment of the rib should intersect the closed profile. Figure 11-77 shows the preview of a filled feature created inside the vent using a closed profile shown in the preview.

Enter the depth of the support area

This spinner is used to specify the depth of the filled area.

Figure 11-77 Preview of the filled feature

Enter the offset of the support area

This spinner is used to specify the offset value for the filled area. You can reverse the offset direction by choosing the **Select Direction** button on the right of this spinner.

CREATING FREEFORM FEATURES

CommandManager:	Features > Freeform	*(Customize to Add)*
Menu:	Insert > Features > Freeform	
Toolbar:	Features > Freeform	*(Customize to Add)*

One of the latest enhancements in this release of SolidWorks is the introduction of the **Freeform** tool. This tool allows you to create freeform features using a four-sided face of an existing feature. You can select the face of an existing feature and deform it to any freeform shape you want. Figure 11-78 shows the model of the tube before deforming the faces and Figure 11-79 shows the same tube after deforming the faces using the **Freeform** tool.

Figure 11-78 Model before deforming the face   *Figure 11-79 Model after deforming the face*

To create the freeform feature, use the following steps:

1. Create the base feature and then invoke the **Freeform** tool; the **FreeformPropertyManager** will be displayed and the **Face to deform** selection area will be active in the **Face Settings** rollout.

2. Select the face that you want to deform; the grid lines mesh will be displayed on the face.

    Next, you need to define a curve and add points to it. Using the points, you will hold the curve and deform it. The same deformation will then be applied to the selected face.

3. Choose the **Add Curves** button from the **Control Curves** rollout of the **Freeform PropertyManager**. Alternative, you can right-click and choose **Add Curve** from the shortcut menu. Next, move the cursor over the selected face; a preview of the curve, parallel to the directions of one set of mesh grid lines, will be displayed.

4. Choose the **Flip Direction (Tab)** button from the **Control Curves** rollout if you want to add curves parallel to the other set of mesh grid lines.

5. Place the one or more curves to deform the face, as shown in Figure 11-80.

6. Next, choose the **Add Points** button from the **Control Points** rollout. Alternatively, you can right-click and choose the **Add Points** option from the shortcut menu.

7. Move the cursor on the curve added and then add control points to the curve, as shown in Figure 11-81. Note that more the number of points, more precise the deformation that can be added to the face.

Figure 11-80 *Partial display of the model with a curve being added*

Figure 11-81 *Partial display of the model with points being added*

8. Right-click and choose **Add Points** again from the shortcut menu to clear this option.

9. Move the cursor over any of the points and then drag it; the selected face will be deformed.

10. Similarly, you can drag the other points to deform the face. You can also use the axes of the triad displayed on the selected control point to deform the face. Figure 11-82 shows the points being dragged to deform the face.

Figure 11-82 Dragging the points to deform the face

Whenever you select a face to deform, four callouts are displayed on it. These callouts control the continuity of the face. After dragging the points and deforming the face, you can click on the white portion of these callouts to modify the continuity of the face.

The options available in the **Freeform PropertyManager** are discussed next.

Face Settings Rollout

The options available in this rollout are discussed next.

Face to deform

This selection box is used to select the face to deform. It is active by default when you invoke the **Freeform** tool.

Direction 1 Symmetry

This check box is available only when the face selected to deform is symmetric in one direction. If you select this check box, the preview of the symmetry plane will be displayed on the selected face. Now, if you add a curve, a similar curve will be added on the other side of the symmetry plane. Also, the points added to one of the curves will be added automatically to the symmetric curve. You can drag the points on any of the symmetric curves to deform the face.

Direction 2 Symmetry

This check box is available only when the face selected to deform is symmetric in both the directions. If you select this check box, the preview of the symmetry plane in the second direction is displayed on the selected face. This option works similar to the **Direction 1 Symmetry** option.

Control Curves Rollout

The options available in this rollout are discussed next.

Control type

This area is used to set the type of control to deform the face. The default option is **Through points**. This is the reason points are added to the curve and you can use these points to deform the face. If you select the **Control polygon** option, polygons will be displayed on all control points on the curve and you can use these polygons to deform the face.

Add Curves

This button is chosen to add a curve to deform the selected face.

Flip Direction (Tab)

This button is chosen to add the curve in the other direction. You can also press the TAB key to add the curve in the other direction.

Control Points Rollout

The options available in this rollout are discussed next.

Add Points

This button is chosen to add points to the control curve. After creating the control curve, choose this button and add the control points. After adding the required control points, choose this button again to start dragging the points.

Snap to geometry

You can also create a sketched curve to match the shape of the deformed face before invoking the **Freeform** tool. If this check box is selected and you drag the control points to the points of the sketched curve, the cursor snaps to the control points of the sketched curve. This way you can match the shape of the face with that of the sketched curve. Note that to use this option, the control curve should be added close to the sketched curve. Figure 11-83 shows the control point of the curve being dragged to the control point of a spline curve.

Figure 11-83 *Dragging the points to the control point of a spline curve*

Triad orientation

This area is used to specify whether the triad will be oriented with reference to the current part file, selected surface, or the control curve. You can select the radio button of the required option.

Triad follows selection

This check box is selected to move the triad to the selected control point. If this check box is cleared, the triad will remain at its current position even if you select some other control point on the curve.

Triad X/Y/Z Direction

These spinners are available in the **Control Points** rollout when you select a point to drag. These spinners are used to move the selected control point along the X, Y, and Z directions. You can also use the thumbwheel provided below these spinners to modify the value.

Display Rollout

The options available in this rollout are discussed next.

Face transparency

This slider is used to set the transparency of the face selected to deform.

Mesh preview

This check box is used to turn on the display of the mesh on the selected surface. If this check box is selected, you can control the density of this mesh by using the slider given below this check box.

Zebra stripes

This check box is selected to display zebra stripes on the selected face. Using the zebra stripes, you can check the change in the curvature of the face.

Curvature combs

This check box is selected to display the curvature combs on the grid lines of the mesh to check the curvature of the face. You can specify the directions, curvature type, scale, and density of the grid curvature combs using the available options.

TUTORIALS

Tutorial 1

In this tutorial, you will create the plastic cover shown in Figure 11-84. The dimensions of this cover are shown in Figure 11-85. Note that a draft angle of 1-degree has to be applied to the side faces of the cover. The parameters of the mounting boss are: Boss diameter = 4.8 mm, Boss height = 14 mm, Draft angle of main boss = 2-degrees, Number of fins = 4, Height of fins = 12 mm, Width of fins = 1.5 mm, Length of fins = 4 mm, Draft angle of fins = 1-degree, Diameter of the inside hole = 2 mm, Height of the inside hole = 5 mm, Draft angle of the inside hole = 1-degree.   **(Expected time: 30 min)**

The steps to be followed to complete this tutorial are discussed next.

a. Create the base feature of the model on the **Front Plane** and extrude it using the **Mid Plane** option, see Figure 11-86.
b. Add the face draft to the side faces of the model and then create the fillets, as shown in Figure 11-87.
c. Create the shell feature and remove the top face, as shown in Figure 11-88.
d. Create the cut feature, as shown in Figure 11-89.

Figure 11-84 *Plastic cover for Tutorial 1*

Figure 11-85 *Dimensions of the plastic cover*

e. Add one of the mounting bosses and then edit its sketch to locate it using dimensions, refer to Figure 11-91.

f. Mirror the mounting boss feature on the other side, refer to Figure 11-92.

Creating the Base Feature

1. Start SolidWorks and then start a new part file.

2. Create the extruded base feature of the model on the **Front Plane** and use the **Mid Plane** option to extrude the sketch. The base feature is shown in Figure 11-86.

Adding Draft and Creating Fillets

1.   Add a draft of 1-degree to all the four vertical side faces of the model using the **Draft** tool.

2.   Add a fillet of radius 8 mm to all the sharp edges of the model, as shown in Figure 11-87.

Figure 11-86 *Base feature of the model*   *Figure 11-87* *After adding the draft and fillet*

Creating the Shell and Cut Features

1.   Create the shell feature of a wall thickness of 2 mm and remove the top face of the model, as shown in Figure 11-88.

2.   Create the extruded cut feature, as shown in Figure 11-89.

Figure 11-88 *Model after shelling*   *Figure 11-89* *After creating the cut feature*

Creating the Mounting Boss

Next, you need to create the two mounting bosses. You will create only one and then mirror it to create the other instance. After creating the mounting boss, you need to edit its sketch, which is a 3D sketch point, to place it at its exact location using dimensions.

1.   Invoke the **Mounting Boss** tool from the **Features CommandManager**; the **Mounting Boss PropertyManager** is displayed and the **Select a face or a 3D point** selection box in the **Position** rollout is highlighted.

2. Click on the horizontal face, close to the top edge, as the face to place the mounting boss; the preview of the mounting boss feature will be displayed, as shown in Figure 11-90.

3. Modify the mounting boss parameters based on the values given in the tutorial statement.

4. Click in the **Select a vector to define orientation of the fins** selection box and the select one of the bottom horizontal edges to reorient the fins in the mounting boss.

5. Choose the **OK** button from the **Mounting Boss PropertyManager**; the mounting boss will be created.

   You will notice that by default, the mounting boss is created at the point where you select the plane. You need to modify this position to locate the mounting boss. This is done by editing the sketch of the mounting boss, which is automatically created when you create the mounting boss.

6. Click on the + sign located on the left of **Mounting Boss** in the tree view to expand it. Now, right-click on the 3D sketch and choose **Edit Sketch** from the shortcut menu.

7. Locate the 3D sketch to its actual position using the **Smart Dimension** tool. Refer to Figure 11-85 for dimensions.

7. Exit the sketching environment; the mounting boss will be created and located at its proper location, as shown in Figure 11-91.

Figure 11-90 *Preview of the mounting boss*

Figure 11-91 *After creating the cut feature*

8. Using the **Mirror** tool, create the mirror image of the mounting boss. Select the **Front Plane** as the mirroring plane. The final model of the plastic cover is shown in Figure 11-92.

Saving the Model

1. Save this model with the name given below:

   My Documents\SolidWorks\c11\c11tut1.sldprt

Figure 11-92 *Final model of the plastic cover*

Tutorial 2

In this tutorial, you will create the plastic cover shown in Figure 11-93. The dimensions of this cover are shown in Figure 11-94. The fillets in Figure 11-94 are suppressed for clarity. In the lower vent, the vertical lines are ribs and the horizontal lines are spars. The other parameters of this vent are given below.

Depth of ribs = 1 mm, Width of ribs = 2 mm, Depth of spars = 0.5 mm, Width of spars = 2 mm, Offset of spars from surface = 0.5 mm.   **(Expected time: 30 min)**

Figure 11-93 *Model for Tutorial 2*

Figure 11-94 *Dimensions of the cover for Tutorial 2*

The steps to be followed to complete this tutorial are discussed next.

a.   Create the base feature of the model on the **Right Plane** and extrude it using the **Mid Plane** option, see Figure 11-95.
b.   Add the required fillets, as shown in Figure 11-96.
c.   Create the shell feature and remove the back and bottom faces, as shown in Figure 11-97.
d.   Create the first vent, as shown in Figure 11-99.
e.   Create the second vent, as shown in Figure 11-101.

Creating the Base Feature

1.   Start a new part file using the **New SolidWorks Document** dialog box.

2.   Create the base feature of the model on the **Right Plane**, as shown in Figure 11-95.

Adding Fillets

1.   Add fillets of radius 3 mm to all the sharp edges of the model, except for the edges on the bottom face. The model, after adding the fillets, is shown in Figure 11-96.

Creating the Shell Feature

1.   Next, create the shell feature with a shell thickness of 1 mm. Remove the back face and the bottom face of the model, as shown in Figure 11-97.

Figure 11-95 Base feature of the model

Figure 11-96 Model after adding fillets

Figure 11-97 Model after shelling

Creating Vents

In the given model, you need to create two vents. The first vent, which has arcs at the two ends, also has fins and spars. However, the upper vent consists only of the boundary. You will first create the lower vent.

1. Define a new work plane at an offset of 20 mm from the front face of the model.

2. Select this plane as the sketching plane and draw the sketch of the vent, as shown in Figure 11-98.

3. Exit the sketching environment and then invoke the **Vent** tool; the **Vent PropertyManager** will be displayed and the selection box in the **Boundary** rollout will be active.

4. Select the outer loop as the boundary of the vent and then select the front face of the model as the face on which the vent will be placed.

5. Select the vertical lines as ribs and then set the parameters of the ribs based on the information given in the tutorial statement.

6. Select the horizontal lines as spars and then set the parameters of the spars based on the information given in the tutorial statement.

7. Choose **OK** to exit the **Vent PropertyManager**. The model, after creating the lower vent, is shown in Figure 11-99.

Figure 11-98 Sketch for the lower vent

Figure 11-99 Model after creating the vent

8. Again, select **Plane1** as the sketching plane and draw the sketch for the second vent, as shown in Figure 11-100.

9. Exit the sketching environment and then invoke the **Vent** tool. Select the sketch as the boundary of the vent and then select the inclined face to create the vent.

10. Exit the **Vent** tool. The final model, after creating the vent, is shown in Figure 11-101.

Figure 11-100 Sketch for the upper vent

Figure 11-101 Final model

Saving the Model

1. Save this model with the name given below:

My Documents\SolidWorks\c11\c11tut2.sldprt

Tutorial 3

In this tutorial, you will create the model of the tube shown in Figure 11-102. The three sections to be used to create the base loft feature are shown in Figure 11-103. The total spacing between Sections 1 and 2 is 200 and between Sections 2 and 3 is also 200. Assume the remaining dimensions. **(Expected time: 30 min)**

Figure 11-102 Model for Tutorial 3

Figure 11-103 Sections for the base feature

The steps to be followed to complete this tutorial are discussed next.

a. Create the first section for the base feature of the model on the **Front Plane**.
b. Create a plane at an offset of 200 from the **Front Plane** and create the second section on this plane, refer to Figure 11-104.
c. Create a plane at an offset of 200 from the previous plane and create the third section on this plane, refer to Figure 11-104.
d. Create the loft feature using these three sections, refer to Figure 11-105.

e. Create the extruded feature with a draft on the front face of the base feature, refer to Figure 11-106.

f. Create the freeform feature on the top and bottom faces of the loft feature, as shown in Figures 107 through 110.

g. Create the fillet and the shell feature to complete the model, refer to Figure 11-111.

Creating the Base Feature

1. Start a new part file and draw the first section for the loft feature on the **Front Plane**, as shown in Figure 11-104.

2. Create a plane at an offset of 200 from the **Front Plane** and create the second section on it, as shown in Figure 11-104.

3. Create a plane at an offset of 200 from the previous plane and create the third section on it, as shown in Figure 11-104.

4. Using these three sections, create the loft feature, as shown in Figure 11-105.

Figure 11-104 Sections for the loft feature

Figure 11-105 The resulting loft feature

Creating the Extruded Feature

1. Draw a circle of 50 diameter on the front face of the base feature and extrude it through a distance of 50 with a draft angle of 6-degrees. The model, after creating this feature, is shown in Figure 11-106.

Figure 11-106 Model after creating the extruded feature

Creating the Freeform Feature

It is recommended that you draw a spline first and then use it to create the freeform feature by snapping to the control points of the spline,

1. Select the **Right Plane** as the sketching plane and draw a spline, as shown in Figure 11-107.

2. Choose **Insert > Features > Freeform** from the menu bar to invoke the **Freeform PropertyManager**.

3. Select the top face of the loft feature as the face to be deformed; the grid mesh is displayed on the face, as shown in Figure 11-108.

Figure 11-107 *Spline drawn to deform the face*

Figure 11-108 *The grid mesh displayed on the face*

4. Right-click and choose **Add Curves** from the shortcut menu. Add a curve below the spline curve drawn earlier.

5. Right-click and choose **Add Points** from the shortcut menu. Add the same number of control points on the curve as in the spline.

6. Right-click and choose **Add Points** again to turn off this option. Make sure the **Snap to geometry** check box is selected in the **Control Points** rollout of the **Freeform PropertyManager**.

7. Drag one of the control points to the control point of the spline; the cursor snaps to the control point of the spline. Also, observe that the face is deformed.

8. Similarly, drag all the control points to their respective control points on the spline. The model, after dragging all the control points, is shown in Figure 11-109.

9. Choose **OK** from the **PropertyManager** and then hide the display of the spline.

10. Similarly, deform the other side of the base feature. In this case, you can drag the control points arbitrarily in the 3D space. You do not need to draw the spline for this. The model, after deforming the other face, is shown in Figure 11-110.

Figure 11-109 *Dragging the control points*   **Figure 11-110** *Model after deforming the other side of the base feature*

Creating the Remaining Features

1. Create the fillet feature of radius 10 on the front edge of the base feature.

2. Create a shell feature of thickness 0.25 and remove the front face of the extruded feature. The final model of the tube is shown in Figure 11-111.

3. You can also add a twist flex and a bend flex to the tube, as shown in Figure 11-112.

Figure 11-111 *Final model of the tube*   **Figure 11-112** *Model after adding a twist and a bend flex*

Saving the Model

1. Save this model with the name given below:

    My Documents\SolidWorks\c11\c11tut3.sldprt

SELF-EVALUATION TEST

Answer the following questions and then compare your answers with those given at the end of this chapter:

1. A concave dome is the one in which the material is removed by creating a cavity in the form of a dome. (T/F)

2. The **Shape** tool is used to create freeform shapes by manipulating the faces of the models. (T/F)

3. The **Deform** tool is used to create free-style designs by manipulating the shape of the entire model or a particular portion of it. (T/F)

4. Mounting boss features cannot be used in the plastic components to accommodate fasteners. (T/F)

5. The vents may or may not have ribs and spars (T/F)

6. The _____ tool allows you to create vents in a solid model.

7. Using the _____ option, you can deform the selected body or bodies by pushing the tool bodies inside them.

8. The _____ are generally created in small plastic boxes to create a push fit type arrangement to close and open the box.

9. The _____ check box is selected to create an elliptical dome feature.

10. _____ are cut features that are created to accommodate the snap hook.

REVIEW QUESTIONS

Answer the following questions:

1. Using the _____ rollout, you can define spars in the vent feature.

2. The _____ rollout is used to specify the boundary of the vent feature.

3. The total thickness of the snap hook at its base can be defined using the _____ rollout.

4. The _____ tool is extremely useful for the packaging industry, industrial designers, and product designers.

5. You can modify the position and location of the trimming planes and the bending axis in the **Flex** tool using the _____.

6. Which tool enables you to perform freeform bending, twisting, tapering, and stretching of a selected body?

    (a) **Flex**   (b) **Indent**
    (c) **Snap Hook**   (d) **Vent**

7. Which tool is used to create a feature to accommodate the snap hook?

    (a) **Snap Hook**   (b) **Snap Groove**
    (c) **Hook**   (d) **Snap Hook Groove**

8. Which option in the **Dome PropertyManager** is used to specify the direction vector in which you need to create the dome feature?

    (a) **Direction**   (b) **Side**
    (c) **Tangent**   (d) None

9. In the **Flex** tool, which radio button is used to twist a body?

    (a) **Rotate**   (b) **Twist**
    (c) **Move**   (d) None

10. Which one of the following operations cannot be performed using the **Flex** tool?

    (a) Twisting   (b) Stretching
    (c) Tapering   (d) Aligning

EXERCISE

Exercise 1

Open the model created in Tutorial 1 and then use the **Flex** tool to twist, bend, and stretch it. Figure 11-113 shows the model after twisting.   **(Expected time: 15 min)**

Figure 11-113 *Twisted body of the plastic cover*

Answers to Self-Evaluation Test
1. T, **2.** T, **3.** T, **4.** F, **5.** T, **6. Vent**, **7. Surface push**, **8.** Snap hooks, **9. Elliptical dome**, **10.** Snap hook grooves

Assembly Modeling-I

Learning Objectives

After completing this chapter, you will be able to:
• *Create bottom-up assemblies.*
• *Add mates to assemblies.*
• *Create top-down assemblies.*
• *Move individual components.*
• *Rotate individual components.*

ASSEMBLY MODELING

An assembly design consists of two or more components assembled together at their respective work positions using parametric relations. In SolidWorks, these relations are called mates. These mates allow you to constrain the degrees of freedom of the components at their respective work positions. To proceed to the **Assembly** mode of SolidWorks, invoke the **New SolidWorks Document** dialog box and choose the **Assembly** button, as shown in Figure 12-1.

*Figure 12-1 The **New SolidWorks Document** dialog box*

Choose the **OK** button to create a new assembly document; a new SolidWorks document will be started in the **Assembly** mode and the **Insert Component PropertyManager** will be invoked, as shown in Figure 12-2.

Types of Assembly Design Approaches

In SolidWorks, the assemblies are created using two types of design approaches: bottom-up approach and the top-down approach. These design approaches are discussed next.

Bottom-up Assembly Design Approach

The bottom-up assembly design approach is the traditional and the most widely preferred approach of assembly design. In this assembly design approach, all components are created as separate part documents and are placed and referenced in the assembly as external components. In this type of approach, the components are created in the **Part** mode and saved as the *.sldprt* documents. After creating and saving all components of the assembly, you will start a new assembly document (*.sldasm*) and insert the components using the tools provided in the **Assembly** mode. After inserting, you will assemble the components using the assembly mates.

*Figure 12-2 Screen display of SolidWorks in the **Assembly** mode*

The main advantage of this assembly design approach is that because there is only a single part in the current file, the view of the part is not restricted. Therefore, this approach allows you to concentrate on the complex individual features. This approach is preferred while handling large assemblies or the assemblies with complex parts.

Top-down Assembly Design Approach

In the top-down assembly design approach, the components are created in the same assembly document, but saved as separate part files. Therefore, the top-down assembly design approach is entirely different from the bottom-up design approach. In this approach, you will start your work in the assembly document and the geometry of one part will help you define the geometry of the other.

Note
You can also create an assembly with a combination of the bottom-up and the top-down assembly approaches.

CREATING BOTTOM-UP ASSEMBLIES

As mentioned earlier, the bottom-up assemblies are those in which components are created as separate part documents in the **Part** mode. After creating the components, they are inserted in the assembly and then assembled using the assembly mates. For starting an assembly design with this approach, you first need to insert the components in the assembly. It is recommended that the first component should be placed at the origin of the assembly document. By doing this the default planes of the assembly and the part will coincide and the component will be in the same orientation as it was in the **Part** mode. When you place the first component in the assembly, that component will be fixed at its placement position. The techniques used to place the components in the assembly file are discussed next.

Placing Components in the Assembly Document

In SolidWorks, there are various options to place the components in the assembly. These options are discussed next.

Placing Components Using the Insert Component PropertyManager

CommandManager:	Assemblies > Insert Components
Menu:	Insert > Component > Existing Part/Assembly
Toolbar:	Assembly > Insert Components

When you start a new SolidWorks document in the **Assembly** mode, the **Insert Component PropertyManager** will be displayed, as shown in Figure 12-3. The **Message** rollout available in the **Insert Component PropertyManager** prompts you to select a part or an assembly and then place the component in the graphics area. When you choose the **Browse** button available in the **Part/Assembly to Insert** rollout, the **Open** dialog box will be displayed. Browse the location where the component is saved and then select the component and choose the **Open** button. The cursor will be replaced by the component cursor and the graphic preview of the component will be also displayed. The name of the selected component will be displayed in the **Open documents** selection box of the **Part/Assembly to Insert** rollout. It is recommended that the origin of the first component should be aligned with the assembly origin. To place the component origin on the assembly origin, choose the **OK** button from the **Insert Component PropertyManager**.

To place the second component, invoke the **Insert Component PropertyManager** again and choose the **Browse** button from the **Part/Assembly to Insert** rollout. Select the component from the **Open** dialog box; the cursor will be replaced by the component cursor and the preview of the component will also be displayed in the drawing area. Select a point anywhere in the drawing area to place the second component.

When you select a component to insert in the assembly, the **Thumbnail Preview** rollout will be displayed in the **Insert Component PropertyManager**. You can invoke this rollout to view the thumbnail preview of the selected component.

The **Start command when creating new assembly** check box available in the **Options** rollout is selected by default and is used to invoke the **Insert Component PropertyManager** automatically when you start a new SolidWorks assembly document. The **Graphics preview** check box available in the **Options** rollout is selected by default and is used to display the graphic preview of the component selected to be inserted.

Insert Component

Message

Select a part or assembly to insert and then place the component in the graphics area. Use the push pin to insert multiple copies of the same or different components.

Hit OK button to insert a component at the origin.

Part/Assembly to Insert

Open documents:

Browse...

Options

☑ Start command when creating new assembly
☑ Graphics preview

*Figure 12-3 The **Insert Component PropertyManager***

Tip. *To place multiple components or multiple instances of the same component, choose the **Keep Visible** button from the **Insert Component PropertyManager** and select the placement points in the drawing area to place the multiple components. The **Keep Visible** button is available on the right of the **Help** button on top of the **Message** rollout.*

*If some part documents are opened in the SolidWorks window and you start an assembly document, those parts will be listed in the **Open documents** selection box. You can directly select the names of the parts from the **Open documents** selection box and place them in the drawing area.*

Starting an Assembly From Within the Part Document

Menu:	File > Make Assembly from Part
Toolbar:	Standard > Make Assembly from Part/Assembly

Tip. *When you insert a component in the assembly, it will be displayed in the* ***FeatureManager Design Tree***. *The convention of naming the first component is* ***(f) Name of Component <1>***. *In this convention (f) denotes that the component is fixed. You cannot move a fixed component. You will learn more about fixed and floating components later in this chapter. Next, the name of the component is displayed. After the name of the component,* ***<1>*** *symbol is displayed. This denotes the serial number of the same component in the entire assembly.*

The (-) symbol implies that the component is floating and is under-defined. You need to apply the required mates to the component to fully define it. You will learn more about assembly mates later in this chapter.

The (+) symbol implies that the component is over-defined.

If no symbol appears before the name of the component, the component will be fully defined.

You can also start an assembly document from within the part document. If the part document of the base component of the assembly is opened, choose the **Make Assembly from Part/Assembly** button from the **Standard** toolbar or choose **File > Make Assembly from Part** from the menu bar. You can also use CTRL+A on the keyboard as the shortcut key. If the **New SolidWorks Document** dialog box is invoked, choose the **OK** button from this dialog box. An assembly document will be started and the **Insert Component PropertyManager** will be invoked. Choose the **OK** button from this **PropertyManager** to place the component at the origin.

Note

If the last time you invoked the ***New SolidWorks Document*** *dialog box in the novice mode, you just need to select the* ***OK*** *button from the* ***New SolidWorks Document*** *dialog box, if it is displayed while creating an assembly from a part document. If you used the* ***New SolidWorks Document*** *in the advanced mode last time, you first need to select the assembly template and then choose the* ***OK*** *button. When you choose the* ***Make Assembly from Part/Assembly*** *button and if a* ***SolidWorks*** *warning box is displayed, choose* ***No*** *from the warning box. The* ***New SolidWorks Document*** *dialog box will be displayed in the advanced mode.*

Placing Components Using the Opened Document Window

Another most widely used method of placing components in the assembly is the use of currently opened part or assembly documents. For example, the assembly that you are going to create consists of three components. Open the part document of the part that you want to insert and then start a new assembly document. Close the **Insert Component PropertyManager**. Now, choose **Window > Tile Horizontally** or **Tile Vertically** from the menu bar; all SolidWorks document windows will be tiled vertically or horizontally, depending on the option selected. You first need to place the first component in the assembly, at the origin. If the origin is not displayed by default in the assembly document, choose **View > Origins** from the menu bar. Now, move the cursor on the component in the drawing window. Press and hold the left mouse button down on the name of the component in the **FeatmreManager Design Tree** and drag the cursor to the assembly origin in the assembly window. When the coincident symbol appears

Tip. *Only the information about the mates is stored in the assembly file. The feature information of parts is stored in the individual part files. Therefore, the size of the assembly file is small.*

It is recommended that all parts of an assembly should be saved in the folder in which the assembly is saved. This is because if the location of the parts is changed, the component will not be displayed in the assembly and it will show errors.

below the component cursor, release the left mouse button. If the **Mate** pop-up toolbar is displayed, choose the **Add/Finish Mate** button to place the component in the assembly. Similarly, place the other components in the assembly. Figure 12-4 displays placing the first component from an opened document window to the assembly document window. If another existing assembly document is opened, you can also drag and drop the part from that assembly document.

Figure 12-4 *Placing a component in the assembly file from an existing window*

Placing Components by Dragging From Windows Explorer

You can also place components in the assembly document by dragging them from the Windows Explorer. Open Windows Explorer and browse to the location where the part documents are saved. Tile the Windows Explorer window and the SolidWorks window such that you can view both windows. Move the cursor on the icon of the part document in the Windows Explorer. Press and hold the left mouse button down and drag the cursor to the assembly document window. Release the left mouse button at the origin of the assembly document to coincide the origin of the part with that of the assembly document. Figure 12-5 shows the part being dropped in the assembly window.

Figure 12-5 *Dropping the part from Windows Explorer to the assembly window*

Placing Components From Internet Explorer

You can also place the components from Internet Explorer. You need Internet Explorer 4.0 or a later version. Browse the location of the SolidWorks part file link on the Web. Drag the hyperlink and drop it in the drawing area of the assembly document. The **Save As** dialog box will be displayed; save the part document at the desired location.

Placing Additional Instances of an Existing Component in the Assembly

Sometimes you need more than one instance of the component to be placed in the assembly document. To do so, press and hold the CTRL key down on the keyboard. Now, select the component in the assembly file and drag the cursor to the location where you want to place the instance of the selected component. Release the left mouse button to drop the new instance of the component. Similarly, you can place as many copies of the existing component as you want by following the above-mentioned procedure.

Placing the Component Using the Feature Palette Window

You can also place a component in the assembly file from the **Feature Palette** window. If you have saved the component in the **Feature Palette** window, you can place that component by dragging and dropping from this window. The **Feature Palette** window is invoked by choosing **Tools > Feature Palette** from the menu bar.

Assembling Components

After placing the components in the assembly document, you need to assemble them. By assembling the components, you will constrain their degrees of freedom. As mentioned earlier, the components are assembled using mates. Mates help you precisely place and position the component with respect to the other components and the surroundings in the assembly. You can also define the linear and rotatory movement of the component with respect to the other components. In addition, you can create a dynamic mechanism and check its stability by precisely defining the combination of mates. There are two methods of adding mates to the assembly. The first method is using the **Mate PropertyManager** and the second and the most widely used method of adding mates to the assembly is using the **Smart Mates**. Both methods are discussed next.

Assembling Components Using the Mate PropertyManager

CommandManager:	Assemblies > Mate
Menu:	Insert > Mate
Toolbar:	Assembly > Mate

In SolidWorks, mates can be applied using the **Mate PropertyManager**. Choose the **Mate** button available in the **Assemblies CommandManager** or choose **Insert > Mate** from the menu bar; the **Mate PropertyManager** will be invoked, as shown in Figure 12-6.

Select a planar face, curved face, axis, or point on the first component and then select the entity from the second component. The selected entities will be highlighted in green. The names of the selected entities will be displayed in the **Entities to Mate** selection box of the **Mate Selections** rollout. The **Mate** pop-up toolbar will be invoked, as shown in Figure 12-7. The most suitable mates to be applied to the current selection set are displayed in the **Mate** pop-up toolbar and in the **Standard Mates** rollout of the **Mate PropertyManager**. The most appropriate mate is selected by default. The preview of the assembly using the most appropriate mate is displayed in the drawing area. You can also select the mates from the given list of the mates that can be applied to the current selection set. As you select some other mate from the **Mate** pop-up toolbar, the preview of the assembly will be displayed using the newly selected mate. Now, choose the **Add/Finish Mate** button from the **Mate** pop-up toolbar; the **Mate PropertyManager** will still be displayed, and you can add other mates to the assembly. After adding all the mates, choose the **OK** button from the **Mate PropertyManager**. Various types of mates that can be applied are discussed next.

*Figure 12-6 The **Mate** PropertyManager*

*Figure 12-7 The **Mate** pop-up toolbar*

Coincident

The **Coincident** mate is applied to make two planar faces coplanar. But you can also apply the **Coincident** mate to other entities. The details of the geometries on which the **Coincident** mate can be applied are shown in Figure 12-8.

When you choose the **Coincident** button from the **Mate** pop-up toolbar, the preview of the model will be displayed according to the current selection of the mate. Also, the model will be assembled in aligned or anti-aligned direction, depending on the current orientation of the model. You can modify the orientation of the assembled component by choosing the **Aligned** or **Anti-Aligned** button from the **Standard Mates** rollout. You can also choose the **Flip Mate Alignment** button from the **Mate** pop-up toolbar to modify the mate alignment. Figure 12-9 shows the faces to be selected to apply the coincident mate. Figure 12-10 shows the resulting mate applied with the **Anti-Aligned** option selected. Figure 12-11 shows the coincident mate applied with the **Aligned** option selected.

ASSEMBLY MATE COMBINATIONS (USING COINCIDENT MATE)		Second Component									
		Cone	Cylinder	Line	Point	Sphere	Circular/ Arc Edge	Extrusion	Surface	Plane	Cam
First Component	Cylinder	X	X	✓	✓	X	✓	X	X	X	X
	Sphere	X	X	X	✓	X	X	X	X	X	X
	Cone	✓	X	X	✓	X	✓	X	X	X	X
	Circular/ Arc Edge	X	✓	X	X	X	✓	X	X	✓	X
	Line	X	✓	✓	✓	X	X	X	X	✓	X
	Point	X	✓	✓	✓	✓	X	✓	✓	✓	✓
	Extrusion	X	X	X	✓	X	X	X	X	X	X
	Surface	X	X	X	✓	X	X	X	X	X	X
	Plane	X	X	✓	✓	X	✓	X	X	✓	X

Figure 12-8 *Table displaying the combinations for applying the **Coincident** mate*

Figure 12-9 *Faces to be selected*

Concentric

The **Concentric** mate is used to align the central axis of one component with that of the other. You need to select the circular faces or circular edges to apply the concentric mate. You can also apply the **Concentric** mate between a point and a circular face or a circular edge. The other combinations of applying the **Concentric** mate are displayed in the table given in Figure 12-12. For applying a **Concentric** mate, invoke the **Mate PropertyManager**. Select circular faces or edges from two different components; the names of the selected entities will be displayed in the **Entities to Mate** selection box. The **Concentric** button will be chosen in the **Mate** pop-up toolbar. If this button is not chosen by default, you need to manually choose it. The preview of the models being assembled, after applying this mate, will be displayed in the graphics area. You can choose the **Aligned** and **Anti-Aligned** buttons on the basis of the design requirement. Finally, choose the **Add/ Finish Mate** button from the **Mate** pop-up toolbar.

Figure 12-10 *The **Coincident** mate applied with the **Anti-Aligned** button selected*

Figure 12-11 *The **Coincident** mate applied with the **Aligned** button selected*

ASSEMBLY MATE COMBINATIONS (USING CONCENTRIC MATE)		Second Component									
		Cone	Cylinder	Line	Point	Sphere	Circular/Arc Edge	Extrusion	Surface	Plane	Cam
First Component	Cylinder	✓	✓	✓	✓	✓	✓	✗	✗	✗	✗
	Sphere	✗	✓	✓	✓	✓	✗	✗	✗	✗	✗
	Cone	✓	✓	✓	✓	✗	✓	✗	✗	✗	✗
	Circular/Arc Edge	✗	✓	✓	✗	✗	✓	✗	✗	✗	✗
	Line	✓	✓	✗	✗	✓	✓	✗	✗	✗	✗
	Point	✓	✓	✗	✗	✓	✗	✗	✗	✗	✗
	Extrusion	✗	✗	✗	✗	✗	✗	✗	✗	✗	✗
	Surface	✗	✗	✗	✗	✗	✗	✗	✗	✗	✗
	Plane	✗	✗	✗	✗	✗	✗	✗	✗	✗	✗

Figure 12-12 *Table displaying the combinations for applying the **Concentric** mate*

Figure 12-13 shows the faces to be selected to apply the concentric mate. Figure 12-14 shows the **Concentric** mate applied with the **Aligned** button chosen and Figure 12-15 shows the **Concentric** mate applied with the **Anti-Aligned** button chosen.

Distance

The **Distance** button is chosen to apply the **Distance** mate between two components. To apply this mate, invoke the **Mate PropertyManager** and select the entities from both components. Choose the **Distance** button from the **Mate** pop-up toolbar; the **Distance** spinner will be displayed in the **Mate** pop-up toolbar. Set the value of the distance in the **Distance** spinner. The preview of the assembly will be updated automatically after you set the value of the distance. Using the **Flip dimension** check box available below the **Distance** spinner, you can reverse the direction of the mate. If needed, you can choose the

Figure 12-13 *Faces to be selected*

Figure 12-14 *The **Concentric** mate applied with the **Aligned** button selected*

Figure 12-15 *The **Concentric** mate applied with the **Anti-Aligned** button selected*

Aligned button or the **Anti-Aligned** button. Figure 12-16 shows the combinations of components to apply the **Distance** mate. Figure 12-17 shows the faces to be selected and Figure 12-18 shows the **Distance** mate applied between two components.

Angle

 The **Angle** button is used to apply the **Angle** mate between two components. This mate is used to specify the angular position between the selected plane, planar face, or edges of the two components. To apply this mate, invoke the **Mate PropertyManager** and select the entities from the two components. Choose the **Angle** button from the **Mate** pop-up toolbar. The preview of the models will be modified with the default value of the angle. Also, the **Angle** spinner will be invoked and you can set the value of the angle in this spinner. You can also change the angle direction using the **Flip Dimension** button provided on the right of the angle spinner. You can choose the **Aligned** button and

ASSEMBLY MATE COMBINATIONS (USING DISTANCE MATE)		Second Component									
		Cone	Cylinder	Line	Point	Sphere	Plane	Extrusion	Surface	Circular/ Arc Edge	Cam
First Component	Cylinder	✕	✓	✓	✓	✕	✓	✕	✕	✕	✕
	Sphere	✕	✕	✓	✓	✓	✕	✕	✕	✕	✕
	Cone	✓	✕	✕	✕	✕	✕	✕	✕	✕	✕
	Plane	✕	✓	✓	✓	✓	✓	✕	✕	✕	✕
	Line	✕	✓	✓	✓	✓	✓	✕	✕	✕	✕
	Point	✕	✓	✓	✓	✓	✓	✕	✕	✕	✕
	Extrusion	✕	✕	✕	✕	✕	✕	✕	✕	✕	✕
	Surface	✕	✕	✕	✕	✕	✕	✕	✕	✕	✕
	Circular/ Arc Edge	✕	✕	✕	✕	✕	✕	✕	✕	✕	✕

Figure 12-16 Table displaying the combinations for applying the Distance mate

Figure 12-17 Selecting the faces to apply the Distance mate

Figure 12-18 The Distance mate applied to the selected faces

the **Anti-Aligned** button on the basis of the design requirement. After adding the mate, choose the **Add/Finish Mate** button from the **Mate** pop-up toolbar. Figure 12-19 shows the table of combinations for applying the **Angle** mate.

Figure 12-20 shows the faces to be selected to apply the **Angular** mate and Figure 12-21 shows the assembly after applying the **Angular** mate with the angle value of 90-degrees.

Parallel

 The **Parallel** button available in the **Mate** pop-up toolbar is used to apply the **Parallel** mate between two components. To apply the **Parallel** mate, invoke the **Mate PropertyManager** and select the two entities from the two components. Choose the **Parallel** button from the **Mate** pop-up toolbar to apply the mate. You can also choose the **Align** button and the **Anti-Aligned** button. After applying the mate, choose the **Add/Finish**

ASSEMBLY MATE COMBINATIONS (USING ANGLE MATE)		Second Component									
		Cylinder	Extrusion	Line	Plane	Sphere	Circular/Arc Edge	Cone	Surface	Point	Cam
First Component	Cylinder	✓	✓	✓	✗	✗	✗	✗	✗	✗	✗
	Extrusion	✓	✓	✓	✗	✗	✗	✗	✗	✗	✗
	Line	✓	✓	✓	✗	✗	✗	✗	✗	✗	✗
	Plane	✗	✗	✗	✓	✗	✗	✗	✗	✗	✗
	Sphere	✗	✗	✗	✗	✗	✗	✗	✗	✗	✗
	Circular/Arc Edge	✗	✗	✗	✗	✗	✗	✗	✗	✗	✗
	Cone	✓	✓	✓	✗	✗	✗	✓	✗	✗	✗
	Point	✗	✗	✗	✗	✗	✗	✗	✗	✗	✗
	Surface	✗	✗	✗	✗	✗	✗	✗	✗	✗	✗

Figure 12-19 Table displaying the combinations for applying the **Angle** mate

Figure 12-20 Faces to be selected to apply the **Angle** mate

Figure 12-21 Assembly after applying the **Angle** mate

Mate button from the **Mate** pop-up toolbar. Figure 12-22 shows the combinations to components on which you can apply the **Parallel** mate. Figure 12-23 shows the entities to be selected to apply the **Parallel** mate and Figure 12-24 shows the assembly after applying the **Parallel** mate.

Perpendicular

The **Perpendicular** button available in the **Mate Settings** rollout is used to apply the **Perpendicular** mate between two components. Invoke the **Mate PropertyManager** and select two entities from the two components. Choose the **Perpendicular** button from the **Mate** pop-up toolbar. You can also toggle between the **Aligned** button and the **Anti-Aligned** button. Choose the **Add/Finish Mate** button from the **Mate**

ASSEMBLY MATE COMBINATIONS (USING PARALLEL MATE)		Second Component									
		Cylinder	Extrusion	Line	Plane	Sphere	Circular/Arc Edge	Cone	Surface	Point	Cam
First Component	Cylinder	✓	✓	✓	✗	✗	✗	✗	✗	✗	✗
	Extrusion	✓	✓	✓	✗	✗	✗	✗	✗	✗	✗
	Line	✓	✓	✓	✓	✗	✗	✗	✗	✗	✗
	Plane	✗	✗	✓	✓	✗	✗	✗	✗	✗	✗
	Circular/Arc Edge	✗	✗	✗	✗	✗	✗	✗	✗	✗	✗
	Sphere	✗	✗	✗	✗	✗	✗	✗	✗	✗	✗
	Cone	✓	✓	✓	✗	✗	✗	✓	✗	✗	✗
	Surface	✗	✗	✗	✗	✗	✗	✗	✗	✗	✗

Figure 12-22 *Table displaying the combinations for applying the **Parallel** mate*

Figure 12-23 *Faces to be selected to apply the* ***Parallel*** *mate*

Figure 12-24 *Assembly after applying the **Parallel** mate*

pop-up toolbar. Figure 12-25 shows the table displaying the combinations for applying the **Perpendicular** mate. Figure 12-26 shows the entities to be selected and Figure 12-27 shows the **Perpendicular** mate applied to the assembly.

ASSEMBLY MATE COMBINATIONS (USING PERPENDICULAR MATE)		Second Component									
		Cylinder	Extrusion	Line	Plane	Sphere	Circular/Arc Edge	Cone	Surface	Point	Cam
First Component	Cylinder	✓	✓	✓	✗	✗	✗	✗	✗	✗	✗
	Extrusion	✓	✓	✓	✗	✗	✗	✗	✗	✗	✗
	Line	✓	✓	✓	✓	✗	✗	✗	✗	✗	✗
	Plane	✗	✗	✓	✓	✗	✗	✗	✗	✗	✗
	Circular/Arc Edge	✗	✗	✗	✗	✗	✗	✗	✗	✗	✗
	Sphere	✗	✗	✗	✗	✗	✗	✗	✗	✗	✗
	Cone	✓	✓	✓	✗	✗	✗	✓	✗	✗	✗
	Surface	✗	✗	✗	✗	✗	✗	✗	✗	✗	✗

Figure 12-25 *Table displaying the combinations for applying the* **Perpendicular** *mate*

Figure 12-26 *Faces to be selected to apply the* **Perpendicular** *mate*

Figure 12-27 *Assembly after applying the* **Perpendicular** *mate*

Tangent

 The **Tangent** button available in the **Mate** pop-up toolbar is used to apply the **Tangent** mate between two components. Figure 12-28 shows the table displaying the combinations for applying the tangent mate. Figure 12-29 shows the entities to be selected to apply the **Tangent** mate and Figure 12-30 shows the **Tangent** mate applied to the assembly.

 Note
*The **Advanced Mates** are discussed in the next chapter.*

ASSEMBLY MATE COMBINATIONS (USING TANGENT MATE)		Second Component								
		Cone	Cylinder	Line	Point	Sphere	Plane	Surface	Cam	Extrusion
First Component	Cylinder	✓	✓	✓	X	✓	✓	✓	✓	✓
	Sphere	✓	✓	✓	X	✓	✓	X	X	X
	Cone	X	X	X	X	✓	✓	X	X	X
	Plane	X	✓	X	X	✓	X	✓	✓	✓
	Line	X	✓	✓	✓	✓	✓	✓	✓	✓
	Extrusion	X	✓	X	X	X	✓	X	X	X
	Surface	X	✓	X	X	X	✓	X	X	X
	Cam	X	X	X	X	X	X	X	X	X

Figure 12-28 *Table displaying the combinations for applying the* **Tangent** *mate*

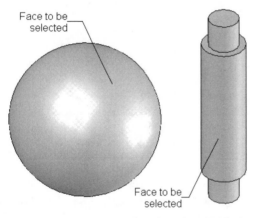

Figure 12-29 *Entities to be selected to apply the* **Tangent** *mate*

Figure 12-30 *Assembly after applying the* **Tangent** *mate*

Creating Multiple Mates

One of the enhancements in this release of SolidWorks is that it allows you to create multiple mates to a common reference. For example, refer to the Base Plate shown in Figure 12-31. There are four Nuts to be assembled with the Base Plate. After applying the concentric mate, you need to apply a coincident mate to the bottom face of the heads of the Bolts and the top face of the Base Plate. You can apply all these mates together using the **Multiple mate mode** option. To use this option, choose the **Multiple mate mode** button available on the left of the **Entities to Mate** selection box in the **Mate Selections** rollout. When you choose this button, the **Common reference** and **Component references** selection areas are displayed. The **Common reference** selection area is highlighted by default. Therefore, you need to select the common reference. In this case, select the top face of the Base Plate. As soon as you select the common reference, the **Component references** selection area will be highlighted. Next, select the bottom face of the head of one of the Bolts; the **Mate** pop-up toolbar will be displayed. You can select the required mate type from this toolbar. Similarly, select the faces of the other Bolts also to apply the mate with the common face. Figure 12-31 shows the top face of the Base Plate selected as the common reference and the four Bolts to be assembled. Figure 12-32 shows the assembly after applying the coincident mate to the bottom faces of the heads of the Bolts and the top face of the Base Plate.

Figure 12-31 *Top face of the Base Plate selected as the common reference*

Figure 12-32 *Assembly after applying multiple mates*

The remaining options available in the **Mate PropertyManager** are discussed next.

Mates
The **Mates** rollout is used to display the mates that are applied between the selected entities.

Options
The **Add to new folder** check box available in this rollout is used to add the currently applied mate in a folder. This folder is placed in the **Mates** mategroup in the **FeatureManager Design Tree**. You can also drag and drop the other mates from the **Mates** mategroup in the newly created folder. The **Show popup dialog** check box is selected by default and is used to display the **Mate** pop-up toolbar. The **Show preview** check box is selected by default and is used to display the dynamic preview of the assembly as you apply the mates to the components. The **Use for positioning only** check box is used only to define the position of the component by applying the mate. This mate is displayed in the **Mates** rollout, but when you exit the **Mate PropertyManager**, this mate will not be displayed in the **Mates** mategroup in the **FeatureManager Design Tree**.

Assembling Components Using the Smart Mates
Smart Mates is the most attractive feature of the assembly design environment of SolidWorks. The **Smart Mates** technology speeds up the design process in the assembly environment of SolidWorks. To add smart mates to the components, choose the **Move Component** button from the **Assembly CommandManager**; the **Move Component PropertyManager** will be displayed.

Now, choose the **SmartMates** button available in the **Move** rollout; the **Move Component PropertyManager** will be replaced by the **SmartMates PropertyManager,** as shown in Figure 12-33. Also, the select cursor will be replaced by the move cursor.

Figure 12-33 The SmartMates PropertyManager

Next, double-click on the entity of the first component to add a mate; the component will appear transparent and the cursor will be replaced by the smart mates cursor. Press and hold the left mouse button down on the selected entity and drag the cursor to the entity with which you want to mate the previously selected entity. The symbol of the constraint that can be applied between the two entities will be displayed below the smart mates cursor. You can use the TAB key to toggle between the aligned and anti-aligned options while applying **Smart Mates**. When the symbol of the mate is displayed below the cursor, release the left mouse button; the **Mate** pop-up toolbar will be displayed. Choose the **Add/Finish Mate** button from this toolbar. Figure 12-34 shows the face to be selected to apply a smart mate and Figure 12-35 shows the component being dragged.

Figure 12-34 *Face to be selected to apply a smart mate*

Figure 12-35 *Component being dragged to apply a smart mate*

Figure 12-36 shows that the concentric symbol appears below the smart mates cursor when the cursor is placed near a circular face of the other component.

Figure 12-36 *Concentric symbol appears below the smart mates cursor*

Figure 12-37 shows a planar face selected to apply a smart mate. You can use the TAB key to toggle between the aligned and anti-aligned mates. Figure 12-38 shows that the coincident symbol appears below the cursor and Figure 12-39 shows the assembly after applying the **Coincident** mate using the smart mate.

Figure 12-37 *Planar face to be selected to apply a mate using smart mates*

Figure 12-38 *Coincident symbol appears after dragging the component near another planar face*

Figure 12-39 *The **Coincident** mate applied to the*
assembly using smart mates

Tip. *You can also add smart mates without dragging the component. To add a smart mate without dragging, invoke the **Smart Mates** tool. Double-click on the entity from the first component. The component will be displayed as transparent. Now, select the entity from the second component. The preview with the most appropriate mate will be displayed and the **Mate** pop-up toolbar is invoked.*

Note
*To apply smart mates without invoking the **SmartMates** tool, press and hold the ALT key down and select the entity of the first component. Drag the component to the entity of the other component to which you need to apply the mate. As you release the left mouse button, the **Mate** pop-up toolbar will be displayed. Choose the **Add/Finish Mate** button from this toolbar.*

When you drag a component for applying a smart mate, the selected entity of the first component will snap all corresponding entities of the second component. You can press the ALT key on the keyboard to exit the snap. To enter the snap mode again, press the ALT key on the key board.

Geometry-based Mates

In the assembly design environment of SolidWorks, you can also add geometry-based mates. Geometry-based mates are also a type of smart mates and are applied while you are placing a component in the assembly environment. Consider a case in which the first component is already placed in the assembly environment. Now, open the part document of the second component. Choose **Window > Tile Horizontal** or **Tile Vertical** from the menu bar.

Suppose you need to insert the revolved feature of the second component in the circular slot of the first component and at the same time align the larger bottom face of the second component with the upper face of the first component. To do so, press and hold the left mouse button down on the edge of the second component, as shown in Figure 12-40. Drag the cursor to the assembly window near the upper edge of the circular slot of the first component; the second component mated with the first component will be displayed in temporary graphics, as shown in Figure 12-41. The coincident symbol will also be displayed below the smart mates cursor.

Figure 12-40 *Edge of the second component to be selected.*

Figure 12-41 *Component being dragged into the assembly window for applying geometry-based mates*

You can also toggle the direction of placement of the component. Figure 12-42 shows that the direction of placement is flipped using the TAB key. Again, press the TAB key to return to the default direction. Release the left mouse button to place the component. On expanding the **Mates** option from the **FeatureManager Design Tree**, you will notice that two mates are applied to the assembly; one is the coincident mate and the other is the concentric mate. Figure 12-43 shows the assembly after adding the geometry-based smart mates.

Figure 12-42 *The placement direction of component is flipped using the TAB key*

Figure 12-43 *Assembly after adding a geometry-based mate*

Tip. *You can add the geometry-based mates between two linear edges, two planar faces, two vertices, two conical faces, two axes, between an axis and a conical face, and between two circular edges.*

Feature-based Mates

In the assembly design environment of SolidWorks, you can also add feature-based mates. For adding feature-based mates, one of the features of the first component must be a circular base or boss feature and the second component must have a hole or a circular cut feature. The feature can be an extruded or a revolved feature. Also, in the assembly document, one of the parts must be placed earlier. Open the part document of the component to be placed using feature-based mates and tile both document windows. In the **FeatureManager Design Tree** of the part document, select the extruded or revolved feature and drag it to the assembly window. Place the cursor at a location where you need to place the component. You can also change the alignment or direction of placement using the TAB key. Release the left mouse button to drop the component. Figure 12-44 shows the component being dragged by selecting the revolved feature from the **FeatureManager Design Tree** of the part document.

Figure 12-44 *Component being dragged by selecting the revolved feature*

Figure 12-45 shows the resulting component assembled using feature-based mates.

Pattern-based Mates

Pattern-based mates are used to assemble the components that have a circular pattern created on the circular feature. The best example for these type of components is the flange or a shaft coupling.

Figure 12-45 *Component assembled using the feature-based mates*

Tip. *The feature-based mates are applied only to the components having cylindrical or conical features. You cannot add feature-based mates using features other than cylindrical or conical geometry. If you are adding feature-based mates to a component having a conical face, the second component also must have a conical face. You cannot add a feature-based mate if the geometry of the feature of one component is cylindrical and that of the other is conical.*

If you are adding feature-based mates using the features having conical geometry, there must be a planar face adjacent to the conical face of both features.

Remember that to create pattern-based mates, all components that will be assembled must have a circular pattern on the mating faces. To create pattern-based mates, select the outer edge of the second component and drag it to the circular edge of the first component that is already placed in the assembly document. The preview of the component assembled with the first component will be displayed. Using the TAB key, you can switch the part with respect to the pattern instances. Release the left mouse button to drop the part. Figure 12-46 shows the component being dragged to the assembly document window. Figure 12-47 shows the preview of the component being assembled and Figure 12-48 shows the component assembled using pattern-based mates.

Assembling Components Using the Mate Reference

CommandManager:	Reference Geometry > Mate Reference *(Customize to Add)*
Menu:	Insert > Reference Geometry > Mate Reference
Toolbar:	Reference Geometry > Mate Reference *(Customize to Add)*

In SolidWorks, you can define the mate reference to the part in the **Part** mode or in the **Assembly** mode. The mate references allow you to define the mating references such as planar surfaces, axis, edges, and so on before assembling the component.

The mate references are created using the **Mate Reference PropertyManager**, which is invoked by choosing the **Mate Reference** button from the **Reference Geometry Command** after customizing it. The **Mate Reference PropertyManager** is shown in Figure 12-49.

Figure 12-46 *Component being dragged into the assembly document*

Figure 12-47 *Preview of the component being assembled using pattern-based mates*

Figure 12-48 *Component assembled using pattern-based mates*

The **Mate Reference Name** edit box is used to define the name of the mate reference. The **Primary Reference Entity** rollout is used to define the primary mate reference. The **Mate Reference Type** drop-down list is used to define the type of mate. The **Mate Reference Alignment** drop-down list is used to define the type of alignment.

The **Secondary Reference Entity** rollout is used to define the secondary mate reference. The **Tertiary Reference Entity** rollout is used to define the tertiary mate reference.

*Figure 12-49 The **Mate Reference PropertyManager***

To assemble a component using the mate reference, you need to define the mate references for two components. Also, the names of the mate references should be the same for both components. After defining the mate references for both components, place the first component coincident with the origin in the assembly document. Now, drag the second component in the assembly document and you will notice that the second component is aligned to the references that were defined as mate references. Therefore, you do not need to apply mates in the assembly environment.

CREATING TOP-DOWN ASSEMBLIES

As mentioned earlier, top-down assemblies are the assemblies in which all components are created in the same assembly file. However, to create the components, you require an environment in which you can draw the sketches of the sketched features and then convert them into features. In other words, you need a sketching environment and a part modeling environment in the assembly file. In SolidWorks, you can invoke the sketching environment and the part modeling environment in the assembly document itself. The basic procedure for creating the components in the assembly, or in other words, the procedure for creating the top-down assembly is discussed next.

Creating Components in the Top-down Assembly

CommandManager:	Assemblies > New Part	*(Customize to Add)*
Menu:	Insert > Component > New Part	
Toolbar:	Assembly > New Part	*(Customize to Add)*

Before creating the first component in the top-down assembly, you first need to save the assembly document. To do so, after starting a new assembly document, choose the **Save** button from the **Standard** toolbar to save the assembly file. It is recommended that you create a new folder and save the assembly file and the other referenced file in the same folder.

Now, choose the **New Part** button from the **Assemblies CommandManager** after customizing it. The **Save As** dialog box will be displayed where you need to specify the name and location to save the new component. Enter the name of the new component in the **File name** edit box and choose the **Save** button. The select cursor will be replaced by the new component cursor. Now, you need to place the new component in the assembly document. Using the left mouse button, place the component on the **Front** assembly plane, which is displayed in the **FeatureManager Design Tree**. The plane on which you place the component is selected as the sketching plane and the sketching environment is invoked automatically. You will notice that the **Edit Part** button available in the **Assemblies CommandManager** is selected. This means that the part modeling environment is invoked in the assembly document. You can draw the sketch of the base feature in the current sketching environment or you can also exit the sketching environment and select any other sketching plane to create the sketch. After creating the sketch of the base feature, exit the sketching environment. Now, as the **Features CommandManager** is not available by default, you need to invoke it and use the tools available in the **Features CommandManager** to convert the sketch into a model. Similarly, create the remaining features in the model.

After creating all the features, choose the **Edit Part** button from the **Assembly** toolbar to exit the part modeling environment. The newly created component will have an **Inplace** mate with the default assembly plane on which it was placed earlier. Therefore, the newly created component is fixed. Using the procedure mentioned above, create other components.

Whenever you create a component in a top-down assembly, the component is fixed using the **Inplace** mate. You can delete this mate by selecting the **Inplace** mate by expanding the **Mates** option available in the **FeatureManager Design Tree**. After selecting the mate, press the DELETE key. Now, this component is floating and you can move it. You can also assemble this component according to your requirement. You will learn more about fixed and floating components later in this chapter.

Note

*As discussed earlier, when you place the first component in the assembly in the bottom-up assembly design approach, it is fixed by default. Therefore, you cannot apply any mates to a fixed component. To add some mates to the fixed component, you first need to float the component. To do so, select the component from the drawing area or from the **FeatureManager Design Tree**. Right-click to invoke the shortcut menu and choose the **Float** option.*

*By default, the components placed after the first component are floating components. If you need to fix a floating component, select the component and invoke the shortcut menu. Choose the **Fix** option from the shortcut menu.*

MOVING INDIVIDUAL COMPONENTS

In SolidWorks, you can move the individual unconstrained components in the assembly document without affecting the position and location of the other components. There are three methods of moving an individual component. Two methods of moving the individual component are discussed next. The third method is discussed later in this chapter.

Moving Individual Components by Dragging

In the **Assembly** mode of SolidWorks, you can move the component placed in the assembly without invoking any tool. To move an individual component, simply select the component and drag the cursor to move the component. Release the left mouse button to place the component at the desired location.

Moving Individual Components Using the Move Component Tool

CommandManager:	Assemblies > Move Component
Toolbar:	Assembly > Move Component

You can also move an individual component using the **Move Component** tool. Choose the **Move Component** button from the **Assemblies CommandManager t**o invoke the **Move Component PropertyManager** is invoked. You will notice that the **Free Drag** option is selected in the **Move** drop-down list in the **Move** rollout. You will be prompted to select a component and drag to move it. The select cursor will be replaced by the move cursor; select the component and drag the cursor to move the component. Release the left mouse button to move the component to the desired location. The other options available in the **Move** drop-down list to move the component are discussed next.

Along Assembly XYZ

Using the **Along Assembly XYZ** option from the **Move** drop-down list, you can move the component dynamically along the X, Y, and Z axes of the assembly document. Select the **Along Assembly XYZ** option from the **Move** drop-down list in the **Move** rollout. An assembly coordinate system in magenta will be displayed in the drawing area and you will be prompted to select a component and drag parallel to an assembly axis to move along that axis. Select the component and drag the cursor to move the component along any one of the assembly axes.

Along Entity

The **Along Entity** option is used to move the component along the direction of the selected entity. When you invoke this option, the **Selected item** selection box will be displayed. You will be prompted to select an entity to drag along, then select a component and drag to move it. Select an entity to define the direction to move the component. The name of the selected entity is displayed in the **Selected item** selection box. Now, select the component and drag the cursor to move the component along the direction of the selected entity.

By Delta XYZ

The **By Delta XYZ** option available in the **Move** drop-down list is used to move the selected component to a given distance in a specified direction. When you select this option, the **Delta X**, **Delta Y**, and **Delta Z** spinners will be invoked and you will be prompted to select a component and enter the distance to move in the PropertyManager. An assembly coordinate system will also be displayed in magenta. Select the component to move and specify the distance in the respective direction spinners in the X, Y, or Z direction. Choose the **Apply** button to move the component.

To XYZ Position

The **To XYZ Position** option is used to specify the coordinates of the origin of the part where the component will be placed after moving. When you select this option, the **X Coordinate**, **Y Coordinate**, and **Z Coordinate** spinners will be invoked and you will be prompted to select a component and enter the X, Y, Z coordinates for the part's origin. An assembly coordinate system will also be displayed in magenta. Select the component and enter the respective coordinates of the part origin in the spinners and choose the **Apply** button to move the component.

ROTATING INDIVIDUAL COMPONENTS

In SolidWorks, you can rotate an individual unconstrained component in the assembly document without affecting the position and location of the other components. The **Rotate Component** tool is used to rotate the component. There are three methods of rotating an individual component, two of which are discussed next and the third method is discussed later in this chapter.

Rotating Individual Components by Dragging

In SolidWorks 2006, you can rotate the component placed in the assembly without invoking any tool. To rotate an individual component, simply select the component using the right mouse button and drag the cursor to rotate the component. Release the right mouse button after attaining the desired orientation of the individual component.

Rotating Individual Components Using the Rotate Component Tool

CommandManager:	Assemblies > Rotate Component
Toolbar:	Assembly > Rotate Component

You can also rotate an individual component using the **Rotate Component** tool. To rotate an individual component using this tool, choose the **Rotate Component** button from the **Assemblies CommandManager**; the **Rotate Component PropertyManager** will be invoked. You will notice that the **Free Drag** option is selected in the **Rotate** drop-down list in the **Rotate** rollout. Therefore, you will be prompted to select a component and drag it to rotate. The select cursor will be replaced by the rotate cursor; select the component and drag the cursor to rotate the component. The other options available in the **Rotate** drop-down list to rotate the component are discussed next.

About Entity

The **About Entity** option in the **Rotate** drop-down list is used to rotate the component with respect to a selected entity. The selected entity is defined as the rotational axis. When you invoke this option, the **Selected item** selection box will be displayed and you will be prompted to select an axis entity to rotate about. Select an entity to define the rotational axis. The name of the selected entity will be displayed in the **Selected item** selection box. Now, select the component and drag the cursor to rotate the component about the selected axis.

By Delta XYZ

The **By Delta XYZ** option available in the **Rotate** drop-down list is used to rotate the selected component by a given incremental angle along the specified axis. When you select this option, the **Delta X**, **Delta Y**, and **Delta Z** spinners will be invoked and you will be prompted to select a component and enter the desired rotation in the PropertyManager. Select the component to rotate and specify the rotation angle in the respective spinners in the direction in which you need to rotate the component. Choose the **Apply** button to rotate the component.

Tip: *You can toggle between the **Move**, **Rotate**, and **SmartMates** PropertyManagers. Invoke this **PropertyManager** and then choose the **Move**, **Rotate**, or **SmartMates** button to invoke its respective **PropertyManager**.*

MOVING AND ROTATING INDIVIDUAL COMPONENTS USING THE TRIAD

To move an individual component using the triad, you first need to select the component and then right-click to invoke the shortcut menu. Choose the **Move with Triad** option from the shortcut menu; the component will appear transparent and the triad, along with the rings, will be displayed on it. Using this triad, you can move the component. Using the rings, you can rotate the component. The different components of the triad and rings are displayed in Figure 12-50.

To move a component along the X direction, press and hold the left mouse button down on the X arm; the select cursor will be replaced by the move cursor. Use the left mouse button to drag the selected component in the X direction. To rotate the component around the X axis, move the cursor on the rotate around the X axis ring and drag the cursor.

If you drag the cursor on the ring, the component will be rotated through an angle of 90-degrees.

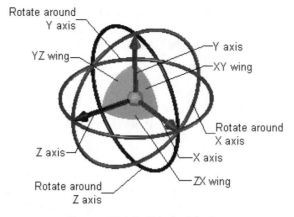

Figure 12-50 *Triad with rings*

To rotate the component through an angle less than 90-degrees, press and hold the left mouse button on the ring and drag the cursor away. Next, start dragging the cursor to rotate the component. Similarly, you can select the Y or the Z arm and drag the cursor to move the component in the Y or Z direction.

You can also move a component in the XY plane. To do so, select the XY wing of the triad and drag the cursor to move the component. To move the component in the YZ plane, select the YZ wing of the triad and drag the cursor to move the component. Similarly, by selecting the ZX wing and dragging the cursor, you can move the component in the ZX plane.

If you select the center sphere and invoke the shortcut menu, various options will be available. These options are discussed next.

Show Translate XYZ Box

The **Show Translate XYZ Box** option available in the shortcut menu is used to display the **Translate XYZ** box. Using this box, you can specify the value of the X, Y, and Z coordinates of the destination where you need to place the selected component. Specify the X, Y, and Z coordinates in the respective edit boxes and then choose **OK** from the box. When you move the component by dragging, the values of the X, Y, and Z spinners will change automatically.

Show Translate Delta XYZ Box

The **Show Translate Delta XYZ Box** option available in the shortcut menu is used to display the **Translate Delta XYZ** box. Using this box, you can specify the incremental value by which you need to move the selected component in the X, Y, or Z direction. Set the incremental value in the X, Y, or Z edit box and then choose **OK** from the box.

Show Rotate Delta XYZ Box

The **Show Rotate Delta XYZ Box** option available in the shortcut menu is used to display the **Rotate Delta XYZ** box. Using this box, you can specify the incremental value by which the selected component will rotate in the X, Y, or Z direction. Set the incremental value in the X, Y, or Z edit box and then choose **OK**.

Align with Component Origin

This option is used to align the triad and the rings to the origin of the selected component.

Align with Assembly Origin

This option is used to align the triad and the rings to the origin of the selected component.

Align to

This option is used to align the triad and the rings to a selected component or a feature.

TUTORIALS

Tutorial 1

In this tutorial, you will create all components of the Bench Vice and then assemble them. The Bench Vice assembly is shown in Figure 12-51. The dimensions of various components of the assembly are given in Figures 12-52 through 12-55.   **(Expected time: 2 hrs 45 min)**

Figure 12-51 *Bench Vice assembly*

The steps to be followed to complete the assembly of this tutorial are listed below.

a.   Create all components in individual part documents and save them. The part documents will be saved in the *My Documents\SolidWorks\c12\Bench Vice* folder.
b.   Open the Vice Body and Vice Jaw part documents and define the mate references in both part documents, refer to Figures 12-56 and 12-57
c.   Create a new assembly document and open all part documents. Place the first component, which is the Vice Body, by dragging and dropping from the part document window. Now, drag and drop the Vice Jaw in the assembly document. It will automatically assemble with

Figure 12-52 *Views and dimensions of the Vice Body*

Figure 12-53 *Views and dimensions of Clamping Plate, Oval Fillister, Set Screw 1, and Set Screw 2*

Figure 12-54 *Views and dimensions of the Vice Jaw*

the Vice Jaw because the mate references are already defined in both part documents, refer to Figures 12-58 and 12-59.

d.   Drag and drop the jaw screw in the assembly document and apply the required mates, refer to Figures 12-61 through 12-66.

e.   Next, analyze the assembly for degrees of freedom of the components.

f.   After analyzing the assembly, apply the required mates to constrain all degrees of freedom, refer to Figures 12-67 and 12-68.

g.   Next, assemble the Clamping Plate, refer to Figures 12-69 through 12-72.

h.   Next, assemble the Oval Fillister using the feature-based mates, refer to Figure 12-73.

i.   Similarly, assemble the other components.

Creating the Components

1.   Create all the components of the Bench Vice assembly as separate part documents. Specify the names of the documents as shown in Figures 12-52 through 12-55. The files should be saved in the folder *My Documents\SolidWorks\c12\Bench Vice*. Make sure that the *Bench Vice* is your current folder.

Figure 12-55 *Views and dimensions of Base Plate, Jaw Screw, Screw Bar, and Bar Globes*

Creating the Mate References

In this tutorial, you need to assemble the first two components of the assembly using the mate references. For assembling the components using the mate references, first you need to create the mate reference. Therefore, you need to open the part documents in which you will add the mate references.

1. Invoke the **Open** dialog box from the **Standard** toolbar.

2. Double-click on the Vice Body; the vice-body part document is opened in the SolidWorks window.

3. Choose **Insert > Reference Geometry > Mate Reference** from the menu bar; the **Mate Reference PropertyManager** is invoked. The selection mode in the **Primary Reference Entity** selection box is active.

4. Select the planar face of the model shown in Figure 12-56 as the primary reference. The selected planar face is highlighted in green.

5. Select the **Coincident** option from the **Mate Reference Type** drop-down list in the **Primary Reference Entity** rollout. The selection mode in the **Secondary Reference Entity** selection box is active.

6. Select the planar face of the model shown in Figure 12-56 of the model as the secondary reference. The selected face is highlighted in magenta.

7. Select the **Coincident** option from the **Mate Reference Type** drop-down list in the **Secondary Reference Entity** rollout.

   The selection mode in the **Tertiary Reference Entity** selection box is active.

8. Select the planar face of the model shown in Figure 12-56 as the tertiary reference. The selected face is highlighted in blue.

Figure 12-56 *Faces to be selected as mate references*

9. Select the **Parallel** option from the **Mate Reference Type** drop-down list in the **Tertiary Reference Entity** rollout.

10. Enter **Vice Mate Reference** as the name of the mate reference in the **Mate Reference Name** edit box available in the **Reference Name** rollout.

11. Choose the **OK** button from the **Mate Reference PropertyManager**.

12. Similarly, create the mate reference in the Vice Jaw part document. The faces to be selected as reference are displayed in Figure 12-57. The name of the mate reference in the **Reference Name** rollout should be the same in both part documents.

13. Close all part documents, except *Vice Body.sldprt* and *Vice Jaw.sldprt*, if they are opened.

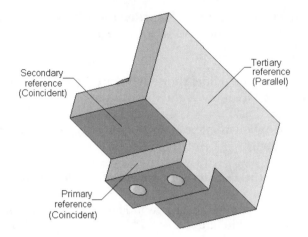

Figure 12-57 Faces to be selected as mate references

Assembling the First Two Components of the Assembly

After creating the mate references in the part documents, you need to assemble the components. To do so, you need to start a new SolidWorks assembly document.

1. Start a new SolidWorks assembly document; the **Insert Component PropertyManager** is invoked automatically and the names of components, which were opened, are displayed in the **Open documents** selection box.

2. Select the Vice Body from the **Open documents** selection box; the preview of the Vice Body is displayed along with the component cursor.

3. Choose the **Keep Visible** button from the **Insert Component PropertyManager** because after placing this component, you also need to place the second component that is displayed in the **Open documents** selection box.

    It is recommended that the first component of the assembly should be placed at the assembly origin.

4. Choose the **OK** button from the **Insert Component PropertyManager** to place the first component coincident to the origin.

    As the **Keep Visible** button is selected, the preview of the Vice Body is again displayed with the component cursor in the drawing area.

5. Change the current view to isometric.

    Next, you need to place the second component in the assembly. As discussed earlier, the second component of the assembly, which is the Vice Jaw, is assembled with the Vice Body using the mate references.

6. Select the Vice Jaw from the **Open documents** selection box; the preview of the Vice Jaw is available in the drawing area.

    When you move the cursor close to the Vice Body in the assembly document, the preview of the Vice Jaw assembled after applying the mates with the Vice Body is displayed in the assembly document.

7. Place the component at the required location. The mates specified in the mate references are applied between the Vice Jaw and the Vice Body. Choose the **Keep Visible** button and exit the **Mate PropertyManager**.

    Figure 12-58 shows the second component being placed in the assembly document and Figure 12-59 shows the isometric view of the Vice Jaw assembled with the Vice Body.

Figure 12-58 Second component being placed

8. Before proceeding further, it is recommended that you close all the part documents. Close the part document windows of all the parts that are placed in the assembly document.

Tip. *The mates that are defined in the mate reference are applied to the components when you place the components in the assembly. You can view the mates applied to both components by expanding the* **Mates** *option from the* **FeatureManager Design Tree** *of the assembly document.*

Figure 12-59 *Vice Jaw assembled with the Vice Body*

Assembling the Jaw Screw

Now, you need to place the Jaw Screw in the assembly document.

1. Choose the **Insert Component** button from the **Assemblies CommandManager**.

2. Choose the **Browse** button from the **Part/Assembly to Insert** rollout to display the **Open**.

3. Double-click on the Jaw Screw to open its part document; the preview of the Jaw Screw is displayed in the drawing area.

4. Click anywhere in the drawing area to place the Jaw Screw.

    Figure 12-60 shows the Jaw Screw placed arbitrarily in the assembly document. Next, you need to add the assembly mates to assemble the components placed in the assembly.

Figure 12-60 *Jaw Screw placed in the assembly document*

5. Press and hold the ALT key down on the keyboard and then select the face from the location shown in Figure 12-61.

6. Drag the Jaw Screw to the hole in the Vice Body, as shown in Figure 12-62; the Jaw Screw appears transparent and the select cursor is replaced by the smart mates cursor. Also, the symbol of the concentric mate is displayed below the cursor.

Face to be selected

Figure 12-61 Face to be selected   *Figure 12-62 Jaw Screw being dragged*

7. Release the left mouse button at this location; the **Mate** pop-up toolbar is displayed and the **Concentric** button is chosen by default, which suggests that the **Concentric** mate is the most appropriate mate to be applied. Choose the **Add/Finish Mate** button from the **Mate** pop-up toolbar. Figure 12-63 shows the Jaw Screw assembled to the Vice Body.

*Figure 12-63 The **Concentric** mate applied between the Jaw Screw and the Vice Body*

Next, you need to apply the coincident mate between the planar faces of the Jaw Screw and the Vice Jaw.

8. Choose the **Mate** button from the **Assemblies CommandManager** to invoke the **Mate PropertyManager**.

9. Rotate the assembly view and select the face of the Vice Jaw, as shown in Figure 12-64. Next, select the face of the Jaw Screw, as shown in Figure 12-65.

Figure 12-64 *Face to be selected*   ***Figure 12-65*** *Face to be selected*

As soon as you select the faces, the **Mate** pop-up toolbar is invoked and the preview of the assembly with the coincident mate is displayed in the drawing area.

10. Choose the **Add/Finish Mate** button from the **Mate** pop-up toolbar. The assembly after adding the **Coincident** mate is displayed in Figure 12-66.

Figure 12-66 *Assembly after applying the **Coincident** mate to the Jaw Screw*

In real world, there are two types of assemblies. The first is the fully defined assembly in which all degrees of freedom of all components are restricted. The other type of assembly is that in which some degrees of freedom of the components are left free so that they can be moved or rotated. These types of assemblies are used for the mechanism, about which you will learn in the next chapter.

After adding the **Coincident** mate, you need to move the assembly to analyze the degree of freedom of the components of the assembly. After analyzing the components of an assembly, you need to add the mates to constrain that degree of freedom.

11. Select the circular face of the Jaw Screw using the left mouse button and drag the cursor.

    You will notice that the Jaw Screw is rotating about its axis and is moving along the X axis. Also, it is forcing the Vice Jaw to move along the X axis. Originally, this degree of freedom of the Vice Jaw and Jaw Screw needs to be left free so that the assembly can function in the mechanism. But in this chapter, you need to restrict this degree of freedom so as to create a fully defined assembly.

12. Select the two faces, one of the Vice Body and the other of the Jaw Screw, as shown in Figures 12-67 and 12-68.

Figure 12-67 *Face to be selected*   *Figure 12-68* *Face to be selected*

13. Choose the **Distance** button from the **Standard Mates** rollout and set the **Distance** spinner value to **10**. As you choose the **Distance** button, the **PropertyManager** changes to the **Distance 1 PropertyManager**.

14. Choose the **OK** button from the **Distance 1 PropertyManager** to again display the **Mate PropertyManager**.

15. Expand the **FeatureManager Design Tree** displayed in the drawing area and select the **Top Plane**. Now, expand the **Jaw Screw** from the **FeatureManager Design Tree** and select the **Top Plane**. The **Mate** pop-up toolbar is displayed.

16. Choose the **Angle** button from the **Mate** pop-up toolbar.

17. Set the value of the **Angle** spinner to **45** and choose the **Add/Finish Mate** button from the **Mate** pop-up toolbar.

18. Choose the **OK** button from the **Mate PropertyManager** to exit.

Assembling the Clamping Plate

Next, you need to assemble the Clamping Plate with the assembly.

1. Invoke the **Insert Component PropertyManager** and choose the **Browse** button to invoke the **Open** dialog box. Open and place the Clamping Plate in the drawing area.

2. Rotate the assembly such that the bottom face of the assembly is displayed, as shown in Figure 12-69.

3. Select the Clamping Plate using the right mouse button and drag the cursor to rotate the Clamping Plate, as shown in Figure 12-70.

Figure 12-69 Rotated assembly   *Figure 12-70* Clamping Plate after rotating

4. Apply the **Concentric** mate between the two cylindrical faces of the clamping plate and the two holes of the Vice Jaw, refer to Figure 12-71. You may have to move the Clamping Plate after applying the first mate.

5. Move the Clamping Plate by dragging. Now, apply the **Coincident** mate between the faces of the Clamping Plate and the Vice Jaw, as shown in Figure 12-72.

Figure 12-71 Faces to be selected to apply mate   *Figure 12-72* Faces to be selected to apply mate

6. Similarly, assemble the Screw Bar, Support Plates, and Bar Globes. The assembly, after assembling all these components, is shown in Figure 12-73.

Assembling the Remaining Components

Next, you need to assemble the Oval Fillister, Set Screw 1, and Set Screw 2. These fasteners are assembled using the feature-based mates.

Figure 12-73 *Assembly after assembling the Vice Body, Vice Jaw, Jaw Screw, Screw Bar, Clamping Plate, Base Plate, and Bar Globes*

1. Open the part documents of Oval Fillisters, Set Screw 1, and Set Screw 2.

2. Choose **Window > Tile Horizontally** from the menu bar to rearrange the windows.

3. Select the **Revolve1** feature from the **FeatureManager Design Tree** of the Oval Fillister part document. Drag the cursor to place the component in the assembly, as shown in Figure 12-74.

Figure 12-74 *Dragging the Oval Fillisters in the assembly using feature-based mates*

4. Drop the component at this location.

   Similarly, assemble Set Screw 1 and Set screw 2 using feature-based mates. Use the TAB key on the keyboard to reverse the direction. The rotated view of the assembly, after assembling Set Screw 1 and Set Screw 2, is shown in Figure 12-75.

Figure 12-75 Viewing the final assembly from the bottom

5. Choose the **Save** button to save the assembly with the name *Bench Vice* in the folder *My Documents\SolidWorks\c12\Bench Vice*.

Tutorial 2

In this tutorial, you will create all components of the Pipe Vice and then assemble them. The Pipe Vice assembly is shown in Figure 12-76. The dimensions of various components of this assembly are given in Figures 12-77 and 12-78.   **(Expected time: 2 hrs 45 min)**

Figure 12-76 Pipe Vice assembly

Figure 12-77 *Views and dimensions of the base*

Figure 12-78 *Views and dimensions of the Screw, Handle, Moveable Jaw, and Handle Screw*

You need to create all components of the Pipe Vice assembly as separate part documents. After creating the parts, you will assemble them in the assembly document. Therefore, in this tutorial, you need to use the bottom-up approach for creating the assembly.

The steps to be followed to complete the assembly of this tutorial are listed next.

a.   Create all components in the individual part documents and save them. The part documents will be saved in *My Documents\SolidWorks\c12\Pipe Vice*.
b.   Place the base at the origin of the assembly.
c.   Place the Moveable Jaw and the Screw in the assembly. Apply the mates between Moveable Jaw and the Screw, refer to Figures 12-79 through 12-81.
d.   Assemble the Screw with the Base.
e.   Place the other components in the assembly and apply the required mates to the assembly, refer to Figure 12-82.

Creating the Components

1. Create all components of the Pipe Vice assembly as separate part documents. Specify the names of the files, as shown in Figures 12-77 and 12-78. The documents should be saved in the folder */My Documents/SolidWorks/c12/Pipe Vice*.

Inserting the First Component in the Assembly

After creating all components of the Pipe Vice assembly, you need to start a new SolidWorks assembly document.

1. Start a new SolidWorks assembly document; the **Insert Component PropertyManager** is invoked by default.

2. Choose the **Browse** button from the **Part/Assembly to Insert** rollout to display the **Open** dialog box. Double-click on Base.

3. Choose the **OK** button from the **Insert Component PropertyManager** to place the Base origin coincident to the origin of the assembly document.

4. Change the view orientation to isometric.

Inserting and Assembling the Moveable Jaw and the Screw

After placing the first component in the assembly document, you need to place the Moveable Jaw and the Screw in the assembly document. After placing these components, you need to apply the required mates.

1. Choose the **Insert Components** button from the **Assemblies CommandManager**. Then, choose the **Keep Visible** button from the **PropertyManager** and invoke the **Open** dialog box by choosing the **Browse** button from the **Part/Assembly to Insert** rollout.

2. Double-click on the Moveable Jaw. Place the component anywhere in the assembly document such that it does not interfere with existing component.

3. Similarly, place the Screw in the assembly document and choose the **OK** button from the **Insert Component PropertyManager**. Figure 12-79 shows the Moveable Jaw, Screw, and Base placed in the assembly document.

    First, you need to assemble the Screw with the Moveable Jaw. Therefore, for assembling the Screw with the Moveable Jaw, you need to fix the Moveable Jaw.

4. Select the Moveable Jaw from the drawing area or from the **FeatureManager Design Tree**. Right-click to invoke the shortcut menu.

5. Choose the **Fix** option from the shortcut menu. The Moveable Jaw is fixed and you cannot move or rotate the Moveable Jaw.

Figure 12-79 *The Moveable Jaw, Screw, and Base placed in the assembly document*

6. Invoke the **Move PropertyManager** and choose the **SmartMates** button from the **Move** rollout. Double-click on the lowermost cylindrical face of the Screw; the Screw appears transparent.

7. Drag the cursor to the hole located on the top of the Moveable Jaw. Release the left mouse button as soon as the concentric symbol is displayed below the cursor. Choose the **Add/Finish Mate** button from the **Mate** pop-up toolbar.

8. Select the Screw and move it up so that it is not inside the Moveable Jaw.

9. Right-click in the drawing area and choose **Clear Selections** to clear the current selection.

10. Rotate the assembly and double-click on the lower flat face of the Screw; the Screw appears transparent.

11. Again, rotate the model and select the top planar face of the Moveable Jaw. The **Coincident** relation is applied between the two selected faces. Choose the **Add/Finish Mate** button from the **Mate** pop-up toolbar.

12. Choose the **OK** button from the **SmartMates PropertyManager**. Figure 12-80 shows the Screw after applying the mates.

    Next, you need to assemble the Screw and the Moveable Jaw with the Base.

13. Select the Moveable Jaw and invoke the shortcut menu. Choose the **Float** option from the shortcut menu.

    Now, the Moveable Jaw and the Screw assembled to it can be moved.

14. Using smart mates, add a **Concentric** mate between the cylindrical face of the Screw and the hole created on the top face of the Base.

15. Invoke the **Mate PropertyManager** and select the front planar face of the Moveable Jaw and the front planar face of the Base.

16. Choose the **Parallel** button from the **Mate** pop-up toolbar and choose the **Add/Finish Mate** button to add a parallel mate between the selected faces.

17. Next, select the faces as shown in Figure 12-81.

Figure 12-80 *The Screw assembled with the Moveable Jaw*

Figure 12-81 *Faces to be selected*

18. Choose the **Distance** button from the **Mate** pop-up toolbar and set the value of the **Distance** spinner to **35**.

19. Choose the **Add/Finish Mate** button from the **Mate** pop-up toolbar and then choose the **OK** button from the **Mate PropertyManager**.

20. Similarly, assemble the other components of the Pipe Vice. Figure 12-82 shows the final Pipe Vice assembly.

21. Choose the **Save** button to save the assembly document in the *\My Documents\SolidWorks\Pipe Vice* folder.

Figure 12-82 *Final Pipe Vice assembly*

SELF-EVALUATION TEST

Answer the following questions and then compare your answers with those given at the end of this chapter:

1. The bottom-up assembly design approach is the traditional and the most widely preferred approach of assembly design. (T/F)

2. In the top-down assembly design approach, all components are created in the same assembly document. (T/F)

3. The **Coincident** mate is generally applied to make two planar faces coplanar. (T/F)

4. The most suitable mates that can be applied to the current selection set are displayed in the **Mate Selections** rollout of the **Mate PropertyManager**. (T/F)

5. Feature-based mates are applied only to the components having cylindrical features. (T/F)

6. Pattern-based mates are used to assemble the components that have a circular pattern created on the circular feature. (T/F)

7. Choose the _____ button from the **Assemblies CommandManager** to invoke the **Rotate Component PropertyManager**.

8. The _____ option available in the **Rotate** drop-down list is used to rotate the selected component by a given an incremental angle about the specified axis.

9. The _____ mate is generally used to align the central axis of one component with that of the other.

10. The _____ option available in the **Move** drop-down list is used to move the component along the direction of the selected entity.

REVIEW QUESTIONS

Answer the following questions:

1. The names of the selected entities are displayed in the _____ selection box of the **Mate PropertyManager**.

2. Choose _____ from the menu bar to place a component in the assembly document.

3. Using the _____ option from the **Move** drop-down list, you can move the component dynamically along the X, Y, and Z axes of the assembly document.

4. The _____ button available in the **Standard Mates** rollout is used to make the two selected entities normal to each other.

5. The _____ option is used to specify the coordinates of the origin of the part where the component will be placed after moving.

6. If you are adding feature-based mates using the features having a conical geometry, then there must be a _____ face adjacent to the conical face of both the features.

7. The most widely used method of adding the mates to the components in the assembly in SolidWorks is

    (a) **Smart Mates**   (b) **Mate PropertyManager**
    (c) By dragging from part document   (d) None of these

8. Which button is used to make the **Mate PropertyManager** available after applying a mate to the selected entities?

    (a) **Help**   (b) **OK**
    (c) **Keep Visible**   (d) **Cancel**

9. Which option available in the **Rotate** drop-down list is used to rotate the component with respect to the selected entity?

    (a) **Along Entity**   (b) **Selected Edge**
    (c) **Reference Entity**   (d) None of these

10. Which option is used to specify the coordinates of the origin of the part where the component will be placed after moving?

    (a) **To XYZ Position**   (b) **Reference Position**

    (b) **Along Entity**   (c) None of these

EXERCISE

Exercise 1

Create the Plummer Block assembly, as shown in Figure 12-83. The dimensions of the components of this assembly are shown in Figures 12-84 through 12-86.   **(Expected time: 1 hr)**

Figure 12-83 Plummer Block assembly

Figure 12-84 *Views and dimensions of Casting*

Figure 12-85 *Views and dimensions of Brasses, Nut, Lock Nut, and Bolt*

Figure 12-86 *Views and dimensions of Cap*

Answers to Self-Evaluation Test

1. T, **2.** T, **3.** T, **4.** T, **5.** T, **6.** T, **7. Rotate Component**, **8. By Delta XYZ**, **9. Coincident**, **10. Along Entity**

Chapter 13

Assembly Modeling-II

Learning Objectives

After completing this chapter, you will be able to:

- *Apply advanced mates.*
- *Create subassemblies.*
- *Delete components and subassemblies.*
- *Edit assembly mates.*
- *Replace mate entities.*
- *Edit components and subassemblies.*
- *Dissolve subassemblies.*
- *Replace components in assemblies.*
- *Create patterns of components in the assembly.*
- *Create mirrored components.*
- *Hide and suppress components in assemblies.*
- *Change the transparency condition of assembly.*
- *Check the interference in an assembly.*
- *Create assemblies for mechanism.*
- *Detect collision while the assembly is in motion.*
- *Create the exploded state of an assembly.*
- *Create the explode line sketch.*

ADVANCED ASSEMBLY MATES

In the previous chapter, you learned to place the components in an assembly document and also to apply assembly mates to them. In this chapter, you will learn to apply advanced mates to the components by invoking the **Mate PropertyManager** and then the **Advanced Mates** rollout available in it. The **Advanced Mates** rollout is displayed in Figure 13-1.

*Figure 13-1   The **Advanced Mates** rollout*

The advanced mates that you will learn in this chapter are the **Symmetric** mate, **Cam** mate, **Gear** mate, and **Limit** mate. All these mates are discussed next.

Applying the Symmetric Mate

 The **Symmetric** mate is applied to create a symmetric relation between two components. To apply this mate, choose the **Symmetric** button available in the **Advanced Mates** rollout; the **Symmetry Plane** selection box is displayed in the **Mate Selections** rollout. Select two similar entities from two components to which you need to apply the symmetric mate. The similar entities can be edges, vertices, planar faces, and so on. Next, you need to select a plane or a planar face that will act as the symmetry plane. Click once in the **Symmetry Plane** selection box to invoke the selection mode and select the symmetry plane; the **Symmetry Plane** callout is attached to the selected plane. Choose the **OK** button from the **Symmetric1 PropertyManager**. Figure 13-2 shows the entities and the plane to be selected to apply the **Symmetric** mate and Figure 13-3 shows the **Symmetric** mate applied to the assembly.

Applying the Cam Mate

You can add a **Cam** mate between a face that is formed by closed and continuous extruded faces from a single profile and a face of the follower. The face of the follower

Figure 13-2 *Entities and the plane to be selected to apply the symmetric mate*

Figure 13-3 *Assembly after applying the symmetric mate*

could be cylindrical or planar, or it could be a vertex. To apply a **Cam** mate, you need to select a chain of continuous tangent faces that will act as a surface of the cam. Next, select a curved face, planar face, or a vertex from the follower that will remain in contact with the selected chain of tangent faces. To apply a **Cam** mate, invoke the **Advanced Mates** rollout of the **Mate PropertyManager**. Choose the **Cam Follower** button from this rollout; the **Cam follower** selection box is displayed in the **Mate Selections** rollout. Select the chain of continuous faces that will act as the cam surface. The selected faces are highlighted in green. Next, click once in the **Cam follower** selection box and select the face from the second component that will act as the surface of the follower. The follower will touch the surface of the Cam and the **Cam Follower** callout will be attached to the selected face. Choose the **OK** button from the **CamMate Tangent1 PropertyManager**. On rotating the cam, the follower will attain the respective linear motion, that is, following the cam surface. Figure 13-4 shows the faces to be selected and Figure 13-5 shows the preview of the assembly, after applying the **Cam** mate.

Figure 13-4 *Faces selected to apply cam mate*

Figure 13-5 *Preview of the assembly with cam mate*

Note

For a better understanding of this mate, make sure that the front faces of the cam and follower are coplanar. Also, ensure that a proper degree of freedom of the components of the cam and follower assembly should be kept free.

Applying the Width Mate

This is the enhancement in the latest release of SolidWorks. Using this mate, you can align a component at an equal distance between the two faces of another component.

The faces between which you want to align another component should be planar faces. However, for the component to be aligned, you can select a nonplanar face also. To apply this mate, choose the **Widthmate** button from the **Advanced Mates** rollout in the **Mate PropertyManager**; the **Mate Selections** rollout will display the **Width selections** and **Tab selections** selection boxes. The two planar faces of the first component between which you want to align the second component should be selected using the **Width selections** selection box. A callout will be displayed on the faces that you select. Next, select the planar or curved faces of the second component that you want to align between the selected width references; the component will be automatically aligned at an equal distance between the two faces of the first component. Figure 13-6 shows the faces of the first component select as the width reference and the cylindrical face of the second component being selected as the tab reference. Figure 13-7 shows the preview of the resulting position of the second component.

Figure 13-6 Selecting the faces for the width and tab references

Figure 13-7 Resulting preview of the location of the second component

Applying the Gear Mate

The **Gear** mate allows you to rotate two components, such as gears, with respect to each other about a selected axis. You can also define a specific gear ratio between the selected components. To apply this mate between two components, invoke the **Advanced Mates** rollout from the **Mate PropertyManager**. Choose the **Gearmate** button from the **Advanced Mates** rollout; the **Ratio** edit boxes and the **Reverse** check box are also invoked. Next, select the references along which the two components will rotate. These references can be cylindrical faces, conical faces, axes, circular edges, or linear edges. Select the required references; the names of references are displayed in the **Entities to Mate** selection box. The **Teeth/Diameter** callouts are also displayed attached to the selected references. You can set the ratio of rotation using the **Ratio** edit boxes or using the **Teeth/Diameter** callouts. The **Reverse** check box is selected to change the direction of rotation of one component with respect to the other. Choose the **OK** button from the **GearMate1 PropertyManager**. After adding this mate, rotate any one of the components and you will observe the other component rotating with the specified gear ratio. Generally, this mate is used to display the rotation of the gears and direction. Figure 13-8 shows the cylindrical faces that you need to select to apply the gear mate. Figure 13-9 shows the **Teeth/Diameter** callouts displayed, after selecting the respective faces.

Figure 13-8 *Faces to be selected to apply gear mate*

Figure 13-9 *Teeth/Diameter callouts attached to the selected faces*

Applying the Rack Pinion Mate

The **Rack Pinion** mate allows you to create a rack and pinion relationship between two components. As a result of this mate, the rack undergoes translation motion and the pinion undergoes rotational motion. To apply this mate, choose the **RackPinionMate** button from the **Advanced Mate** rollout; the **Rack** and **Pinion/Gear** selection boxes will be displayed in the **Mate Selections** rollout. Select the linear edge of the rack and then select the circular edge of the pinion; the **Rack Pinion** mate will be applied to the two components. You can specify the pinion pitch diameter or the distance travel by the rack per revolution of the pinion using the options available in the **Advanced Mates** rollout.

Applying the Limit Mate

The introduction of the limit mate is another major enhancement in the recent releases of SolidWorks. It is used to apply a distance mate or angle mate to the selected components, but the difference between a simple distance or angle mate and limit mate is that in limit mate you can move the component within a specific range of values. To apply a limit mate, invoke the **Advanced Mates** rollout from the **Mate PropertyManager** and then apply the distance or the angle mate, as required. Next, specify the maximum and minimum values of the limit mate in the **Maximum Value** and the **Minimum Value** spinners, respectively. Choose the **OK** button from the **PropertyManager**.

CREATING SUBASSEMBLIES

In the previous chapter, you learned to place the components in the assembly document and apply the assembly mates to them. In this chapter, you will also learn to create the subassemblies and place them in the main assembly.

For placing the subassemblies in the main assembly, there are two approaches that are followed in the assembly design environment. These two approaches are discussed next.

Bottom-up Subassembly Design

In the bottom-up subassembly design approach, the subassembly is created in the assembly environment and then saved as an assembly file. To place the subassembly in the main assembly, open the main assembly document and invoke the **Insert Component PropertyManager**. On choosing the **Browse** button, the **Open** dialog box is displayed; select **Assembly** (**.asm, *.sldasm*) from the **Files of Type** drop-down list. All assemblies saved in the current location will be displayed in the selection box. Select the subassembly from the selection box and choose the **Open** button from the **Open** dialog box. Select a point in the drawing area to place the subassembly. Now, using the assembly mates, assemble the subassembly with the main assembly. Figure 13-10 shows a subassembly of a piston and an articulated rod. Figure 13-11 shows the main assembly of the piston and master rod.

Figure 13-10 The subassembly

Figure 13-11 The main assembly

Top-down Subassembly Design

The top-down subassembly design approach is the most flexible subassembly design approach. In this, you create a new subassembly in the main assembly document. The approach is generally used in conceptual design or while managing a large assembly. To create a new subassembly in the assembly document, choose **Insert > Component > New Assembly** from the menu bar. The **Save As** dialog box is displayed; save the subassembly in the current location. You can drag and place the components in the new subassembly from the **FeatureManager Design Tree**. You will learn more about this approach, while discussing the editing of assemblies and subassemblies.

DELETING COMPONENTS AND SUBASSEMBLIES

After creating the assembly, at a certain stage of your design cycle you may need to delete a component or the subassembly. To delete a component of the assembly, select the component from the drawing area or from the **FeatureManager Design Tree**. Invoke the shortcut menu and choose the **Delete** option. You can also delete the selected component by pressing the

Tip. *You can also place a subassembly in the main assembly using the drag and drop method that was discussed in the previous chapter.*

*When you place a subassembly in the main assembly, an assembly icon will be displayed, with the name of the subassembly in the **FeatureManager Design Tree**. If you expand the subassembly in the **FeatureManager Design Tree**, all the parts assembled in the subassembly will be displayed.*

*You can also create a subassembly of the components that are already placed in an assembly file. Press and hold down the CTRL key and select the components from the drawing area or from the **FeatureManager Design Tree**. Invoke the shortcut menu and choose **Form New Sub-assembly Here** or **Assembly from [Selected] Components**. The **Save As** dialog box is displayed; you need to enter the name of the subassembly and save it in the current location. You will observe that the selected components will be combined and an assembly icon will be displayed in the **FeatureManager Design Tree**.*

DELETE key on the keyboard. When you delete a component, the **Confirm Delete** dialog box is displayed. The name of the component and the items dependent on it are displayed in this dialog box. Choose the **Yes** button from the **Confirm Delete** dialog box.

To delete the subassembly, select it from the **FeatureManager Design Tree** and press the DELETE key. The **Confirm Delete** dialog box is displayed; choose the **YES** button from it. Note that on deleting the subassembly, all the components of the subassembly are also deleted.

EDITING ASSEMBLY MATES

You may need to edit the assembly mates, after creating the assembly or during the process of assembling the components. The editing operations that can be performed include modifying the type of the assembly mate or angle and offset values, changing the component to which the mate was applied, and so on. To edit the mates in SolidWorks, you first need to expand the **Mates** option available at the bottom of the **FeatureManager Design Tree**. Next, select the mate that you need to modify and invoke the shortcut menu. Choose the **Edit Feature** option from the shortcut menu. The **Mate PropertyManager** and the **Mate** pop-up toolbar are displayed. The name of the **Mate PropertyManager** will depend on the name and sequence of the mate applied. Figure 13-12 shows a partial view of the **Mate PropertyManager** to edit the **Coincident** mate. You can edit the entities to mate, type of mate, value of offset, value of angle, and so on using this **PropertyManager**.

Figure 13-12 Partial view of the **Mate PropertyManager**
to edit the **Coincident** mate

 Tip. *The entities used in the mate are highlighted in red in the drawing area, when you move the cursor on a mate in the **FeatureManager Design Tree**. On selecting the mate from the **FeatureManager Design Tree**, the entities used in the selected mate will be highlighted on the drawing area in green.*

Replacing Mated Entities

As discussed, you can edit the mate entities using the **Mate PropertyManager**. They can also be modified using the **Mated Entities PropertyManager**. Select the **Mates** option from the **FeatureManager Design Tree,** invoke the shortcut menu, and choose the **Replace Mate Entities** option; the **Mated Entities PropertyManager** is displayed, as shown in Figure 13-13. You can customize the **Assemblies CommandManager** and then select the specific mate whose entities you need to replace. Next, choose the **Replace Mate Entities** button from the **Assemblies CommandManager**. On invoking the **Mated Entities PropertyManager**, you are prompted to select the entity to be replaced. Select the entity from the **Mate Entities** selection box. You can also expand the entity tree to edit an individual mate. After selecting, the selected face will be highlighted in the drawing area in green and its name will be displayed in the **Replacement Mate Entity** selection box. You are prompted to select the entity to be mated. Select the entity that will replace the previously selected entity. The SolidWorks warning

*Figure 13-13 The **Mated Entities PropertyManager***

box, informing the possible cause of error, will be displayed if the selected entity over defines the mate, or the mating is not possible between the entities.

The **Flip Mate Alignment** button is used to flip the direction of mate. The **Disable Preview** button is used to disable the preview of the assembly after replacing the mate entity. The **Show All** check box is used to display all the mated entities.

Tip. *Select the **Mates** option from the **FeatureManager Design Tree** and invoke the shortcut menu. Choose the **Parent/Child Relationship** option from the shortcut menu. The **Parent Child Relationship** dialog box will be displayed. You can display the child and parent relationship of any component placed in the assembly using the **Parent Child Relationship** dialog box.*

EDITING COMPONENTS

CommandManager: Assemblies > Edit Component
Toolbar: Assembly > Edit Component

At some stage of your design cycle, you may need to edit the components, after placing and mating them in the assembly document. This may include editing the features, sketches, and sketch planes. To edit the components, you first need to select the component and invoke the part modeling environment in the assembly document. To do so, select the component from the drawing area or from the **FeatureManager Design Tree** and choose the **Edit Component** button from the **Assembly CommandManager**. The part modeling environment will be invoked and the entire assembly, except the component to be edited, is displayed in transparent. If not, choose the **Assembly Transparency** button available in the **Features CommandManager** that is displayed; a flyout is invoked and the options available in it can be used to set the transparency of the assembly. On choosing the **Opaque** option, all components of the assembly are set to opaque. The **Maintain Transparency** option retains the default transparency settings of the individual components. If the **Force Transparency** option is chosen, all components of the assembly, except the component being edited, are set as transparent. The name of the component to be edited will be displayed in blue in the **FeatureManager Design Tree**. Select the desired feature to edit, and invoke the respective **PropertyManager**. The **PropertyManager** corresponding to that feature will be displayed and you can easily edit the feature parameters. If required, you can also add new features to the component. This type of editing is technically termed as **Editing in the Context of Assembly**. After editing the component, again choose the **Edit Component** button from the **Assembly CommandManager** to return to the assembly environment.

*Tip. You can also modify the dimensions of a component assembled or those placed in the assembly by double-clicking on the desired feature of that component. All dimensions of that feature will be displayed in the drawing area. Invoke the **Modify** dialog box by double-clicking on the dimension to be modified. Enter the new dimension in the **Modify** dialog box and press the ENTER key on the keyboard; the dimension will be modified, but the geometry of the feature will not be changed. You need to rebuild the assembly to reflect the modifications. To do so, choose the **Rebuild** button from the **Standard** toolbar or use the CTRL+B key on the keyboard.*

*While in the part editing mode in the assembly document, you can use the **Move/Size Features** tool to edit the features dynamically using editing handles.*

Note
*To edit components separately in their part documents, select the component, invoke the shortcut menu and select the **Open Part** option from it. The part document of the selected component will be opened. You can edit the component individually in the part document. After editing, save the part, close the part document and return to the assembly document. The **SolidWorks 2007** dialog box will be displayed, which will inform you that the models contained within the assembly have changed. It will further prompt you to specify whether you would like to rebuild the assembly now. Choose the **Yes** button from this dialog box.*

EDITING SUBASSEMBLIES

CommandManager:	Assemblies > Edit Component
Toolbar:	Assembly > Edit Component

To edit subassemblies, select them from the **FeatureManager Design Tree** and choose the **Edit Component** button from the **Assembly CommandManager**. You can set the transparency setting using the **Assembly Transparency** button available in the **Assemblies CommandManager**. You can add components in the subassembly, modify the mates, and replace the components while in the editing mode. After editing the subassembly, choose the **Edit Component** button to exit the editing mode.

Note

*For editing a component of the subassembly, select the component from the drawing area, invoke the shortcut menu and choose the **Edit Part** option from it. The part editing mode will be invoked in the assembly document.*

*You need to expand the desired subassembly from the **FeatureManager Design Tree** to select its components. All the components assembled in that subassembly will be displayed once the subassembly is expanded.*

DISSOLVING SUBASSEMBLIES

Dissolving the subassembly means the components of the selected subassembly become the components of the next higher level subassembly. When you dissolve a subassembly, it is removed from the assembly and the components of the subassembly become the components of the assembly or the subassembly in which it was inserted. To dissolve a subassembly, select the subassembly from the **FeatureManager Design Tree**. Invoke the shortcut menu and choose the **Dissolve Sub-assembly** option from the shortcut menu. The subassembly will be removed from the **FeatureManager Design Tree** and its components will be displayed as the components of the assembly or the subassembly in the **FeatureManager Design Tree**.

REPLACING COMPONENTS

Sometimes, in the assembly design cycle, you may need to replace a component of the assembly with some other component. To replace a component, select the component to be replaced, invoke the shortcut menu, expand it and choose the **Replace Components** option to display the **Replace PropertyManager**, as shown in Figure 13-14. You can also invoke the **Replace PropertyManager** by choosing the **Replace Components** button from the **Assemblies CommandManager** after customizing it.

On invoking the **Replace PropertyManager**, you are prompted to select components to be replaced. If the component is already selected before invoking this tool, then it will remain selected. The name of the selected component is displayed in the **Components to be Replaced** selection box. Next, you need to specify the replacement component. Choose the **Browse** button from the **Selection** rollout; the **Open** dialog box will be displayed. Select the replacement component and choose the **Open** button from the **Open** dialog box. The name

Figure 13-14 The Replace PropertyManager

and location of the replacement component is displayed in the **Replacement Component** area.

The **All instances** check box available in the **Selection** rollout is used to replace all the instances of the selected component. The options available in the **Configuration** area are used to define the selection procedure of the configurations. You will learn more about configurations later.

The **Re-attach mates** check box is selected by default. On exiting the **Replace PropertyManager** with this check box selected, the **What's Wrong** dialog box is displayed. Choose **Close** from this dialog box. The **Mated Entities PropertyManager** is displayed. You can replace the mate entities by using the **Mated Entities PropertyManager**.

If the **Re-attach mates** check box is cleared, the **What's Wrong** dialog box is displayed after you exit the **Replace PropertyManager**. This dialog box informs you the name of the mates that contain errors. Therefore, you need to redefine the mates. To do so, expand the **Mates** option from the **FeatureManager Design Tree**. Select the mate that has an error symbol on the left. Invoke the shortcut menu and choose the **Edit Feature** option. The **Mate PropertyManager** will be displayed and you can edit the mate entities.

Figure 13-15 shows the assembly in which the bolt is to be replaced by a pin. Figure 13-16 shows the faces of the pin to be used as mate entities, after replacing the component. Figure 13-17 shows the isometric view of the assembly after bolts are replaced by pins.

Figure 13-15 *Bolt to be replaced by a pin*   **Figure 13-16** *Mating entities to be replaced*

Figure 13-17 *Bolt replaced by pin in the assembly*

Tip. *The exclamation symbol displayed on the **Mates** option in the **FeatureManager Design Tree** means that the mates group has errors in it. Expand the mates group; the mate that displays the exclamation sign will have some errors. Select that mate and invoke the shortcut menu. Choose the **What's Wrong?** option to display the **What's Wrong** dialog box. The possible cause of the error will be displayed in it.*

*If you choose the **Mate Diagnostics** option from the shortcut menu, the **Diagnostics PropertyManager** will be displayed. The **Diagnose** button in this **PropertyManager** is used to display the entities that are the cause of errors in the mate. Right-click on the mate and choose the **Edit Mates** option from the shortcut menu to edit the mate with errors.*

CREATING PATTERNS OF COMPONENTS IN AN ASSEMBLY

Menu: Insert > Component Pattern > Linear Pattern/ Circular Pattern/ Feature Driven

While working on a complex assembly, you may need to assemble more than one instance of the component about a specified arrangement. For example, consider the case of a flange coupling where you have to assemble eight instances of nuts and bolts to fasten the coupling. In this case, you need to assemble eight instances of the nuts and bolts with the couplings. However, this is a very tedious and time-consuming process. Therefore, to reduce time, SolidWorks has provided a tool to create the patterns of the components. The three types of component patterns provided in SolidWorks are discussed next.

Feature-driven Pattern

The feature driven pattern is used to pattern the instances of the components using an existing pattern feature created while creating the component. To create this type of pattern, choose **Insert > Component Pattern > Feature Driven** from the menu bar; the **Feature Driven PropertyManager** is displayed, as shown in Figure 13-18.

Figure 13-18 The Feature Driven PropertyManager

You are prompted to select the driving feature pattern and the components to be patterned. Select the components to be patterned from the drawing area; the selected components will be displayed in green. Click once in the **Driving Feature** selection box and select a pattern feature that will drive the component pattern. The preview of the resulting pattern is displayed in the drawing area. Choose the **OK** button from the **Feature Driven PropertyManager**.

Figure 13-19 shows the components to be selected to be patterned and an instance of an existing pattern feature to be selected. Figure 13-20 shows the assembly after creating the derived pattern feature.

Figure 13-19 *Components and the instance of the pattern feature to be selected*

Figure 13-20 *Assembly after creating the derived component pattern*

In order to skip some of the instances of the pattern after it has been created, select the derived pattern feature from the **FeatureManager Design Tree** and invoke the shortcut menu. Choose the **Edit Feature** option from the shortcut menu; the resulting **PropertyManager** is displayed. Click once in the **Instances to Skip** selection box. Filled dots in magenta are displayed with the preview of the instances of the pattern. Select the dot on the instance that you need to skip; the selected instances disappear from the display and the color of the dot changes to red. To retain the instances again, select the dot. After selecting the instances to skip, choose the **OK** button from the **PropertyManager**.

Note

The number of instances of the component pattern are automatically modified when you change the number of instances of the pattern feature that was used to derive the component pattern. This indicates the associative nature of the derived component pattern.

*You may have to choose the **Rebuild** button, after editing the number of entities in the pattern feature.*

Remember that you need to modify the mates if the feature that was used to assemble the seed component is deleted while reducing the number of features in the pattern. This is because the original feature on which the mates were applied does not exist any more and so there is an error in associating the elements to mate.

Local Pattern

You can also create the patterns of the components individually, even if there is no pattern feature. This type of a component pattern is known as a local pattern. You can create two types of local patterns. They are the linear pattern and the circular pattern. Both types of the local patterns are discussed next.

Tip. *You will observe that after creating a derived circular pattern, the*
DerivedCirPattern1 *feature will be displayed in the* ***FeatureManager Design***
Tree. *The name of the feature will be* ***DerivedLPattern1***, *if the derived pattern*
creates a rectangular pattern of the components. The number at the end of the
feature displays the sequence number of the derived pattern feature.

On expanding the component pattern feature, all instances of the patterned
component are displayed. Select the instance to be skipped from the ***FeatureManager***
Design Tree *and press the DELETE key. The* ***Confirmation*** *dialog box will be*
displayed; choose the ***Yes*** *button from it.*

To restore the skipped pattern instance, select the derived pattern from the
FeatureManager Design Tree *and invoke the shortcut menu. Choose the* ***Edit***
Feature *option. Select the skipped instance from the* ***Instances to Skip*** *rollout*
and invoke the shortcut menu. Choose the ***Delete*** *option; the instance is restored.*

Linear Pattern

Choose **Insert > Component Pattern > Linear Pattern** from the menu bar for creating the
local linear pattern; the **Linear Pattern PropertyManager** is displayed. Also, you are prompted
to select an edge or axis for direction reference and the components to be patterned. Select
the direction reference and then the component to pattern from the drawing area. Other
options available in this **PropertyManager** are the same as those discussed while creating a
linear pattern of features, faces, and bodies in earlier chapters.

Circular Pattern

For creating the local circular pattern, choose **Insert > Component Pattern > Circular
Pattern** from the menu bar. The **Circular Pattern PropertyManager** is displayed and you are
prompted to select an edge or an axis for direction reference, and the components to pattern.
Select the direction reference and then the component to be patterned from the drawing
area. Other options available in this **PropertyManager** are the same as those discussed while
creating circular pattern of the features, faces, and bodies in earlier chapters.

Tip. *If one instance of the component pattern is modified or edited, the other*
instances of the component will also be modified.

You can also create the component pattern of a component pattern feature.

MIRRORING COMPONENTS

Menu:	Insert > Mirror Components

In the **Assembly** mode of SolidWorks, you can also mirror a component to place the new
instance of the component in the assembly document. To mirror the component, choose
Insert > Mirror Components from the menu bar; the **Mirror Components PropertyManager**
is displayed. Expand the rollouts, if they are not expanded, to display the options, as shown
in Figure 13-21.

Figure 13-21 *Partial view of the* **Mirror Components PropertyManager**

Select the planar face or plane that will act as a mirror plane, as shown in Figure 13-22. Next, select the component to mirror; you will observe that the name of the component with a check box is displayed in the **Components to Mirror** area. Leave this check box cleared and choose the **Next** button from the **Mirror Components PropertyManager**. The preview of the mirrored component is displayed, as shown in Figure 13-23. The **Orientation** rollout is displayed and using the options available in this rollout, you can change the orientation of the mirrored component. Choose the **OK** button from the **Mirror Components PropertyManager**. The mirrored instance of the selected component is displayed in the drawing area, as shown in Figure 13-24.

If you select the check box available with the name of the selected component in the **Components to Mirror** area, a new component is created that is mirrored along the selected mirror plane and saved in a specified location. Select the check box available along the name

Face selected as
the mirror plane

Figure 13-22 *Face to be selected as mirror plane*

Figure 13-23 *Preview of the mirrored component*

Figure 13-24 *Instance created by mirroring the component*

of the selected component and choose the **Next** button; the **Filenames** rollout is displayed. Choose the **Browse** button available in the **Filenames** rollout. This button is used to specify the name and location where the file will be saved. You can save all the mirrored instances in one folder by selecting the **Place files in one folder** check box. You can also add a suffix or a prefix to the file name by using the **Add** drop-down list.

SIMPLIFYING ASSEMBLIES USING THE VISIBILITY OPTIONS

When you are assembling the components in an assembly, whether it is a large assembly or a small assembly, you may need to simplify the assembly using the visibility options. By simplifying, you can hide the components or set its transparency at any stage of the design cycle. You can also suppress and unsuppress the components at any stage of the design cycle. The various methods of simplifying the assembly are discussed next.

Hiding Components

CommandManager:	Assemblies > Hide/Show Components
Menu:	Edit > Hide > This Configuration
Toolbar:	Assembly > Hide/Show Components

In order to hide the component placed in the assembly, select the component from the drawing area or from the **FeatureManager Design Tree**. You can select more than one component to hide by using the CTRL key. Right-click to invoke the shortcut menu and choose the **Hide** option from it; the display of the component will be turned off. The icon of the hidden component is displayed in gray in the **FeatureManager Design Tree**. To turn on the display of the hidden component, select the icon of the component from the **FeatureManager Design Tree** and invoke the shortcut menu. Select the **Show** option from the shortcut menu. The hidden component will be redisplayed in the drawing area. You can also select the component and choose the **Hide/Show Components** button from the **Assembly CommandManager** to hide or show the components.

Tip. *You will observe that the **Lightweight** check box is provided in the **Open** dialog box. On selecting this check box before opening the assembly file, the assembly will be opened only with the lightweight components.*

*A lightweight component is one in which the feature information is available in the part document, and only the graphical representation of the component is displayed in the assembly document. Therefore, the assembly environment becomes light. An icon of a lightweight component is displayed as a feather attached to the component icon in the **FeatureManager Design Tree**.*

*To get the feature information of the lightweight component, you need to resolve the component to the normal state. Therefore, select the component from the drawing area or from the **FeatureManager Design Tree** and invoke the shortcut menu. Select the **Set to Resolved** option from this shortcut menu. To set a resolved component to a lightweight component, select the component and invoke the shortcut menu. Select **Set to Lightweight** from the shortcut menu.*

Suppressing Components

CommandManager:	Assemblies > Change Suppression State
Menu:	Edit > Suppress > This Configuration
Toolbar:	Assembly > Change Suppression State

You can also suppress the components placed in the assembly to simplify the assembly representation. To do so, select the component from the drawing area or from the **FeatureManager Design Tree,** invoke the shortcut menu, and choose **Suppress**. The component will not be displayed in the assembly document and the icon of the suppressed component will be displayed in gray in the **FeatureManager Design Tree**. To unsuppress the suppressed component, select the component to be resolved from the **FeatureManager Design Tree,** invoke the shortcut menu and choose the **Set to Resolve** option from it.

You can also suppress the component using the **Change Suppression State** button from the **Assembly CommandManager**. You cannot only suppress the selected component but also set the selected component to lightweight by using the **Change Suppression State** button. When you select the component and choose the **Change Suppression State** button from the **Assembly CommandManager**, a flyout is displayed. This flyout has three options: **Suppress**, **Lightweight**, and **Resolve**. The **Resolve** option is used to set the suppressed or lightweight components to resolve state.

Changing the Transparency Conditions

In SolidWorks, you can change the transparency of the components or selected faces to simplify the assembly. First, you will learn how to change the transparency of the components. Select the component to change its transparency and invoke the shortcut menu. Choose the **Component Properties** option from the **Component** area of the shortcut menu; the **Component Properties** dialog box will be displayed. Choose the **Color** button available in this dialog box; the **Assembly Instance Color** dialog box is displayed, as shown in Figure 13-25.

Figure 13-25 *The **Assembly Instance Color** dialog box*

Choose the **Advanced** button from this dialog box; the **Advanced Properties** dialog box is displayed, as shown in Figure 13-26. You can set the transparency of the component from the **Transparency** slider. You can also set the various other advanced color settings such as **Ambient**, **Diffuse**, **Specularity**, **Shininess**, and **Emission** from this dialog box.

You can also change the transparency of a face. To do so, select the face, invoke the shortcut menu and choose the **Properties** option from the **Face** area of the shortcut menu; the **Entity Property** dialog box is displayed. Choose the **Advanced** button from this dialog box to invoke the **Advanced Properties** dialog box that can be used to set the transparency of the selected face.

Tip. *The face that has been made transparent cannot be selected by clicking. You need to select some other faces, and then choose the **Select Other** option from the shortcut menu. Right-click until the desired face is highlighted and then left-click to select it. Now, right-click anywhere in the drawing area to display the shortcut menu.*

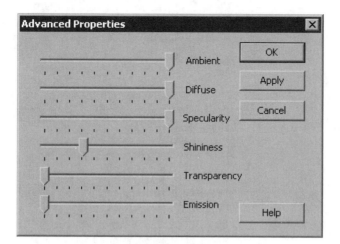

Figure 13-26 The *Advanced Properties* dialog box

CHECKING INTERFERENCES IN AN ASSEMBLY

CommandManager:	Assemblies > Interference Detection
Menu:	Tools > Interference Detection
Toolbar:	Assembly > Interference Detection

 After creating the assembly design, the first and the most essential step is to check the interference between the components of the assembly. If there is interference, the components may not assemble properly after they roll out from the machine shop or tool room. Therefore, before sending the part and assembly files for the detailing and drafting purpose, it is essential to check the interference. To do so, choose the **Interference Detection** button from the **Assemblies CommandManager**; the **Interference Detection PropertyManager** is displayed. The name of the current assembly is displayed in the **Components to Check** selection box in the **Selected components** rollout. You can also check the interference between two or more than two components. To select the components, first clear the current selection set and select the components from the assembly. Next, choose the **Calculate** button from this **Selected components** rollout to check the interference. If there is any interference between the components in the assembly, it will be displayed in the assembly and also the interfering components will be displayed in the **Results** rollout, as shown in Figure 13-27. Expand the names of the interfering components to view the cause of interference. You can select a component/interference from the **Results** rollout and choose the **Ignore** button to ignore that particular component/interference while calculating the interference.

The **Treat coincidence as interference** check box available in the **Options** rollout considers the **Coincident** mates also as interference. The **Show ignored interferences** check box is selected to show the interferences that you ignored while using the **Ignore** button in the **Results** rollout. If you select the **Treat subassemblies as components** check box, all subassemblies in the current assembly will be treated as single components and any interference in the subassembly will be ignored. The **Include multibody part interferences** check box is selected to analyze the multibody parts for interference. If the **Make interfering**

***Figure 13-27** Interfering parts displayed in the*
Interference Detection PropertyManager

parts transparent check box is selected, the interfering parts are made transparent in the drawing window. The **Create Fasteners Folder** check box is selected to place the interfering fasteners in a separate folder in the **Results** rollout.

The **Non-interfering Components** rollout is used to select the display option for the non-interfering parts. After analyzing the assembly, you can edit or modify the part.

CREATING ASSEMBLIES FOR MECHANISM

As mentioned earlier, there are two types of assemblies. The first one is a fully defined assembly in which the relative movement of all the components is contained. The second type is the one in which the components are not fully defined and some degree of freedom is kept unconstrained. As a result, they can move in a certain direction with respect to the surroundings of the assembly. This flexibility in turn helps you to create mechanisms and then you can move the assembly to check the mechanisms that you have designed. Consider the case of a Bench Vice, in which you are assembling the Vice Jaw with the Vice Body. For this assembly to work, the linear movement of the Vice Jaw, when placed on the Vice Body, should be free. Therefore, while creating this assembly for mechanism, you should not apply the mates for constraining the linear motion of the Vice Jaw with respect to the Vice Body. Figure 13-28 shows the degree of freedom that is required to be free to create an assembly for motion.

The degree of freedom in this direction should be free for the translational motion

Figure 13-28 Direction in which the degree of freedom should be free

After creating the assembly for mechanism by defining minimum mates, invoke the **Move Component** tool. Select one of the faces of the component that you need to move and drag the cursor to move the assembly. The options available for analyzing the assembly, while moving the assembly for mechanism design, are discussed next.

Analyzing Collisions Using the Collision Detection Tool

In SolidWorks, you can also analyze any collision between the components of the assembly while the assembly is in motion. Invoke the **Move Component PropertyManager** and then the **Options** rollout. Select the **Collision Detection** radio button, as shown in Figure 13-29; the **Check between** area is displayed. The options available in this area are used to specify the components between which the collision will be detected. These options available in the **Check between** area are discussed next.

*Figure 13-29 The **Options** rollout of the Move Component PropertyManager*

All components

This radio button is selected to check the collision between all components of the assembly.

These components

The **These components** radio button is selected to check the collision only between the selected components when the assembly is in motion. On selecting this radio button, the **Components for Collision Check** selection box and the **Resume Drag** button is displayed in the **Options** rollout, as shown in Figure 13-30. The name of the components, between which the collision is to be detected, is displayed in the **Components for Collision Check** selection box. After selecting the components, choose the **Resume Drag** button from the **Options** rollout and drag the cursor to move the assembly.

*Figure 13-30 The **Options** rollout with the **These** components radio button selected*

Stop at collision

The **Stop at collision** check box is selected to stop the motion of the assembly when one of the components collides with another component during the assembly motion.

Dragged part only

The **Dragged part only** check box should be selected when you need to detect the collision only between the components that you selected to be moved. If this check box is cleared, the collision is determined between the components that you have selected to move and any other component that moves because of the mates with the selected components.

After setting the options in the **Options** rollout, drag the assembly using the **Move Component** tool or the **Rotate Component** tool. If a component of the assembly collides with another component while the assembly is in motion, the faces of the components that collide with each other, will be displayed in green. If the **Stop at collision** check box is selected, the motion of the assembly will be stopped, when one of the components collides with another component of the assembly.

Consider the assembly shown in Figure 13-31. In this assembly, you need to move the slider in the given direction. Invoke the **Move PropertyManager** and select the **Collision Detection** radio button from the **Options** rollout. Drag the slider to move in the given direction. Figure 13-32 shows that the slider collides with the extrusion feature created in the vertical column of the base component. The faces of the components that collide are displayed in green. If the **Stop at collision** check box is selected, you cannot move the component further, after it collides with one of the components of the assembly.

Figure 13-31 *Direction in which the slider will be moved inside the base*

Figure 13-32 *The faces of the components highlighted in green after collision*

Once the collision is detected in the assembly, you can edit and modify the components that collide during the assembly motion.

CREATING THE EXPLODED STATE OF AN ASSEMBLY

CommandManager:	Assemblies > Exploded View
Menu:	Insert > Exploded View
Toolbar:	Assembly > Exploded View

In SolidWorks, you can create an exploded state of the assembly using the **Explode PropertyManager**. To invoke this **PropertyManager**, choose the **Exploded View** button from the **Assemblies CommandManager**. You can also invoke this **PropertyManager** by first invoking the **ConfigurationManager** and then selecting the **Default** option from the **ConfigurationManager** for invoking the shortcut menu. Choose the **New Explode View** option from it. The **Explode PropertyManager** is shown in Figure 13-33.

The **Explode PropertyManager** allows you to explode an assembly using the manipulator. After invoking the **Explode PropertyManager**, select the component to be exploded; the manipulator is displayed on the component and the name of the component is displayed in the **Component(s) of the explode step** selection box of the **Settings** rollout. Now, to explode the component along any of the axes of the manipulator, move the cursor over the arrowhead of that axis. When the cursor changes into the move cursor, press and hold the left mouse

*Figure 13-33 The **Explode PropertyManager***

button down and drag the cursor to explode the component. You can also set the exact numeric value of the explode distance. To do this, select the direction from the manipulator and set the value of the explosion distance in the **Explode distance** spinner provided in the **Settings** rollout. Now, choose the **Apply** button provided below this spinner. You can select an edge or a face to define the direction of explosion.

If the **Auto-spec components after drag** check box is selected in the **Options** rollout, the explosion is displayed as **Chain 1** in the **Existing explode steps** area of the **Explode Steps** rollout. However, if the **Auto-spec components after drag** check box is cleared, the explosion is displayed as **Explode Step 1**. You will learn more about the **Auto-spec components after drag** check box later in this chapter. To edit the **Chain 1** or **Explode Step 1**, select it and invoke the shortcut menu. Choose the **Edit Step** option from the shortcut menu. Edit the position of the selected component.

You can delete an explode step by selecting it and choosing the **Delete** option from the shortcut menu. After exploding a component, select another component to be exploded. Similarly, you can create as many explode steps as you want.

You can also perform the auto-explosion by selecting all the components of the assembly together. You can drag a window across the assembly to select all its components. Now, select the direction from the manipulator, along which you need to explode all the components. Set the value of the explode distance in the **Explode distance** spinner. Choose the **Apply** button.

The options available in the **Options** rollout, shown in Figure 13-34, are used to specify the explode options. The **Auto-space components after drag** check box is used to specify an automatic spacing between the components, after exploding them using the auto-explode method. The **Adjust the spacing between the chain components** slider bar is used to adjust the spacing between the chain of components in order to define the automatic spacing between the components after dragging. The **Select sub-assembly's parts** check box is used to select the components of the subassembly also for exploding.

The **Re-use Sub-assembly Explode** button is chosen to reuse the explode steps of a subassembly also in the current assembly.

Figure 13-34 The Options rollout of the Explode PropertyManager

Figure 13-35 shows the assembly exploded using the auto-explode method. Figure 13-36 show assemblies exploded using the **Explode PropertyManager**.

Figure 13-35 Auto-explosion of an assembly   *Figure 13-36 A systematic exploded state of an assembly*

Creating the Explode Line Sketch

CommandManager:	Assemblies > Explode Line Sketch
Menu:	Insert > Explode Line Sketch
Toolbar:	Assemblies > Explode Line Sketch

Explode lines are the parametric axes that display the direction of explosion of the components in the exploded state. Figure 13-37 shows an exploded assembly with explode lines.

To create an explode line sketch, choose the **Explode Line Sketch** button from the **Assembly CommandManager**; the sketching environment is invoked and the **Explode Sketch** toolbar is displayed. Also, the **Route Line PropertyManager** is displayed, as shown in Figure 13-38. You are prompted to select a cylindrical face, planar face, vertex, point, arc, or line entities. One by one, select the cylindrical faces of the two components to create an explode line between them. For example, in order to create an explode line between the Oval Fillister and the Vice Jaw, select the cylindrical face of the Oval Fillister that goes inside the Vice Jaw. Now, select the cylindrical hole of the Vice Jaw. The preview of the explode line appears. Choose

Figure 13-37 Explode line sketch created on an exploded assembly

*Figure 13-38 The **Route Line PropertyManager***

OK to create the explode line. The names of the selected faces are displayed in the **Items To Connect** selection box. When you select an entity to create an explode line, an arrow is also displayed with the line. You can use that arrow or select the **Reverse** check box from the **Options** rollout to reverse the direction of the explode line creation. Next, choose the **OK** button from the **Route Line PropertyManager** and exit the sketching environment.

TUTORIALS

Tutorial 1

In this tutorial, you will create the radial engine assembly shown in Figure 13-39. This assembly will be created in two parts: one will be the subassembly and the second will be the main assembly. You will also create the exploded state of the assembly and then create the explode line sketch. The exploded state of the assembly is displayed in Figure 13-40. The views and dimensions of all the components of this assembly are displayed in Figures 13-41 through 13-44.   **(Expected time: 3 hrs)**

Figure 13-39 *The radial engine assembly*

Figure 13-40 *Exploded view of the assembly*

Figure 13-41 *Views and dimensions of the Piston*

Section A—A

Figure 13-42 *Views and dimensions of the Articulated Rod*

Figure 13-43 *Views and dimensions of other components*

Section A–A

Figure 13-44 *Views and dimensions of the Master Rod*

You need to break this assembly in two steps because it is a large assembly. One will be the subassembly and the other will be the main assembly. First, you need to create the subassembly consisting of Articulation Rod, Piston, Piston Rings, Piston Pin, Rod Bush Upper, Rod Bush Lower, and Piston Pin Plug. Next, create the main assembly by assembling the Master Rod with the Piston, Piston Rings, Piston Pin, Rod Bush Upper, and Piston Pin Plug. Finally, you will assemble the subassembly with the main assembly.

The steps to be followed to complete this tutorial are listed next.

a. Create all components of the assembly in the **Part** mode and save the components in a folder named *Radial Engine Assembly*.
b. Start a new assembly document and assemble the components to complete the subassembly, refer to Figures 13-45 through 13-47.
c. Start a new assembly document and assemble the components of the main assembly, refer to Figure 13-48.

d.   Assemble the subassembly in the main assembly, refer to Figures 13-49 through 13-53.

e.   Create the exploded view of the assembly and then create the explode line sketch, refer to Figures 13-54 through 13-56.

Creating the Components

1.   Create a folder with the name *Radial Engine Assembly* in the */My Documents/ SolidWorks/c13* folder. Create all components in the individual part documents and save them in this folder.

Note
While creating the Master Rod, make sure that the holes on the left of the Master Rod should be created using the sketch-driven pattern. This is done because while assembling the Link Pin you will create the derived pattern of the Link Pin using the sketch-driven pattern feature.

Creating the Subassembly

As discussed earlier, you will first create the subassembly and then assemble it with the main assembly.

1.   Start a new SolidWorks assembly document and exit the **Insert Component PropertyManager**. Next, save it with the name **Piston Articulation Rod Subassembly** in the same folder in which the parts are created.

2.   First place the Articulated Rod at the origin of the assembly and then place the other components such as Piston, Piston Pin, Piston Pin Plug, Rod Bush Upper, and Rod Bush Lower in the assembly document.

3.   Apply the required mates to assemble these components. Figure 13-45 shows the sequence required to assemble the components. The exploded view and the explode line sketch is given only for your reference. The assembly, after assembling the Articulated Rod, Piston, Piston Pin, Piston Pin Plug, Rod Bush Upper, and Rod Bush Lower, is shown in Figure 13-46.

Figure 13-45 Assembly of the Articulated Rod, Piston, Piston Pin, Piston Pin Plug, Rod Bush Upper, and Rod Bush Lower

Figure 13-46 First instance of the Piston Ring assembled with the Piston

It is clear from the assembly that you need to assemble four instances of the Piston Ring. You will assemble only one instance of the Piston Ring at the uppermost groove of the ring and then create a local linear pattern.

4. Insert the Piston Ring in the assembly document and assemble the Piston Ring at the uppermost groove of the Piston using the assembly mates, see Figure 13-46. In this figure, the color of the Piston Ring is changed by selecting it and choosing the **Component Properties** option from the shortcut menu. Choose the **Color** button from the **Component Properties** dialog box to change the color.

Next, you need to create the local linear pattern of the Piston Ring.

5. Choose **Insert > Component Pattern > Linear Pattern** from the menu bar; the **Linear Pattern PropertyManager** is displayed.

6. Select any one of the horizontal edges of the Articulated Rod to define the direction of pattern creation.

7. Click once in the **Components to Pattern** selection box and select the Piston Ring from the drawing area.

The preview of the linear pattern with the default settings is displayed in the drawing area.

8. Select the **Reverse Direction** button to reverse the direction of pattern creation, if required.

9. Set the value of the **Spacing** spinner to **5** and the value of the **Number of Instances** spinner to **4**.

10. Choose the **OK** button from the **Linear Pattern PropertyManager**.

The subassembly, after patterning the Piston Ring, is shown in Figure 13-47

The subassembly is completed. Save and close the assembly document.

Creating the Main Assembly

Next, you will create the main assembly and then assemble the subassembly with it.

1. Start a new SolidWorks assembly document and exit the **Insert Component PropertyManager**. Now, save it with the name **Radial Engine Subassembly** in the same folder in which the parts are created.

2. First, place the Master Rod at the origin of the assembly and then place the Piston, Piston Pin, Piston Pin Plug, Piston Ring, Rod Bush Upper, and Master Rod Bearing in the current assembly document.

3. Using the assembly mates and the local linear pattern option, assemble all components of the main assembly.

    The components, after assembling in the main assembly, are displayed in Figure 13-48.

Figure 13-47 Subassembly after patterning the Piston ring

Figure 13-48 Components assembled in the Main assembly.

Assembling the Subassembly With the Main Assembly

Next, you will place the subassembly in the main assembly and then assemble them together.

1. Choose the **Insert Components** button from the **Assemblies CommandManager**; the **Insert Component PropertyManager** is displayed.

2. Choose the **Browse** button available in the **Part/Assembly to Insert** rollout; the **Open** dialog box is displayed.

3. Choose **Assembly** (**.asm, *.sldasm*) from the **Files of type** drop-down list.

4. Double-click on *Piston Articulated Rod Subassembly* and place the subassembly in the main assembly. Figure 13-49 shows the subassembly and the main assembly placed together.

5. Using the assembly mates, assemble the subassembly with the main assembly. Refer to Figure 13-50, which shows the assembly structure to help you in assembling the instances of the subassembly.

Tip. *You can create more than one instance of the subassembly by holding down the CTRL key; select and drag the subassembly from the **FeatureManager Design Tree**. Release the left mouse button to place the assembly in the current assembly document.*

Figure 13-49 *Subassembly and the main assembly placed together*

Figure 13-50 *Assembly structure*

Figure 13-51 shows all instances of the subassembly assembled with the main assembly.

Assembling the Link Pin

After assembling the subassembly with the main assembly, you need to assemble the Link Pin with the main assembly.

1. Place the Link Pin in the current assembly document and using the assembly mates, assemble the Link Pin with the main assembly. Figure 13-52 shows the first instance of Link Pin assembled with the main assembly.

Figure 13-51 *Subassembly assembled to the main assembly*

Figure 13-52 *First instance of the Link Pin assembled with the main assembly*

As discussed earlier, the other instances of the Link Pin will be assembled using the sketch-driven pattern feature of the holes created on the left of the master rod.

2. Choose **Insert > Component Pattern > Feature Driven** from the menu bar; the **Feature Driven PropertyManager** is displayed.

3. Select the Link Pin from the main assembly; its name is displayed in the **Components to Pattern** selection box.

4. Click once in the **Driving Feature** selection box to activate the selection mode.

5. Select any one of the hole instances from the master rod. The name of the sketch pattern feature will be displayed in the **Driving Feature** selection box and the preview of the resulting pattern is also displayed.

6. Choose the **OK** button from the **Feature Driven PropertyManager**.

Figure 13-53 displays the final assembly.

Exploding the Assembly

After creating the assembly, you need to explode it using the **Assembly Exploder** tool.

1. Choose the **Exploded View** button from the **Assemblies CommandManager**; the **Explode PropertyManager** is displayed.

2. Click once in the **Explode direction** selection box to highlight it. Select any vertical edge from the assembly to define the direction in which the components will be exploded. The **Component(s) of the explode step** selection box is automatically highlighted.

Figure 13-53 *The final assembly*

The **Select sub-assembly's parts** check box has to be selected, if it is cleared in the **Options** rollout. If this check box is cleared then selecting a component selects the complete sub-assembly. On selecting this check box, you can select the individual components of the sub-assembly.

3. Select the **Select sub-assembly's parts** check box. From the assembly, select all the Piston Pin Plugs that are assembled on the upper hole of the piston.

    Ensure that the **Auto-space components after drag** check box is cleared in the **Options** rollout.

4. Set the value of the **Explode distance** spinner to **170**, choose the **Apply** button from the **Settings** rollout and then choose **Done**. The selected instances of the Piston Pin Plug are exploded and the components removed from the selection set. Also, this sequence of explosion is displayed as **Chain 1** in the **Existing explode steps** area of the **Explode Steps** rollout.

5. Click once in the **Explode direction** selection box and again select the same vertical edge to define the direction of explosion. Choose the **Reverse direction** button available on the left of the **Explode direction** selection box to reverse the direction of explosion.

6. Rotate the view of the assembly and select all instances of the Piston Pin Plug that are assembled with the lower holes of the Pistons.

    The explosion value in the **Explode distance** spinner shows a value of 60. You can accept this value to explode the lower Piston Pin Plugs.

7. Choose **Apply** and then choose **Done** to explode the selected components.

8. Click in the **Explode direction** selection box again and select the same vertical edge to define the explosion direction. Now, select all instances of the Piston Pin from the assembly.

9. Set the value of the **Distance** spinner to **140**. Choose **Apply** and then choose **Done**.

10. Similarly, explode the other components of the assembly and then choose **OK** to exit the **Explode PropertyManager**. The assembly, after exploding the components, is shown in Figure 13-54.

Figure 13-54 Final exploded assembly

Creating the Explode Line Sketch

After exploding the assembly, you need to create the explode line sketch of the exploded state of the assembly.

1. Choose the **Explode Line Sketch** button from the **Assemblies CommandManager**; the **Route Line PropertyManager** is displayed and you are prompted to select a cylindrical face, planar face, vertex, point, arc, or line entities.

2. Choose the **Keep Visible** button, if not chosen automatically, from the **Route Line PropertyManager**, to keep it visible on the screen.

3. Select the cylindrical face, as shown in Figure 13-55, as the first selection; the name of the selected face will be displayed in the **Items To Connect** selection box. Also, the preview of the explode line sketch is displayed at the center of the selected face.

4. Refer to Figure 13-55 and select the other cylindrical faces to create the explode line sketch.

5. Next, choose the **OK** button; an exploded line will be created.

First selection

Third selection—

Second selection

Fourth selection

Fifth selection—

Sixth selection—

Figure 13-55 Faces to be selected to create explode line sketch

6. Similarly, create explode lines between other parts of the exploded assembly. Figure 13-56 shows the assembly after creating the explode line sketch.

Figure 13-56 Explode line sketch created to the exploded state of the assembly

7. Invoke the **ConfigurationManager** and expand the **Default** option. Select **ExplView1** and invoke the shortcut menu. Choose the **Collapse** option from the shortcut menu to switch back to the collapse state of the assembly.

8. Save and close the assembly document.

Tutorial 2

In this tutorial, you will modify the assembly created in Tutorial 1 (Bench Vice) of Chapter 12. You will modify the design of the components of the assembly and then suppress some mates that enable it to move along a particular degree of freedom. Next, check the assembly for collision detection when the assembly is in motion and then modify the assembly and check the interference. **(Expected time: 1 hr)**

The steps that will be followed to complete this tutorial are listed next.

a.   Save the Bench Vice assembly folder in *c13* directory and then open the Bench Vice assembly.
b.   Modify the design of the components within the context of the assembly, refer to Figures 13-57 through 13-61.
c.   Suppress the mate to enable the Vice Jaw to move along the slide ways of the Vice Body.
d.   Check the new assembly design for collision detection when the assembly is in motion. Modify the design, if there is any collision between the components, refer to Figures 13-62 and 13-63.
e.   Check the interference in the modified assembly.

Opening the Bench Vice Assembly

The assembly created in Tutorial 1 of Chapter 12 is the Bench Vice assembly. You need to copy and save it in the current folder of Chapter 13.

1.   Copy the folder in which the Bench vice assembly is saved and paste it in the *c13* folder.

2.   Invoke the **Open** dialog box and browse the Bench Vice assembly document. Double-click on it to open the assembly document.

Modifying the Design of the Components of the Bench Vice Assembly

You need to modify the components in the context of the assembly because of some alteration in the design of some of the components.

Before you start modifying the components, it is recommended that you hide some of them. This will simplify the assembly and facilitate in the selection of components while editing and modifying them.

1.   Press and hold down the CTRL key on the keyboard and select the Clamping Plate, Base Plate, all four Set Screw 1, both Set Screw 2, Oval Fillister, Screw Bar, and Jaw Screw from the **FeatureManager Design Tree**.

2.   Invoke the shortcut menu and choose the **Hide** option from the **Component** area of the shortcut menu.

The display of the selected components is turned off and is not displayed in the drawing area of the assembly document.

The design alteration includes creating a through slot on the right face of the Vice Jaw. To modify its design, you first need to enable the part editing environment.

3. Select the Vice Jaw from the assembly and choose the **Edit Component** button from the **Assemblies CommandManager**. The part modeling environment is invoked in the assembly document.

4. Make sure that the Vice Body is transparent. If not, choose the **Assembly Transparency** button from the **Assemblies CommandManager**; a flyout is displayed. Choose the **Force Transparency** option from the flyout. The Vice Body is displayed in transparent, as shown in Figure 13-57.

5. Select the right face of the Vice Jaw and invoke the sketching environment.

6. Create the sketch of the slot, as shown in Figure 13-58.

Figure 13-57 *Vice Jaw in the part edit mode in the assembly document*

Figure 13-58 *Sketch of the slot*

7. Invoke the **Cut-Extrude PropertyManager**.

8. Create the cut feature using the **Through All** option.

9. Choose the **Edit Component** button to exit the part editing environment.

Figure 13-59 shows the assembly after modifying the design of the Vice Jaw.

10. Similarly modify the design of the Vice Body. You need to create a blind extruded boss feature up to 60 mm depth on the right face of the component. You also need to reverse the direction of feature creation.

The sketch of the feature is shown in Figure 13-60. Figure 13-61 shows the assembly, after exiting the part editing environment.

Figure 13-59 Modified Vice Jaw

Figure 13-60 Sketch of the extruded boss feature

Figure 13-61 Modified assembly

11. Choose the **Save** button from the **Standard** toolbar. The **SolidWorks** information box is displayed and you are informed that some models referenced in the document are modified and they must be saved. Choose **Yes** to save the referenced models also.

Suppressing the Mate to Make the Movement of Vice Jaw Free in a Specified Direction

To analyze the movement of the Bench vice assembly, you need to make the movement of the Vice Jaw free in the X direction. By doing so, the Vice Jaw will slide on the sideways of the Vice Body.

1. Expand the **Mates** mategroup from the **FeatureManager Design Tree** and select the **Distance1** mate. The planar faces of the Vice Jaw and the Vice Body, to which this mate is applied, are highlighted in green.

2. Invoke the shortcut menu. Choose the **Suppress** option from the shortcut menu.

    Now, the degree of freedom in the X direction is free.

3. Choose the **Move Component** button from the **Assemblies CommandManager** and select a horizontal edge of the Vice Jaw. On dragging the cursor, you will observe that you can move the Vice Jaw in the X direction.

4. Drag the Vice Jaw back to its original position and choose the **OK** button from the **Move Component PropertyManager**.

Analyzing the Collision Between the Components When the Assembly is in Motion

Next, you will analyze the collision between the components of the assembly when the assembly is in motion.

1. Again, choose the **Move Component** button from the **Assemblies CommandManager**. Select the **Collision Detection** radio button from the **Options** rollout.

2. Select Vice Jaw and drag the cursor to move it in the direction shown in Figure 13-62.

3. On moving the Vice Jaw in the specified direction, you will observe that the right face of the Vice Jaw and the newly created extrusion feature of the Vice Body are highlighted in green, as shown in Figure 13-63.

Figure 13-62 *Direction in which the Vice Jaw will be moved*

Figure 13-63 *Faces of the Vice Jaw and the Vice Body highlighted in green*

This indicates that the Vice Jaw collides with the Vice Body. Leave the assembly at this location.

4. Choose the **OK** button from the **Move Component PropertyManager**.

The collision is detected in the assembly, and so you need to modify the design of one of the components. In this case, you will modify the dimensions of the extruded boss feature.

5. Double-click the newly created extrusion feature of the Vice Body; the dimensions of the newly created feature will be displayed.

6. Double-click the dimension that has a of value **6**; the **Modify** dialog box is displayed; set the value of the dimension to **4** and press the ENTER key.

7. Press CTRL+B on the keyboard to rebuild the entire assembly.

8. Choose the **Interference Detection** button from the **Assemblies CommandManager**. The **Interference Detection PropertyManager** is displayed.

9. You will observe that **No Interferences** is displayed in the **Interference Results** selection box in the **Results** rollout of this **PropertyManager**.

10. Choose the **Cancel** button from the **Interference Detection PropertyManager**.

Next, you need to show all the components of this assembly.

11. Press and hold the CTRL key, select the hidden components from the **FeatureManager Design Tree,** and invoke the shortcut menu. Choose the **Show** option from the shortcut menu.

12. Save the assembly document and all the referenced part documents.

SELF-EVALUATION TEST

Answer the following questions and then compare your answers with those given at the end of this chapter:

1. You can create subassemblies in the assembly environment of SolidWorks. (T/F)

2. You cannot create a subassembly of the components that are already placed in an assembly document. (T/F)

3. When you move the cursor on a mate in the **FeatureManager Design Tree**, the entities used in the mate are highlighted in red in the drawing area. (T/F)

4. You cannot edit the assembly mates. (T/F)

5. While in the part editing mode in the assembly document, you can use the **Move/Size Features** tool to edit the features dynamically using editing handles. (T/F)

6. The component patterns created individually without the use of any existing pattern feature are known as _____ patterns.

7. The component patterns created using an existing pattern feature are known as _____ patterns.

8. In _____ component, the feature information is available in the part document and only the graphical representation of the component is displayed in the assembly document.

9. After selecting the component, choose the _____ option from the shortcut menu to change the transparency condition of the selected component.

10. To create the explode line sketch, choose the _____ button from the **Assemblies CommandManager**.

REVIEW QUESTIONS
Answer the following questions.

1. Which option is used to open a component separately in the part document?

    (a) **Modify**   (b) **Edit**
    (c) **Open Part**   (d) None of these

2. Which option is used to define whether a component collides with another component of the assembly or not?

    (a) **Collision Detection**   (b) **Interference Detection**
    (c) **Mass Properties**   (d) None of these

3. Which check box is selected in the **Open** dialog box to open an assembly with lightweight parts?

    (a) **Lightweight**   (b) **Open Lightweight**
    (c) **Lightweight parts**   (d) **Lightweight assembly**

4. Which button available in the **Assembly CommandManager** is used to suppress a component?

    (a) **Change Suppression State**   (b) **Suppress**
    (c) **Hide/Show Component**   (d) **Move Component**

5. Which button is selected from the **Assemblies CommandManager** to create an exploded view?

    (a) **Exploded View**   (b) **Assembly Exploder**
    (c) **Mate**   (d) None of these

6. The _____ radio button is used to create a local linear pattern.

7. To show the hidden component, select the icon of the component from the **FeatureManager Design Tree,** invoke the shortcut menu, and choose the _____ option from it.

8. The _____ option is used to pattern the instances of the components using an existing pattern feature.

9. The explode state of the assembly is created using the _____ dialog box.

10. The _____ check box is selected to stop the motion of the assembly, when one of the component collides with another component, when the assembly is in motion.

EXERCISE

Exercise 1

Create the assembly shown in Figure 13-64. Ensure that the back plate is fixed and the entire assembly can move in the Y direction with respect to the back plate. Keep the rotational degree of freedom of the screw rod free so that it can also rotate on its axis. After creating the assembly, explode it and create the explode line sketch. The exploded view of the assembly with the explode line sketch is shown in Figure 13-65. The dimensions of the model are given in Figures 13-66 through 13-70. Assume the missing dimensions.

(Expected time: 4 hrs)

Figure 13-64 Shaper tool holder assembly

Figure 13-65 *Exploded view of the Shaper tool holder assembly with explode lines*

Figure 13-66 *Views and dimensions of the Back Plate*

Figure 13-67 *Views and dimensions of the Vertical Slide*

Figure 13-68 *Views and dimensions of the Swivel Plate*

***Figure 13-69** Views and dimensions of the components*

Figure 13-70 *Views and dimensions of the components*

Answers to Self-Evaluation Test
1. T, **2.** F, **3.** T, **4.** F, **5.** F, **6. Local, 7. Derived, 8. Lightweight, 9. Component Properties, 10. Explode Line Sketch**

Chapter 14

Working With Drawing Views-I

Learning Objectives

After completing this chapter, you will be able to:
- *Generate standard three views.*
- *Generate model views.*
- *Generate relative views.*
- *Generate predefined views.*
- *Generate projected views.*
- *Generate section views.*
- *Generate aligned section views.*
- *Generate broken-out section views.*
- *Generate auxiliary views.*
- *Generate detail views.*
- *Generate crop views.*
- *Generate broken views.*
- *Generate alternate position views.*
- *Generate the view of an assembly in the exploded state.*
- *Work with interactive drafting.*
- *Edit the drawing views.*
- *Change the scale of the drawing views.*
- *Delete drawing views.*
- *Modify the hatch pattern of the section views.*

THE DRAWING MODE

After creating the solid models of the parts or assemblies, you need to generate the two-dimensional (2D) drawing views. These views are the lifeline of all the manufacturing systems because at the shop floor or machine floor, the machinist mostly needs the 2D drawing for manufacturing. SolidWorks has provides a specialized environment, known as the **Drawing** mode, that has all the tools required to generate and modify the drawing views and add dimensions and annotations to them. In other words, you can get the final shop floor drawing using this mode of SolidWorks. You can also sketch the 2D drawings in the **Drawing** mode of SolidWorks using the sketching tools provided in this mode.

In other words, there are two types of drafting methods available in SolidWorks: Generative drafting and Interactive drafting. Generative drafting is a technique of generating the drawing views using a solid model or an assembly. Interactive drafting is a technique of using the sketching tools to sketch a drawing view in the **Drawing** mode. In this chapter, you will learn about generating the drawing views of parts or assemblies.

One of the major advantages of working in SolidWorks is that this software is bidirectionally associative in nature. This property ensures that the modifications made in a model in the **Part** mode are reflected in the **Assembly** mode and the **Drawing** mode, and vice versa.

STARTING A DRAWING DOCUMENT

To generate the drawing views, you need to start a new drawing document. There are two methods of starting a drawing document in SolidWorks 2006. You can use the **New SolidWorks Document** dialog box or the option available in the part of assembly document to start a drawing document. Both these methods are discussed next.

Starting a New Drawing Document Using the New SolidWorks Document Dialog box

To start a new drawing document for generating the drawing views, invoke the **New SolidWorks Document** dialog box. Choose the **Drawing** button, as shown in Figure 14-1, and choose the **OK** button. A new drawing document is started and the **Sheet Format/Size** dialog box is also displayed. Figure 14-2 shows the initial screen of the drawing document with the **Sheet Format/Size** dialog box. Select the available drawing template file from this dialog box. A new drawing document will be started.

The Model View PropertyManager is invoked automatically when you start a new drawing document. Its appearance will depend on whether any part or assembly document was opened or not when you started the new drawing document.

Tip. *If you start a new drawing document by choosing the **drawing** template from the **Tutorial** tab of the **New SolidWorks Document** dialog box, when used in the **Advanced** mode, the **Sheet Format/Size** dialog box is not displayed.*

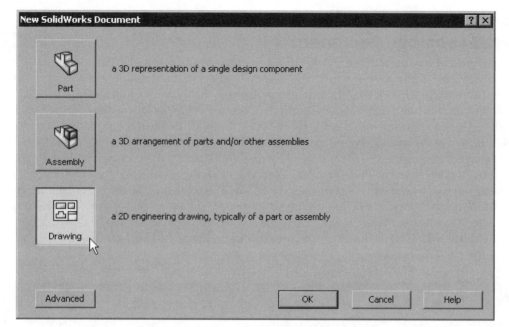

Figure 14-1 The *New SolidWorks Document* dialog box

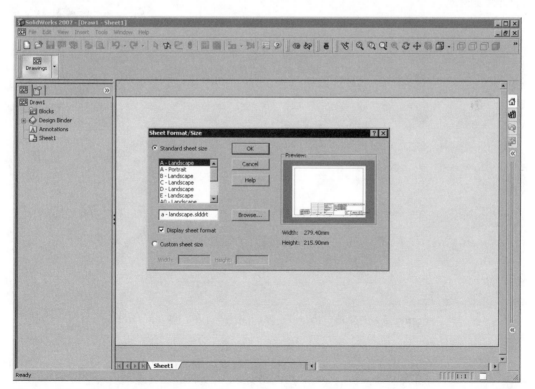

Figure 14-2 The initial screen of the drawing document with the *Sheet Format/Size* dialog box

Starting a New Drawing Document From Within the Part/Assembly Document

This method of starting a new drawing document is recommended when the part or the assembly document of which you want to generate the drawing views is open. In this case, choose the **Make Drawing from Part/Assembly** button from the **Standard** toolbar of the part or assembly document; the **New SolidWorks Document** dialog box will be displayed if you are using it in the advanced mode. Select the drawing template and choose the **OK** button; a new drawing document will be started and the **Sheet Format/Size** dialog box will be displayed. You can select the required format and size of the sheet from this dialog box. A new drawing document will be started and the **View Palette** will be displayed on the right of the drawing window, as shown in Figure 14-3. The **View Palette** shows the preview of all the views of the component in the part file that was used to start this drawing file. You can drag the required view from this window to the drawing sheet. As soon as you drag a view to the drawing sheet, the **View Palette** will be closed and the **Projected View PropertyManager** will be displayed to create the projected views.

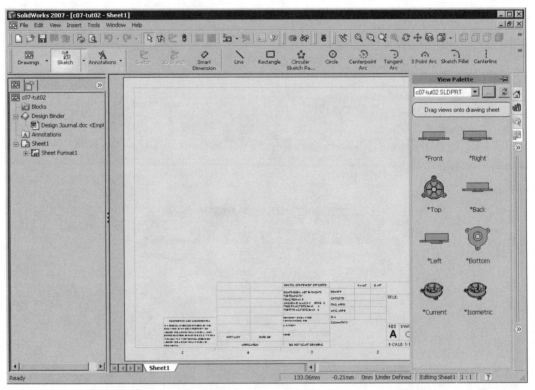

*Figure 14-3 A new drawing document with the **View Palette***

Tip. *If you choose the **Cancel** button from the **Sheet Format/Size** dialog box, a blank custom sheet of size 431.80 mm x 279.40 mm will be inserted in the drawing document.*

TYPES OF VIEWS

You can generate nine types of views in SolidWorks. Generally, you first need to generate a standard view, such as the top view or the front view, and then use it to derive the remaining views from the standard view. The following are the types of views that you can generate.

Model View

The model view is used to create the base view in the drawing sheet. You can generate orthogonal views such as the front, top, left, and so on as the model view. You can also generate isometric, trimetric, or dimetric views as the model view.

Projected View

The projected view is generated by taking an existing view as the parent view. It is generated by projecting the lines normal from the parent view or at an angle. The resulting view will be an orthographic view or a 3D view.

Section View

A section view is generated by chopping a part of an existing view using a plane and then viewing the parent view from a direction normal to the section plane. In SolidWorks, the section plane is defined using one or more sketched line segments.

Aligned Section View

An aligned section view is used to section the features that are created at a certain angle to the main section planes. Align sections straighten these features by revolving them about an axis that is normal to the view plane. Remember, that the axis about which the feature is straightened should lie on the cutting planes.

Auxiliary View

An auxiliary view is generated by projecting the lines normal to a specified edge of an existing view.

Detail View

A detail view is used to display the details of a portion of an existing view. You can select the portion whose detailing has to be shown in the parent view. The portion that you have selected will be magnified and placed as a separate view. You can control the magnification of the detail view.

Broken View

A broken view is the one in which a portion of the drawing view is removed from in between, keeping the ends of the drawing view intact. This type of view is used to display the components whose length to width ratio is very high. This means that either the length is very large as compared to the width or the width is very large as compared to the length. The broken view will break the view along the horizontal or vertical direction such that the drawing view fits the required area.

Broken-out Section View

A broken-out section view is used to remove a part of the existing view and display the area of the model or the assembly that lies behind the removed portion. This type of view is generated using a closed sketch associated with the parent view.

Crop View

A crop view is used to crop an existing view enclosed in a closed sketch associated to that view. The portion of the view that lies inside the associated sketch is retained and the remaining portion is removed.

Alternate Position View

The alternate position view is used to create a view in which you can show both the maximum and minimum range of motion of the assembly. The main position is displayed in the drawing view in continuous lines and the alternate position of the assembly is shown in the same view in dashed lines (phantom lines).

GENERATING STANDARD DRAWING VIEWS

A standard view is generally the first view that you generate in the current drawing sheet. There are a number of methods of generating the standard drawing views. All these methods are discussed next.

Generating Model Views

Command Manager:	Drawing > Model View
Menu:	Insert > Drawing View > Model
Toolbar:	Drawing > Model View

As mentioned earlier, the model views can be used to generate the base view in the drawing sheet. Whenever you start a new drawing document, the **Model View PropertyManager** is automatically invoked.

If you start the new drawing document from within the part or the assembly document, the part or the assembly is automatically selected and you can place the view using the **View Palette**. However, if you start the new drawing document using the **New SolidWorks Document** dialog box, a message will be displayed in the **Model View PropertyManager** and you will be prompted to select a part or assembly to generate the drawing view. If any part or assembly document is opened, it will be displayed in the selection box of the **Part/Assembly to Insert** rollout. You can preview the part or the assembly document by opening the **Thumbnail Preview** rollout, as shown in Figure 14-4.

You can also choose the **Browse** button and use the **Open** dialog box to select the document; the **Model View PropertyManager** is automatically modified and now provides the options related to

Figure 14-4 Selecting the document to generate the model views

generating the standard views, as shown in Figure 14-5. The options available in this **PropertyManager** are discussed next.

Number of Views Rollout

The radio buttons available in this rollout allow you to specify whether you want to generate only a single view or multiple views. To generate multiple views, select the **Multiple views** radio button and then choose the buttons of the required views from the **Orientation** rollout.

Orientation Rollout

The buttons available in the **Orientation** rollout are used to specify the orientation of the view. You can select additional orientations by selecting the required check box from the **Mere views** list box. Selecting the **Preview** check box allows you to preview the drawing view before it is placed.

Note

*You can change the orientation of the model view, even after placing it. To do this, place the view and make sure that it is still selected. This can be confirmed by the box that appears around the model view. The view is selected, if the box is displayed in green with a grip point. Now, double-click on the required view orientation from the **Orientation** rollout in the **Model View PropertyManager**. The orientation of the view is automatically modified.*

Figure 14-5 Partial view of the Model View PropertyManager after selecting the document to generate the drawing views

Options Rollout

The **Auto-start projected view** check box available in this rollout is used to automatically invoke the **Projected View** tool to generate the projected view immediately after placing the model view. The model view that you generate will be automatically taken as the parent view to generate the projected view. Note that this rollout will not be displayed if you select to generate the isometric view of the model.

Display Style Rollout

The options available in this rollout are used to specify the display styles for the model view. These display styles are similar to those available in the **View** toolbar to display parts or assemblies in the part or assembly documents.

Scale Rollout

A default scale to generate the drawing views is automatically defined when you select any template to start the new drawing sheet. This is the reason the **Use sheet scale** radio button is selected in the **Scale** rollout. If you want to define a custom scale for the model view, select the **Use custom scale** radio button and specify the scale factor in the edit boxes available below this radio button.

Dimension Type Rollout

The radio buttons available in this rollout are used to specify whether the model view will have true dimensions or projected dimensions. The true dimensions are the exact model dimensions that were specified while creating the model. The projected dimensions are reduced dimensions that are used in case of isometric, dimetric, or trimetric view. Generally, the value of the projected dimension is about 81.6% of the value of true dimension.

Using the View Palette to Place the Drawing Views

One of the latest enhancements in this release of SolidWorks is the **View Palette** that is automatically displayed when you start a new drawing file from within the part or assembly document. You can also display the **View Palette** manually by displaying the task pane and choosing the **View Palette** button. The **View Palette** is shown in Figure 14-6.

Figure 14-6 The View Palette

To place a view using the **View Palette**, select the preview of the view in the **View Palette** and then drag it to the drawing sheet at the desired location; the **Projected View** tool will be invoked to place the projected views taking the view placed using the **View Palette** as the parent view. You can choose the **Browse to select a part/assembly** button from the **View Palette** to browse and select a part or an assembly file to generate the drawing views.

Tip. *The drawing views will be generated depending on the default projection type of the current sheet. If the sheet is configured for first angle projection, the drawing views will be generated according to that. If the drawing sheet is configured for third angle projection, the views will be generated accordingly.*

To change the projection type of the current sheet, right-click on Sheet Format1 in the FeatureManager Design Tree and choose Properties from the shortcut menu to display the Sheet Properties dialog box. Set the required projection type using the Type of projection area.

Generating the Three Standard Views

CommandManager:	Drawing > Standard 3 View
Menu:	Insert > Drawing View > Standard 3 View
Toolbar:	Drawing > Standard 3 View

You can generate three default orthographic views of the specified part or assembly by using the **Standard 3 View** option. To create the three standard views, choose the **Standard 3 View** button from the **Drawing CommandManager**; the **Standard 3 View PropertyManager** will be displayed. If any part or assembly document is opened in the current session of SolidWorks, it will be displayed in the list box available in the **Part/Assembly to Insert** rollout, as shown in Figure 14-7.

Figure 14-7 The Standard 3 View PropertyManager

You can select the document from this list box. You can use the **Browse** button to select the part or assembly document, if no documents are opened. As soon as you select a document, three standard views are generated based on the default scale of the current sheet. Figure 14-8 shows the three standard views of a model generated in the third angle projection using the **Standard 3 View** tool.

Figure 14-8 *Three standard views generated using the **Standard 3 View** tool*

Note

*You will observe that the name of the part document whose drawing views are generated is displayed in the **DWG NO.** text box of the title block. The size of the sheet is also displayed at the lower right corner of the title block. Try changing the sheet format, if these parameters are not displayed.*

*You will observe that the center marks are automatically created on generating the drawing views. If they are not generated automatically, you can set the option to do so. Invoke the **System Options** dialog box and choose the **Document Properties** tab; the **Detailing** tab is chosen by default. Select the **Center marks-holes** check box from the **Auto insert on view creation** area. You can also set auto-insertion of centerlines, balloons, and so on using the options provided in this dialog box.*

Tip. *You need to move the view generated using the **Standard 3 View** if it overlaps the title block. Place the cursor over the view to move it; the bounding box of the view is displayed in dashed red lines. At this point, click to select the view. Next, move the cursor to the boundary of the selected view; the cursor is replaced by the move cursor. Press and hold down the left mouse button and drag the cursor to move the view. Remember that on moving the parent view, all the views generated using it are also moved.*

Generating Standard Views Using the Relative View Tool

CommandManager:	Drawing > Relative View *(Customize to Add)*
Menu:	Insert > Drawing View > Relative To Model
Toolbar:	Drawing > Relative View *(Customize to Add)*

The **Relative View** tool is used to generate an orthographic view. The orientation of the view is defined by selecting two reference planes or the planar faces of the model. This option is very useful if you need the orientation of the parent view other than the default orientations.

Open the part or the assembly document and tile it vertically or horizontally with the drawing document in order to create a relative view. Invoke the **Relative View** tool and click once in the part or assembly document; the **Relative View PropertyManager** is displayed in that document, as shown in Figure 14-9, and you are prompted to select a planar face of the model.

Figure 14-9 The *Relative View PropertyManager*

Select the orientation for the first plane or planar face from the drop-down list available in the **First** area. Then select the plane or planar face of the model to be oriented in that direction. For example, you can select the **Top** option from this drop-down list and then select the top planar face of the model.

The selection box in the **Second** area is highlighted on specifying the first reference. Select the orientation for the second reference from the drop-down list and then select a plane or planar face. Next, choose the **OK** button from the **Relative View PropertyManager**. You will return to the drawing document. Place the view at the required location. Figure 14-10 shows the faces of the model selected to generate a standard view and Figure 14-11 shows the resulting view.

Generating Standard Views Using the Predefined View Tool

Toolbar:	Drawing > Predefined View *(Customize to Add)*
Menu:	Insert > Drawing View > Predefined
Toolbar:	Drawing > Predefined View *(Customize to Add)*

Second selection
(Oriented using Top option)

First selection
(Oriented using Front option)

Figure 14-10 *Faces to be selected*

Figure 14-11 *Resulting view*

Predefined
View

The **Predefined View** tool is used to create empty views with the predefined orientation. After their creation, you can populate them by dragging a part from the other window by holding the name of the part document in the **FeatureManager Design Tree**. All the predefined views will be populated. This option adds the empty views in the drawing document and then saves it as a drawing template. You just need to drag and drop a part from another window to the current window to populate it with all the predefined views. To create predefined views, choose the **Predefined View** button from the **Drawing CommandManager**; an empty view will be attached to the cursor. Specify a point in the drawing document to place the predefined view; a rectangle defining the boundary of the view will be placed in the drawing document and the **Drawing View PropertyManager** will be displayed, as shown in Figure 14-12.

Figure 14-12 The Drawing View1 PropertyManager

Select the view orientation from the **View Orientation** area of the **View Orientation** rollout and choose the **OK** button from the **Drawing View PropertyManager**.

You need to define the alignment option while placing the next predefined view. To create additional predefined views, invoke the **Predefined View** tool and place the view in the drawing sheet. The bounding box of the view is displayed. Right-click inside the bounding box and choose **Alignment > Align Horizontal by Center/Align Vertical by Center**. Next, select the previous predefined view to align the corresponding view. Similarly, add the other predefined views using this tool.

After creating all the predefined views, open the part or assembly document and tile the document windows horizontally or vertically. Next, press and hold the left mouse button down on the name of the part or assembly in the **PropertyManager** and drag the component or the assembly in the drawing document; all the predefined views will be populated. You can also populate individual predefined views by selecting them and choosing the **Browse** button from the **Insert Model** rollout of the **Drawing View PropertyManager**.

Figure 14-13 shows the selected predefined views with the orientation, in which the views are created, and Figure 14-14 shows the drawing document after populating the drawing views.

Figure 14-13 *Various predefined views*

Figure 14-14 *Views created after populating the predefined views*

Note

*The views generated in the **Drawing** mode of SolidWorks are automatically scaled on the basis of the size of the sheet.*

The views will also be scaled automatically if the drawing contains more than one predefined view.

*One predefined view placed in the drawing document will be scaled with respect to the **Custom Scale** value, if specified. Otherwise, it will be scaled with the default scale factor of the drawing sheet. You can change the view scale using the **Sheet Properties** dialog box. You will learn more about scaling the views in the next chapter.*

GENERATING DERIVED VIEWS

All views generated from a view already placed in the drawing document are known as derived views. These include:

1. Projected view
2. Section view
3. Aligned Section view
4. Broken-out Section view
5. Auxiliary view
6. Detail view
7. Crop view
8. Broken view
9. Alternate Position view

The methods of generating the various derived drawing views are discussed next.

Generating Projected Views

CommandManager:	Drawing > Projected View
Menu:	Insert > Drawing View > Projected
Toolbar:	Drawing > Projected View

As mentioned earlier, the projected views are generated by projecting the normal lines from an existing view or at an angle from an existing view. To generate a projected view, choose the **Projected View** button from the **Drawing CommandManager**; the **Projected View PropertyManager** is displayed. If there are multiple views on the sheet, you will be prompted to select a drawing view to project the normal lines. If there is only one view, it will be automatically selected as the parent view. Select the parent view and move the cursor vertically to generate the top view or the bottom view or move the cursor horizontally to create right or left view. If you move the cursor at an angle, a 3D view will be created. Specify a point on the drawing sheet to place the view. For generating more than one projected views, choose the **Keep Visible** button to pin the **Projected View PropertyManager**. Figure 14-15 shows the front view generated from the top view.

Figure 14-15 *Front view generated from the top view*

Tip. *The drawing view is aligned to the parent view when you generate a projected drawing view. To place the projected view that is not in alignment with the parent view, press and hold down the CTRL key before placing it. Next, move the cursor to the desired location and place the view.*

All the standard and derived views such as projected views, section view, detailed view, and so on are linked to their parent view by a Parent-Child relationship. If you select the child view, the bounding box of the parent view will also be displayed.

*Select the child view, invoke the shortcut menu, and choose the **Jump to Parent View** option from it. The parent view will be selected automatically.*

Generating Section Views

CommandManager:	Drawing > Section View
Menu:	Insert > Drawing View > Section
Toolbar:	Drawing > Section View

As mentioned earlier, section views are generated by chopping a portion of an existing view, using a cutting plane (defined by sketched lines), and then viewing the parent view from a direction normal to the cutting plane.

In SolidWorks, you can use the **Section View** tool to create a full section view, or a half section view, as shown in Figures 14-16 and 14-17, respectively. A full section view is defined using a single line segment but a half section view is defined using three line segments. Note that the section plane for a full section view can be defined after invoking the **Section View** tool. But to generate a half section view, you need to draw the line segments to define the section plane before invoking the **Section View** tool. To do this, select the drawing view that you want to use as

Figure 14-16 *Full section view*

Figure 14-17 *Half section view*

the parent view and choose the **Sketch** button from the **CommandManager**; the sketching environment will be invoked. You can use the inferencing lines to draw the lines for the section plane.

To create a full section view, activate the view in which you need to draw the section line. The view symbol will be displayed below the cursor and the bounding box of the view will also be displayed. Now, choose the **Section View** button from the **Drawing CommandManager**. The **Section View PropertyManager** is displayed and you will be prompted to sketch a line to continue view creation.

After activating the view, draw a line that will define the section plane. On specifying the endpoint of the section line, the view is defined and is attached to the cursor. Also, the other options in the **Section View PropertyManager** are displayed.

To generate a half section view, select all the line segments that define the section plane and then invoke the **Section View** tool. The section view is defined and is attached to the cursor.

Move the cursor and specify a point on the drawing sheet to place the section view. The name and the scale factor of the drawing view is displayed below the section view and the **Section View PropertyManager** is invoked, as shown in Figure 14-18.

Figure 14-18 Partial view of the **Section View** *PropertyManager*

You can use the **Flip direction** check box to flip the direction of the section view. The view will be automatically modified in the drawing sheet. You can also flip the direction of the viewing section view using the TAB key on the keyboard before placing the section view. The **Scale with model** check box is used to scale the drawing view, if the model is scaled in the part document. You will learn more about scaling the model in the next chapter.

Tip. *On creating a section view and moving the cursor to place the section view, you will observe that the view is aligned to the direction of arrows on the section line. In order to remove this alignment to place the section view, press and hold down the CTRL key and move the view to the desired location. Select a point in the drawing sheet to place the view.*

Note
The default hatch pattern in the section view depends on the material assigned to the model. Also, you may need to increase the spacing of the hatch pattern, if it is not correct. You will learn more about editing the hatch pattern later in this chapter.

Some other options available in the **Section View PropertyManager** to create a partial section view and the surface section view are discussed next

Creating the Partial Section View

If the section line does not cut through the model, the **SolidWorks** information box will be displayed. This dialog box informs you that the section line does not completely cut through the bounding box of the model in this view. It then prompts you whether you want this to be a partial section cut? For creating the partial section view, choose the **Yes** button from this dialog box. If you choose the **No** button from this dialog box, a full section view will be created. Figure 14-19 shows a partial section view generated from the top view.

Figure 14-19 A partial section view

Creating the Surface Section View

A surface section view is the one in which only the sectioned surface is displayed in the section view. To create a surface section view, you first need to create the section view and then select the **Display only surface** check box from the **Section View** rollout of the **Section View PropertyManager**. Figure 14-20 shows a surface section view.

Tip. *Sometimes, the sectioned view is generated upside down, even if you have set the projection type to third angle. In such cases, you need to flip the direction of the section line from the **Section View PropertyManager**.*

Generating the Section View of an Assembly

According to the drawing standards, when you create the section view of an assembly, some components, such as fasteners, shafts, keys, and so on should not be sectioned. Therefore, when you create the section view of an assembly, the **Section View** dialog box is displayed, as shown in Figure 14-21.

This dialog box allows you to select the components that will be excluded from the section cut. You can also select the components from the parent view. But if the components are not visible

SECTION B−B

Figure 14-20 *A surface section view*

Figure 14-21 *The **Section View** dialog box*

in the parent view, you can invoke the **FeatureManager Design Tree** and expand the parent drawing view. Next, expand the assembly tree view to display all the components of the assembly. Select the components that are not required to be sectioned. The name of the selected component is displayed in the **Excluded components** selection box.

The **Auto hatching** check box is used to automatically define the hatch patterns. You can even change them if required. The method of changing hatch patterns is discussed later. This release of SolidWorks provides you with an option to exclude the fasteners that are inserted in the assembly using the **Toolbox** application. Toolbox, one of the add-ins of SolidWorks, is used to insert standard fasteners to the assembly. To exclude the fasteners that are inserted using this option, select the **Exclude fasteners** check box from the **Drawing View Properties** dialog box.

The **Flip direction** check box is used to flip the direction of viewing of the section view.

In case you have more than one instance of the component in the assembly, and you need to exclude all the instances of the component from the section view, select the component from the drawing sheet and also the name of the component from the **Exclude components** selection box. Select the **Don't cut all instances** check box from the **Section Scope** dialog box. All instances of the selected component will be excluded from the section view. Figure 14-22 shows an assembly section view with fasteners excluded from the cut.

SECTION A—A

Figure 14-22 Section view of an assembly with some of the components excluded from the cut

Tip. *You can add or remove the components that are sectioned by right-clicking the drawing view and choosing* **Properties** *from the shortcut menu. Next, choose the* **Section Scope** *tab and add or remove the components.*

Generating Aligned Section Views

CommandManager:	Drawing > Aligned Section View
Menu:	Insert > Drawing View > Aligned Section
Toolbar:	Drawing > Aligned Section View

This tool is used to generate a section view of the component in which at least one of the features is at an angle. In the aligned section view, the sectioned portion revolves about an axis normal to the view such that it is straightened. For example, refer to Figure 14-23.

Figure 14-23 *Aligned section view*

This figure explains the concept of an aligned section view of a model. Notice that the inclined feature sectioned in this view is straightened. As a result, the section view is longer than the parent view. Activate the view to create the aligned section view. Choose the **Aligned Section View** button from the **Drawing CommandManager**. Draw the sketch that defines the section plane. The aligned section view will be attached to the cursor; place the view at an appropriate location in the drawing sheet. Note that the resulting view will be projected normal to the line drawn at the end in the section sketch. Therefore, to get the aligned section view similar to that shown in Figure 14-23, the inclined line in the section sketch should be drawn first, followed by the vertical line. Figure 14-24 shows the aligned section view in which the vertical line in the section sketch is drawn first. This is the reason the section view is projected normal to the inclined line that is drawn last. On the other hand, Figure 14-25 shows the view in which the inclined line is drawn first.

You can also create a section view and aligned section views from a crop view, detail view, and an orthogonal exploded views.

Note
*You can also create a sketch associated to a view. This sketch can be selected as the section plane for generating the section view. To create an associated sketch, activate the view and draw the sketch that defines the section plane, using the **Line** tool.*

*If you create a sketch to define the section plane for the aligned section view before invoking the **Aligned Section View** tool, the view will be projected normal to the line that you select last. However, if you select the sketch by dragging a window around it, the view will be projected normal to the line that was drawn last.*

Figure 14-24 Aligned section view   *Figure 14-25* Aligned section view

Tip. *With this release of SolidWorks you can also use more than two lines to create an aligned section view. To do this, you need to draw the lines prior to invoking the* **Aligned Section View** *tool.*

Generating Broken-out Section Views

CommandManager:	Drawing > Broken-out Section
Menu:	Insert > Drawing View > Broken-out Section
Toolbar:	Drawing > Broken-out Section

This tool is used to create a broken-out section view that is used to remove a part of the existing view and display the area of the model or the assembly behind the removed portion. This view is generated using a closed sketch that is associated with the parent view. To create a broken-out section view, activate the view on which you need to create the broken-out section view. Choose the **Broken-out Section** button from the **Drawing CommandManager**. The **Broken-out Section PropertyManager** is displayed and it prompts you to create a closed spline to continue the section creation. The cursor will be replaced by the spline cursor. Draw a closed sketch using the spline cursor. If you do not want a spline profile, select a closed profile before choosing the **Broken-out Section** button. Figure 14-26 shows an associated sketch created for creating a broken-out section view.

Figure 14-26 Sketch for creating a broken-out section view

When you draw a closed sketch, the options are displayed in the **Broken-out Section PropertyManager**, as shown in Figure 14-27, and you are prompted to specify the depth of the broken-out section.

*Figure 14-27 The **Broken-out Section PropertyManager***

Select the **Preview** check box to preview the broken-out section view. The **Auto hatching** check box, which is available only for assemblies is used to automatically define the hatch pattern to the section drawing view of the assembly. The **Exclude fasteners** check box, which is also available only for assemblies, is used to exclude fasteners from getting sectioned in the broken-out section view. Figure 14-28 shows the preview of the broken-out section view of a part.

Figure 14-28 Preview of the broken-out section view

Set the value of the depth of the broken-out section in the **Depth** spinner. The preview of the section will be modified dynamically in the drawing view. After setting the value of the depth of the broken-out section, choose the **OK** button from the **Broken-out Section PropertyManager**. Figure 14-28 shows a broken-out section view with a different depth value.

Figure 14-29 Broken-out section view

Generating Auxiliary Views

CommandManager:	Drawing > Auxiliary View
Menu:	Insert > Drawing View > Auxiliary
Toolbar:	Drawing > Auxiliary View

An auxiliary view is a drawing view that is generated by projecting the lines normal to a specified edge of an existing view. SolidWorks also allows you to create a line segment associated to the view that can be used to generate the auxiliary view. For this, the associated line segment needs to be created before invoking this tool.

To create an auxiliary view, choose the **Auxiliary View** button from the **Drawing CommandManager**; the **Auxiliary View PropertyManager** is displayed and you will be prompted to select a reference edge to continue. Select the edge or the associated sketch; a view will be attached to the cursor and some options will be displayed in the **Auxiliary View PropertyManager**, as shown in Figure 14-30. Also, you will be prompted to specify the location to place the view.

*Figure 14-30 Partial view of the **Auxiliary View PropertyManager***

The check box available in the **Arrow** rollout is used to display the arrow of the viewing direction in the drawing views. The name of the auxiliary view is specified in the **Label** edit box. Using the **Flip Direction** check box, you can flip the viewing direction for creating the auxiliary view. Figure 14-31 shows the reference edge to be selected to create the auxiliary view.

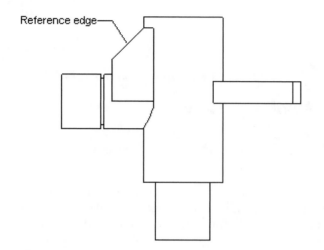

Figure 14-31 *Reference edge to be selected to create the auxiliary view*

Figure 14-32 shows the auxiliary view created with the default viewing direction. Figure 14-33 shows the auxiliary view created with the **Flip Direction** check box selected.

Figure 14-32 *Auxiliary view created with the* ***Flip Direction*** *check box cleared*

Figure 14-33 *Auxiliary view created with the* ***Flip Direction*** *check box selected*

While generating the auxiliary view of an assembly, the **Display State** rollout will also be displayed. This rollout allows you to select the display state whose auxiliary view will be generated.

Generating Detail Views

CommandManager:	Drawing > Detail View
Menu:	Insert > Drawing View > Detail
Toolbar:	Drawing > Detail View

A detail view is used to display the details of a portion of an existing view. You can select the portion whose detailing has to be shown in the parent view. The portion that you select will be magnified and placed as a separate view. You can control the magnification of the detail view. To create a detail view, activate the view from which you will generate the detail view. Next, choose the **Detail View** button from the **Drawing CommandManager**; the **Detail View PropertyManager** is displayed and you are prompted to sketch a circle to continue the view creation. The cursor is replaced by a circle cursor. Create the circle on the portion of the view that is to be displayed in the detail view. To use a profile other than the circle, you need to create it associated to the sketch before invoking the **Detail View** tool.

As soon as you draw the circle, the detail view is attached to the cursor and the options are displayed in the **Detail View PropertyManager**, as shown in Figure 14-34. You are also prompted to select a location for the new view. Specify a point on the drawing sheet to place the view. The options available in the **Detail View PropertyManager** are discussed next.

*Figure 14-34 The **Detail View PropertyManager***

Detail Circle

This rollout is used to define the options to display the circle of the detail view. You can also apply the leader to the detail view, using the options available in the rollout, which are discussed next.

Style

The **Style** area has the **Style** drop-down list to specify the style of a closed profile. By default, the **Circle** radio button is selected below the **Style** drop-down list. Therefore, the portion of the parent view that is shown in the detail view is highlighted in the circle. Select the **Profile** radio button, if you have already created a closed profile for defining the portion to be shown in the detail view. The options available in the **Style** drop-down list are discussed next.

Per Standard. The **Per Standard** option is used to create the detail view as per the default standards.

Broken Circle. The **Broken Circle** option is used to display the area of the parent view to be displayed in the detailed view in a broken circle.

With Leader. The **With Leader** option is used to add the leader to the callout of the detail view.

No Leader. The **No Leader** option is used to remove the leader from the callout of the detail view.

Connected. This option is used to create a line that connects the detail view with the closed profile in the parent view.

Detail View

This rollout is used to set the parameters of the detail view. The various options available in this rollout are discussed next.

Full outline

The **Full outline** check box is used to display the complete outline of the closed profile in the detail view.

Pin position

The **Pin position** check box is used to pin the position of the detail view.

Scale hatch pattern

While creating a detail view of a section view, the **Scale hatch pattern** check box is used to scale the hatch pattern with respect to the scale factor of the detail view.

If you create a detail view with another detail view or a crop view as the parent view, the default scale factor of the resulting detail view is twice of the immediate parent view. Figure 14-35 shows the detail view created using the **Detail View** tool.

Figure 14-35 Detail views generated using the existing views

Tip. *When you create a detail view, by default it is scaled as 1:1. You can define the default scale factor in the **System Options** dialog box so that the detail view will be created with the scaling factor provided by you. To specify the scale factor for the detail view, invoke the **System Options** dialog box and select the **Drawings** option from its left. Set the value of the scale factor of the detail view in the **Detail view scaling** edit box and choose the **OK** button. Hence forth, the detail view will be created of the scale factor defined in the **System Options** dialog box.*

Cropping Drawing Views

CommandManager:	Drawing > Crop View
Menu:	Insert > Drawing View > Crop
Toolbar:	Drawing > Crop View

This tool is used to crop an existing view using a closed sketch associated to it. The portion of the view that lies inside the associated sketch is retained and the remaining portion is removed. To crop the view, you first need to create a closed profile that defines the area of the view that will be displayed. The area of the view outside this closed profile will not be displayed when you crop the view. Select the closed profile and choose the **Crop View** button from the **Drawing CommandManager**. Figure 14-36 shows the closed profile used to crop the view and Figure 14-37 shows the cropped view.

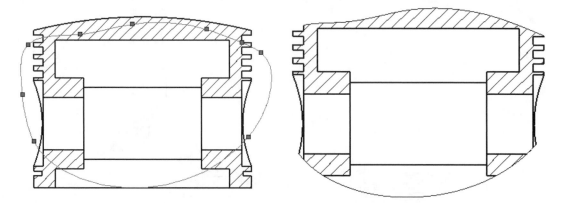

Figure 14-36 *Closed profile to crop the view*   **Figure 14-37** *Resulting crop view*

> **Tip**. *You can remove the cropping of the view by selecting the crop view and invoking the shortcut menu. Choose* **Crop View** > **Remove Crop** *from the shortcut menu. The initial view will be displayed in the drawing sheet.*
>
> *To edit the closed profile of the crop view, select the crop view and invoke the shortcut menu and choose* **Crop View** > **Edit Crop** *from it. The sketch of the closed profile and the complete view is displayed in the drawing sheet. Edit the closed profile and choose the* **Rebuild** *button from the* **Standard** *toolbar or use CTRL+B on the keyboard.*

Generating Broken Views

CommandManager:	Drawing > Break
Menu:	Insert > Drawing View > Break
Toolbar:	Drawing > Break

A broken view is the one in which a portion of the drawing view is removed from in between, keeping the ends of the drawing view intact. This view is used for displaying the component whose length to width ratio is very high. This means that either the length is very large as compared to the width or the width is very large as compared to the length. The broken view will break the view along the horizontal or vertical direction such that the drawing view fits the area you require. To create a broken view, choose the **Break** button from the **CommandManager** and then select the view; the **Broken View PropertyManager** will be displayed. Depending on the direction in which you need to break the view, choose the **Add vertical break line** or the **Add horizontal break line** button; a break line will be displayed on the selected view. Place the first break line and then place the second break line; the model will be broken between the two break lines, as shown in Figure 14-38.

Similarly, you can continue adding the break lines to create multiple breaks in the drawing view, as shown in Figure 14-39.

Figure 14-38 *Break lines added to the view*

You can define the gap between the broken lines using the **Gap Size** spinner of the **Broken View PropertyManager**. You can also modify the style of the break line. This is done using the **Break line style** drop-down list of the **Broken View PropertyManager**. Figure 14-40 shows a view with curved break lines.

Figure 14-39 *Multiple break lines*   ***Figure 14-40*** *Curved break view*

You can also break an isometric view; the procedure of breaking an isometric view or any 3D view is the same as discussed earlier. Figure 14-41 shows a broken isometric view.

Figure 14-41 *A broken isometric view*

Note

You can select and drag the break lines to increase or decrease the gap between the broken view. On moving the break line, the broken view is modified dynamically.

If you generate a projected view from a broken view, the resulting projected view is also a broken view.

If you break the isometric view of a component placed horizontally, the two parts of the view will lose their alignment because of the break.

Tip. *You can also change the style of the break line by selecting it and invoking the shortcut menu. The various break line styles available are straight cut, curve cut, zig zag cut, and small zig zag cut.*

*To unbreak the broken view, select the view, invoke the shortcut menu and choose the **Un-Break View** option from it.*

*Select the view, invoke the shortcut menu and choose the **Break View** option to again break the view.*

If you select the break lines and press the DELETE key on the keyboard, the broken view will be replaced by the parent view.

Generating Alternate Position Views

CommandManager:	Drawing > Alternate Position View
Menu:	Insert > Drawing View > Alternate Position
Toolbar:	Drawing > Alternate Position View

The alternate position view is used to create a view in which you can show the maximum and minimum range of the motion of an assembly. The main position is displayed with continuous lines in the drawing view, while the alternate position of the assembly is shown in the same view with dashed (phantom) lines. To create an alternate position view, activate and select the view of the assembly drawing on which you need to create the alternate position view. Choose the **Alternate Position View** button from the **Drawing CommandManager**. The **Alternate Position PropertyManager** is displayed, as shown in Figure 14-42.

The **Alternate Position PropertyManager** prompts you to select a new configuration, click OK or enter and define the new configuration parameters. If you have not created any configurations, the **New Configuration** radio button will be automatically selected to create one. Enter the name of the configuration in the edit box given below and choose the **OK** button from the **Alternate Position PropertyManager**. Choose **OK** from the **Tangent Edge Display** dialog box, if displayed.

The assembly document is opened and the **Move Component PropertyManager** is displayed in the assembly document. The **Move Component PropertyManager** prompts you to move the desired components to the position to be shown in the alternate view. Note that the component

Figure 14-42 *The **Alternate Position PropertyManager***

or components that you need to move should have that particular degree of freedom free. These components should not be fully defined in the assembly. Select and drag the cursor to move the components to the desired location. After defining the alternate position of the components, choose the **OK** button from the **Move Component PropertyManager**. You will return to the drawing document automatically. The alternate position of the components that are moved will be displayed in the phantom lines in the drawing view, as shown in Figure 14-43.

Figure 14-43 *Alternate position view*

You can also create the alternate position view of an isometric view or of any 3D view. The procedure of creating the alternate position view of a 3D view is the same as that discussed earlier. Figure 14-44 shows the alternate position view of an isometric view.

Figure 14-44 *Alternate view of an isometric view.*

Note
*On creating an alternate view of an assembly, a new configuration is created inside the assembly document with the same name that is specified to the configuration while creating the alternate position view. Open the assembly document and invoke the **ConfigurationManager**; you will observe that a new configuration has been created along with the default configuration. By default, the newly created configuration is selected. Therefore, the assembly is displayed with the components moved to their extreme positions. To switch back to the default configuration, select **Default** from the **ConfigurationManager**, invoke the shortcut menu and choose the **Show Configuration** option from it. You will observe that the assembly will be displayed with the moved components back at their original positions. If the **Show Configuration** option is not available in the shortcut menu, the assembly is at the default configuration.*

Generating Drawing Views of the Exploded State of an Assembly

You can create the drawing view of the exploded state of the assembly. For this, you need to have an exploded state defined in the assembly document. Generate the isometric view of the assembly on the drawing sheet. Select the view, invoke the shortcut menu, and choose the **Properties** option from it. The **View Properties** tab of the **Drawing View Properties** dialog box is displayed. Select the **Show in exploded state** check box from the **Configuration information** area and choose the **OK** button. Figure 14-45 shows the drawing view of the exploded state of assembly with explode lines.

Figure 14-45 *Drawing view of the exploded state with explode lines*

Tip. *All the views of the assembly will be generated in the exploded state, if the assembly in the assembly document is in the exploded state and you drag and drop the assembly to generate the drawing views.*

To collapse the exploded state in the drawing view, select the view and clear the **Show in exploded state** *check box from the* **View Properties** *tab of the* **Drawing View Properties** *dialog box.*

WORKING WITH INTERACTIVE DRAFTING IN SolidWorks

As mentioned earlier, you can also sketch the 2D drawings in the drawing document of SolidWorks. In technical terms, sketching 2D drawings is known as interactive drafting. Before starting the drawing, it is recommended that you insert an empty view. To create an empty view, choose **Insert > Drawing View > Empty** from the menu bar. An empty view is attached to the cursor. Select a point at the desired location to place an empty view. Now, select the empty view to activate and use the tools in the **Sketch CommandManager** to sketch the view.

The sketched entities will also move if you move the empty view by selecting and dragging it. This is because the sketch that you draw is associated to the empty view.

EDITING AND MODIFYING DRAWING VIEWS

In SolidWorks, you can perform various kinds of editing operations and modifications on the drawing views. For example, you can change the orientation of the view, or the view scale, or you can delete the view. All these operations are discussed next.

Changing the View Orientation

You can change the orientation of the views generated using the **Model View** or the **Predefined View** option. To change the orientation, select the view; the **Drawing View PropertyManager** is displayed in both the cases. Double-click on the view orientation that you want as the current one from the **Orientation** rollout. The orientation of the selected view will be modified. Choose the **OK** button from the **Drawing View PropertyManager**.

All the derived views will also change their orientation, when you change the orientation of the parent view.

Changing the Scale of Drawing Views

In SolidWorks, you can also change the scale of the drawing views. For doing so, select the drawing view and then select the **Use custom scale** radio button from the **Scale** rollout. Set the new scale of the drawing view in the edit boxes available below this radio button. You can also change the scale of the derived views. However, the scale of the parent view will not be changed if you change the scale of a derived view.

Deleting Drawing Views

The unwanted views are deleted from the drawing sheet using the **FeatureManager Design Tree** or directly from the drawing sheet. Select the view to be deleted from the **FeatureManager Design Tree**. Next, invoke the shortcut menu and choose the **Delete** option from it. The **Confirm Delete** dialog box will be displayed. Choose the **Yes** button from this dialog box. You can also delete a view by selecting it directly from the drawing sheet and pressing the DELETE key on the keyboard. The **Confirm Delete** dialog box is displayed; choose the **Yes** button from this dialog box. On deleting a parent view, the projected views are not deleted. However, if you delete the parent view from which a section, auxiliary, or a detail view is generated, the name of the dependent view will also be displayed in the **Confirm Delete** dialog box. If you choose **Yes**, the dependent views will also be deleted.

Rotating Drawing Views

SolidWorks allows you to rotate a drawing view in the 2D plane. Select the view and choose the **Rotate View** button from the **View** toolbar. The **Rotate Drawing View** dialog box is displayed, as shown in Figure 14-46. You can enter the value or rotation angle in this dialog box or you can also dynamically rotate the drawing view by dragging the mouse. If you select the **Dependent views update to change in orientation** check box, the views dependent on the rotated view will also change their orientation.

*Figure 14-46 The **Rotate Drawing View** dialog box*

Tip. *You can also copy and paste the drawing view in the drawing sheet. To do so, select the view to copy and press CTRL+C on the keyboard. Now, click anywhere on the drawing sheet to select the sheet and press CTRL+V on the keyboard to paste the drawing view.*

MODIFYING THE HATCH PATTERN IN SECTION VIEWS

As discussed earlier, when you generate a section view of an assembly or a component, a hatch pattern is applied to the component or components. This hatch pattern is based on the material assigned to the components in the part document. If you need to modify the default hatch pattern, select it from the section view; the **Area Hatch/Fill PropertyManager** is displayed, as shown in Figure 14-47. The options available in this dialog box are discussed next.

Figure 14-47 The Area Hatch/Fill PropertyManager

Properties Rollout

The **Properties** rollout is used to define the type of hatch pattern and its properties. Some of the options in this area are not available by default. This is because by default, the material-dependent hatch pattern is applied to the component. If you want to make the other options also available, clear the **Material crosshatch** check box. The options available in this area are discussed next.

Preview

The **Preview** area displays the preview of the hatch pattern with the current setting.

Hatch

The **Hatch** radio button is selected to apply the standard hatch patterns to the section view. On selecting this button, some options available in the dialog box are invoked to define the properties of the hatch pattern. The options available to define the properties of the hatch pattern are discussed next.

Solid

The **Solid** radio button is used to apply the solid filled hatch pattern to the section view. By default, black color is applied to the solid filled hatch pattern.

None

Select the **None** radio button, if you do not need to apply any hatch pattern in the section view.

Hatch Pattern

The **Hatch Pattern** drop-down list is used to define the style of the standard hatch pattern you need to apply to the section view. The preview of the hatch pattern selected from this drop-down list is displayed in the **Preview** area of the **Area Hatch/Fill** dialog box.

Hatch Pattern Scale

The **Hatch Pattern Scale** spinner is used to specify the scale factor of the standard hatch pattern selected from the **Pattern** drop-down list. When you change the scale factor using this spinner, the preview displayed in the **Preview** area updates dynamically.

Hatch Pattern Angle

The **Hatch Pattern Angle** spinner is used to define an angle to the selected hatch pattern.

Material crosshatch

The **Material crosshatch** check box is selected to apply the hatch pattern based on the material assigned to the model. Clear this check box to change the type of the hatch pattern.

Apply to

The **Apply to** drop-down list is used to specify whether you need to apply this hatch pattern to the selected component, region, body, or to the entire view. Note that some of these options are available only while modifying the hatch pattern of an assembly section view.

Options Rollout

The **Options** rollout provides the **Apply changes immediately** check box, which when selected applies the changes immediately on the view and the preview is modified dynamically. If you clear this check box, you need to choose the **Apply** button, after making the changes to reflect the changes in the preview.

TUTORIALS

Tutorial 1

In this tutorial, you will generate the front view, top view, right view, aligned section view, detail view, and isometric view of the model created in Tutorial 3 of Chapter 9. Use the Standard A4 Landscape sheet format for generating the views.   **(Expected time: 30 min)**

The steps to be followed to complete this tutorial are listed next.

a. Copy the part document of Tutorial 3 of Chapter 9 in the folder of the current chapter.
b. Open the copied part document and start a new drawing document from within the part document.
c. Select the standard A4 landscape sheet format and generate the parent view using the **Model View** tool, refer to Figure 14-48.
d. Generate the projected views using the **Projected View** tool, refer to Figure 14-48.
e. Generate the aligned section view using the **Aligned Section View** tool, refer to Figures 14-49 and 14-50.
f. Generate the detail view, refer to Figure 14-51.
g. Save and close the drawing document.

Copying and Opening the Part Document

1. Create a folder with the name *c14* in the *SolidWorks* directory and copy *c09tut3.sldprt* from the *\My Document\SolidWorks\c09* folder to this folder.

2. Start SolidWorks and open the part document of Tutorial 3 of Chapter 9 that you copied in the folder of the current chapter.

Starting a New Drawing Document

As mentioned earlier, one of the latest enhancements of SolidWorks 2006 is its ability to let you start a new drawing document from within the part document. This way, the model in the part document is automatically selected and you can generate its drawing views.

1. Choose the **Make Drawing from Part/Assembly** button from the **Standard** toolbar.

If you are in the practice of using the advanced form of the **New SolidWorks Document** dialog box, this dialog box will be displayed every time you choose the **Make Drawing from Part/Assembly** button.

2. From the **New SolidWorks Document** dialog box, select the drawing template from the **Template** tab and choose **OK**.

Remember that if you are not using the advanced form of the **New SolidWorks Document** dialog box, this dialog box is not displayed. Instead, a new drawing document is started directly and the **Sheet Format/Size** dialog box is displayed.

3. Select the **A4 - Landscape** sheet from the list box available in this dialog box and choose the

OK button. The new drawing document is started with the standard A4 sheet and the **View Palette** is displayed automatically. The model of Tutorial 3 of Chapter 9 is selected by default for generating the drawing views.

Generating the Parent View and the Projected Views

Before you proceed with generating the drawing views, you need to confirm whether the projection type for the current sheet is set to the third angle.

1. Click anywhere on the sheet to close the **View Palette**. Select **Sheet1** from the **FeatureManager Design Tree** and then right-click on it. Choose the **Properties** option from the shortcut menu to display the **Sheet Properties** dialog box.

2. Select the **Third angle** radio button from the **Type of projection** area. Close this dialog box.

3. Now, open the task pane and choose the **View Palette** button, if the **View Palette** is not displayed by default.

4. Select the **Front** view from the **View Palette** and drag it to the middle left of the drawing sheet just above the title block. Drop the view at this location to place the front view, refer to Figure 14-48.

   The front view will be generated and placed at this location. This view is generated at a 1:1 scale. Note that because you selected the option to start projected views immediately after generating the front view, the **Projected View PropertyManager** is invoked and the preview of the projected view is attached to the cursor. This view is being generated by referencing the front view as the parent view.

5. Move the cursor above the front view and specify a point to place the top view, refer to Figure 14-48. The top view of the model is generated and the preview of another projected view with the front view as the base view, is attached to the cursor.

6. Move the cursor to the right of the front view and place the right view, refer to Figure 14-48.

7. Similarly, move the cursor horizontally toward the right and then move it upward; the preview of the isometric view is displayed. Specify a point to place the isometric view. Now, exit the **Projected View PropertyManager**.

   The current location of the isometric is such that it will interfere with the aligned section view that you need to place next. Therefore, you need to move the isometric view close to the top right corner of the drawing sheet.

Tip. *If you suppress the features of a model whose drawing views have been generated, the suppressed features will not be displayed in the drawing views. The feature, on suppressing, will be displayed in the drawing views.*

When you hide or suppress the components of an assembly, the hidden or suppressed components are not displayed in the drawing views.

8. Move the cursor over the isometric view; the bounding box of the view is displayed in red.

9. Click to select the view; the border of the view is displayed in green.

10. Move the cursor on one of the border lines of the view; the cursor changes to the move cursor.

11. Press and hold the left mouse button and drag the view close to the upper right corner of the drawing sheet. The drawing sheet, after generating and moving the drawing view, is shown in Figure 14-48.

Figure 14-48 Drawing sheet after generating the front, top, right, and isometric views

Tip. *You can turn off the origins displayed in the drawing views by using the **View** menu.*

Center marks are automatically created in the drawing views of the circular features in the model.

Generating the Aligned Section View

Next, you need to generate the aligned section view. The line segments, used to generate this view, will be drawn before invoking the **Aligned Section View** tool. Remember that the view is projected normal to the line selected last, irrespective of the last line drawn. This means that you can draw any line first. In this tutorial, you will first select the inclined line and then the vertical line.

1. Click on the top view to activate the view.

2. Choose the **Sketch** button from the **CommandManager** to invoke the sketching tools. Using the **Line** tool, draw the sketch and apply the relations and dimensions to the sketch, as shown in Figure 14-49.

Figure 14-49 Sketch to be used as the section sketch for the aligned section view

3. Select the dimension and invoke the shortcut menu. Choose the **Hide** option from the shortcut menu.

    Next, you need to select the lines to generate the aligned section view. Note that the vertical line should be selected last to generate the view normal to this line. It will be difficult to select the line because the vertical line coincides with the center marks. You will use the **Select Other** option to select this line.

4. Select the inclined line. Make sure you do not select any segment of the center mark.

5. Next, press and hold the CTRL key down and move the cursor to the vertical line. Right-click on the vertical line and choose the **Select Other** option from the shortcut menu; the **Select Other** list box is displayed.

6. Select the **Line** option from the **Select Other** list box. Also, because the CTRL key was pressed, the inclined line will still be in the current selection set.

7. Now, choose the **Aligned Section View** button from the **Drawing CommandManager**. The aligned section view will be attached to the cursor.

    The view generated is normal to the vertical line. If the direction of viewing the aligned section view is reversed, you need to flip it after placing the view.

8. Move the cursor to the right of the top view and place the aligned section view. The **Section View PropertyManager** is displayed. Select the **Flip direction** check, if the direction of viewing is not as required. Click anywhere on the sheet to exit the **PropertyManager**. The sheet, after generating the aligned section view, is shown in Figure 14-50.

Figure 14-50 Sheet after generating the aligned section view

Modifying the Hatch Pattern of the Aligned Section View

The gap between the hatching lines in the aligned section view is large. Therefore, you need to modify the spacing.

1. Select the hatch pattern from one of the sections in the aligned section view; the **Area Hatch/Fill PropertyManager** is displayed.

2. Clear the **Material crosshatch** check box; the **Hatch Pattern**, **Hatch Pattern Scale**, and

Hatch Pattern Angle options are available. Set the value of the **Hatch Pattern Scale** spinner to **2** and select **View** from the **Apply to** drop-down list. Exit the **PropertyManager**.

Generating the Detail View

Next, you need to generate the detail view of the right circular feature of the model. Before doing so, you need to activate the view from which you will drive the detail view.

1. Activate the top view and choose the **Detail View** button from the **Drawing CommandManager**; the **Detail View PropertyManager** is displayed and you are prompted to sketch a circle to continue to view the creation. Also, the cursor is replaced by the circle cursor.

2. Draw a small circle on the right circular feature of the model in the top view, refer to Figure 14-51. As you draw the circle, the detail view is attached to the cursor.

3. Place the view on the right side of the drawing sheet above the title block, refer to Figure 14-51.

4. Set the value of the scale factor of the detail view to **3:1** and choose the **OK** button from the **Detail View PropertyManager**.

You may need to move the drawing view and its label so that the view does not overlap the title block. Figure 14-51 shows the final drawing sheet, after generating the detail view from the top view.

Figure 14-51 *The detail view derived from the top view*

Saving the Drawing

1. Choose the **Save** button from the **Standard** toolbar and save the drawing document with the name given below.

\My Documents\SolidWorks\c14\c14tut1.slddrw

2. Choose **File > Close** to close this document. Also, close the part document of Tutorial 2.

Tutorial 2

In this tutorial, you will generate the drawing view of the Bench Vice assembly created in Chapter 12. You will generate the top view, sectioned front view, right view, and isometric view of the assembly in the exploded state.   **(Expected time: 45 min)**

The steps to be followed to complete this tutorial are listed next.

a. Copy the folder of the Bench Vice assembly from Chapter 12 to the *c14* folder.
b. Create the exploded state of the Bench Vice assembly, refer to Figure 14-52.
c. Start a new drawing document from within the assembly document using A4 landscape sheet format. Generate the top view using the **Model View** tool, refer to Figure 14-53.
d. Generate the section view using the **Section View** tool, refer to Figure 14-54.
e. Generate the right view using the **Projected View** tool, refer to Figure 14-55.
f. Generate the isometric view and change the state of the isometric view to the exploded state, refer to Figure 14-56.
g. Save and close the drawing and assembly documents.

Copying the Folder of the Bench Vice Assembly

First, you need to copy the folder of the Bench Vice assembly to *c14* folder.

1. Copy the folder of the Bench Vice assembly from the *\My Document\SolidWorks\c12* folder to the *c14* folder.

Creating the Exploded View of the Assembly

Before proceeding further to generate the drawing views of the assembly, you need to create the exploded state of the assembly in the **Assembly** mode.

1. Open the Bench Vice assembly and create the exploded state and the explode lines, as shown in Figure 14-52.

It is recommended that whenever you create an exploded state of an assembly, you must revert to the collapsed state. On saving the assembly in the exploded state, whenever you generate the drawing views of the assembly, it will generate views with the exploded state.

Figure 14-52 *Exploded view of the assembly with explode lines*

2. Right-click on **Bench Vice Configuration(s)** in the **ConfigurationManager** and choose **Collapse** to unexplode the assembly.

3. Save the assembly.

Starting a New Drawing Document From Within the Assembly Document

As mentioned earlier, you can also start a drawing document from within the assembly document.

1. Choose the **Make Drawing from Part/Assembly** button from the **Standard** toolbar. Start a new drawing document from the **Templates** tab of the **New SolidWorks Document** dialog box, if it appears.

A new SolidWorks drawing document is started and the **Sheet Format/Size** dialog box is displayed.

2. Select the **A4 - Landscape** sheet. Right-click on **Sheet Format1** and choose **Properties** from the shortcut menu. Using the **Sheet Properties** dialog box, set the current projection type to third angle.

Generating the Top View

1. Invoke the **Model View** tool and double-click on **Bench Vice** in the **Part/Assembly to Insert** rollout.

2. Select the **Top** button from the **Standard views** area of the **Orientation** rollout of the **Model View PropertyManager**.

3. Select the **Use custom scale** radio button from the **Scale** rollout.

4.   Set the value of the scale factor to **1:2** and then select the **Preview** check box from the **Orientation** rollout. The preview of the top view of assembly is displayed.

5.   Make sure the **Auto-start projected view** check box in the **Options** rollout is cleared.

6.   Place the view close to the top left corner of the drawing sheet, refer to Figure 14-53. Click anywhere on the sheet to exit the **PropertyManager**.

Figure 14-53 Top view generated using the Model View tool

Creating the Sectioned Front View

Next, you need to generate the sectioned front view that is derived from the top view.

1.   Activate the top view and choose the **Section View** button from the **Drawings CommandManager**.

The **Section View PropertyManager** is displayed and you are prompted to sketch a line in order to continue to view the creation. The cursor will be replaced by the line cursor.

2.   Draw a horizontal line such that it passes through the center of the Bench Vice assembly.

On specifying the endpoint of the line, the **Section View** dialog box is displayed. This dialog box is used to exclude the components from the section cut.

3.   Click on the + sign located on the left of the **Drawing View1** to display the name of the assembly. Next, expand the assembly.

4.   Select Screw Bar, Bar Globes, Jaw Screw, Oval Fillister, Set Screw1, and Set Screw2. Next, click on the **Section View** dialog box in the drawing area to activate it. Select one of the components displayed in the **Exclude components** selection box and then select the **Don't cut all instances** check box. Similarly, one by one select all components from this selection box individually and then select the **Don't cut all instances** check box.

5.   Next, select the **Auto hatching** check box and choose the **OK** button from the **Section View** dialog box.

     The preview of the section view is displayed in the drawing sheet as you move the cursor up and down.

     If the direction of viewing of the section view is not what is required, flip the direction by selecting the **Flip direction** check box from the **Section Line** rollout.

6.   Place the section view below the top view. Click anywhere on the sheet to exit the **PropertyManager**.

7.   Modify the hatch scale for the components. Figure 14-54 shows the section view generated using the **Section View** tool, after modifying the hatch scale.

SECTION A-A
SCALE 1 : 2

*Figure 14-54 Section view generated using the **Section View** tool*

Generating the Right-Side View

The next view that you need to generate is the right-side view derived from the sectioned front view and it will be generated using the **Projected View** tool.

1.   Select the sectioned front view and invoke the **Projected View** tool. The **Projected View PropertyManager** is displayed and a projected view is attached to the cursor.

2. Move the cursor to the right of the sectioned front view and place the view on the right of the sectioned front view.

3. Choose **OK** from the **PropertyManager**. The sheet, after generating the projected view, is shown in Figure 14-55.

*Figure 14-55 Right-side view generated using the **Projected View** tool*

Creating the Isometric View of the Assembly in the Exploded State

The last view to be generated is the isometric view of the assembly in the exploded state.

1. Using the **Model View** tool, generate the isometric view and place it close to the upper right corner of the drawing sheet.

2. Set the scale factor of the drawing view to **1:2**.

3. Right-click on the view to invoke the shortcut menu. Choose the **Properties** option from the shortcut menu; the **Drawing View Properties** dialog box is displayed.

4. Select the **Show in exploded state** check box from the **View Properties** tab of the **Drawing View Properties** dialog box and choose the **OK** button.

5. Move the views to place all of them in the drawing sheet. Figure 14-56 shows the final drawing sheet after generating all the drawing views.

Figure 14-56 *Drawing sheet after generating all the views*

Saving the Drawing

Next, you need to save the drawing document.

1. Choose the **Save** button from the **Standard** toolbar and save the drawing document with the name given below.

    \My Documents\SolidWorks\c14*c14tut2.slddrw*

2. Close the drawing and assembly documents.

SELF-EVALUATION TEST

Answer the following questions and then compare your answers with those given at the end of this chapter:

1. The **Standard sheet size** radio button is selected by default in the **Sheet Format/Size** dialog box. (T/F)

2. The **Display sheet format** check box is selected if you want to use the empty sheet without any margin lines or a title block. (T/F)

3. The **Relative View** tool is used to generate an orthographic view by defining its orientation using reference planes or planar faces of the model. (T/F)

4. An auxiliary view is a drawing view that is generated by projecting the lines normal to a specified edge of an existing view. (T/F)

5. You cannot change the style of the break line in a broken view. (T/F)

6. In technical terms, creating a 2D drawing in the drawing document is known as _____.

7. To start a new drawing document from within the part document, choose the _____ button from the **Standard** toolbar.

8. The _____ check box available in the **Detail View** rollout of the **Detail View PropertyManager** is used to display the complete outline of the closed profile in the detail view.

9. To change the scale of the drawing views, select the drawing view and select the _____ radio button from the **Scale** rollout.

10. To rotate a drawing view, select the view and choose the _____ button from the **View** toolbar.

REVIEW QUESTIONS

Answer the following questions:

1. Choose the _____ button from the **Drawings CommandManager** to create an alternate position view.

2. The _____ dialog box is used to modify the hatch pattern of a section view.

3. The _____ check box needs to be cleared to modify the scale of the hatch pattern.

4. A _____ view is a section view in which only the sectioned surface is displayed in the section view.

5. The _____ dialog box is displayed to confirm the deletion of the views.

6. The views that are generated from a view already placed in the drawing sheet are known as the

    (a) Child views   (b) Derived views
    (c) Predefined views   (d) Empty views

7. By default, the detail view boundary is in which shape?

    (a) Circle   (b) Ellipse
    (c) Rectangle   (d) None

8. In which edit box is the name of the auxiliary view specified?

    (a) **Label**   (b) **Arrow**
    (c) **Name**   (d) **Detail view label**

9. From which rollout can you select the view orientation in the **Named View PropertyManager**?

    (a) **Orientation**   (b) **Define View**
    (c) **Specify View**   (d) **Scale View**

EXERCISE

Exercise 1

In this exercise you will generate the front view, section right view, isometric view, and the alternate position view on the isometric view of Exercise 1 of Chapter 11. You need to scale the parent view to the scale factor of **1:3**. The views that you need to generate are shown in Figure 14-57.

(Expected time: 30 min)

Figure 14-57 Views of Exercise 1

Answers to Self-Evaluation Test
1. T, **2.** T, **3.** T, **4.** T, **5.** F, **6.** Interactive drafting, **7. Make Drawing from Model/Assembly**,
8. Full outline, **9. Use custom scale**, **10. Rotate View**

Chapter 15

Working With Drawing Views-II

* *Add annotations to the drawing views.*
* *Add reference dimensions.*
* *Add notes to drawing views.*
* *Add surface finish symbols to drawing views.*
* *Add datum feature symbols to drawing views.*
* *Add geometric tolerance to drawing views.*
* *Add datum target symbols to drawing views.*
* *Add center marks and centerlines to drawing views.*
* *Add hole callouts to drawing views.*
* *Add cosmetic threads to drawing views.*
* *Add multi-jog leader to drawing views.*
* *Add dowel pin symbol to drawing views.*
* *Edit annotations.*
* *Add Bill of Material (BOM) to the drawing sheet.*
* *Add balloons to the assembly.*
* *Add new sheets in the drawing document.*
* *Edit the sheet format.*
* *Create a user-defined sheet format.*

ADDING ANNOTATIONS TO DRAWING VIEWS

After generating the drawing views, you need to generate the dimensions and add other annotations, such as notes, surface finish symbols, geometric tolerance, and so on. Two types of annotations can be displayed in the drawing views. The first type are the generative annotations that are added while creating the part in the **Part** mode. For example, the dimensions that you add to the sketch and features of the part. The second type are added manually to the geometry of drawing views such as reference dimensions, notes, surface finish symbols, and so on. Both these types of annotations are discussed next.

Generating Annotations Using the Model Items Tool

CommandManager:	Annotations > Model Items
Menu:	Insert > Model Items
Toolbar:	Annotation > Model Items

 The **Model Items** tool is used to generate the annotations that were added while creating the model in the **Part** mode. To invoke this tool, choose the **Model Items** button from the **Drawing Annotation CommandManager**; the **Model Items PropertyManager** is displayed, as shown in Figure 15-1. The options available in this **PropertyManager** are discussed next.

Source/Destination Rollout

The drop-down list available in the **Source/Destination** rollout defines the options from where the annotations are imported. These options are discussed next.

Entire model

When a feature of a model is selected from the **FeatureManager Design Tree** in the **Drawing** mode, the **Entire model** option is selected to import the annotations from the entire model. In case of assemblies, the annotations from the entire assembly are imported, even if a single component of the assembly is selected.

Selected component

The **Selected component** option is available only when you generate the drawing views of an assembly. This option is selected to import the annotations from only the selected component.

Selected feature

The **Selected feature** option is selected to import the annotations from only the selected feature or features.

Only Assembly

The **Only Assembly** option is also available only when you generate drawing views of an assembly. This option is selected to import the annotations that are applied to the assembly in the **Assembly** mode, such as the offset distance and so on.

Figure 15-1 The Model Items PropertyManager

Import items into all views

This check box is selected to import the dimensions in all the drawing views available on the sheet. This check box is selected by default. If this check box is cleared, the **Destination view(s)** selection box is displayed in this rollout. Using this selection box, you can select the drawing views in which the dimensions will be placed.

Dimensions Rollout

This rollout is used to select the type of dimensions, pattern annotations, and the hole annotations that you need to generate in the drawing views. You can choose the button of the required annotation type. You can also select the **Select all** check box to select all the options. The **Eliminate duplicates** check box is selected to remove duplicate instances of annotations.

Annotations Rollout

The **Annotations** rollout is used to select the annotations that are to be generated in the drawing views. Using the buttons available in this rollout, you can generate the cosmetic thread, datums, datum targets, dimensions, geometric tolerances, notes, surface finish, and weld symbols. You can also select the **Select all** check box to select all the options.

Reference Geometry Rollout

The **Reference Geometry** rollout is used to generate the reference geometries that were used in creating the part. You can generate axes, curves, planes, surfaces, and so on. Select the check box of the type of reference geometry that you need to generate in the drawing views. You can also select the **Select all** check box to select all the options.

Options Rollout

The options available in this rollout are discussed next.

Include items from hidden features

The **Include items from hidden features** check box is selected to display the annotation that belongs to a hidden feature of the model. By default, this check box is cleared. It is recommended to keep this check box cleared because it will eliminate the display of unwanted annotations.

Use dimension placement in sketch

This check box is selected to place the dimension at the exact location where it was placed in the sketch while creating the part.

Layers Rollout

This rollout allows you to select the layers in which the dimensions will be placed.

After setting all the parameters in the **Insert Model Items** dialog box, choose the **OK** button to display the annotations.

Tip. *You can toggle the display of annotations when the **Model Items** **PropertyManager** is displayed by right-clicking on the annotation.*

The annotations mostly overlap each other when they are generated. Therefore, you may need to move the annotations after generating them. To move an annotation, move the cursor on the annotation; the annotation is highlighted in red. Press and hold down the left mouse button and drag the cursor to place the annotation at the desired location. Release the left mouse button when the cursor is placed at the desired location.

The dimensions generated, while generating the annotations, are the same as the ones used to create the model. These dimensions are linked to the model because of the bidirectional associativity in SolidWorks.

*Double-click on the dimension to modify it. The **Modify** dialog box is displayed, using which, you can modify the value of the dimension. Next, rebuild the drawing views using the **Rebuild** button. The change in the dimension will also be made in the original model. If the model is used in an assembly, the changes will also be reflected in the assembly.*

Adding Reference Annotations

You can add reference annotations in the drawing views in SolidWorks. These include reference dimensions, notes, surface finish symbols, datum feature symbol, geometric tolerance, and so on. The method of adding reference annotations is discussed next.

Adding Reference Dimensions

CommandManager:	Annotations > Smart Dimension
Menu:	Tools > Dimensions > Smart
Toolbar:	Annotations > Smart Dimension

 You can use the **Smart Dimension** tool to add reference dimensions to the drawing views in the **Drawing** mode of SolidWorks. This tool is similar to the **Smart Dimension** tool discussed in the sketching environment of SolidWorks.

You can also use the **Dimension/Relations CommandManager** to add dimensions. For example, you can use this **CommandManager** in the **Drawing** mode to add chamfer dimensions. The technique of adding chamfer dimensions to the drawing views in the **Drawing** mode of SolidWorks is discussed next.

Chamfer Dimension

The **Chamfer Dimension** tool is used to add the reference dimension to the chamfers in the drawing view. To add a chamfer dimension, choose **Chamfer Dimension** from the **Dimension/Relations CommandManager**. The cursor is replaced by the chamfer dimension cursor. Now, select the inclined chamfered edge and then select a horizontal or vertical edge. The chamfer dimension will be attached to the cursor. Select a point on the sheet to place the dimension. Figure 15-2 shows a chamfer dimension created using the **Chamfer Dimension** tool.

*Figure 15-2 Chamfer dimension added using the **Chamfer Dimension** tool*

Adding Notes to Drawing Views

CommandManager:	Annotations > Note
Menu:	Insert > Annotations > Note
Toolbar:	Annotation > Note

In SolidWorks, you can add notes to the drawing views in the **Drawing** mode. To do so, choose the **Note** button from the **Annotations CommandManager**. The partial view of the **Note PropertyManager** is displayed, as shown in Figure 15-3.

Figure 15-3 Partial view of the Note PropertyManager

On invoking the **Note PropertyManager**, a shape defined using the **Style** drop-down list in the **Border** rollout is attached to the cursor. If you move the cursor close to an edge in a drawing view, a leader will be displayed with the text box. This is because the **Auto Leader** button is chosen in the **Leader** rollout. From this release onward, you can also place a multijog leader line. After selecting the edge, place the endpoint of the leader at the desired location; the **Formatting** toolbar and the **Text** edit box will be invoked in the drawing area. Enter the text in the edit box. Next, choose **OK** from the **Note PropertyManager**. The other options available in the **Note PropertyManager** are discussed next.

Favorites

You can save a note as a favorite using the options available in the **Favorites** rollout. The options available in this rollout are the same as those discussed in Chapter 3.

Text Format

The **Text Format** rollout is used to set the format of the text such as font, size, justification, and rotation of the text. You can also add symbols and hyperlinks to the text using the options available in this rollout.

Leader

The options available in the **Leader** rollout are used to define the style of arrows and leaders that are displayed in the notes.

Border

The options available in the **Border** rollout are used to define the border in which the note text will be displayed. You can use various types of borders from the **Style** drop-down list. The **Size** drop-down list available in this rollout is used to define the size of the border in which the text will be placed.

Adding Surface Finish Symbols to Drawing Views

CommandManager:	Annotations > Surface Finish
Menu:	Insert > Annotations > Surface Finish Symbol
Toolbar:	Annotation > Surface Finish

 You can add the surface finish symbols to the edges or faces in the drawing views using the **Surface Finish** tool. To do so, choose the **Surface Finish** button from the **Annotations CommandManager**. The **Surface Finish PropertyManager** is displayed, as shown in Figure 15-4. When you invoke this tool, a surface finish symbol is attached to the cursor. The options available in the **Surface Finish PropertyManager** dialog box are discussed next.

Favorites

With this release of SolidWorks, you can use the options available in the **Favorites** rollout to save a surface finish as a favorite. The options available in this rollout are the same as those discussed in Chapter 3.

Symbol

The **Symbol** rollout is used to define the type of surface finish symbol that you need to add to the drawing views. The surface finish symbols include the **Basic** surface finish symbol, **Machining Required**, **Machining Prohibited**, **JIS Basic**, **JIS Machining Prohibited**, **JIS Machining Prohibited**, and so on.

*Figure 15-4 Partial view of the **Surface Finish PropertyManager***

Symbol Layout

The options available in the **Symbol Layout** rollout are used to define the parameters of the surface finish symbol.

Format

The options available in the **Format** rollout are used to define the font size and the orientation of the surface finish symbol.

Angle

The options available in the **Angle** rollout are used to define the angle of the surface finish symbol. You can enter the angle value in the spinner provided in this rollout or choose the buttons available below the spinner.

The other options available in the **Surface Finish PropertyManager** are the same as those discussed while adding notes.

Adding a Datum Feature Symbol to Drawing Views

CommandManager:	Annotations > Datum Feature
Menu:	Insert > Annotations > Datum Feature Symbol
Toolbar:	Annotation > Datum Feature

The **Datum Feature** tool is used to add a datum feature symbol to an entity in the drawing view. The datum feature symbols are used as datum references while adding the geometric tolerances in the drawing view. To add the datum feature symbol, choose the **Datum Feature** button from the **Annotations CommandManager**. The **Datum Feature PropertyManager** is displayed and a datum feature symbol with default parameters is attached to the cursor. The **Datum Feature PropertyManager** is displayed in Figure 15-5. The options available in the **Datum Feature PropertyManager** are discussed next.

Filled Triangle

Filled Triangle With Shoulder

Empty Triangle With Shoulder

Empty Triangle

*Figure 15-5 The **Datum Feature PropertyManager***

Label

The **Label** edit box in the **Settings** rollout is used to define the label to be used in the datum feature symbol. You can use alphabets or numeric characters as labels.

Use document style

This check box is selected to use the datum feature style defined in the document to display the datum feature symbol.

Square

The **Square** button is displayed below the **Use document style** check box, when you clear it. This button is used to place the text of the datum feature inside a square. By default, the text of the datum feature is placed using this option. Therefore, by using the buttons available below the **Square** button, you can set the type of datum feature such as filled triangle, filled triangle with shoulder, empty triangle, empty triangle with shoulder.

Round (GB)

The **Round (GB)** button is displayed below the **Use document style** check box, when you clear it. This button is used to place the text of the datum feature inside a circle. To do so, you first need to clear the **Use document style** check box and then choose the **Round (GB)** button. On choosing this button, additional buttons are displayed below the **Round (GB)** button. These buttons are used to set the style of the datum feature.

After defining all parameters of the datum feature symbol, specify a point on an existing entity in the drawing sheet. Next, move the cursor to define the length and the placement of the datum feature symbol. As soon as you place one datum feature symbol, another datum feature symbol is attached to the cursor. Therefore, you can place as many datum feature symbols as you want using the **Datum Feature PropertyManager**. The sequence of the names of the datum feature symbols automatically follows the order based on the labels, as you place multiple datum feature symbols.

Adding a Geometric Tolerance to Drawing Views

CommandManager:	Annotations > Geometric Tolerance
Menu:	Insert > Annotations > Geometric Tolerance
Toolbar:	Annotation > Geometric Tolerance

In a shop floor drawing, you need to provide various other parameters, along with the dimensions and dimensional tolerance. These parameters can be geometric condition, surface profile, material condition, and so on. All these parameters are defined using the **Geometric Tolerance** tool. To add the geometric tolerance to the drawing views, choose the **Geometric Tolerance** button from the **Annotations CommandManager**; the **Properties** dialog box will be displayed, as shown in Figure 15-6. Also, a geometric tolerance is attached to the cursor.

*Figure 15-6 The **Properties** dialog box used to apply the geometric tolerance*

Both rows in this dialog box are separate frames. You can add additional frames using the **Frames** spinner provided on the right of the **Tertiary** edit box. The parameters that can be added to these frames are geometric condition symbols, diameter symbol, value of tolerance, material condition, and datum references. The options available in the **Properties** dialog box, to add the geometric tolerance to the drawing views, are discussed next.

Symbol

The **Symbol** drop-down list is used to define the geometric condition symbol. When you choose the down arrow button, the **Symbols** flyout is displayed, as shown in Figure 15-7. This is used to define the geometric condition symbols in the geometric tolerance. You can select the standard of the geometric condition symbol from this flyout. As soon as you select a symbol, the flyout is closed and the selected symbol is displayed in the **Symbol** edit box. Also, the preview of the geometric tolerance is displayed in the preview area.

Figure 15-7 The Symbols flyout used to define the geometric condition symbols

Tolerance 1

The **Tolerance 1** edit box is used to specify the tolerance value with respect to the geometric condition defined using the **Symbols** flyout. You can use the buttons available above the rows of the frames to add symbols such as diameter, spherical diameter, material conditions, and so on.

Tolerance 2

The use of the **Tolerance 2** edit box is the same as that discussed earlier. This edit box is used to define the second geometric tolerance, if required.

Primary

The **Primary** edit box is used to specify the characters to define the datum reference added to the entities in the drawing view using the **Datum Feature Symbol** tool.

Similarly, you can define the **Secondary** datum reference and the **Tertiary** datum reference.

Frames

The **Frames** spinner is used to increase the frames for applying more complex geometric tolerances.

Projected tolerance

The **Projected tolerance** button is the last button available above the frame rows. This button is chosen to define the height of the projected tolerance. When you choose this button, the **Height** edit box will be enabled and you can specify the projected tolerance zone height in this edit box.

Composite frame

The **Composite frame** check box is selected to use a composite frame to add the tolerance.

When you select this check box, the tolerance frame is converted into a composite frame and the preview is modified accordingly.

Between two points

The **Between two points** edit boxes are used to apply a geometric tolerance between two points or entities. To do so, specify the tolerance in the edit boxes provided in the **Between two points** area.

Figure 15-8 shows a drawing, after adding annotations to some of the entities in the drawing view.

Figure 15-8 A drawing after adding some annotations

Adding Datum Target Symbols to Drawing Views

CommandManager:	Annotations > Datum Target
Menu:	Insert > Annotations > Datum Target
Toolbar:	Annotation > Datum Target

The **Datum Target** tool is used to add datum targets to the entities in the drawing view. To add the datum targets, choose the **Datum Target** button from the **Annotations CommandManager**. The cursor is replaced by the datum target cursor and the **Datum Target PropertyManager** is displayed, as shown in Figure 15-9. Select a model face, edge, or line from the view on which you need to add the datum target and then place the datum target.

This **PropertyManager** is used to define the properties of the datum target symbol. Set the parameters of the datum target symbol in the **Settings** rollout of this **PropertyManager**. You can set the target shape as a point, circle, or rectangle. You can also define the diameter of the target area, if the shapes of the target are selected as a point and a circle. If the shape of the target selected is a rectangle, you need to define its width and height. You can specify datum references to the datum target symbol by using the **First reference**, **Second reference**,

Figure 15-9 *The **Datum Target PropertyManager***

and the **Third reference** edit boxes. Figure 15-10 shows the datum target symbols added to the entities in the drawing view.

Figure 15-10 *Datum target symbols added to the model*

Adding Center Marks to Drawing Views

CommandManager:	Annotations > Center Mark
Menu:	Insert > Annotations > Center Mark
Toolbar:	Annotations > Center Mark

The **Center Mark** tool is used to add center marks to the circular entities. As discussed earlier, center marks are automatically generated when you generate the model. But if the center marks are not generated while generating the drawing view, or if you have sketched a view, you can use this tool to add the center marks to the drawing views. To add the center marks to the drawing views, choose the **Center Mark** button from the **Annotations CommandManager**; the **Center Mark PropertyManager** will be displayed, as shown in Figure 15-11.

Figure 15-11 The Center Mark PropertyManager

When you invoke the **Center Mark PropertyManager**, the cursor is replaced by the center mark cursor and you are prompted to select a circular edge or an arc for the center mark insertion. By default, the **Single Center Mark** button is chosen in the **Options** rollout of the **Center Mark PropertyManager**. Select the circular edge or arc to add the center mark. Figure 15-12 shows the center marks added using the **Single Center Mark** button.

The **Propagate** button appears on the center marks that are added to holes, which are part of a linear or circular pattern. If you choose this button, the center marks are added to all the remaining instances of the pattern.

The center marks in rectangular and circular patterns can also be applied using the **Linear Center Mark** and **Circular Center Mark** buttons. You can add the center marks in the linear pattern format by using the **Linear Center Mark** button from the **Options** rollout. The center marks will be connected using the centerlines because the **Connection lines** check box is selected by default, as shown in Figure 15-13.

You can create the center mark in the circular pattern format by using the **Circular Center**

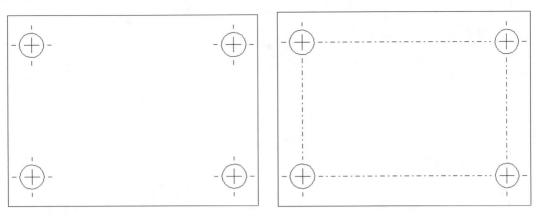

Figure 15-12 *Center marks added using the* **Single Center Mark** *option*

Figure 15-13 *Center marks added using the* **Linear Center Mark** *option*

Mark button. When you choose this button, the **Circular lines**, **Radial lines**, and **Base center mark** check boxes are displayed. The **Circular lines** check box is used to create a circular line passing through the centers of the circles arranged in the form of a circular pattern. The **Radial lines** check box is used to display the radial lines from the center of the pattern to the center of each instance. The **Base center mark** check box is used to display the center mark at the center of the pattern. Figure 15-14 shows the center mark created with the **Base center mark** check box cleared. Figure 15-15 shows the center mark created with the **Base center mark** check box selected. Figure 15-16 shows the center mark created with the **Radial lines** check box selected. Observe that in all these figures, the **Circular lines** check box is selected.

Figure 15-14 *Center marks created with the* **Base center mark** *check box cleared*

Figure 15-15 *Center marks created with the* **Base center mark** *check box selected*

The **Display Attributes** rollout available in the **Center Mark PropertyManager** is used to define the size of the center mark and the extended lines. The **Angle** rollout is used to rotate the center mark at an angle.

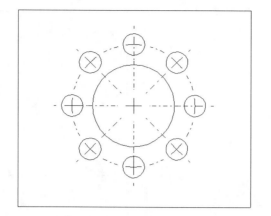

Figure 15-16 *Center marks created with the **Radial lines** check box selected*

Adding Centerlines to Drawing Views

CommandManager:	Annotations > Centerline
Menu:	Insert > Annotations > Centerline
Toolbar:	Annotation > Centerline

The **Centerline** tool is used to add centerlines to the views by selecting two edges/sketch segments or a single cylindrical/conical face. To add a centerline, choose the **Centerline** button from the **Annotations CommandManager**. The **Centerline PropertyManager** is invoked and it prompts you to select two edges/sketch segments or a single cylindrical/conical face. Select the entity or entities from the view to add the centerline. Figure 15-17 shows the centerlines added to the drawing views by selecting the surface of the cylinder.

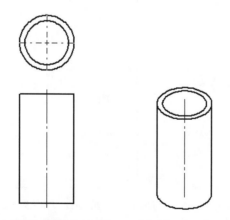

Figure 15-17 *Centerlines added to the front and isometric views using the **Centerline** tool*

Tip. *You can also set the option for the automatic creation of a centerline while generating the drawing views. Choose **Tools** > **Options** from the menu bar to invoke the **System Options- General** dialog box and select the **Document Properties** tab from it. Also, select the **Centerlines** check box from the **Auto insert on view creation** area and choose **OK** to close the dialog box.*

You can also directly select a view to add the centerlines.

Adding a Hole Callout to the Views

CommandManager:	Annotations > Hole Callout
Menu:	Insert > Annotations > Hole Callout
Toolbar:	Annotation > Hole Callout

The **Hole Callout** tool is used to generate the hole callouts that are created in the **Part** mode using the **Hole PropertyManager**, the **Hole Wizard** tool, or the cut option. To generate a hole callout, choose the **Hole Callout** button from the **Annotations CommandManager**; the cursor will be replaced by the hole callout cursor. Select the hole from the drawing views; the hole callout will be attached to the cursor. Pick a point on the drawing sheet to place the hole callout. The **Dimension PropertyManager** is displayed when you place the hole callout. Exit this **PropertyManager**. Figure 15-18 shows a drawing view with hole callouts generated using the **Hole Callout** tool.

Figure 15-18   Hole callouts generated using the Hole Callout tool

Adding Cosmetic Threads to Drawing Views

CommandManager:	Annotations > Cosmetic Thread (*Customize to Add*)
Menu:	Insert > Annotations > Cosmetic Thread
Toolbar:	Annotation > Cosmetic Thread (*Customize to Add*)

The **Cosmetic Thread** tool is used to add the cosmetic threads that will display the thread conventions in the drawing views. To do so, select the circular edge from the drawing view on which you need to apply the cosmetic thread. Now, choose the **Cosmetic Thread** button from the **Annotations CommandManager**;

the **Cosmetic Thread PropertyManager** is displayed, as shown in Figure 15-19.

Figure 15-19 The Cosmetic Thread PropertyManager

The options available in the **Cosmetic Thread PropertyManager** are discussed next.

Thread Settings

The options available in the **Thread Settings** rollout are used to define various parameters of the cosmetic thread. On invoking this tool, you are prompted to select the edges for the threads and set the parameters. Select the required circular edges on which you need to add a cosmetic thread. The name of the selected edge is displayed in the **Circular Edges** selection area. Specify the end condition and set the minor diameter of the thread.

Thread callout

The **Thread Callout** edit box is used to specify the text to be used in the thread callout for the cosmetic thread.

After setting all the parameters, choose the **OK** button from the **Cosmetic Thread PropertyManager**. When you add a cosmetic thread to a generated drawing view, the thread convention will be displayed in all the drawing views. Figure 15-20 shows the cosmetic thread added to the drawing views.

Tip. *If you add cosmetic threads to the drawing views, you can also view them in the part document because of the bidirectional associativity. You can use any display mode to view the cosmetic threads in the model.*

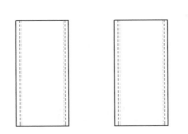

Figure 15-20 *Cosmetic threads added to the drawing views*

Note

*The thread conventions, once added in the drawing view, can be deleted only from the part document. You cannot delete the thread convention from the drawing document. To delete the thread convention in the part document, expand the **Hole** or **Cut** feature in the **FeatureManager Design Tree**. Now, select the thread convention and delete it.*

Adding the Multi-jog Leader to Drawing Views

CommandManager:	Annotations > Multi-jog Leader	*(Customize to Add)*
Menu:	Insert > Annotations > Multi-jog Leader	
Toolbar:	Annotation > Multi-jog Leader	*(Customize to Add)*

You can add a multi-jog leader line to the drawing views by using the **Multi-jog Leader** tool. A multi-jog leader is basically a leader in which you can add multiple jog lines with arrowheads at both the ends. To add a multi-jog leader, choose the **Multi-jog Leader** button from the **Annotations CommandManager**; the cursor will be replaced by the multi-jog line cursor. Select a point on the sheet or on an entity from where you need to start the leader. Now, specify the points on the drawing sheet to specify the jogs and then select the second entity, where the end of the leader will be placed. A multi-jog leader will be created. You can also double-click anywhere on the sheet to specify the second end of the multi-jog leader. Figure 15-21 shows a multi-jog leader added to the drawing view. Note that in this figure, the text is written separately.

Adding the Dowel Pin Symbols to Drawing Views

CommandManager:	Annotations > Dowel Pin Symbol *(Customize to Add)*	
Menu:	Insert > Annotations > Dowel Pin Symbol	
Toolbar:	Annotation > Dowel Pin Symbol *(Customize to Add)*	

The **Dowel Pin Symbol** tool is used to add the dowel pin symbol to the holes in the drawing views. It is also used to confirm the size of the selected hole. To create a dowel pin symbol, select a hole or circular edge from the drawing view and choose the **Dowel Pin Symbol** button from the **Annotations CommandManager**.

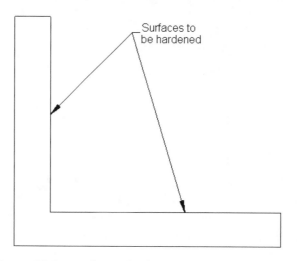

Figure 15-21 *Multi-jog leader added to the drawing view*

The **Dowel Pin Symbol PropertyManager** is displayed. You can flip the direction of the dowel pin symbol by using the **Flip symbol** check box in the **Display Attributes** rollout.

EDITING ANNOTATIONS

You can edit the annotation added to the drawing views by selecting them or by double-clicking on them to display their respective **PropertyManagers** or dialog boxes in which you can edit the parameters of the selected annotation.

ADDING THE BILL OF MATERIAL (BOM) TO A DRAWING

CommandManager:	Annotations > Tables > Bill of Materials
Menu:	Insert > Tables > Bill of Materials
Toolbar:	Annotation > Tables > Bill of Materials

The Bill of Materials (BOM) is a table that displays the list of the components used in the assembly. This table can also be used to provide information related to the number of components in an assembly, their names, quantity, and any other information required to assemble the components. Remember that the sequence of the parts in the BOM depends on the sequence in which they were inserted in the assembly document. The BOM, placed in the drawing document, is parametric in nature. Therefore, if you add or delete a part from the assembly in the assembly document, the change will be reflected in the BOM in the drawing document.

To insert a BOM in the drawing file containing the assembly drawing views, select any one view from the drawing document and choose the **Bill of Materials** button from the **Annotations CommandManager**; the **Bill Of Materials PropertyManager** is invoked, as shown in Figure 15-22. The options available in the **Bill Of Materials PropertyManager** are discussed next.

Figure 15-22 The partial view of the **Bill of Materials PropertyManager**

Table Template

The **Table Template** rollout is used to define the template to be used in the BOM. By default, the **bom-standard** template is selected. If you choose the **Open table template for Bill of Materials** button, the **Select BOM Template** dialog box is displayed. You can choose any of the default templates available in SolidWorks by using this dialog box.

Table Anchor

The buttons available in the **Table Anchor** rollout are used to select the corner of the BOM, using which, the corner will be attached to the drawing sheet. If the **Attach to anchor** check box is selected, the table will be automatically attached to the anchor point of the drawing sheet.

BOM Type

The **BOM Type** rollout is used to specify the level of the assembly. The options available in this rollout are discussed next.

Top level only

The **Top level only** radio button is used to list only the parts and the subassemblies in BOM. The parts of the subassemblies are not listed in the BOM.

Parts only

If you select the **Parts only** radio button, the subassemblies will not be listed in the BOM. The components of the subassemblies are listed as individual components in the BOM.

Indented assemblies

The **Indented assemblies** radio button is selected to list the components and the subassemblies. The components of the subassemblies are listed as indented below their respective subassemblies and are not listed with their respective item number.

Configurations

The **Configurations** rollout is used to specify the configuration for creating the BOM. By default, the **Default** configuration is selected.

Part Configuration Grouping

This rollout is used to set the grouping options for a part having more than one configuration. Selecting the **Display as one item number** check box ensures that if a component has multiple configuration, all of them are listed in the BOM with the same item number. Selecting the **Display configurations of the same part as separate items** radio button ensures that if a component has multiple configurations, they are listed as separate items in the BOM. Selecting the **Display all configurations of the same part as one item** radio button ensures all configurations of a part are listed as one item in the BOM. Similarly, selecting the **Display configurations with the same name as one item** radio button ensures that if multiple components have configurations with the same name, they are listed as a single item in the BOM.

Keep Missing Items

After creating the BOM, if a component is deleted from the assembly, it will also be deleted from the BOM. To retain the deleted component in the BOM, select the **Keep Missing Items** check box; the **Keep Missing Items** rollout is also invoked. The name of the missing components will be displayed in the BOM with a strikeout by selecting the **Strikeout** check box available in the **Keep Missing Items** rollout.

Zero Quantity Display

The options available in the **Zero Quantity Display** rollout are used to set the option to display the component using -, 0, blank in the BOM if that component is not displayed in a particular configuration.

Item Numbers

You can specify a numeric value from where the sequence of the components starts in a BOM. You can set this value in the **Start at** edit box in this rollout. Additionally, you can specify the increment for the numeric value in the BOM using the **Increment** edit box.

After setting all the parameters in the **Bill Of Materials PropertyManager,** choose the **OK** button. A BOM will be attached to the cursor. Specify a point on the drawing sheet to place the BOM. Figure 15-23 shows a BOM added to a drawing sheet.

Figure 15-23 BOM added to the drawing sheet

ADDING BALLOONS TO DRAWING VIEWS

After adding the BOM, you need to add the balloons to the components in the drawing views. The balloons can be added using the **Balloon** tool or the **AutoBalloon** tool. Both these methods of adding balloons to the components in the drawing views are discussed next.

Adding Balloons Using the Balloon Tool

CommandManager:	Annotations > Balloon
Menu:	Insert > Annotations > Balloon
Toolbar:	Annotation > Balloon

The **Balloon** tool is used to manually add the balloons to the components of the assembly in the drawing view. The naming of balloons depends on the sequence of the parts in the BOM. To add balloons to the drawing view, choose the **Balloon** button from the **Annotations CommandManager;** the **Balloon PropertyManager** is displayed. The partial view of the **Balloon PropertyManager** is displayed in Figure 15-24.

On invoking the **Balloon PropertyManager**, you are prompted to select one or more locations to place the balloons. Select the components from the assembly drawing view to add the balloons. If you select the face of a component, the balloon will have a filled circle at the attachment point. However, if you select an edge of the component, the balloon will have a closed filled arrow. After adding the balloons to all components, choose the **OK** button from the **Balloon PropertyManager**. Figure 15-25 shows the drawing sheet in which the balloons have been added.

Figure 15-24 *Partial view of the **Balloon** PropertyManager*

Figure 15-25 *Balloons added to the assembly drawing view*

Adding Balloons Using the AutoBalloon Tool

CommandManager:	Annotations > AutoBalloon
Menu:	Insert > Annotations > Auto Balloon
Toolbar:	Annotation > AutoBalloon

The **AutoBalloon** tool enables you to add balloons automatically. To do so, select the drawing view in which you need to add the balloons and choose the **AutoBalloon** button from the **Annotations CommandManager**. Balloons are added to the selected drawing view with the default settings and the **Auto Balloon PropertyManager** is displayed, as shown in Figure 15-26. The options available in the **Auto Balloon PropertyManager** are discussed next.

Figure 15-26 *Partial view of the **Auto
Balloon** PropertyManager*

Balloon Layout

The options available in the **Balloon Layout** rollout are used to set the layout of the balloons, when they are placed automatically. By default, the balloons are placed in a square form, because the **Square** button is chosen in the **Balloon Layout** rollout. You can also arrange the balloons in circular, aligned to top, aligned to bottom, aligned to left, and aligned to right forms. The **Ignore multiple instances** check box is selected by default to eliminate the creation of multiple instances of a balloon.

Balloon Settings

The **Balloon Settings** rollout is used to set the style, size, and type of the text of balloons.

After setting all parameters, choose the **OK** button from the **AutoBalloon PropertyManager**.

ADDING NEW SHEETS TO DRAWING VIEWS

You can also add new sheets to the drawing document. A multisheet drawing document can be used to generate the drawing views of all the components and the drawing views of the assembly in the same document. You can switch between the sheets easily to refer to the drawings of the different parts of an assembly within the same document. Also, you do not need to open the separate drawing documents. To add a sheet to the drawing document, select **Sheet1** from the **FeatureManager Design Tree** and invoke the shortcut menu. Choose the **Add Sheet** option to add a sheet to the drawing document or else choose **Insert > Sheet** from the menu bar; the **Sheet Properties** dialog box is displayed. You can specify the name, standard sheet format, and scale projection type for the drawing sheet to be added by using this dialog box. Choose the **OK** button from this dialog box; a new sheet will be added in the drawing document. Figure 15-27 shows a drawing document with four drawing sheets added, with the **Sheet 5** as the active sheet.

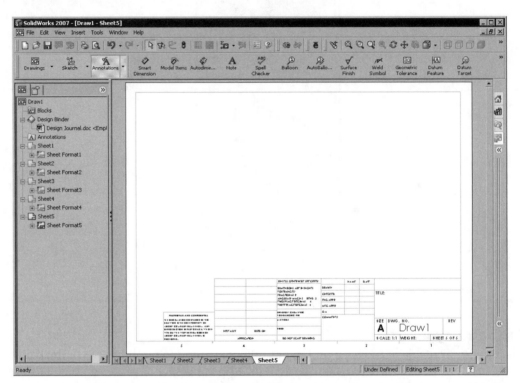

Figure 15-27 *Drawing sheets added to the drawing document*

To activate a drawing sheet, select it from the **FeatureManager Design Tree**. Next, invoke the shortcut menu and choose the **Activate** option from it. You can also activate the sheet by selecting the sheet tab from the bottom of the drawing document.

EDITING THE SHEET FORMAT

You can edit the standard sheet format according to your requirement. To do so, ensure that the required sheet is active and select it from the **FeatureManager Design Tree**. Right-click on the sheet, invoke the shortcut menu, and choose the **Edit Sheet Format** option from it. All the entities, annotations, and views will disappear from the drawing sheet. You can edit the sheet format by using the sketching tools available in the **Sketch CommandManager**. After editing the sheet format, select the active sheet and invoke the shortcut menu. Choose the **Edit Sheet** option from the shortcut menu to switch back to the edit sheet environment.

CREATING USER-DEFINED SHEET FORMATS

You can also create a user-defined sheet format in SolidWorks. To do so, start a new drawing document with a custom size. On the basis of your design requirements, you can set the size of the sheet in the **Width** and **Height** edit boxes available in the **Sheet Format/Size** dialog box. After defining the sheet, select **Sheet1** from the **FeatureManager Design Tree**. Next, invoke the shortcut menu and choose the **Edit Sheet Format** option from it. The edit sheet format environment is invoked. You can create or modify the sheet format by using the standard sketching tools available in the **Sketch CommandManager**. After creating or modifying the sheet format, switch back to the edit sheet environment. Choose **File > Save Sheet Format** from the menu bar. The **Save Sheet Format** dialog box is displayed. Browse to the location where you need to save the sheet format. Specify the name of the sheet format and choose the **Save** button from the **Save Sheet Format** dialog box. Next time when you invoke the **Sheet Format/Size** dialog box, you can retrieve the saved sheet format by selecting the **Standard sheet format** radio button. Using the **Browse** button, browse to the location where you have saved the sheet format. Figure 15-28 shows a user-defined sheet format.

Figure 15-28 *A user-defined sheet format*

TUTORIALS

Tutorial 1

In this tutorial, you will open the drawing created in Tutorial 1 of Chapter 14 and generate dimensions and add annotations to it. Next, you will change the display of the front and the right view to hidden lines visible and the display of the isometric and aligned section views to the shaded mode.   **(Expected time: 45 min)**

The steps to be followed to complete this tutorial are listed next.

a. Copy the part and the drawing document in the folder of the current chapter.
b. Configure the font settings and generate the dimensions using the **Model Items** tool.
c. Arrange the dimensions and delete the unwanted dimensions, refer to Figures 15-30 and 15-31.
d. Add the datum symbol and geometric tolerance to the drawing views, refer to Figures 15-32 and 15-33.
e. Change the model display state of the drawing views, refer to Figure 15-34.

Copying the Documents in the Folder of the Current Chapter

Before proceeding, you need to copy the model and the drawing document in the folder of the current chapter.

1. Create a folder with the name *c15* in the *SolidWorks* folder and copy *c09-tut03.sldprt* and *c14-tut01.slddrw* from the *\My Document\SolidWorks\c14* folder to this folder.

Opening the Drawing Document

Next, you need to open the drawing document in the SolidWorks window.

1. Invoke the **Open** dialog box and open the *c14-tut01.slddrw* document from the folder of the current chapter.

The drawing document, in which you need to add the detailing, is displayed in the drawing area, as shown in Figure 15-29.

Figure 15-29 Drawing views generated in Chapter 14

Applying the Documents Settings

Before generating the model dimensions, you need to configure the document settings. These settings will allow the dimensions and other annotations in the current sheet to be viewed properly.

1. Invoke the **Document Properties - Detailing** dialog box and select the **Annotations Font** option from the area on the left.

2. Select the **Note** option from the **Annotation type** area; the **Choose Font** dialog box will be invoked.

3. Select the **Points** radio button from the **Height** area and set the value of the font size to **9** from the list box.

4. Choose the **OK** button from the **Choose Font** dialog box. Similarly, set the font size for **Dimension**, **Detail**, and **Section** options to **9**.

5. Now, select the **Arrows** option from the area on the left. The options related to size and shape of the arrows are displayed.

6. Set the value of the **Height** as **1**, **Width** as **3**, and **Length** as **6** in the **Size** area.

7. In the **Section/View size** area, set the value of the **Height** as **2**, **Width** as **4**, and **Length** as **8**.

8. Choose the **OK** button from the **Document Properties - Detailing - Arrows** dialog box.

Generating the Dimensions

Next, you need to generate the dimensions using the **Model Items** tool. As discussed earlier, if you do not select any view on generating the dimensions using the **Model Items** tool, all the dimensions will be displayed in all the views. Sometimes, the dimensions overlap each other. Therefore, you will select the view in which you need to generate the dimension and then you will invoke the **Model Items** tool.

1. Select the top view and choose the **Model Items** button from the **Annotation CommandManager**. The **Insert Model Items** dialog box is displayed. The name of the selected view is displayed in the **Import to views** selection area.

2. Choose the **OK** button from the **Insert Model Items** dialog box.

The dimensions of the model that can be displayed in the selected view are generated. Any radial dimension attached to the counterbore hole in the top view needs to be deleted because you will add a hole callout to this counterbore hole later.

3. Select the radial dimension and press the DELETE key to delete the dimension. Similarly, delete the dimension of diameter **20**.

Note that if SolidWorks 2007 is configured for the ANSI system on your machine, the dimension arrowheads are displayed as not filled. You need to change the arrowheads to filled.

4. Drag a window such that all the dimensions are enclosed inside it. Release the left mouse button to select all the generated dimensions. The **Dimension PropertyManager** is displayed.

5. Select the **Filled Arrow** option from the **Style** drop-down list of the **Arrow** rollout. Choose **OK** to close the **Dimension PropertyManager**.

    The arrowheads will be changed to filled arrowheads. Note that the generated dimensions are scattered arbitrarily on the drawing sheet. Therefore, you need to arrange the dimensions by moving them to the required locations.

6. Select the dimension one by one and drag them to the desired location, refer to Figure 15-30. You can reverse the direction of arrowheads by clicking on the control point that is displayed on them.

Figure 15-30 Top view after generating and arranging the dimensions

7. Select the aligned section view and generate the dimensions using the **Model Items** tool. After placing the dimensions, move them to the appropriate places, refer to Figure 15-31. You may need to change the arrowheads to closed filled, if they are not already filled.

8. Choose the **Hole Callout** button from the **Annotation CommandManager** and select the outer circle of one of the counterbore features in the top view. The hole callout will be attached to the cursor. Pick a point on the drawing sheet to place the hole callout.

Adding the Datum Feature Symbol to the Drawing View

After generating the dimensions, you need to add the datum feature symbol to the drawing

Figure 15-31 *Partial view of the sheet after generating and arranging the dimensions in the aligned section view*

view. Datum feature symbols are used as the datum reference for adding the geometric tolerance to the drawing views.

1. Select the edge of the outer cylindrical feature from the top view and then choose the **Datum Feature** button from the **Annotations CommandManager**. The **Datum Feature PropertyManager** is displayed and a datum callout is attached to the cursor.

2. Place the datum symbol at an appropriate location, refer to Figure 15-32.

Figure 15-32 *Datum feature symbol hole description added to the top view*

3. Choose the **OK** button from the **Datum Feature PropertyManager**.

Adding the Geometric Tolerance to the Drawing View

After defining the datum feature symbol, you will add the geometric tolerance to the drawing view.

1. Select the circular edge that has a diameter of 12 from the top view and choose the **Geometric Tolerance** button from the **Annotation CommandManager**.

    The **Properties** dialog box is displayed. It is used to specify the parameters of the geometric tolerance.

2. Choose the **GCS** button corresponding to the first row in the **Feature control frames** area; the **Symbols** dialog box is displayed.

3. Select the **Concentricity and coaxiality** option from the list box and choose the **OK** button from the **Symbols** dialog box.

4. Set the value of tolerance in the **Tolerance 1** edit box to **0.002**.

5. Specify **A** in the **Primary** edit box to define the primary datum reference.

6. Choose the **OK** button from the **Properties** dialog box. The geometric tolerance will be placed attached to the selected circular edge. You may need to move the geometric tolerance, if it overlaps the dimensions. Figure 15-33 shows the drawing view, after adding and rearranging the geometric tolerance.

Figure 15-33 *Geometric tolerance added to the drawing view*

Changing the View Display Options

After adding all the annotations to the drawing views, you need to change the display setting of the drawing views.

1. Press and hold down the CTRL key, and select the front view and the right-side view from the drawing sheet.

2. Choose the **Hidden Lines Visible** button from the **View** toolbar. You can also choose this button from the **Display Style** rollout of the **Multiple Views PropertyManager** that is displayed when you select the two views.

    The hidden lines will be displayed in the selected drawing views.

3. Now, select the isometric view and the aligned section view from the drawing sheet.

4. Choose the **Shaded With Edges** button from the **View** toolbar or the **Multiple Views PropertyManager**. Figure 15-34 shows the final drawing sheet after changing the display view settings.

Figure 15-34 *Final drawing sheet*

5. Save and close the drawing document.

Tutorial 2

In this tutorial, you will generate the BOM of the Bench Vice assembly and then add balloons to the isometric view in the exploded state.   **(Expected time: 45 min)**

The steps to be followed to complete this tutorial are listed next.

a. Copy the Bench Vice folder that contains parts, assembly, and the drawing document to the folder of the current chapter.
b. Delete the views that are not required in the drawing sheet, refer to Figure 15-36.
c. Move to arrange the views in the drawing sheet, refer to Figure 15-36.
d. Set the anchor on the drawing sheet where the BOM will be attached.
e. Generate the BOM, refer to Figure 15-37.
f. Add balloons to the isometric view, refer to Figure 15-38.

Copying the Bench Vice Assembly Folder to the Current Folder

1. Copy the Bench Vice folder from the *\My Document\SolidWorks\c14* folder to the folder of the current chapter.

Opening the Drawing Document

After copying the folder, you need to open the drawing document in the SolidWorks window.

1. Open the *c14-tut02.slddrw* document.

The drawing document, in which you need to generate the BOM and balloons is displayed in Figure 15-35.

***Figure 15-35** Drawing views generated in Chapter 12*

Deleting the Unwanted View

You need to delete the right view because it is not required in this tutorial.

1. Select the right-side view and press the DELETE key on the keyboard; the **Confirm Delete** dialog box will be displayed.

2. Choose the **Yes** button from this dialog box. The view will be deleted from the current drawing sheet.

Moving the Isometric View

You need to move the exploded isometric view, because the BOM will be generated and placed at the top right corner of the drawing sheet.

1. Select the isometric view; the border of the view is displayed in green.

2. Move the cursor to the border; the cursor will be replaced by the move cursor.

3. Drag the cursor to move the drawing view. Place it at the required location, refer to Figure 15-36.

Figure 15-36 Drawing sheet after moving the drawing view

Setting the Anchor for the BOM

Before generating the BOM, you need to set its anchor. The anchor is a point on the drawing sheet on which one of the corners of the BOM coincides. By default, the anchor is defined at the top left corner of the drawing sheet. But in this tutorial, you need to add the BOM on the top right corner of the drawing sheet. Therefore, you need to set the anchor before generating the BOM.

1. Expand **Sheet1** from the **FeatureManager Design Tree** and then expand **Sheet Format1**.

2. Select the **Bill of Materials Anchor1** option, right-click to invoke the shortcut menu and choose the **Set Anchor** option from it. The drawing views will disappear from the sheet.

3. Specify the anchor point on the inner top right corner of the drawing sheet. A point will be placed at the selected location.

After you specify the anchor point, the drawing views automatically are displayed in the sheet because the sheet editing environment is automatically invoked.

Generating the BOM

Next, you need to generate the BOM. As discussed earlier, the BOM generated in SolidWorks is parametric in nature. If a component is deleted or added in the assembly, the change is automatically reflected in the BOM. But before you generate the BOM, you need to set its text parameters.

1. Invoke the **Document Properties - Detailing - Annotation Font** dialog box. Select the **Tables** option from the **Annotation type** area to display the **Choose Font** dialog box.

2. Select the **Points** radio button from the **Height** area and set the value of the font size to 9 point. Close both the dialog boxes.

3. Similarly, change the text height of balloons to 12 points.

4. Select the isometric view and choose **Bill of Materials** from the **Tables** flyout in the **Annotations CommandManager**. The **Bill Of Materials PropertyManager** is displayed.

5. Choose the **Top Right** button from the **Anchored corner** area of the **Table Anchor** rollout. Also, select the **Attach to anchor** check box.

6. Choose the **OK** button from the **Bill Of Materials PropertyManager**.

    The BOM is generated. You will notice that the **Description** column is also displayed in the BOM. But this column is not required and so you need to delete it.

7. Move the cursor over the heading **Description** and right-click to display the shortcut menu. Choose **Delete > Column** from the cascading menu. This column will be deleted. The drawing sheet, after generating the BOM and deleting the **Description** column, is displayed in Figure 15-37.

Note

*If the color of the BOM is gray and is not clearly visible, invoke the **System Options - Colors** dialog box. Select the **Imported Annotations (Driven)** from the **System colors** list box and change its color to black.*

Adding the Balloons to the Components

After generating the BOM, you need to add the balloons to the components. Before proceeding further, make sure that you have changed the font height of balloons to 12 point in the last section.

ITEM NO.	PART NUMBER	QTY.
1	vice-body	1
2	vice-jaw	1
3	screw-bar	1
4	base-plate	2
5	bar-globes	2
6	jaw-screw	1
7	clamping-plate	1
8	set-screw-2	2
9	oval-fillister	1
10	set-screw-1	4

Figure 15-37 Drawing sheet after generating the BOM

1. Select the isometric view and choose the **AutoBalloon** button from the **Annotations CommandManager**; balloons are automatically added to all the components in the isometric view and the **Auto Balloon PropertyManager** is also displayed.

    The multiple instances of any component are ignored because the **Ignore multiple instances** check box is selected in the **Balloon Layout** rollout.

2. Select **1 Character** from the **Size** drop-down list in the **Balloon Settings** rollout. Choose **OK** to close this **PropertyManager**.

    The balloons are added to all the components, except the Clamping Plate. This is because the clamping plate is not visible in the isometric view. You will notice that the balloons are not properly arranged on the sheet and are placed arbitrarily. Therefore, you need to manually drag each balloon and place it properly.

3. Move the cursor over one of a balloon and when it is highlighted, drag it to place it at a better location, refer to Figure 15-38.

4. Similarly, drag and place the remaining balloons also at the proper locations. The final drawing sheet, after adding and rearranging balloons, is shown in Figure 15-39.

5. Save the drawing and close the document.

ITEM NO.	PART HUMBER	QTY.
1	vice-body	1
2	vice-jaw	1
3	screw-bar	1
4	base-plate	2
5	bar-globes	2
6	jaw-screw	1
7	clamping-plate	1
8	set-screw-2	2
9	oval-fillister	1
10	set-screw-1	4

SECTION A-A
SCALE 1 : 2

Figure 15-38 Final drawing sheet after adding balloons

SELF-EVALUATION TEST

Answer the following questions and then compare your answers with those given at the end of this chapter:

1. You cannot add annotations while creating the part in SolidWorks. (T/F)

2. You can add the surface finish symbols to the drawing views. (T/F)

3. The **Projected tolerance zone** area is used to define the quality of the projected tolerance. (T/F)

4. You can set the target shape as a point, circle, or rectangle, while adding a datum target. (T/F)

5. You can also set the option for the automatic creation of the centerline while generating the drawing views. (T/F)

6. The _____ spinner is used to define the major diameter of the thread.

7. The _____ tool is used to add the balloons to the components of the assembly in the drawing view.

8. You can also create automatic balloons using the _____ tool.

9. Using the _____ rollout available in the **Bill Of Materials PropertyManager,** you can specify the template needed to create the BOM.

10. The _____ tool is used to create a hole callout.

REVIEW QUESTIONS

Answer the following questions:

1. The _____ tool is used to add the cosmetic threads that are used to display the thread conventions in the drawing views.

2. The _____ tool is used to add reference dimensions to the drawing views.

3. You can change the model display setting from hidden lines removed to hidden lines visible, or wireframe, or shaded using the options available in the _____ toolbar.

4. Select the _____ check box from the **Auto insertion on view creation** area to automatically create centerlines, while generating the view.

5. The _____ tool is used to create the centerlines in the views.

6. Which **PropertyManager** is invoked to add automatic balloons to the selected drawing view?

    (a) **AutoBalloon**   (b) **Balloon**
    (c) **Properties**   (d) **Center Mark**

7. Which **PropertyManager** is displayed when you choose the **Cosmetic Thread** button from the **Annotations CommandManager**?

    (a) **Cosmetic Thread Properties**   (b) **Cosmetic Thread**
    (c) **Cosmetic Thread Convention**   (d) None of these

8. Which **PropertyManager** is used to add center marks to the drawing views?

    (a) **Add Center Mark**   (b) **Create Center Mark**
    (c) **Center Mark**   (c) **Cosmetic Thread**

9. Which rollout available in the **Cosmetic Thread PropertyManager,** is used to define the depth of the cosmetic thread?

    (a) **Thread Settings**   (b) **Thread Depth**
    (c) **Cosmetic Thread**   (d) None of these

10. Which **PropertyManager** is used to add balloons in the drawing views?

    (a) **Add Balloons**   (b) **Balloon Properties**
    (c) **Balloons**   (d) None of these

EXERCISE

Exercise 1

Generate the isometric view in the exploded view of the assembly created in Tutorial 1 of Chapter 13 on the standard A4 sheet format. The scale of the view will be 1:5. After generating the view, generate the BOM and add balloons to the assembly view shown in Figure 15-39.

(Expected time: 30 min)

Figure 15-39 *Drawing view for Exercise 1*

Answers to Self-Evaluation Test
1. T, **2.** T, **3.** F, **4.** T, **5.** T, **6. Minor Diameter**, **7. Balloon**, **8. AutoBalloon**, **9. Table Template**, **10. Hole Callout**

Index

Other Publications by CADCIM Technologies

The following is the list of the other publications by Prof. Sham Tickoo and the CAD Engineers of CADCIM Technologies.

SolidWorks Textbooks
- SolidWorks 2006 for Designers
  CADCIM Technologies, USA
- SolidWorks 2006 for Designers
  Piter Publishing Press, Russia
- SolidWorks 2006 for Engineers & Designers
  Dreamtech Press, India
- SolidWorks for Designers, Release 2005
  CADCIM Technologies, USA
- SolidWorks for Designers, Release 2005
  Piter Publishing Press, Russia
- SolidWorks for Designers, Release 2004
  CADCIM Technologies, USA
- SolidWorks for Designers, Release 2004
  Piter Publishing Press, Russia
- SolidWorks for Designers, Release 2003
  CADCIM Technologies, USA
- SolidWorks for Engineers and Designers, Release 2003
  Dreamtech Press, India

NX Textbooks
- NX 4 for Designers
  CADCIM Technologies, USA
- NX 3 for Designers
  CADCIM Technologies, USA
- NX 3 for Engineers & Designers
  Dreamtech Press, India

Solid Edge Textbooks
- Solid Edge V18 for Designers
  CADCIM Technologies, USA
- Solid Edge V18 for Engineers & Designers
  Dreamtech Press, India
- Solid Edge for Designers, Version 16
  CADCIM Technologies, USA

- Solid Edge for Designers, Version 15
  CADCIM Technologies, USA
- Solid Edge for Engineers and Designers, Version 15
  Dreamtech Press, India

CATIA Textbooks

- CATIA V5R16 for Designers
  CADCIM Technologies, USA
- CATIA V5R16 for Engineers & Designers
  Dreamtech Press
- CATIA V5R15 for Designers
  CADCIM Technologies, USA
- CATIA V5R15 for Engineers & Designers
  Dreamtech Press
- CATIA for Designers, V5R14
  CADCIM Technologies, USA
- CATIA for Engineers & Designers, V5R14
  Dreamtech Press
- CATIA for Designers, V5R13
  CADCIM Technologies, USA
- CATIA for Engineers and Designers, V5R13
  Dreamtech Press

Autodesk Inventor Textbooks

- Autodesk Inventor 11 for Designers
  CADCIM Technologies, USA
- Autodesk Inventor 11 for Engineers & Designers
  Dreamtech Press
- Autodesk Inventor for Designers, Release 10
  CADCIM Technologies, USA
- Autodesk Inventor for Designers, Release 9
  CADCIM Technologies, USA
- Autodesk Inventor for Designers Release 6 with Release 7 Update Guide
  CADCIM Technologies, USA
- Autodesk Inventor for Designers, Release 6
  CADCIM Technologies, USA
- Autodesk Inventor for Designers: Update Guide Release 6
  CADCIM Technologies, USA
- Autodesk Inventor for Engineers and Designers, Release 6
  Dreamtech Press
- Autodesk Inventor for Designers, Release 5
  CADCIM Technologies, USA

Pro/ENGINEER Textbooks

- Pro/ENGINEER Wildfire 3.0 for Designers
  CADCIM Technologies, USA

- Pro/ENGINEER Wildfire for 3.0 Engineers & Designers
  Dreamtech Press, India
- Pro/ENGINEER Wildfire for Designers Release 2.0
  CADCIM Technologies, USA
- Pro/ENGINEER Wildfire for Engineers & Designers Release 2.0
  Dreamtech Press, India
- Pro/ENGINEER Wildfire for Designers
  CADCIM Technologies, USA
- Pro/ENGINEER for Designers, Release 2001
  CADCIM Technologies, USA
- Pro/ENGINEER Wildfire for Engineers and Designers
  Dreamtech Press, India
- Pro/ENGINEER for Engineers and Designers, Release 2001
  Dreamtech Press, India
- Designing with Pro/ENGINEER, Release 2001
  Dreamtech Press, India

Autodesk Revit Building Textbooks
- Autodesk Revit Building 9 for Designers & Architects
  CADCIM Technologies, USA
- Autodesk Revit Building 8 for Designers & Architects
  CADCIM Technologies, USA
- Autodesk Revit for Building Designers & Architects, Release 7.0
  CADCIM Technologies, USA

AutoCAD LT Textbook
- AutoCAD LT 2007 for Designers
  CADCIM Technologies, USA
- AutoCAD LT 2006 for Designers
  CADCIM Technologies, USA

Mechanical Desktop Textbook
- Mechanical Desktop Instructor, Release 5
  McGraw Hill Publishing Company, USA

AutoCAD Textbooks (US Edition)
- AutoCAD 2007: A Problem-Solving Approach
  Autodesk Press
- Customizing AutoCAD 2007
  Autodesk Press
- AutoCAD 2006: A Problem-Solving Approach
  Autodesk Press
- Customizing AutoCAD 2006
  Autodesk Press

- AutoCAD 2005: A Problem-Solving Approach
  Autodesk Press
- AutoCAD LT 2004: A Problem-Solving Approach with Update Guide AutoCAD LT 2005
  Autodesk Press
- Customizing AutoCAD 2004 and 2005
  Autodesk Press
- AutoCAD 2004: A Problem-Solving Approach
  Autodesk Press
- AutoCAD LT 2004: A Problem-Solving Approach
  Autodesk Press
- Customizing AutoCAD 2004
  Autodesk Press

AutoCAD Textbooks (Russian Edition)

- AutoCAD 2005
  Piter Publishing Press, Russia
- AutoCAD 2004
  Piter Publishing Press, Russia
- AutoCAD 2002
  Piter Publishing Press, Russia
- AutoCAD 2000
  Piter Publishing Press, Russia

AutoCAD Textbooks (Italian Edition)

- AutoCAD 2000 Fondamenti
- AutoCAD 2000 Tecniche Avanzate

AutoCAD Textbook (Chinese Edition)

- AutoCAD 2000

AutoCAD Textbooks (Indian Edition)

- AutoCAD 2006 for Engineers and Designers
  Dreamtech Press, India
- Understanding AutoCAD 2006: A Beginner's Guide
  Dreamtech Press, India
- AutoCAD 2005 for Engineers and Designers
  Dreamtech Press, India
- AutoCAD 2004 for Engineers and Designers
  Dreamtech Press, India
- Understanding AutoCAD 2004: A Beginner's Guide
  Dreamtech Press, India

3D Studio MAX and VIZ Textbooks

- Leaning 3ds max5: A Tutorial Approach
  (Complete manuscript available for free download on *www.cadcim.com*)

- Learning 3DS Max: A Tutorial Approach, Release 4
  Goodheart-Wilcox Publishers (USA)
- Learning 3D Studio VIZ: A Tutorial Approach
  Goodheart-Wilcox Publishers (USA)
- Learning 3D Studio R4: A Tutorial Approach
  Goodheart-Wilcox Publishers (USA)
- Learning 3D Studio MAX/VIZ 3.0: A Tutorial Approach
  BPB Publishers (India)

Paper Craft Book
- Constructing 3-Dimensional Models: A Paper-Craft Workbook
  CADCIM Technologies

Coming Soon: New Textbooks from CADCIM Technologies
- Solid Edge V19 for Designers
- CATIA V5R17 for Designers
- ANSYS for Design Analysts

Rendered Image of the Pipe Vice Assembly

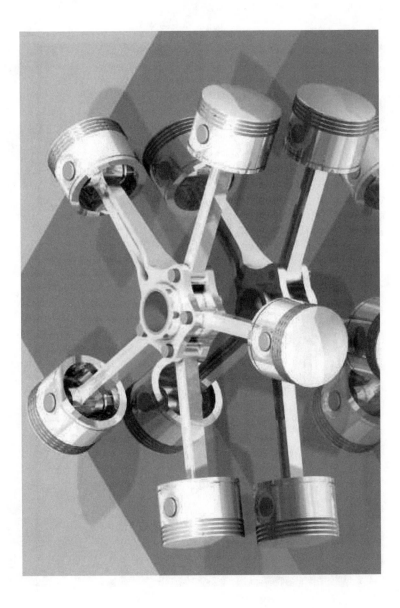

Rendered Image of the Radial Engine Subassembly

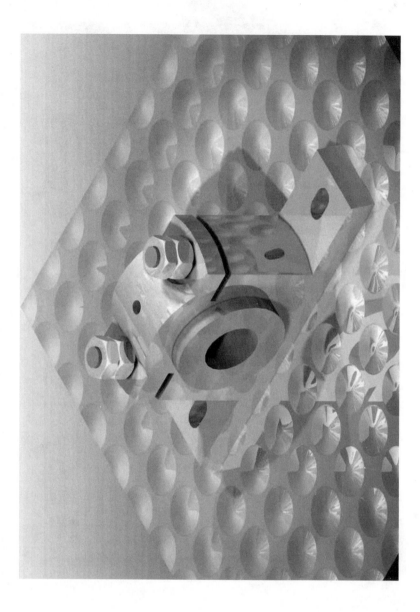

Rendered Image of the Plummer Block Assembly